100 ARMENIAN TALES

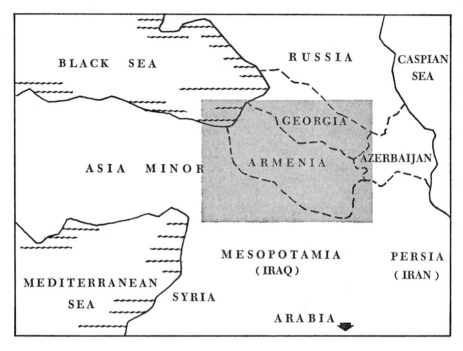

The birthplaces of informants who contributed tales to this collection are indicated in the map of Armenia.

The above maps are based on the *London Times Atlas* (1895 ed.) Map 76 and (1922 ed.) Map 51. Maps drawn by Joanne Colman.

100 ARMENIAN TALES

and Their Folkloristic Relevance

Collected and Edited
by Susie Hoogasian-Villa

Wayne State University Press, Detroit, 1966

Published simultaneously in Canada by Ambassador Books, Limited
Toronto, Ontario, Canada

Library of Congress Catalog Card Number: 66–10502

Second Printing, January 1967

Grateful acknowledgment is made to the Ford Foundation,
Thelma G. James, Mr. and Mrs. Edward Mardigian
for financial assistance in publishing this book.

Permission was graciously granted by Indiana University Press and
Stith Thompson to use motif-index numbers and motifs selected
from Stith Thompson's The Motif-Index of Folk Literature
(6 vols.; Bloomington: Indiana University Press, 1955–58).

To my mother, Hripsima Hoogasian,
my husband, John J. Villa, and
our children, John Kazar,
Nancy Emelyn and Jimmy

CONTENTS

Map of Armenia   *frontispiece*

Foreword BY THELMA G. JAMES   11

Preface   14

I. Background for the Detroit Armenian Folktales
Folklore in the Metropolis   21
Delray and Its People   23
Armenia's Past: A Brief Survey   29
The Oral Tradition   36

II. The Armenian Folktale
Published Collections of Armenian Folktales   43
The Detroit Collection   47
    Story Distribution   47
    Parallels in Other Collections   49
    Kinds of Stories   54
    General Characteristics   56
    Motifs   60

III. The Folktales
Märchen   77
    1. The Ogre's Soul   77
    2. Nourie Hadig   84
    3. The Fairy Child   91
    4. Clever Daniel   96
    5. The Giant-Slayer   102
    6. Wisely Spent   109
    7. The Seven Giant Brothers   113
    8. Abo Beckeer   119
    9. The Giantess Leader   124
    10. The Miller and the Fox   127
    11. The Work of the Genii   133
    12. The Magic Bird-Heart   137

CONTENTS

13. *The Magic Figs* — 145
14. *The Magic Horse* — 153
15. *The Huntsman* — 159
16. *The Dreamer and His Dream* — 167
17. *The Patient Suitor* — 175
18. *The Country of the Beautiful Gardens* — 180
19. *The Riddles* — 189
20. *The Magic Ring* — 193
21. *Hagop's Wish* — 197
22. *The Monster's Hairs* — 202
23. *The Turtle Skin* — 210
24. *The Golden Box* — 216
25. *The Magic Box* — 217
26. *The King of Snakes* — 224
27. *The Nine-Seeded Apple* — 229
28. *Tanzara and Dyeer* — 232
29. *Mundig* — 235
30. *Cinderella* — 240
31. *The Golden-Haired Twins* — 245
32. *The Story of Mariam* — 253
33. *Yeghnig Aghpar* — 255
34. *The World Below* — 266
35. *The Son of the Gray Horse* — 273
36. *The Helpful Spirit* — 290
37. *Ludwig and Iskander* — 293
38. *Buzz-Buzz Aunty* — 296
39. *The Halva-Maker* — 299
40. Tushcoon *Eigna* — 302

Moralistic Tales — 309

41. *The Rich Boy and the Poor Boy* — 309
42. *The Devoted Son* — 315
43. *The Ditch-Digger Falls into His Own Ditch* — 321
44. *Foretelling the Future* — 322
45. *The Soul-Taking Angel* — 323
46. *The Gold Piece* — 327
47. *The Emperor's Lesson* — 328
48. *Honor* — 331
49. *Nature's Ways* — 338
50. *The Shepherd's Dream* — 340
51. *The Soul-Taker* — 344
52. *There Is Righteousness* — 345
53. *The Test* — 348

54. *The Ball of Gold*   350
Anecdotes   351
55. *A Treasure Hunt*   351
56. *The Curse*   352
57. *A Great Catch*   354
58. *One Way To Catch a Fish*   354
59. *What a Fish!*   355
60. *Saint Snakes*   356
61. *The Rising Snake*   357
Humorous Tales   357
62. *Fool's Luck*   357
63. *Ingratitude*   359
64. *Outwitting Giants*   361
65. *Vhy, Vhy, Vhy*   364
Tales of Trickery and Wit   369
66. *The Ashman's Money*   369
67. *The Clever Boy*   372
68. *The Dead Snake and the Young Wife*   374
69. *The Dilemma*   375
70. *It Happened in a Bath*   376
71. *Quick-Witted*   379
72. *Matching Wits*   383
73. *The Story of the Robbers*   388
74. *The Test of the Chicken*   391
75. *The Devil's* Yallehr   392
76. *Rooster-Brother*   393
Anti-Feminine Tales   396
77. *The Honorable Wife*   396
78. *The Rooster's Advice*   401
79. *The Talkative Wife*   402
80. *Today's Laughter, Tomorrow's Sadness*   403
Sagas and Legends   405
81. *Gohc* Amu *and the Tax Officials*   405
82. *Aryohn,* Gullah   406
83. *Gohc* Amu *and the* Toot   407
84. *Gohc* Amu *and the Running Water*   408
85. *Gohc* Amu *and the* Matzoon   408
86. *The Bear Husband*   409
87. *The Town of Stone*   411
88. *Retribution*   413
89. *The Old Fort*   413
90. *Under Suspicion*   414

CONTENTS

91. *The Woman in Blue*   417
92. *The Prize Bull*   418
93. *The Sacred Sheet*   419
94. *The Servant in the Monastery*   420
Cumulative Stories   422
95. *From Bad to Worse*   422
96. *It Started with a Thorn*   423
97. *Munuck*   425
Myths   426
98. *Lochman Hehkeem*   426
99. *The Seven Stars*   429
100. *The Sunset Lad*   430

IV. Comparative Studies

Appendices   535
A. Narrator Sketches   535
B. Index of Motifs   538
C. Bibliography of Comparative Sources   594
D. Additional References   599

Notes   600

FOREWORD

URBAN FOLKLORE AS found in the cities of the United States is rich
and varied. Carried here in the minds and hearts of those who
have left their homelands for many reasons, it represents, for the
first generation, a bridge between the old and the new. The parallels and the differences are sources of security and of fear. For
the early arrivals there is bound to be a desperate clinging to and
a very conscious preserving of the old ways and beliefs, arts and
crafts, food, festivals, tales, songs, proverbs. Much of this material
is still functionally effective because the social and family struc-
tures in the ethnic enclaves remain virtually unchanged. Tradition
and structure are mutually supportive; the functions of the folk
patterns are still close to those of the homelands.

For the second and later generations, moving out of the en-
clave, the new world customs are corrosive; many economic, social, political and religious pressures act to ridicule, debase, sup-
press, change, destroy and finally obliterate the old language,
names, beliefs, arts and crafts. The melting-pot has done its work.
Later generations recover a new pride in their heritage, and, out
of the shreds and pieces which remain, something that is a curious
blend of the romanticized old, the ever-present new and strange
intermediate materials can be found. Obviously, the functions of
these materials are quite different from those of the earlier days.
One point, often overlooked, is that all of the stages are present at
any one historical moment, for while the number of immigrants
changes, there continue to be some recent arrivals in almost every
ethnic group, and some of the early comers still live in quite isolated circumstances, hidden shyly in families and neighborhoods.
They are old now, their memories are weakened, but their revival
for someone interested is astonishing.

For the scholar these survivals of folklore are peripheral and
frequently much less "contaminated" than they might be in the
homelands where wars, famine and population movements have
obliterated and changed them in folk memory and practice. These
texts probably come closer to their oldest forms than those now to
be found in Europe. Here is one of the greatest contributions that

our ethnic communities have made to the American heritage. This mingling of traditions, not the obliteration of the melting-pot, is one of the sources of our vastly rich intellectual, artistic and spiritual spectrum. Often unnoticed, undervalued and unappreciated, such books as this one bring them profitably to our attention. In *Voices in the Valley, Mythmaking and Folk Belief in the Shaping of the Middle West* (University of Wisconsin Press, 1964) Frank R. Kramer has studied in some depth the processes by which the continuing assimilations of new ideologies into folk memory and subsequent public action develop. The chief weakness of this book lies in its almost total neglect (aside from the birth of labor unions) of the ethnic factors so powerful in the development of the Middle West, and especially of such a city as Detroit. Nor is this historian alone in his unrealistic appraisal.

It is, consequently, extremely important that we secure accurate, firsthand reports of the ethnic folklore contributions. There is such a rare and priceless record in this collection of Armenian folktales. The author is an American-born girl who lived in her warm and affectionate home composed of an Armenian-born grandmother, her Armenian-born parents and her American-born brother. After her marriage to John Villa, of Mexican ancestry, she continued to live with her family for some time. Her mother continues to be a much loved and frequent companion of Mrs. Villa's three children, none of whom speaks Armenian.

This daughter was to become the bridge for her family between the old world and the new. Her eyes were open to the values inherent in her heritage when, as a high school student, she met Professor Emelyn E. Gardner whose early perception of the existence and importance of urban, ethnic lore was to enable her to pioneer in this work in the United States. Susie Hoogasian (Villa) was to be one of many students whom Professor Gardner found and trained to record faithfully the lore of their families and friends.

These students lived with their informants, shared their memories and recorded them accurately; with comparative study, they came to rich understanding and pride in these treasures of tradition. These students adapted to their foreign–American status; they were never absorbed by that process. Their collections constitute a founding section of the Wayne State University Archives which have continued to specialize in the collecting of urban, ethnic lore and to further the study of the impact of these materials on individuals and on the community.

As the old Delray, River Rouge sections of Detroit have changed, the stores, halls, homes and churches have altered their patrons, names, wares and events. The Armenian people are scattered throughout the city and its suburbs, but many of them continue the old contacts. Recently fine cultural centers have been erected, new churches built, language courses offered in the university—these things provide a focal center. Once almost exclusively employed on the automobile production lines and as itinerant sellers of rugs and laces, Armenians are today to be found in all of the professions.

There remains a common pride in their ethnic heritage, a great bond in the knowledge of the tragedies of the homeland's past and of the present land's promise. This, like the other ethnic sub-cultures in America's vast tapestry of folk heritage, shares in the world's folk heritages. Here is the true common ground, best revealed by comparative studies of types and motifs to be found in these Armenian folktales. That they are often blended types, often astonishing variants, reflects the geographical and historical situations of Armenia as a bridge between the Near East and Western Europe. In this volume is to be found the second, even longer bridge between Europe and America.

Further study may well reveal even more astonishing relationships with the tales of the Orient. Thus the circle will be completed; if so, these old Armenian tales, collected, archived and now published in Detroit, will be seen, as I believe they are, to be the connecting, hitherto missing link in the long chain of the world's folktales. Others will study the songs, proverbs, customs, but none will give a better report of the Armenian social and family contexts in which the folk materials were to survive. Through the insight and encouragement of Professor Gardner, and the dedication of her student, they have survived.

THELMA G. JAMES
Professor of English
Wayne State University

Detroit, Michigan
15 September 1964

PREFACE

AMONG MY EARLIEST childhood memories are the happy times I spent listening to the wonderful *hekiats,* or fairy tales, which my grandmother told. Not only did she have a large repertoire of tales, she was never too busy or too impatient to share them with my brother and me. Years later these tales became the nucleus of the collection of Armenian folktales, now a part of the Wayne State University Archives, Detroit, Michigan. The primary purpose of this volume is to present a selection of the folktales which I recorded from the oral tradition of the Armenian community in Delray, one section of industrial Detroit, in 1940–42. My collecting activity during this period was by no means definitive: I am certain that many more tales can and should be collected in the Armenian communities of this city even today.

To create a better understanding of the Armenian scene which influenced the storytellers and their tales, a brief review of Armenian history and a discussion of Armenian life, both in the native land and in the new homeland, have been prepared. A summary of the characteristics of the Armenian folktale, its style and main motifs or story materials particularly as found in Detroit, is presented to serve as general background. Although I have attempted to assemble such information for the reader, this book is not meant to be a scholarly study of Armenian history and culture or a complete analysis of the Armenian folktale.

Because the folk material, interesting as it is in relation to the Armenian culture, can also be of value to serious folklorists throughout the world, the stories have been classified according to the Aarne-Thompson and Eberhard-Boratav Types. Similarities between the Detroit Armenian tales and those of other Armenian collections as well as those of lands geographically and historically linked with Armenia have been pointed out. Bolte-Polívka references, when available, have been indicated for the stories.[1] This material is found in the Comparative Studies which follow the folktales. Motif listings are located in Appendix B.

Throughout the book, foreign words which cannot be translated readily have been italicized, and their closest translations are given immediately following in brackets. The Armenian words have been given in the simplest phonetic form.

The storyteller for each tale in the collection has been identified on the opening page of the story. A discussion of narrator techniques as well as further information about individual informants are to be found in Appendix A.

It was Professor Emeritus Emelyn E. Gardner of the English department, Wayne State University, who first inspired me as a freshman student to collect folklore. I listened to the stories in Armenian and wrote them with Gregg shorthand in English. This is not as surprising as it might sound: in my adolescent years Armenian was more my mother tongue than was English. Furthermore, I had been trained in high school as a fast and accurate stenographer; this enabled me to transcribe the stories quickly and thus insure vividness and preserve idiomatic expression. These translations present plot, motif, conversation, soliloquy and detail just as the storyteller re-created the tale. Even obvious memory lapses have not been improved by the addition of transitions.

The translations have not been "prettied" or "enriched" to make a more favorable impression on the reader. Nor have items been deleted which might embarrass the sensitive person. In preparing the stories for this volume, great care has been taken to preserve the genuineness of the folk material. At times simpler English usage or clearer expression has been selected than that which was mine as an undergraduate in the original translation.

I was aware, even as a young collector, of the real danger ever present in recording literary versions of a story rather than the representative oral tradition. For this reason I asked each informant how he had come upon the story. If he had read the tale or if it had been read to him, I did not record it. It is important to state that the most prolific storytellers in the Detroit group were unlettered. Furthermore, it must be emphasized that the reading of Armenian folktale collections, even for those informants in the group who could read, would have proved difficult: collections of Servantstian, Tcheraz, etc. are rare and almost impossible to locate.

Because of the structure of the Armenian folktale, it has been extremely difficult to assign Aarne-Thompson Type classifications with any degree of accuracy. A glance at the Comparative Studies reveals that only a few stories can be analyzed with a single Aarne-Thompson Type number. I am indebted to Dr. Sven Liljeblad of Sweden, who, in the summer of 1946, spent many hours verifying my Aarne-Thompson studies. Dr. Warren Roberts of Indiana University made the definitive Aarne-Thompson Type classifications for the Detroit Armenian stories in the spring of 1963. His experience and stature as a folktale scholar and his association with Dr. Stith Thompson, dean of American folklorists, bring a final authority to this phase of the Armenian folktale research. To Dr. Roberts I am grateful, also, for the Eberhard-Boratav Turkish Type assignments of the Detroit stories.

I am grateful to the many people whose help and interest have spurred this publication. As I recorded story after story, it was Professor Gardner who showed me the significance of the material and the necessity for recording it to prevent its loss in the adopted homeland. She inspired, she guided, she developed appreciation of the cultural heritage which was taken so much for granted by me and my contemporaries. Her influence as a folklore scholar and her continued faith in "our book" have, to a large extent, made this publication possible.

In 1948 a stylistic study of these folktales was prepared as a graduate thesis under the supervision of Professor Thelma G. James, Wayne State University. In her role of literary godmother, Professor James's encouragement and help have been invaluable in the selection and classification of these stories. Her careful reading of the entire manuscript for both content and style is greatly appreciated. She has made herself available for guidance on every phase of this volume.

The critical analysis of the introductory material by Dr. Wayland Hand of the Center for the Study of Comparative Folklore and Mythology, UCLA, was of considerable help to me in the final draft. I appreciate the review of the introductory materials made just prior to publication by Rev. R. P. Rubyan, teacher of Armenian language at Wayne State University.

I acknowledge the contribution of Mardiros Tarpinian, presently of Los Angeles, who has permitted the publication in this volume of several stories which he collected in his freshman days at Wayne State University. I am grateful to my translators: Mrs. Margareta Berker, Mrs. Lillian Wilson, Mrs. Siret Yener.

My appreciation is due the editors of the *Journal of American Folklore* for permission to reprint portions of an article written in cooperation with Miss Gardner in June 1944.

I am indebted to the staffs of the Folklore Library of Indiana University, the Detroit Public Library, Wayne State University

Library, Harvard University Library and the Library of Congress. I am grateful to Dr. George J. Maciuszko, director of the John G. White Folklore Division, Cleveland Public Library, who made valuable resources available to me. Without the loyalty and cooperation of Miss Jeanne Lloyd, director of my local Baldwin Public Library in Birmingham, Michigan, and her excellent staff, much of my comparative work would have been impossible.

My gratitude and recognition are unlimited to my editors, Miss Francine Rosemberg and Mrs. Gene Tendler, who with skill and patience worked on this manuscript, ever mindful of the value of the folk material in their hands. I appreciate the encouragement which Dr. Harold Basilius, director of the Wayne State University Press, has given me, as well as the many courtesies extended to me by members of his staff.

To the members of my family, particularly my husband, John J. Villa, my brother, Vaughn and my mother, Mrs. Hripsima Hoogasian, I am grateful for the understanding and encouragement which enabled me to devote the necessary time to this project. For the readings in the Armenian of comparative sources, I am again indebted to my mother.

The Delray of my childhood, the friends and neighbors who gave of their love and inspiration to make Armenia live in one corner of this metropolis, I shall always remember. To Miss Vehanoush Zakarian and Ardashes Hoogasian (unfortunately, no familial ties), teachers in the Zavarian Armenian School, my contemporaries and I owe appreciation for devoted teaching and guidance.

It is with appreciation and gratitude that I acknowledge the contribution of my storytellers, even those like Koran Rahanian whose stories do not appear in the present volume. I cherish the memory of my tiny grandmother, Mrs. Mariam Serabian, who first planted and nurtured my love for these folktales. Although a number of my informants are no longer alive, it is my hope that this volume will fulfill their frequently expressed wish: that Armenia will live forever in the stories of her people.

S. H.-V.

1

Background for the Detroit Armenian Folktales

FOLKLORE
IN THE METROPOLIS

IN THE ARMENIA of old, *ashoughs* sang the songs and told the tales which captivated listeners, rich and poor alike.* These wandering minstrels were welcomed eagerly, particularly in the vast countryside of this agricultural land. The rich oral tradition in Armenia was not limited to these professional storytellers, however. In the absence of radio, television, motion pictures and frequently even the written word, the country folk looked to the local storyteller to pass away the long, cold and lonely winter nights.

It is to be expected that Armenia, situated as it is in the Asia Minor continent, would possess a rich stock of folktales. What is surprising, however, is that these folktales, vivid and meaningful to the Armenian people, should be found in such abundance and detail in this industrial American city. But Detroit is not unique in this respect; the same folktale-collecting activity can be repeated profitably in Boston, Hartford, New York, Chicago, Fresno, Los Angeles, San Francisco or in any community of Armenians who found refuge on the American continent after World War I. In this new homeland these persecuted people settled close to each other and tried to create an Armenian spirit in the new environment. However, the activity of these Armenians was not different from that of other foreign-language-speaking groups upon their arrival in America.

Frequently handicapped by an inadequate knowledge of English, immigrants from any particular country settled close together, established stores, churches, restaurants, and formed, perhaps without actually setting out to do so, a subculture of their own. Such a group created a speech island of a few streets in the

* August von Haxthausen, in *Transcaucasia* (London, 1854), pp. 348–49, says that *ashoughs*, who were wandering singers, were almost always Armenian by birth although their songs and stories were frequently told in the Tatar language which served in the south Caucasus in the same capacity as French did in the rest of the world of that time. He observed: ". . . the facility with which the Armenians acquire foreign languages and become assimilated to any nationality is remarkable. And this enables them to make their way so well in foreign countries."

metropolis.[1] Several speech islands, each representing a different tongue, were frequently placed back-to-back or several streets apart and lived in relative harmony. They adapted their lives to the American milieu, respecting the customs and language of their neighbors, but preserving their arts and crafts, native foods, religious observances and patriotic days. Their folk songs were sung, folktales told, riddles and sayings remembered, folk cures practiced, and children's games played. Midst the noise and smokestacks of the crowded city, these ethnic groups maintained their folkways until the adaptive process was completed.

The transplanted folk cultures were perpetuated in the form in which they were brought to this land. In some instances powerful influences on European life had produced corresponding changes in the native folktales. However, similar changes rarely appeared in the American versions because the newly arrived groups feared the loss of their folk heritage. The folktales, particularly, lived in a relatively fixed state, and it was in this form that I recorded them. Illustrative of this, in 1941 I collected "The World Below," along with numerous other stories, from Hovhannes Kaprelian. In 1963 I had occasion to hear this same storyteller repeat this story and found both versions perfectly similar in every detail. Furthermore, the only complete parallel of "The Shepherd's Dream" which I have been able to trace is found in Baron von Haxthausen's *Transcaucasia* published in 1854. It seems that the Armenian story collected in Detroit in 1941 has been perfectly preserved for almost a century.

At one time it was the consensus that folklore lived in the rural areas of America. The immigration of a great number of people of diverse nationalities during this century undoubtedly brought many people to the rural areas of our country. But certainly a good number of them found work in the large cities also where labor was needed to keep the industries working at capacity. Too frequently the role our large urban centers play in perpetuating ethnic folkways has been overlooked. At the time of my folktale recording in the 1940's, folklore was being collected at Wayne State University by Italian, Hungarian, Finnish, Polish and Estonian students, to name only a few. Even today, rich sources of difficult-to-find Chaldean and Lebanese folklore, for example, are available to the interested collector in this metropolis.

It is the older generation, or the first generation in America, who remembers and keeps alive the folk material. If this ethnic lore is to be recorded and preserved for future study, it must be collected before the Americanization process becomes complete. Our urban universities have a challenge as well as a responsibility here.

DELRAY AND ITS PEOPLE

THE INDUSTRIAL COMMUNITY of Delray, located in southwest Detroit, was, between World Wars I and II, composed of various ethnic groups. Along the eastern edge of this area, the Italian families were most numerous. Between the Italians and the large Hungarian colony, the Armenians were to be found, and the Poles lived on the western fringe of the Hungarian group. On the margin, between the Armenian and Hungarian colonies, a Negro group had long existed.

Within the Armenian ten- to fifteen-block area were four or five Armenian grocery stores which specialized in the beloved lamb, favorite vegetables and the special cereal grains such as *bulghour, sissair, gorgod* and *vosp* which were essential to the Armenian cook. The pungent spicy scent of *pastourma* [dried beef sausage, highly seasoned] and *feta* [fresh Greek cheese made of goat's milk] greeted us as we entered these stores. *Halva* [candy] and large black olives were always on display, and large loaves of brick and Muenster cheese were available for the delicious *beurek* [pastries filled with cheese and parsley] so popular with the Armenian families.

Two excellent Macedonian bakeries specialized in the baking of *peda* [flat crusty bread], the favorite of Armenian families. Several times a day the scent of freshly made bread enveloped the streets.

The only baked goods which the Armenian woman bought, however, was the *peda*. She made her own *paklavas*, starting the dough with her recipe. But her recipe alone did not make *paklava*, as many of us less gifted modern cooks have since discovered. The layers and layers of tissue-like dough demand great skill and experience; the Armenian housewife possessed both and took pride in this accomplishment.

And *gatah!* What heavenly *gatah* [coffee rolls, unsweetened usually] these women made! There is nothing as satisfying and delicious as fresh, warm *gatah* just out of the oven, golden brown and thickly sprinkled with sesame seeds. When a special occasion was in sight, the busy housewife started preparing huge recipes of the special yeast dough and the rich, unsweetened fillings which she needed for the family's *gatah*. The baking was frequently an all-day affair, but the large quantities prepared never lasted long enough. Frequently, at the time the housewife made *gatah*, she made a large supply of *lavash* or *dahn hatz*, the large flat breads reminiscent of enormous pancakes. These would be stored in tall piles and, if they lasted that long, stayed fresh for weeks. These breads, when dampened with water and wrapped around a piece of cheese and roasted green pepper, made the best lunch one could wish for.

Each region of Armenia was noted for a food speciality of one kind or another. While women from one part were noted for their excellent pastries, another region would boast the best *pastourmas*, another the most delicious *roejig* [a string of walnut halves dipped a number of times into cooked fruit pulp]. The speciality of Kharput, the region of many of the Detroit storytellers, was *kheyma* [steak which has all fat removed, is ground twice, kneaded with fine *bulghour* and water, and eaten uncooked].

With the advent of World War II and the housing problems created by it, a greater geographical intermingling occurred among various groups in the community, and finally, an almost new pattern appeared. Delray today is not at all the Armenian center it was prior to the war. Families have moved into newer communities, and the Little Armenia which existed during my youth is now a thing of the past. Although cultural centers and churches have been established in newer neighborhoods, the Armenian population of metropolitan Detroit today is widely scattered and well assimilated into the American scene. Armenians who no longer live in concentrated areas such as Delray frequently have moved to neighborhoods where, within a few streets, a number of other Armenian families are located. It is this grouping within the assimilative process which would enable a folklorist to collect today.

While many Armenians in Delray prior to World War II found work in the numerous automobile plants, some entered small businesses of their own. They bought and rented homes close to one another. Some homes were two-family flats; others were private dwellings. There was nothing unusual about these homes: they could have been duplicated without difficulty in other sections of Detroit. The Armenians were good homeowners: whenever financially able, they repainted their homes; lawns, flowers and trees were well-tended. Frequently, when families needed extra income, rooms would be rented to bachelors who sometimes ate meals with the family and shared evenings discussing news of the day. Reminiscing about their homes in Armenia often led to the telling of folktales.

Families, although not large, experienced financial difficulties which were magnified by the depression of the 1930's and the limitations of opportunities inherent in a community of newly settled and relatively unskilled people. Consequently, children frequently found part-time work and contributed their earnings to meet expenses. This working-together-for-the-common-good created a great sense of unity and responsibility among family members which is characteristic of the Armenian family even today. In spite of the economic problems of this period, Armenian children lived in an atmosphere of love and acceptance. Broken homes, desertions and divorces were almost nonexistent. However, since the Armenian woman seldom worked outside her home, the death of a husband meant the almost complete financial collapse of the family.

Grandparents rarely lived alone. They were respected members of the family group and, as the older generation, brought Armenia a little closer to their American-born grandchildren. My grandmother, for example, lived with us when she came to America in 1923. She was so much a part of my family that I called her "*Mairig*" [Little Mother]. From my earliest childhood my grandmother slept with me, telling me one *hekiat* after another until I fell asleep. Not only folktales and folk remedies, but native superstitions and beliefs were vivid in the memories of these grandparents and practiced in their everyday lives. Frequently, this older generation spoke only Armenian and made few attempts to adjust to the new culture. Adaptations were made slowly, with reluctance and with a remembrance of other days and other values.

Thus, Delray represented an interesting transition between the old and the new. Grandparents lived in the past and yielded to the American milieu only when unavoidable. Their children, the transition generation, had the tasks of earning a living, making a home and raising a family in the new land. Behind them, they

25

had the memories of their youth, their happinesses, as well as their losses and sufferings. Ahead of them, they had the problems of American parenthood. They attempted a fusion of the two cultures, not only in speech but also in philosophy and behavior.

In the Delray of this period the Armenian family was patriarchal; the father's authority was not questioned, his decisions remained firm. The household was organized around his comfort: the women cleaned, cooked and served to please him. In seeking more freedom and more understanding, the American-born Armenian children frequently found that their mothers and grandmothers made excellent intermediaries. For, while the father was the head of the house, the women were the heart. It was the mother who, loving with one hand and spanking with the other, interceded for the children. She visited the public schools, somehow communicating with the teachers in her unsteady English, helping to make the necessary adjustments for her bilingual children. With the approval and knowledge of her menfolk, the Armenian woman established local chapters of, and actively participated in, the Armenian Red Cross, the benevolent societies to help needy Armenians still abroad, the Armenian church and the Armenian language schools to preserve and perpetuate the Armenian culture. Bazaars, dances and membership dues pieced together out of tight budgets paid for these expenses.

Armenian children spent several afternoons a week, after regular school hours, learning not only to read and write Armenian, but learning Armenian literature, songs and history as well. Even Armenian plays and operettas were presented by these youngsters.

The Armenian church played an important part in the life of Delray. In addition to the usual weddings, baptisms and funerals observed by the church, the priest blessed the graves of the departed and visited each Armenian home at least once a year, blessing the house and each occupant.

Although for many education had been curtailed at an early age because of finances and lack of school facilities, Armenian parents knew full well the value of an education and took pride in their children's scholastic achievements. In the public schools these Armenian children were accepted readily, encouraged to develop their abilities to the fullest and inspired to greater levels of learning and scholarship. Most teachers conveyed to the children that, although their cultural heritage was different from the teacher's own, it was a rich and valuable one. Most important, discrimination because of national origin was almost nonexistent.

In the midst of Little Armenia stood the Delray Community Center, established and serviced by the Presbyterian Church. For the people of Delray the community house offered many things: a Presbyterian Sunday School, after-school recreation and hobby programs, a library, young people's groups, adult language classes, child-care classes, a public health and social service center and a small playground. Some Armenian youths participated and even taught in the Presbyterian Sunday School, while, later that same morning, they would cross the street to their Armenian Apostolic Church, don choir robes and chant the liturgy of their forefathers.

The young Armenians of Delray were loyal to each other. Not only was their camaraderie remarkable, there was a uniting to beat all rivals. The most intensely fought basketball, baseball and football games were those played against neighboring Hungarian and Italian teams.

In social matters, as in traditional Armenia, a more liberal code of behavior was permitted to the young male of the family, while the daughter was highly protected. Her comings and goings were monitored, her social life was restricted. Dating, as we know it in American life, was not permitted. Although prior to World War II marriages were still arranged by the parents of the young people, this custom became less prevalent and, during the war years, almost nonexistent. Armenian boys married non-Armenians, but an Armenian girl broke every tradition when she did the same.

Rarely did children address their neighbors with the prefixes "Mr." or "Mrs." A sign of respect and acceptance was the honorary "Aunt" or "Mr. Hovhannes" (using the first name instead of the surname). Each person in the community was interested in the well-being of the young people; one dared not do something bad. If parents, aunts or relatives did not observe, a neighbor or family friend was certain to. Without fail, the matter was immediately brought to the attention of the parental authority.

In the summer young and old alike sat on their front porches after dinner and greeted passersby, exchanging news of the day. Families visited one another, particularly on winter evenings and Sunday afternoons. The young daughter of the house made and served numerous cups of thick, sweet Turkish coffee. Attractive brass coffee-makers of various sizes were in constant use. When the coffee was completely drunk, the demitasse was turned upside down on its saucer. The last few drops of thick coffee ran down the side of the cup and made unusual patterns. If a fortune teller was present, each person would eagerly have his coffee cup read.

The Turkish coffee was also served in the ever-popular coffee houses. On one Delray street, set aside for living quarters for the bachelors, several restaurants served homemade Armenian food. A number of coffee houses, catering to both single and married men, served as social centers where the Armenian newspapers were read and discussed and sometimes gossip was exchanged over loud, lively games of *tavlu* or *khoz*. It was not unusual for an older man to sit contemplatively with his *khehriba* [loosely strung amber conversation beads] clicking away in his hands, thinking about things past. In one corner a small group might be reminiscing and recalling scenes of their youth in Armenia. As the Delray community changed and families moved to newer neighborhoods, the function of the coffee houses remained. Sometimes the new cultural center provided these same facilities; sometimes the men traveled back to their favorite "clubs" in the old community.

In Delray many traditions and ceremonies, with minor changes, were observed as they had been in Armenia. Festivals, special church and patriotic days were celebrated with meetings, social events and picnics. Armenians, fervent picnickers, boarded special buses and, singing both patriotic and folk songs, enjoyed the long ride. Once at the picnic grounds, relatives grouped themselves near one another and enjoyed shish kebab and pilaff cooked over an open fire. Greeting neighbors and friends from the greater Detroit area became the object for some, while folk dancing to the *davoul, zourna* [drum, horn, and frequently also violin and zither] was eagerly anticipated by others. Frequently, a speech or commemorative ceremony, such as the blessing of the grapes, was the highlight of an afternoon.

It was from such a community that these Armenian tales were collected. Although such stories were told among the older folk for entertainment, the pressures and values of modern living did not foster this activity. The cures, superstitions and customs were losing their importance to even the transition generation because of their desire to conform with the "American" youth. It was with pride and a certain pleasure that the informants told their stories to an interested member of the younger group, even though it is obvious that some of the stories were imperfectly remembered.

ARMENIA'S PAST:
A BRIEF SURVEY

In the everyday lives of the Armenian people folktales originally found their real function as entertainment or a means of escape, as a lesson in wit or trickery, as the recall of past and glorious days or the teaching of moral values. Events such as wars, massacres, invasions of powerful neighbors, as well as economic, cultural, geographic and social conditions affected the people and, consequently, their repertoire of tales.

To give a brief picture of these influences involves some discussion of the geography and history of Armenia. Such a background, sketchy as it may be, will serve to put the stories into better perspective. The often striking similarities of motifs and story outline, as presented in the Comparative Studies, will have greater meaning.

Although Armenia's boundaries have varied frequently throughout her turbulent history, in modern times this country has been divided among the powers of Turkey, Russia and Persia (Iran). Traditional Armenia (see Frontispiece), was a land-locked country in Transcaucasia, bounded by the Black Sea on the north, present Azerbaijan and Georgia (Iberia) on the northeast, the Taurus Mountains and Mesopotamia on the south, Persia on the east and the rest of Asia Minor on the west. The Euphrates River divided the country in two; Armenia Major was the area in the east, and Armenia Minor (Sophene) was to the west.

Armenia was a plateau region with an abundance of mountains and deep valleys. The mighty Ararat, popularly called *"Massis"* by the Armenians, was situated in the heart of Armenia and served as a cradle of much folk belief and superstition. Ararat's snow-bound peaks were visible from areas which were three or four days walking distance from it. Distinct geographical features divided the country into such definite regions that generations living adjacent to one another sometimes had little com-

29

munication; localization of some dialects as well as folk beliefs, folk songs and folktales frequently occurred.

The beginnings of the Armenian people are still a source of interest and research for archaeologists and historians. Some believe the Armeno-Phrygians arrived in Thrace from the Russian steppes many centuries before the present era then traveled eastward across the Bosphorus about 1250 B.C. Before the eighth century B.C. the Armens had separated from the Phrygians and moved eastward to the Ararat region during the eighth and seventh centuries. The powerful Urartu people, who had successfully absorbed numerous groups including the Mitannites, Hittites, Hurrians, Chaldeans and the Nairi people, were then conquered by the Armen invaders who formed the new Armenian nation. This theory of Armenian origins is accepted by most scholars today; the Armenian language is placed among the Indo-European family of languages.

Another theory popularly held by the Armenian folk, is found in the writings of Moses of Khoren, the Armenian Herodotus who lived in the fifth century A.D. Moses of Khorene, whose sources and accuracy have been questioned in recent times, related that the brave Haig, the founder of the Armenian nation, rebelled against the Babylonian Bel during the civil wars among the Sumerian states, moved northward with his son Armenach and his followers, and settled in the Ararat region. Haig, according to the legend, was the great grandson of Japhet, son of Togormah, and thus related to Noah. The belief that the original Garden of Eden was situated in the valley of the Araxes, surrounded by the Euphrates, Tigris, Kura and Araxes Rivers, strengthens this theory. The Armenians proudly remind the world that Noah's ark rested on Mt. Ararat.[*]

A third theory of Armenian origin, denying that the nation was formed by great waves of immigration, suggests that a combination of various peoples such as the Urartians, Chaldeans, Hurrians, Mitannites, Azzies and Hayasans formed the Armenian nation.[2] Indications are that in the second millennium B.C. the Hittites had borrowed a large vocabulary and expressions of religious, technical and moral nature from the Hurrians, a group of people who saw their beginning in the third millennium B.C. and

---

[*] Vahan Kurkjian, in *A History of Armenia* (New York, 1958), p. 2, emphasizes Genesis 8:4: "The Ark landed upon the mountains of Ararat" (the Hebrew name for Armenia itself, not necessarily Mt. Ararat exclusively).

were submerged during the Assyrian period in the Urartu nation.[3] The Hittites, whose power was formidable in Asia Minor, transmitted the Hurrian culture westward as far as Cappadocia and Cilicia. Since Hittite is considered an Indo-European language, some scholars believe that Armenia might well be the cradle of the Aryan civilization.[4]

The Urartu or Armenian nation had hardly been formed when, in the sixth century B.C., it became a subject and ally of the powerful Medes and saw the destruction of the once great Assyrian Empire. Under King Cyrus of Persia the Achaemian Rule in Armenia was established from 559 to 330 B.C., stimulating prosperity and expanding trade in that land. This period was followed by that of Alexander the Great whose Macedonian rule in Armenia, beginning in 330 B.C., brought Hellenistic culture— literature, science and philosophy—to Armenia. Seleucid rule followed until 190 B.C. when the empire fell to the Romans. Artaxias and Zareh, military governors who ruled Armenia Major and Armenia Minor, took advantage of this defeat; they revolted, proclaiming independence for Armenia. Artaxias established the mighty Artaxian Dynasty, but his attempts to rally the Armenian people into one nation were hampered by the comparative geographical isolation of areas which was created by the rivers and mountains of Armenia. He did succeed in developing a spirit of nationalism among the people and made it compulsory to use the Armenian language throughout the land. Since Artaxias was an admirer of Hellenistic culture, he encouraged its dissemination in all places. With the advice of Hannibal, who, defeated by Rome, was seeking temporary refuge in Armenia, the new capital, Artaxata, was built strategically on the Araxes River.

The Parthians, who had subjugated Media, Persia, Babylonia and Mesopotamia, went into battle over boundaries with Artaxias' son, Artavazd II. The Parthian forces met great resistance in Armenia but succeeded in taking the heir Tigranes as hostage, releasing him in 94 B.C. only after considerable concessions of territory. Known as Tigranes the Great, King of Kings, King of Armenia, he became Armenia's most renowned ruler. During his reign he united the land, vastly extended its borders and encouraged the spread of culture. He finally met defeat by the Romans led by Lucullus and Pompey. The Artaxian Dynasty, an illustrious period of Armenian independence, ended in 2 B.C.

Both Parthia and Rome exerted influence on Armenia from 2 B.C. to 53 A.D. at which time the Armenian Arsacid Dynasty

(53–429 A.D.) came into power. During this period St. Thaddeus and St. Bartholomew went to Armenia after the crucifixion of Christ to preach Christianity. They established the Armenian Apostolic Church and were martyred in the middle of the first century. In 301 A.D., under the leadership of St. Gregory the Illuminator, King Tiridates III accepted Christianity and established this faith as the national religion. Thus, Armenia became the first Christian nation in the world.[5] As Christians, the Armenians looked to the West instead of the East for cultural ties.

In 405 A.D., St. Sahag and St. Mesrop, both men of the church, created the Armenian alphabet. This was the necessary predecessor to the Golden Age of Armenia which occurred in the fifth through the seventh centuries. Schools were established, the teaching of Christianity became widespread and monastic education in Armenia greatly progressed. Translations into Armenian were numerous, including a translation of the Bible.

During the Persian rule of Armenia (430–634 A.D.) the historic Battle of Avarair, the first war for religious freedom, was fought. In 451 A.D., led by the Armenian nobleman Vardan Mamikonian, the Armenian people valiantly fought the mighty armies of Persia. Although defeated, the Armenians refused to accept Zoroastrianism and clung to their religion. This event is celebrated even today in Armenian churches throughout the world.

The Armenian church, although somewhat similar to the Greek Orthodox, was separate from both Rome and Byzantium and has remained to this day a national church. The Armenian church and the people are one: each finds existence within the other. The establishment of the Armenian church, the creation of the unique Armenian alphabet and the acceptance of Christianity in the midst of Mohammedans and non-believers served to encourage the spirit of nationalism among the people.

With the fall of the Persian Empire in 625 A.D., the Byzantine governors-general tried to seize power in Armenia. They vied with the Arabs who overran the country in 639 A.D. and ruled with cruelty for almost two centuries. The Arabs considered their campaign a holy war and were determined that the Armenians would accept Mohammed. Meanwhile the Byzantine Court, according to historians, was intolerant of religious views different from its own.[6] So the Armenians were attacked by both powers, Arabian and Greek, because of religious convictions.

In this period of Arabian rule, Paulican Protestantism, a

movement in search of free religious expression, gained popularity in Byzantium and Armenia. Although some authorities place the Paulicans as early as the fifth century, the first church was established by the reputed leader of this movement, Constantine of Mananalis (a village in the Armenian mountains) in 660 A.D. This group of puritans and critics of the church was persecuted for their religious views, causing them to flee from Armenia in 844 A.D. They traveled westward, carrying their missionary activity to the Balkans and influencing the Protestant Reformation in Europe in the centuries to come.[7]

The Arabian caliph appointed Ashot as king of Armenia, the first of the Bagratid Dynasty, in 885 A.D. This third period of Armenian independence was characterized by a resurgence of industry and agriculture and the establishment of peace and prosperity. The city of Ani, the heart and love of Armenia which was reputed to have one thousand and one churches, was built by the Bagratid rulers. In the eleventh century Armenia was attacked first by the Byzantine forces, then by the Seljuk Turks. In 1048 the Seljuks devastated the Van region and, in 1064, ransacked and destroyed Ani, the magnificent city.

With the fall of Ani, a large settlement of Armenians under Ruben I left their homeland and founded a new barony in Cilicia, establishing the Rubenian Dynasty. Known as New Armenia, Cilician Armenia was a kingdom from 1196 until 1375 A.D. and was the seat of the Armenian kings. Leo V of the French-Armenian dynasty, the last Armenian king, reigned from 1374–75 and died in Paris in 1393.

The era in Cilicia, known as the Silver Age, was culturally productive even when the country was devastated by successive attacks of Seljuk Turks, Mamelukes and Mongols. During this period also, contact between East and West occurred with the Crusades. Undoubtedly, considerable exchange of culture, intermarriage and some migration westward occurred. Friendship existed between English and Armenian kings as exemplified by the following: "Leon II of Armenia, in the spring of 1191, and Richard the Lion-Hearted of England met on the classic soil of Cyprus at Richard's wedding, where Leon II acted as chief of the bridegroom's friends (the best man)."[8]

Cilician Armenia fell to the Egyptian Mamelukes in the latter part of the fourteenth century. Armenia Major, meanwhile, was being attacked by waves of Mongols. Conflicts with Persia and Russia occurred, too; finally, the Turks succeeded in establishing their rule over Armenia until 1918. Following the Russo-Turkish War of 1877–78 when Bulgaria was liberated, the Turks feared that the Armenians also might achieve independence. Their ferocious repression of the Armenian people, their inhuman massacres and the plundering of these Christians have been a record of history. After World War I the Armenian Republic was established from 1918–20; it then became part of the Soviet Union and is known today as the Armenian Socialist Soviet Republic. Thus, the ancient land of the Armenians is divided in modern times among Turkey, Russia and Iran.

With powerful neighbors on all sides, Armenians felt their influences on politics and religion as well as in social and economic matters. As part of the Christianized West, Armenia has served as a bridge between Europe and Asia, transmitting European culture to the Asian continent and bringing Asia and the Orient to Europe.

After the fall of the Armenian kingdom in 1375, Armenians looked for refuge everywhere in the world. Certainly, conditions in Armenia throughout the years had encouraged migrations, some voluntary, some in search for a less violent political climate. Other Armenians, utilizing their abilities in trade and commerce, looked elsewhere for new business opportunities. Many left their mark on the lands in which they settled as wise businessmen, talented artisans, bright and gifted students of the arts and government and as hard-working, honest tillers of the soil.[9]

The coming of the Crusades had familiarized the Armenians with the Latin nations; the trade routes opened by the Romans made westward movement considerably easier. Many Armenians settled in Venice, Rome, Milan, Leghorn, Pisa, Marseilles. Others moved to Bulgaria, Romania, Moldavia, Austria-Hungary, Egypt, Cyprus, Crete, Syria and Iran. Permanent colonies were established in Poland, the Crimea and in Amsterdam. A number of the best ports of India in 1497 were controlled by Armenians, and several communities of them made their way to Bombay, Calcutta and even eastward to China.* Many Armenians, during their country's turbulent history, have scattered northward to all corners of Russia.

In describing these migrations, the historian Jacques de

---

* According to Louise Nalbandian, *The Armenian Revolutionary Movement* (Berkeley and Los Angeles, 1963), pp. 34–36, the first book using the Armenian alphabet was printed in Venice in 1512; the first journal in the Armenian language, *Aztarar*, was published in 1794 in Madras.

Morgan wrote that from Lwow, Poland in the seventeenth century, some ten thousand Armenians went to Moldavia. In 1671, however, they were forced during the Turco-Polish Wars to settle in Bukowina and Transylvania (from 1699–1848, this territory was part of Hungary).[10]

The most notable of these relocations occurred in 1717 when the Armenian Mekhithar from the province of Sebaste established the Mekhitharist Monastery of the Roman Catholic Church on the Island of St. Lazar in Venice.* Later a second colony was established in Vienna. These two groups of scholars, originally drawn from Armenia, have spread the Roman, Germanic and European influences into Armenia. They have furthered the education of those interested in Armenian scholarship and have themselves served as scholars and translators of Armenian literary and historical works.†

As early as 1655 two Armenians were brought to America by the Virginia colonists as experts on silkworm breeding. Although in 1834 the first Armenian students arrived in this country, it was after the Russo-Turkish War of 1877 that the first sizable migrations to the United States occurred.

The greatest influx of Armenians reached the United States immediately after World War I when they fled their homeland to escape Turkish massacres. Men frequently preceded their wives and families, seeking a means of livelihood as well as a shelter for their loved ones. It was not at all unusual for those who had already emigrated to send financial aid to relatives and friends still abroad. Unmarried men, or men whose families had been lost in the war, married the war widows and young ladies who looked to America for refuge.

Many Armenian immigrants settled along the eastern coast and, for one reason or another, were unwilling to venture far into the interior. Others found in the rich industrial Midwest better

---

* Haxthausen, op. cit., p. 341, discusses the losses which have occurred to Armenian literary manuscripts during the destructions of villages and towns. Some manuscripts which escaped destruction have been scattered throughout libraries in Rome, Paris and the Mekhitharist Monastery in Venice. "The celebrated library at Etchmiadzin [Holy See of the Armenian faith] itself was partly destroyed and plundered and suffered to perish from neglect. There was not even a catalogue of it until one was published by M. Brosset in 1840, illustrated with notes."

† Aram Raffi, in Noel Buxton's Travels and Politics in Armenia (New York, 1914), p. 229, indicated that Lord Byron stayed at St. Lazar and studied Armenian. He actually took part in the preparation of an Armenian-English dictionary and grammar.

sources of employment. More ambitious ones discovered that the West, particularly California, most nearly duplicated the fertile fields and vineyards of the home they had left behind.*

THE ORAL TRADITION

A FOLKTALE, ALTHOUGH it is a literary artifact, lies dormant in the memory of the folk, ready for quick recall. With the proper stimulation, the storyteller will produce for his listeners the familiar events of the story, told in the traditional folktale manner. It is to be expected, then, that the re-creation and recall of the folktale at any particular time is influenced not only by the social, political and economic milieu of the informant but also by his background, memory, personality and emotional attitude. Furthermore, these highly personalized factors determine not only the selection of the motifs used in the tale, but also the manner in which the tale is told.

Storytelling situations in the life of the Armenian folk were numerous. However, there can be no overall generalizations about Armenian life for conditions in the villages were very different from those in the towns. Since the bulk of the Armenian population was found in the rural areas, the following discussion of the oral tradition will be concerned with village ways.

Under the paternal pattern of culture in Armenia during the nineteenth century when a son was old enough to marry, his

---

* According to James Tashjian, *The Armenians of the United States and Canada* (Boston, 1947), pp. 20–26:
   Of the 26,146 Armenian immigrants to come to America between 1920–31, 4770 settled in Massachusetts and an estimated 17,000 settled in Detroit, Michigan.
   He presents the following estimated survey made in 1945 of the Armenian population in America:

New England	64,000
Mid-Atlantic	66,000
Mid-Western	35,000
Southern	5,000
Western	45,000
Canada	8,000
Total in the United States	215,000
Grand Total	223,000

parents selected a wife for him. This new bride left her father's home and, with her new husband, lived at the home of her father-in-law. Commonly then, several generations and numerous family branches were to be found under the same roof; the property, meanwhile, remained undivided. Such groupings of generations in the villages made the patriarch and his wife the oldest members of the family and the objects of reverence.

Families lived close together in small villages. As many as one hundred might be situated around a *mairakaghak* [mother city] which served as a cultural and business center. Kharput, the *mairakaghak* of many Detroit informants:

> . . . is built on a hill. The dwellings are for the most part constructed of mud and brick with two stories, in striking contrast to the underground burrows elsewhere. . . . Armenians are in a great minority in the city but they have a large preponderance among the inhabitants of the surrounding regions. It has been estimated that not less than 130–50 villages are situated in the vicinity.[11]

While the men went some distance to herd the sheep, tend their orchards and vineyards and enjoy the abundant supply of fish in nearby waters, the women were taught the intricacies of the household: cooking, baking, embroidery, spinning and weaving, as well as the abundant lore associated with the many events of everyday life. Having many women under one roof made it necessary to establish a control so as to achieve harmony in these large households of numerous sons, wives and grandchildren.

This discipline was accomplished by observing the rule of silence, at least until the bride bore her first son. Although the Armenian girl was veil-less and bareheaded before her marriage, things were different after marriage, especially in the small villages. The new bride could speak to no one except the children in the absence of the men and elder women. She could speak to her husband in privacy.[12]

The older woman, on the other hand, enjoyed freedom of movement and expression. She was afforded great respect, and in the event of her husband's death, she inherited the responsibilities of head of household and exercised authority over grown and married sons.

Life was difficult for the Armenian, for not only was the heavy Turkish taxation a great problem to the villager, he was in constant terror of raids and pillage. Living conditions in the villages frequently caused many men to go to the large cities to find work as hamals, the lowest of laborers. The money these porters earned went back to the village to pay the high taxes. The life of the hamals was one of deprivation and sadness. Treated as unskilled, undesirable labor, they were kept socially distant from even their wealthy compatriot merchants.

In spite of these intolerable conditions, a resurgence of the Armenian intelligentsia occurred in mid-nineteenth century. These men were concerned with political and social problems and effected a renaissance in Armenian literature and journalism concentrated in the areas of language, church and politics. There was a rebirth of learning, a movement away from the traditional church language, *krapar,* to the commonly spoken language, *ashkharapar.* A number of newspapers and journals were established. Gifted writers and editors contacted, motivated and inspired their people to a national consciousness and a spirit of protest.

Although patriotic literature was dangerous to read and dangerous to possess in Turkish Armenia, it was secretly circulated. The villagers soon discovered that the oral transmission of heroic stories about guerilla leaders had advantages: no writing could be confiscated by the oppressors—with the attendant reprisals; the villager who could not read or had no access to reading material could be inspired by a skillful storyteller; and, at one telling, a large number of villagers could be contacted. So it was that during this period, the oral tradition became even more important in the life of the folk.

Several male informants told of climbing to a small balcony above the stables on winter nights where, in the warmth of the room, the men would pass away the night listening to and telling stories.* On several occasions *fedayihs* [guerilla fighters] who were pursued by the Turks found refuge in the villages. In the evenings these patriots would tell of their experiences to the spellbound audience.

Since Armenia is an agricultural country which has hot summers and cold winters, the people had to adjust to extremes in weather. They worked hard all summer, building supplies of food and other necessities. The winter nights were made pleasant as the family gathered around a warm fire to card and soften the wool sheared from their sheep and the storyteller told tale after

* J. S. Wingate, in *Folk-Lore,* XXI (1910), 218, in speaking of the popularity of storytelling among the Armenian men, describes a similar scene in her introduction to Servantstian's stories from *Manana.*

tale during the monotonous work. When one storyteller stopped, another would begin, striving to outshine his predecessor. The older women had good reason to be competent storytellers for when the supply of tales was exhausted, the carding of wool stopped.

Similarly, much of the work involved in preparing the wheat for table consumption was done by hand. When fully ripe, wheat was cut with a scythe and gathered in sheaves. A team of oxen pulling a heavy weight broke the wheat stalks into pieces which were put into a machine to separate the wheat kernels from the straw used in the stables for the animals. While some wheat was left raw, the rest was boiled until pink and was later dried in the sun on large white sheets atop the flat *daneeks* [flat earthen roofs], later to be ground.* During the tedious sifting of wheat for tiny chips of stone and other impurities, the women told stories to each other.

Some other situations conducive to storytelling were associated with everyday events in the life of the villagers. Cotton blossoms were picked and carried to the house in containers. In the circle of friends and relatives gathered around the fire on a cold winter night, the storyteller would begin to relate treasure after treasure. The fascinated listeners would deftly lift the cotton from the outer shell, remove the seeds and pull the cotton apart with their fingers to soften it as the stories unfolded.

Armenia was a fertile land and produced magnificent fields of luscious grapes. To avoid theft from these valuable vineyards, the common practice was to station two men as guards every night until the fruit was picked. Shepherds, too, stayed with their flocks all night to prevent loss and injury. These men, over a small fire in the dark of the night, kept each other awake by telling tales until sunrise. More than one informant has told of hearing many stories in this manner.

In both town and village, women prepared dough for the large quantity of noodles needed by the family for some months ahead. The women folk all helped, passing away the long hours with one story after another. The young children of the house gathered around the women and listened with fascination until the last story was told.

If there were no urgent household tasks, families visited close neighbors, particularly in the towns. The most welcome guest was

* These *daneeks* were regularly leveled and kept in good condition. They were used for storytelling and for sleeping on warm summer nights.

the gifted storyteller, but all who were present had an opportunity to entertain the group. An example of this occurs in "Honor."

Although these are the more common situations, it is obvious that informal storytelling to children, regardless of age, and among women would take place at all times. And it is not at all surprising to learn that women found the long hours at the spinning wheel and the loom passed more quickly with a good storyteller nearby.

II

The Armenian Folktale

PUBLISHED COLLECTIONS
OF ARMENIAN FOLKTALES*

THE COLLECTION AND study of Armenian folklore throughout the world is today still in its infancy. Komitas *Vartabed* [member of Armenian church order] devoted his life (1869–1939) to collecting Armenian folksongs, even in the remotest villages of his homeland, arranging this music and making it available for performance. In recent years several gifted composers and musicians have followed in his tradition.[1]

In folktale collecting, however, only the surface of the rich Armenian oral tradition has been scratched. *Catholicos* [Armenian: Pope] Khrimian (1820–1907), affectionately called *Hairig* [Little Father], studied and traveled principally in Armenia. He stirred the patriotism of his people by means of preaching and writing combined with his active political role. His concern was for the poorer classes, the common folk.

It is not surprising that Khrimian's student, Bishop Garegin Servantstian (1840–92) was among the first collectors of the Armenian folktale. In his travels throughout the land he became aware of the rich oral tradition of the Armenians. Bishop Servantstian disguised himself as a layman to hear the tales in their complete form when he discovered that storytellers were shy in the presence of dignitaries.[2] Among his writings *Manana* (1876) and *Hamov-Hodov* (1884) are particularly concerned with the folktale. *Hamov-Hodov* [spicy-fragrant] which contains twenty-seven stories (fourteen Märchen), was translated into French by Frédéric Macler in 1905. Known as *Contes armeniens,* this book presents twenty-one stories. *Manana* has been impossible to find in the original Armenian, but J. S. Wingate's translations in *Folk-Lore* have made this material available in English.[3]

Several Armenian stories appeared in Baron August von Haxthausen's *Transcaucasia* (1854). The baron, however, was more interested in the description and background of his travels than in folktales.

* Full bibliographical data for works cited in this section will be found in Appendix C.

43

As Volume IV of *Armenische Bibliothek*, Grikor Chalatianz published *Märchen und Sagen* (1887). In his Foreword, Chalatianz indicated that these stories are from a larger private collection in the Lasarew Institute for Oriental Languages in Moscow. *Märchen und Sagen* consists of five Märchen and one moralistic tale collected in Erivan. These stories, beautifully written and complete in detail, are available in less splendor in Wingate's translations from *Manana*.[4]

The French collection by E. Henry Carnoy and Jean Nicolaïdes, *Traditions populaires de l'Asie Mineure* (1889) contains only one Armenian Märchen. The German collection by Dr. Heinrich von Wlislocki, *Märchen und Sagen der Bukowinaer und Sieburbürger Armenier* (1892) offers fewer than five good Märchen among its fifty stories. This volume is heavily weighted with myths, legends, moralistic tales, stories of wit and of the supernatural (ghosts, vampires, etc.). Thus, the motifs as well as kinds of stories in Wlislocki's collection show considerable evidence of the new culture to which the Armenians had adapted themselves. The effectiveness of this adaptation is evidenced by Wlislocki's statement:

> In just a few years, the Armenians have intermingled with the Hungarians very completely. The Armenian language is not taught any more and is used only in the church and among the older people in conversation.[5]

Lucy Garnett, in *Women of Turkey and Their Folklore*, Volume I (1890), printed several Armenian stories. Although her discussion of Armenian life and folkways is quite subjective and limited, this book still serves as a valuable source of Armenian tales for the English-speaking student.

In Cleveland, Ohio, A. G. Seklemian published a book of Armenian fairy tales, *The Golden Maiden* (1898). These twenty-nine stories, which he had collected in his schoolmaster days in Erzerum, Armenia, were somehow combined with Servantstian's stories to present more "complete" tales.[6]

In Seklemian's collection American cultural influences are not evident. However, Servantstian's stories show some American influences even though they were collected primarily in Van and Moush. In "Tiflis Duenna Gizeli," the hero boards a ship for America, is shipwrecked and reaches an island. There he discovers the magical fruits which cause and reverse transformations and then returns to the town of the World Beauty, dressed as an

American doctor, Dr. Carabobo.[7] It is interesting indeed that the American element entered the story collected in Armenia—undoubtedly because letters were arriving from family members and friends who had already emigrated to America; this same story—collected and recorded in Detroit—does not use the same American data.

In speaking of American influence, some is apparent in the Detroit collection of Armenian tales, but not as much as one might expect. Undoubtedly this is due to the slowness of the assimilative process for the storytelling generation. The most notable effect has been on the living arrangements described in the stories, e.g., the appearance of kitchens, kitchen tables and chairs, balconies, American money denominations. Letter writing, gunpowder and dynamite, mentioned in some stories, although not too common in Armenia, were known to the generation which emigrated to America.

In a bibliography of Armenian folk material Macler speaks of Raffi's *Contes persans* published in Paris in 1902. However, from the folklorist's point of view, this minute, artistic volume has little value because it contains no folktales.

Several additional translations into French by Macler of Armenian material in addition to *Contes armeniens* have been of interest to folklorists during this century. His *Contes et légendes de l'Armenie* (1911) and *Contes, légendes et épopées populaires d'Armenie* (1928) have made material available which is almost extinct in the original Armenian.

Minas Tcheraz, editor of *L'Armenie*, regularly wrote a series from 1889–1906 known as *"L'Orient inedit."* Published as part of *Contes et chanson populaires*, Tome XXXIX (1912), the book *L'Orient inedit* presents nine Märchen in a total of twenty-six stories and numerous anecdotes, legends and beliefs. Tcheraz, who was born into the high society of Constantinople, was particularly interested in the poor and those who ". . . having received no instruction and not being perceptibly changed since the early ages of the planet, still kept intact the traditions of the past."[8] Tcheraz was one of the few Armenian collectors who noted the background of his material in his collecting method. He found women to be the best storytellers: "Endowed with a strong memory and a brilliant imagination, they [old women] still keep all the handed-down legends of the past."[9]

I. Khatchatrianz' collection of sixteen stories, *Armenian Folk Tales* (1946), was translated from the Russian. The volume discloses nothing about informants, the time of the collecting activity or the technique used. These tales bear much resemblance to the stories of Servantstian. There is considerable similarity between the names of Chalatianz and Khatchatrianz, and the story origins of the two books are from Russian Armenia. Furthermore, in Chalatianz' Foreword he indicates that a large collection of material is deposited at the University of Moscow. Is it unreasonable to question whether the 1946 book is a further translation of the material deposited in the archives in 1887?

In the Foreword to Khatchatrianz' stories the fact is noted that the Russian way of life has affected the Armenian tale. For example, the heroine in one story has the privilege of choosing her own husband instead of accepting her father's decision. This motif appears a number of times in the Detroit collection also (see, among others: "The Monster's Hairs," "The Son of the Horse," "Honor," for free speech).

Zabelle Boyajian's artistic *Armenian Legends and Poems,* originally published in 1916 in London and reissued in 1959, is a collection of the historical legends (e.g., the story of Ara and Shameramis) and poetry of Armenia. The book, unfortunately, contains no folktales.

Only two of the four Armenian stories are Märchen in the Azerbaijan collection, *Die Prinzessin von Samarkand* (1951). Alfred Hermann, one of the editors, mentions that a wealth of Armenian tales which had been intended for publication is now lost.

In several volumes of Armenian tales which have been published in Egypt and in other countries in the Armenian language, no mention is made of the background of the stories. Whether these are really folktales taken from the oral tradition or whether they are artistic stories based on folk material is not clear. One of Armenia's most beloved writers, Hovhannes Toumanian (1869–1959) frequently used folk material as an inspiration to create literary works.

Undoubtedly there are other collections of folktales in the original Armenian which, if only one could obtain them, would be valuable for comparative studies. The volumes of Lalayan and Eminian at Harvard and the University of California, for example, are rare and irreplaceable and could not be trusted to the mails. Therefore, it was impossible to make use of these valuable ethnographic works in the comparative studies of the Detroit collection.

THE DETROIT COLLECTION

Story Distribution

THIS DETROIT COLLECTION of Armenian folktales contains numerous stories told by relatively few informants whose birthplaces or origins, with one exception, are geographically closely linked to Kharput. Tcheraz' collection, essentially an urban one, drew upon people who had come from the various provinces of Armenia with the prime concern of earning a livelihood in Constantinople; Servantstian collected his material in the areas of Van and Moush. Thus, several questions arose about the degree of similarity of these Detroit tales to stories in other Armenian collections and about whether the stories recorded in Detroit are representative of the oral tradition of more than Kharput and its environs.

A further concern was the comparison of the Armenian oral tradition, particularly in the Detroit stories, with variant tales of those countries which have influenced or have been influenced by Armenia through geographical locale, history, travel or migration. In the examination of these variants greater emphasis has been given to the Armenian material since this is most difficult to find, even in the Armenian language.

In attempting to determine whether the Detroit stories were provincial or representative of a larger oral tradition, various Armenian collections in the Armenian language, in French, German and English were used for comparative reading. Fifty-four parallels were located for the one hundred Detroit stories in the Armenian collections researched. Similarities between the Detroit Armenian tales and those stories in the comparative sources other than Armenian were even greater—sixty-seven of the one hundred stories have such parallels. Furthermore, in the study of both Armenian and other ethnic traditions, the largest groups of stories without parallels were among the anecdotes and legends, both of which are personal and localized in nature.

Specifically, in the forty Märchen, or fairy tales, presented in this volume, only seven have no Armenian parallels located to date. However, of these seven, parallels for all but four appear in folktale collections from other countries.

Of the fourteen moralistic stories next presented in this collection, parallels for all but five have been found in Armenian collections. Only three of these Detroit stories have no parallels in other folktale collections.

Anecdotes (seven presented in the Detroit collection) are generally localized since they are developed from some personal experience. Except for "The Curse," no other parallels, either in Armenian collections or others, have been located for the anecdotes in this volume.

Only one of the four humorous tales in this collection has no discoverable parallel. Of the eleven stories classified as pertaining to trickery and wit, two have Armenian parallels. However, nine of these stories have variants among other folktales.

Of four classified as anti-feminine stories, two have no parallels. However, all four stories have variants among the stories of other countries.

Legends (eleven presented here), like anecdotes, are localized and explain some unusual event. Except for one Armenian parallel, only scattered motifs appear in three stories in the comparative literature studied.

Of the three cumulative stories in this collection, one has a close Armenian parallel as well as a variant in the other collections. Only one of the three stories classified as myths is without an Armenian parallel; one story in this group has a variant in the folktales from other lands.

In summary, the evidence of comparative literature discloses that although the folktales in this Detroit collection are from informants who lived within a small geographical radius, these tales are not typically localized. Generally, even when parallels are not found in other Armenian collections, such parallels are frequently available in the folktale collections of other countries. The lack of Armenian parallels indicates either that not enough Armenian folktales have been collected or that collections which have been made are unavailable for comparative studies.

It is entirely possible that a wealth of Armenian folk material has been lost because the serious Armenian scholar in the nineteenth century was too much concerned with educating and patriotically motivating his people to appreciate the folktales as living history. It is possible, too, that these Armenians who fled the Turkish sword have been too much concerned—and necessarily so—with problems of adjustment and survival in a new land to record and thus preserve their oral tradition.

Parallels in Other Collections

Folklorists, anthropologists and philologists, aware of the remarkable similarities in folktales throughout the world, have explored through the years numerous theories in attempting to explain these similarities.[10] The Comparative Studies reveal also that the motifs and plots in the Detroit folktales are not unique to the Armenian people alone. On the basis of the striking similarities between the Armenian folktales and those of other national collections, some assumptions can be made about the tales collected in Detroit.

However, certain geographical and historical facts mentioned earlier make it impossible to say with finality that one or another event influenced the Armenian oral tradition in a specific manner. To say specifically what influence the Armenian migrations, both early and recent, have had on the folktales of the new land is equally difficult. Furthermore, since Armenians have scattered to all parts of the world, they have taken their stories with them. Few, if any, collectors identify their informants, and the possibility that the informant might be a first or second generation Armenian cannot be overlooked.

In the following paragraphs, brief summary statements indicate the apparent relationship between the Detroit Armenian tales and the tales in those oral traditions used for comparison. These similarities, which are concerned almost solely with the appearance and arrangement of motifs (the smallest story segment which can exist alone in the oral tradition) into plot and subplot, are arranged so that the most important similarities or influences are discussed first.

Greek. Perhaps the most striking similarities to the Detroit collection of Armenian tales appear in the Greek stories collected in Asia Minor, from various islands, as well as Greece. In *Modern Greek Folktales,* R. M. Dawkins, in presenting one representative story of each type from a number of collections of Greek folktales, comments on how frequently the best versions are found in the eastern Hellenic regions—even as far as the Pontos and Asia Minor.[11]

Although it might be said that the Greek stories collected in Asia Minor by Dawkins as well as by Carnoy and Nicholaïdes bear close resemblance to the Armenian tales because of their comparative geographic proximity, such proximity did not necessarily influence the similarity of the stories in *Modern Greek Folktales* or *Forty-Five Stories from the Dodekanese*. Yet the similarities of motif and motif arrangement are evident in the Märchen, the moralistic tales, myths, witty tales and stories of humor.

Russian. Considerable parallels to the Russian appear in the Märchen, moralistic tales, anti-feminine stories, witty stories, humorous stories—even in a legend ("The Bear Husband"). A large number of parallels appear well scattered through the entire collection.

As a Christian neighbor, Russia received many Armenians who fled their homeland during various periods of oppression. It is not inconceivable that some oral tradition traveled with these settlers.

Turkish. Since the folktales in the Detroit collection came from that part of Armenia which was under Turkish rule, even a glance at the Comparative Studies will indicate that numerous Turkish parallels to the Detroit stories exist. Although such variants are labelled "Turkish," it is important to distinguish between the Turkish people as such and the people who lived in Turkey. There is no way of knowing whether the informant for a "Turkish" tale was a real Turk, or a Greek, Armenian, Kurd or Jew who was telling the story in the Turkish language. Although the "outward trappings" of the Detroit Armenian stories such as settings, names, words, supernatural characters may show Turkish influence, the stories represent Armenian values, particularly in the moralistic, witty and humorous tales:

> It should not be forgotten that the Turk and the Christian were living side by side, that the Turkish society influence on the life and language of the Christian of the Empire was very great and that the Sultan's vizier and his other officials were just as important persons to them as they were to the Turk.[12]

Similarities between Armenian and Turkish stories occur chiefly among the Märchen in the use of motif and plot. Other similarities appear in the humorous, witty, moralistic tales and even in one myth.

Georgian. The number of Georgian parallels to the Armenian is not surprising. Geographical proximity and historical factors have contributed to the folk heritage:

The Armenian Emperor Mauricius placed upon the throne of Iberia the first Bagratid sovereign of the country, Gouaram (575–600 A.D.). Thereafter, Georgia, Aghouania, Mingrelia, and all the small Kartvelian states of the southern slope of the Caucasus were governed by Armenian rulers, and the last of the Georgian kings, Erekle II (1737–1797 A.D.) was still a Bagratid descendant.[13]

Azahaghan Handes, a magazine published in Tiflis, capital of Georgia, in the Armenian language during the years 1896–1916 (suspended during 1909, 1914–15) was concerned with the ethnographical material of the Armenian people.

Although most Armenian and Georgian parallels are found among the Märchen, two similarities occur in the moralistic tales, two in the humorous stories; one story is classified as wit and another as myth.

Siberian. The large Siberian collection, *Siberian Folk Tales* by C. Fillingham Coxwell, has been valuable in this comparative study. Most of the variants cited are limited to the Märchen; in addition, variants can be found for two moralistic tales, one witty story, one anti-feminine tale, one legend and one cumulative tale. In this respect the Siberian tales are different from the Russian parallels because of their limited range of similarity.

Gypsy. The large number of gypsy story parallels to not only the Armenian but to stories of neighboring cultures is one of the most astonishing results of the comparative readings. The Welsh-Gypsy, Romanian-Gypsy, Bukowina-Gypsy and Transylvania-Gypsy tales offer the most parallels among the gypsy collections. These similarities occur not only in the Märchen; four parallels occur in the moralistic tales, two in humorous, one witty, one legend and one myth.

The large number of gypsy parallels are difficult to explain. Francis H. Groome, who spent a lifetime collecting material about and studying the gypsy tribes, believed that the gypsies came from India and, in their wanderings across Europe, carried folktales with them. He speaks of the Romanian-Gypsy word *bakt* which, in one form or another, occurs in every gypsy dialect. Groome indicates that the occurrence of this word as a loan word in modern Greek and Turkish suggests a profound influence of the gypsies on the folklore of the Balkan peninsula. He adds that *bakt* is also good Persian.[14] *Bakt* is also used by Armenians in speaking of fortune. Several informants of the Detroit collection spoke of seeing gypsies occasionally but added that they were not welcome visitors.

Hungarian. The Hungarian parallels are most numerous in the Märchen, although variants occur in two moralistic tales, two witty tales and one anti-feminine tale. Interesting variants appear for the Märchen "Abo Beckeer," "Story of Mariam" and "Yeghnig Aghpar." Although Hungary has had no direct contact with Armenia either historically or geographically, it lies just north of the Balkan peninsula and was among the centers of Armenian migrations.

Italian. The greatest similarities among the Italian tales occur in the Märchen, although there are parallels for two moralistic tales, one humorous story, two tales of wit and one cumulative tale.

Persian. Although relatively few Persian stories were available for comparative purposes, the similarities are many and with only a few exceptions, are limited to the Märchen. Parallels are available for "The Cliff," "Fool's Luck," "Rooster's Advice," and only scattered motifs appear for "Foretelling the Future" and "*Vhy, Vhy, Vhy.*"

Among the probable reasons for this similarity is the fact that the boundaries between the two lands have undoubtedly been crossed many times and in both directions.

Azerbaijan. The Azerbaijan stories, although few in number, are interesting parallels to the stories in this collection. These variants which are limited to the Märchen are particularly noteworthy for the Detroit stories "Tanzara and Dyeer" and "The Country of the Beautiful Gardens." Undoubtedly, geographic proximity must be considered as one of the primary contributing factors for this similarity.

Romanian and Serbian. Romanian and Serbian collections are rich in parallels to the Detroit Armenian stories. Although most similarities are found among the Romanian Märchen, two parallels also occur for the moralistic tales, one each in humorous and anti-feminine stories.

Westward migrations must be considered as contributing factors for this similarity; a large Armenian settlement in Europe was in Bukowina which prior to World War I was a province of Austria-Hungary and later became part of Romania.

Basque. In his unique *Gypsy Folk Tales,* Francis H. Groome's quotation of Rev. Wentworth Webster's remark: "the ease with which Basque scholars acquire Magyar and the Hungarian, Basque," stimulated comparative readings in Basque folktales.[15] Although the parallels were many among the Märchen, similarities were found in three moralistic tales, one humorous and one witty tale.

Albanian. As a Balkan nation, Albania would be expected to offer tales with similarities to the Armenian. Most of these variants occur among the Märchen; there are some similarities among the stories of trickery and humor also.

Israeli. In using Dov Noy's *Folktales of Israel* as reference, it became apparent that the variants of the Detroit Armenian stories came from Jewish informants whose origins are the Middle East (with one exception from Lithuania). The absence of variants from a larger geographic area is in itself impressive. Most of these similarities occur among the Märchen, but there are parallels to three moralistic tales, one humorous and one witty story.

Scotch. Perhaps it is surprising to see Scotch stories in the Comparative Studies. A remark about the similarity between Scotch and Armenian food prompted this investigation.[16] However, similarities of folktales seem to be limited to the Märchen and do not greatly differ from other folktales in the Anglo-Saxon tradition.*

Arabian and Iraqi. The Arabian influence, as such, is difficult to measure. Both the period of Arabian conquest and the geographic location of Arabia have brought the two nations into frequent contact. The similarities of the Arabian stories collected by C. G. Campbell to those in the present collection are limited to several Märchen and moralistic tales.

E. S. Stevens' *Folk Tales from Iraq* bear interesting similarities to the Detroit stories. In the introduction the author indicates that she collected from Christian and Moslem alike; in fact, several stories were told by Armenian informants. Although the similarities are greatest among the Märchen, three parallels appear among the moralistic tales, one humorous, one witty and one anti-feminine tale.

* It is interesting to find a reference to the "kingdom of Sasunn" in J. Campbell's *Popular Tales of the West Highlands,* I (London, 1890–93), 128. Sassoun is the scene of the great Armenian national epic of David (see Leon Surmelian, *Daredevils of Sassoun* [Denver, 1964]).

Polish. The Polish stories, expected to be rich in comparisons, proved disappointing; it is very possible that the sources available were inadequate. Large numbers of Armenians have found refuge in Poland over the centuries and some evidences of this should have been evident in their folktales. The Armenian exiles, long before the fall of the Armenian kingdom in 1375:

> . . . carrying with them a handful of their native soil wrapped in cloth, scattered into southern Russia, into the Caucasus, and the land of the Cossacks, and forty thousand of them reached Poland. . . . They settled chiefly in the cities and in many places became the nucleus of Polish middle class life.[17]

In general then, we can say that although folklorists are in search of profound theories concerning the distribution of individual folktales, some influences and borrowings in both directions are evident in comparing the Armenian folktales with tales from other countries. No definite conclusions can be drawn at this time as to when or how these similarities have occurred. Generally, they have been caused either by transmission across geographical boundaries, the supplantation of cultures as political influences were felt, or the implantation of native folk tradition upon and from the land in which the Armenians made a new home.

Kinds of Stories

The typical Armenian story is the Märchen or *hekiat*, the fairy tale which is full of magical elements. The stories in this collection have been arranged so that the Märchen are found at the beginning of the volume and the more realistic stories toward the end.

Since the Armenian Märchen relies so much on magic for its plot development, some comment on the function of magic is necessary. Magic is used chiefly as an instrument—the means by which an impossible task is accomplished or the magical help is received from grateful animals. Frequently the search for a magical object serves as a hero task or a spur for the development of plot—even for the necessity for discovering the external soul of the wicked villain.

Magic is classified by folklorists as contagious or homeopathic.[18] A study of the magical motifs in this collection shows a considerable preference for contagious magic in which things,

54

having once been in contact, continue to act on each other at a distance even after the physical contact has been severed. Thus, two strands of hair from a helpful animal give the folktale hero the same magical help as the entire animal would give if it were present. In homeopathic magic, like produces like, or an effect resembles its cause. An example of this form of magic in these stories is the destruction of the external soul, thus causing the death of the "owner" who may be great distances away.

Not only is magic necessary for bringing about certain desirable conditions, it is used to retain such conditions through the use of tabu motifs. Among the more popular uses of the tabu are: precautions against rubbing, looking behind, entering a forbidden room, looking at the sun, seeing or dealing with the opposite sex, splashing water on oneself, complaining, revealing the secret of origin and calling aloud the magic name.

The moralistic tale, the collection's second most popular kind of story, uses fewer magical elements and is concerned more with moral values. In Christian Armenia the moralistic tale was a popular tool for parents, church and school in teaching youth about duty and wisdom; therefore, moral influence is apparent in these Detroit stories. At the end of most of these stories a specific virtue is either strongly implied or definitely stated.

The stories of humor as well as of wit and trickery generally involve real life situations with a minimum of magic used. Because the Armenians greatly value the qualities of intelligence and cunning, such tales are popular in the oral tradition.

The anecdote is a short, localized story having one or more motifs. It seems highly probable that the anecdote is an outgrowth of an unusual personal experience which has been repeated so often, or elaborated upon to such a degree, that it has entered into the stream of the oral folk tradition.

The sagas and legends are localized, having some basis in historical fact. The tellers of these tales seem usually to believe that the events which they relate happened at one time.

The anti-feminine tales, popular with the male audience and the male storyteller, poke fun at women as being ridiculous and second best. Unusual as it may seem, women told some of these stories about themselves.

The cumulative stories are not intended to be either reasonable or sensible. Frequently, pleasant word sounds or mere repetition of phrases are the only goals of the storyteller, and the plot is of minor consideration. The addition of one ridiculous event upon another makes these stories fun to hear.

The fact that there are only a few myths among the stories is noteworthy. The nature myths, like other pre-Christian interpretations of the world, were discouraged by the church. If the festival or deity could be Christianized, well and good. Otherwise, the church frowned on its use. The myths in the collection seem to indicate some degree of speculation about the phenomena of nature.

General Characteristics

Style. The style of the Detroit Armenian folktales shows a number of noteworthy characteristics. Fatalism and determinism are essential to plot development as well as to characterization. If a character has a dream, that dream will be fulfilled. If a prediction is made at the beginning of the story, there is no escaping or changing the course of events. In this sense the Armenian folktale is comparable to Greek tragedy. Fate is the one prevailing victor throughout the collection.

Sometimes the violence, cruelty and undeserved punishment in these stories shocks the modern reader. However, when considered as realities in the life of the subjugated Armenian villager, these elements are easier to understand.

The tempo of the Armenian folktale is slow, the story unfolding unhurriedly, gradually reaching its climax and ending when the narrator feels like stopping. The Märchen are characteristically long, but the rest of the stories are considerably shorter. In the moralistic tales and the anecdotes the same leisurely unfolding of events occurs; in the humorous tales and tales of trickery the action is somewhat livelier.

The mood of the Detroit Armenian folktale is achieved by several methods, one of which is the choice of an appropriate hero. In the Märchen the hero is courageous and fearless; the reader is ready for a story full of adventure. In the stories of trickery the hero is extremely clever, and the entire story takes on an air of excitement and cunning. In the humorous or numskull stories the hero always seems foolish and dumb but is truly the only one who comes out well at the end of the tale; the hero prepares us for the ridiculous events which follow.

Characterization. This device of determinism affects the choice of the folktale characters, too. There is no manifestation of free will or natural unfolding of character. Instead, in story after story stock characters appear. Inevitably, contrasting qualities emphasize the goodness of the hero and the badness of the villain. From the moment these stock characters come on the scene, the experienced folktale reader or hearer can predict what events will probably follow.[19]

Since many Armenians believe that a child born late in the married life of his parents is more gifted than his siblings, the hero is always either the third son of a king, the only son or the third son of a poor family. He is tricky and brave, frequently the possessor of supernatural strength or help, compassionate with the deserving and cruel to the wicked. The heroine is either an abused stepdaughter, the third daughter of a king or a poor family, or the only daughter of the king. She is beautiful, kind, unselfish and unsuspecting. Brothers and sisters generally appear in the tales as wicked people. Their purpose is to do all they can to add difficulty upon difficulty for the hero or heroine.

Parents have more varied roles. Fathers, for some unknown reason, generally appear as weak-willed and easily dominated by their wives—exactly the opposite of Armenian family life. Stepmothers are always presented in a bad light. The cruel woman is anxious to harm her stepchildren, and frequently does. Whenever the stepmother has a daughter of her own, she is certain to be very ugly, while the stepdaughter is beautiful.

Kings and queens are the instigators of hero tasks of one kind or another, as bridegroom tests to win the princess, tests to select the new ruler, cures to be secured for sickness or blindness, or tasks assigned just cruelly with the hope of destroying the hero. In the Lear pattern, kings are frequently led to believe the flattery of their elder daughters and do not recognize the truth and justice which the youngest speaks. Frequently kings are only head men of their villages; princesses do menial work.

Supernatural creatures appear in dual roles; they can be either helpful or destructive to the folktale hero. Animals, as a rule, are helpful, as are genii, fairies and dervishes. Demons or *devs*, more popularly giants, are less predictable. Sometimes they serve in the capacity of villains; in some stories they are not only good characters, but the heroes. Villains are selfish people who, no matter how strong, are eventually defeated by the hero. These bad men, or frequently giants and monsters, possess all the opposite qualities of the hero. If the hero is generous, the villain is not. If the hero is brave, the villain is not. Indeed, the law of extremes

57

is the guiding principle of character development within these stories.

The characters in the Detroit folktales generally do not have proper names. The narrator refers to them as the "boy," the "father," the "princess," or the "king." Furthermore, they seem to be ageless. One moment we are told that the hero is a small boy, the next, that he is anxious to marry the princess.

Although the number of characters in the tales varies from two to twenty, depending upon the length and complexity of the plot, not more than two or three appear before the reader in an active role at one time. The ingenious device of constantly shifting groups of characters to bring about the desired events is used.

Structure. In order to discover a predictable pattern of story structure, the tales in this collection were divided into introduction, body and conclusion. It became apparent that there are two kinds of introductions as well as two kinds of conclusions: the formula introduction and the introduction proper, and the formula conclusion and the conclusion proper.

The introductions and conclusions proper involve the motifs or motif cycles which occur as the tale begins or ends. It is evident that while introductions proper are highly individualistic for each story—differing widely even for versions of the same story—the conclusions proper are either absent or short.

The formula introductions and conclusions are tagged onto the tales and are totally unnecessary for the development of a specific story. When formula introductions appear, seldom are more than one used for an individual story. The concluding formulas, however, are elaborate, frequently numbering as many as five at the end of an individual story. Concluding formulas are attached to stories which have conclusions proper as well as to those stories which do not have them. The Märchen are more apt to have elaborate conclusions than are other tales.

Formula introductions are more variable than the formula conclusions. The most popular of these in the collection are: "Once upon a time," "Once there was," "There was once," "There was and there was not, there was," and "At one time there was and there was not."

The most popular tags appearing in the Armenian collections used in the Comparative Studies are: (Servantstian) "There was and there was not, God was there," "There was and there was not, there was a boy"; (Tcheraz) "There was someone, there was no one"; (Chalatianz) "There lived, there was"; (Nazinian) "There was, there was not, there was."

The most popular concluding formulas of the Detroit collection are: "They lived happily ever after," "They reached their purpose, and may we reach ours," "The boy married the girl, and there was a wedding for seven days and seven nights" (or forty days and forty nights), "From the sky fell three apples: one to me, one to the storyteller and one to the person who has entertained you," "They were tied to the tails of wild jackasses who were whipped and driven over mountainous trails: the largest piece they found later was only an ear," and "The story is ended: there is no more."

While each Detroit storyteller claimed all three apples in the closing tag for himself, this was in contrast to some closing tags found in other Armenian sources: "From the sky fell three apples: one for me, one for he who listens, one for he who understands"; "From the sky fell three apples: one for the storyteller, one for the listener and one for the reader." From Servantstian's stories these tags are most common: "They reached their purpose, may we reach ours from [with the help of] St. Mourad and St. Garabed"; "They reached their earthly purpose, may we reach our heavenly one"; "They reached their purpose and may St. Sarkis [supernatural helper in this particular story] help you reach yours."

In summary then, no predictable structure can be identified for the Armenian folktale as found in the Detroit collection; introductions proper and conclusions proper are variable, even with different versions of the same story; introductory tags appear with introductions proper as well as without them; and concluding tags appear with or without conclusions proper. While seldom more than one introductory tag appears with a single story, as many as four or five concluding tags may appear in one tale.*

Settings. The narrator is least concerned with the settings for the stories. If a place of action is suggested, it is always Armenia. In the realistic stories the informant may use his own village or that of one of his audience as the locale. The time element is quickly disposed of by saying, "Many years ago," or "Not many years ago." Since this is true of all the tales, regardless of the various narrators involved, it might be said that one characteristic

* This is in contrast to the Turkish stories in Naki Tezel, *Istanbul Masallari* (Istanbul, 1938). In these stories a great many introductory tags are used for a single story, but the ending formulas, when used, are short and simple.

of the Armenian folktale is the neglect of the storyteller to supply an appropriate background for the story which is to follow. In this respect the folktale is markedly different from the literary tale.

Motifs

The story structure of the Detroit tales might be described as a cycle of motifs which appear together, forming a chain reaction. When one motif cycle appears, the next can be expected, and subsequent ones will develop from that. Several of these cycles, then, are combined through the skill and memory of the storyteller to form the story.

Since these Armenian stories cannot be classified fully by the Aarne-Thompson Type, they are presented below according to motif groups. Furthermore, this same plan has been used for the arrangement of the stories in the Comparative Studies. Since many of the stories have more than one important motif cycle, the one which allows the simplest classification has been chosen. This choice has been purely an arbitrary one; numerous stories could have been grouped under one classification just as easily as under another; for example, "The Magic Box," which is classified under unusual births, can be placed with the stories concerning the object of search.

The Stith Thompson *Motif-Index* has been used to identify the motifs in the groups discussed below: external soul, magical source, magic sleep, transformations, supernatural creatures, tasks, marriage, unusual childbirth and the evil-doer.[20] The stories, as numbered in the table of contents and in which these motif cycles occur, are indicated throughout this section in parentheses. The listing of individual motifs is found in Appendix B.

The discussion in the following pages concerns the old beliefs of the Armenian people. Very few of these superstitions and customs are practiced by the people today, although some remnants are found in their folktales. Therefore, the active voice and present verb tense by no means imply present belief or practice.

External Soul (Story 1). Beliefs concerning the soul and life itself were undoubtedly important to primitive people. Therefore, it is not unusual to find evidences of these ideas preserved in the folktales. Manuk Abeghian used authorities from different periods of Armenian literature in developing his study of the soul beliefs of the Armenians. I am indebted to his research for much of the material in this section.[21]

Abeghian refers to the first and basic interpretation of soul as breath or wind and speaks of the interchangeability of the words in Armenian for breath (*shounch*), air (*ott*), and soul (*hokee*). He emphasizes that ghost and soul are called by the same word and were thought of as being of the same substance. Another belief about the soul regarded it as a shining light which came from heaven when a child was born. It lived in the heart itself in an indefinite shape or as a body of light.

Since it was believed that the soul left the mouth in death, it lived on apart from the body and was invisible. It could assume physical shape somewhat smaller than the body, or an animal shape, the most important of which was a bird (see "Ogre's Soul," "Son of the Horse"). Even inanimate objects, such as trees, were associated with soul beliefs, and the poor health of a tree symbolized that the human owner was in danger, too (see "Nine-Seeded Apple").

Departed souls could appear as good or evil. Good ghosts were associated with angels and holy beings; bad ghosts were considered to be the souls of sinners. Armenians believed that these bad ghosts were formerly scoundrels, Turks or suicides and credited them with doing much harm. In the shape of animals or men these unclean souls appeared before men and brought misfortune to them. Such departed bad souls constantly pursued the living and were eager to take them along. To prevent this, the living flattered the dead with attention and honored them with a funeral. They provided a *hokeh-hatz* [funeral dinner] with abundant food for the mourners. If, however, flattery was ineffective, the evil force of the soul might be destroyed by eating part of the dead man's heart, which was, and still is, considered the seat of the soul (see "Tanzara and Dyeer").

The belief that the soul of the departed needs special care exists even today. Special prayers for the peace of the departed are still said in church and until recently were chanted in individual homes on Saturday nights over the faint glow of incense. On the Monday after Easter the great celebration of *Merelotz* [Memorial Day] occurs. In Armenia whole families spent the afternoon at the cemeteries of their departed. It is still believed that the dead are happy to be remembered, and special graveside blessings and prayers are offered by priest and family even today in America.

Armenians believed it a great misfortune when a couple was childless. Not only were the joys of parenthood denied them, but there was the fear that no one would take care of the soul after death. Therefore, the soul would always wander because it was unhappy. For the same reason it was considered a misfortune when a person died in a far-off country because there, again, no one would be concerned with taking care of the soul.

The father's soul and his grave were held in special reverence by his sons. In the first story, "Ogre's Soul," the hero's adventure begins when the candle he is holding as he stands vigil at his father's new grave is suddenly extinguished.[22]

Magic Sleep (*Stories 2–3, 87–89*). The motif of a magic, death-like sleep and its close variant, petrification, appear numerous times in the Detroit tales.

Since the Armenians believed that the soul could leave the body and roam, during this period the body remained unconscious and awaited the soul's return. For all practical purposes this period of waiting was death-like. No one knew quite where the soul was or when it would return. Belief in a life token, interpreted broadly as the seat of the soul or the outward manifestation of the soul, makes it easier to understand why the body must lie in a death-like sleep when the token (necklace, sword) is removed.[23]

Supernatural Creatures (*Stories 4–11*). There seems to have been some confusion among the Detroit informants in the rigid classifications of supernatural creatures in these stories. *Devs*, dragons and snakes were frequently interchanged by the storytellers as were *devs*, fairies, *kaches*. *Elks* or *als*, *torx* or *torches* and dwarfs were sometimes spoken of as one group, at other times as separate, specific entities. Sometimes *elks* and *kaches* served identical functions, while at other times they were very different. Whether this designation is due to the memory lapse of the storyteller or the similarity of the classification in the folk mind itself is difficult to determine. Sometimes when supernatural creatures could not be identified, the classifications of "monster" or "spirit" were used by the collector.

The role of the supernatural creature is vital in the Armenian folktale for his work gives impetus to the plot. The helpful genie or dervish enables the hero to do almost impossible tasks. The evil giant or dwarf adds excitement and adventure to the tale. Several stories even have supernatural creatures as folk heroes.

Many stories depend upon the tricking or defeat of the supernatural adversary for the development of their action; when this
is accomplished, the story is done.

The most popular of these supernatural creatures is the *dev*
or demon. A distinction should be made here between the popular, modern version of the *dev* and the older one. Tcheraz speaks
of the *dev* of old, the mischievous spirit with superhuman
strength who could be mistaken for the devil. Chalatianz refers
to the dragon as the personification of Ariman (chief devil) who
was bent on exterminating the human race. Ananikian describes
devs in Armenian mythology who, in the form of wild beasts,
frightened men. Both male and female, they appeared as humans
during waking hours or took form of snakes.[24]

Modern Armenians still use the *dev* as a reference for great
strength or endurance: *devi ooj ounie* [he has the strength of a
dev]; *devi bes goudeh* [he eats like a *dev*]; *devi hasag ounie* [he
has the height of a *dev*].[25] Informants, when asked to specify the
characteristics of the *dev*, described and named "giant." All giants,
which are used interchangeably with *devs* in this discussion, do
not look alike; in fact, some look so much like humans that giant-
human marriage is practiced. Some giants are grotesque, with
one lip touching the heavens, the other, the earth. Some giants
have one head; others have as many as seven. There are blond
as well as red-headed giants.

The appearance of the orthodox giantess is impressive. She
has such huge breasts that the right one must be thrown over the
left shoulder, the left over the right shoulder. By throwing oneself upon a giantess' breast, a human being will be considered her
child and will receive no harm at her hands. The motif of kissing
the giantess' breasts occurs in Greek stories, too.[26]

Many human abilities are attributed to the giant in the Detroit collection. He is able to read, write, experience fear, make
love, run, feel grief, cry and has the power of transformation.
Some giants, like men, live in houses; others live in deep wells,
stony caves or thick forests surrounded with great treasures of
gold and silver. The magic, fiery, flying horses—sources of wisdom and magical aid for the folktale hero—are in their hands,
too. *Devs* appear alone or in groups of three, seven or forty brothers. They are usually strong, but foolish, and are more frequently
overcome with trickery than strength.

The belief appears in these stories that a giant parent cannot harm his children and that a giant, in turn, cannot harm his

parents. Whether this is an injection into the stories of Christian doctrine or whether it is actual "giant code" is for speculation. Some giants are highly interesting folktale characters because of their possession of the external soul.

The most unusual external soul motif which happens to appear in the giant stories closely resembles the Pandora story. The heroine breaks a tabu and opens a small box, thereby liberating a bee which is the soul of her giantess mother-in-law (see brief outline of "Mark in Her Palm" in the Comparative Studies for the story "Abo Beckeer").

The eating habits of giants have always been of concern to the characters in folktales. In these stories some giants eat indiscriminately, at all times. Others eat only once a month and don't seem to crave food for the rest of the month. All giants, no matter what their eating habits, seem to have the same cry in all these stories: "I smell human flesh!"

The death of a giant is always a serious affair. Again and again throughout these stories we learn that to kill a giant, one must hit him only once. A second blow renews his life.

In some stories a giant is buried just as any human would be. However, in one spectacular death scene there are great noises and screams beneath the earth, the ground breaks open, giants fall in and the earth closes over them (see "Abo Beckeer").

In these stories the dervish is a supernatural creature whose primary function is to cause transformations and encourage fertility in barren women. The dervishes, perhaps the second most popular supernatural creature in the stories, did exist in Armenia and were wise men who depended on the public favor for their survival.

The *torx* is a demon of either gigantic or dwarfish size. The *torx* appears in the Detroit stories as a dwarf no more than eighteen inches in height, possessing unusual strength and ability of one kind or another. One *torx* is a master card player and a gigantic eater. The most unusual dwarf in these stories possesses the external soul (see "Son of the Horse"). It was believed that these tiny people, who lived at the end of the world, were becoming smaller and smaller, and when they could pass through the eye of a needle, the world would come to an end.[27]

Elks, who have no motif classification unless they are considered elves or dwarfs, were believed to be the demons who attacked a woman in childbirth, pulling out her liver, strangling both her and her child, or stealing the human child and leaving behind a changeling. Since it is believed that the unborn child is fully developed by seven months, at this time the *elk* was most apt to cause miscarriage and future sterility.

Although referred to as men, *elks* could be of either sex and were believed to be half man, half animal, possessing one fiery eye, copper claws, iron teeth and fangs of a wild boar.[28] Their power was all the more terrifying because of their invisibility, effected by a pointed bonnet covered with small round bells which they wore constantly.[29]

To prevent the ever-present danger for an expectant mother, certain precautions were taken. Under her pillow was kept a sword, knife or something else of iron to ward off evil spirits. During birth, those near the mother swished the air with their hands, hoping to kill or frighten away the invisible *elks*. It was believed that the *elk*, when he wrenched away the mother's liver, had to touch it to water before he could eat it and harm the woman (see "The Curse").[30] Therefore, the same swishing procedure was carried on by the stream, to frighten away the *elk* if he should be there dipping the liver in water.

Several unusual stories explain the destructiveness of the *elks:* God created Adam and gave him the *al* (*elk*) for a companion, but since Adam was made of earth and the *al* was fiery, they were incompatible.[31] So God created Eve, an arrangement which excluded the *al* who became so jealous and upset that he cursed woman, vowing that he would get the best of her. Another story tells that Christ saw the *al* running with a human liver in his hand and commanded the demon to stop. The *al* begged for his life, promising that if he were set free, he would not harm any woman who cried for help in Christ's name; thus, special prayers are necessary during childbirth.

Known as *kaches* [brave ones, usually male] and *javerza-harses* [perpetual brides, nymphs—female], fairies were considered vain and unpredictable creatures. Armenians to this day call this group of spirits the "brave ones" or "better than us." Fairies rarely lived in waters but in high mountains, caves, deep valleys. In stories *javerzaharses* appeared with wings or as birds, and when these wings were removed, beautiful maidens stepped forth. It was generally believed that fairies were beings of air or wind who liked to linger under trees, especially nut trees. (One of the beliefs recalled by a Detroit informant concerned the nut tree's great power of drawing objects close to it. Therefore, it was the custom that only an old man could plant a walnut tree for fear of an early death, perhaps from the hands of the tricky *kaches.*)

Since they were soul-less, fairies were like animals: they could not learn anything or forget what they knew.[32] *Kaches* were mortal because they were born and could die, were both visible and invisible. They were dependent on human midwives to help their women bear children and rewarded these frightened midwives with onion and garlic skins which magically turned to gold.[33] Tcheraz, in speaking of midwives helping at fairy births, said that it was a bad omen to burn the skins of garlic or onion because they were the money of fairies. Even today the traditional Armenian Easter eggs are dyed by boiling the eggs with onion skins.

Since spirits are unable to touch iron, the female fairies could not sew and needed to borrow clothes from humans for weddings and feasts. To prevent this, the people put a cross among their clothes or hid a needle somewhere on a dress, making it impossible for the clothes to be worn by such a spirit (see "The Curse" for example of the power of a needle).

Animals as supernatural helpers are extremely popular in Armenian life and in the folktales. Rarely, however, is an animal the central character. More often he has the role or function of a supernatural helper, dispensing magic and advice and, for this reason, is discussed in the present section. The vagueness concerning the supernatural creatures in these Detroit stories encourages the analysis of these folktales by function or action performed rather than by specific actor. Therefore, the appearance of animals as supernatural creatures fits well into this discussion.[34] The tales in which animals appear are highly animistic —all the traits of humans are given to these creatures. They talk, marry, have young, possess wisdom and magical ability.

The horse is the animal which appears most frequently in the collection, and only rarely is it cast in an evil role. The magic *hureghen* [fiery, heavenly, or even flying horse] speaks, gives advice, possesses great jumping ability and is brave and cunning in fighting sea horses and water buffalo. Because of his fiery nature even his hoofs can cause the villain to burn to death.

The sea horse, although a fierce fighter, is important because his milk causes the regaining of youth, which is frequently set as a hero task. Furthermore, the new-born colt of a sea mare is endowed with great speed and magical powers. In the Armenian folk epic of David, Sanassar escaped the evil king of Baghdad with his twin brother. When they came to the sea, Sanassar threw himself in, the waves made a path for him and Sanassar descended under the sea to a beautiful garden. There he saw the beautiful, heavenly, fiery, flying horse Jallali who was saddled and carried a sword of lightning. In conversation with the horse the young boy proved that he was born from the sea (his mother became pregnant by drinking from a fountain). The horse recognized Sanassar as master and served him well.[35]

Snakes are the second most popular supernatural animal to appear in the Detroit stories. They speak, have great magical powers and are the source of knowledge, particularly medical knowledge. The stories tell of transformations to snakes and of the touching of a snake's tongue which serves as a source of knowledge. Magic objects are usually kept under the tongue of the king of snakes.

A number of informants have discussed saint snakes, the ancestral spirits which appear in the form of snakes, with considerable clarity. In many areas of Armenia it was believed that each home had a genie, a landlord in the form of a snake or turtle who protected his old home.[36] The saint snake, which was sometimes invisible, was supposed to be the luck of the house and to treat it badly, causing it to depart, was not wise. Instead, milk was left for it to drink for it was known that snakes love milk. It was foolhardy to hurt house snakes or saint snakes, which usually appeared in pairs, for the mate and its children would pursue the snake killer, no matter how many times he moved his residence. The best way that one could escape such a dreaded snake was to cross a wide body of water for it was believed that snakes cannot cross water.*

The folklore scholar Alexander Krappe believed that Armenian folktales originated from India because there, poisonous snakes which were both common and feared were believed to take on human shape.[37] In light of the common acceptance of saint snakes in the Armenia of these narrators, Krappe's supposition is not entirely accurate.

A close connection exists between the snake and the dragon in Armenian folklore. Chalatianz tells of the long life these terrifying dragons reportedly had.[38] The dragon grew to be very tall and very large. To prevent him from consuming the world's food

* Minas Tcheraz, in *L'Orient inédit* (Paris, 1912), p. 146, describes another method of escaping snakes. Because snakes cannot tolerate the odor of burning eggshell, creating this smell effectively chases away the unwanted snake.

supplies and thus destroying mankind, the angels descended from heaven, bound the wrists of the dragon with chains and pulled him up so high that the sun burned him to ashes. There was a sizzling sound, the dragon whined and his tail fell off and descended to earth (see "The Rising Snake").

Stories of the thunder snakes, called *veeshabs* or dragons, tell that their fighting caused a charge of thunder. This was a personification of the thunder whirlwind and thunder clouds. As a storm being, the thunder god was pictured as living high in the mountains. People believed that the screams of the dragon were the thunder. They believed, too, that when the dragon was cut into pieces, it fell to earth as snakes.[39]

In speaking of the role of birds in the Armenian towns, Garnett indicates that the public reverence of birds was so great that amazing numbers are found throughout the land. Indeed, in Erzerum as many as 175 varieties were counted.[40] The Armenian believed that it was a worthy thing to purchase a bird, hold it on one's right hand, circle it around one's head three times and then let it fly, saying, "Be free and carry my troubles away."[41]

In the Detroit stories the bird is used again and again as the object of search. The motif of selecting a new ruler by the flight of a bird is also a popular one (see "Magic Bird-heart," "Shepherd's Dream"). And, of course, we must not forget the beautiful birds who remove their wings and become lovely maidens and marry love-struck mortals.

Transformation (Stories 12–13). These Detroit stories are rich in the use of the transformation motif. Why this device should be so popular among the Armenians is conjectural. Perhaps the folk imagination or the numerous physical changes evident everywhere in plant and animal life helped popularize the idea of transformations. Certainly the belief that the human soul could exist apart from the body and assume human or animal form in restless visits to the living world must not be overlooked as contributing to the popularity of transformations.

To bring about the reversal of the transformation from animal to man, water, which is considered a purifier, is thrown into the face of the enchanted one in most instances.* In one

* It is interesting to speculate whether the girl-eating dragon or monster which appears several times in these stories and the scarcity of water which accompanies his appearance are remnants of the days of water worship and sacrifice. Grikor Chalatianz, in *Märchen und Sagen* (Leipzig, 1887), pp. x– xi, wrote that the historian Moses of Khorene mentioned one of the eastern

reversal the transformation is broken by burning the animal skin. Enchanted fruit—figs and apples—not only cause transformations from man to animal but cause the reversal as well.

Tasks (*Stories 14–19*). Every wonder tale is rich in the use of magic and must have some task for its hero to accomplish. Since many stories in this collection are wonder tales, the object of search or the motivation of the story is important for our consideration.

In these stories various physical qualities enable the hero to overcome great obstacles. Frequently, he is aided by superhuman companions in fulfilling tasks. These helpers have great prowess in running, throwing, eating, hearing, drinking and lifting.

In several stories tasks are given the hero by a jealous ruler even though he has already married the beauty. Demands for a huge rug, an enormous loaf of bread, many nails, and the world's greatest Bible which can be balanced on a thumb, are made of the hero.

Unusual suitor tasks are: the exact repetition of a phrase three times, discontinuing the work of a *halva*-maker [candy-maker] to gain the princess, dueling to win the beauty. And in several stories tricky tasks are required by the heroines when an undesirable marriage seems inevitable. The suitor is required to produce magic objects which the girl knows that only the hero possesses.

---

provinces of Armenia where, in 400 A.D., two black dragons were honored and given two young girls as a sacrifice. Manuk Abeghian, in *Der Armenische Volksglaube* (Leipzig, 1899), pp. 57, 61–62, indicated that Armenians, who even today believe flowing water is holy and must not be defiled, regarded certain wells as Christian holy places in front of which a sacrifice of hens was made, incense burned and special prayers said. Such wells had the special powers to cure illness and protect health (see stories 100. "The Sunset Lad" and 32. "The Story of Mariam").

The celebration of *Veejak* [Fate] on Ascension Day, an annual event in villages across the land, was described by several Detroit informants. The gaily dressed village girls in complete silence picked seven kinds of wild flowers and collected water from seven brooks. The flowers were placed in a clay jug along with a possession from each girl (ring, necklace, etc.). This vessel was hidden in full moonlight because it was believed that the stars which shined on it shaped man's destiny.

A little girl, dressed in white, personified Fate and stuck her hand into the jug, withdrawing objects at regular intervals. Meanwhile, a song of prophecy was sung by the girls. The sad or happy fate of this verse belonged to the owner of the object withdrawn.

Another Water Festival still observed by Armenians is *Vardevar* on Transfiguration Sunday when people sprinkle each other with water when they meet. No position in life affords protection, and no one is too high or holy to escape this shower.

An evil ruler often sets the hero on a difficult task with the hope that he will never return. Some of the objects which he must bring home are a talking bird, ivory, a beautiful bird and a beautiful maiden. Frequently, an evil task results in a suitor task for the hero, especially is this so when a maiden or bird (transformed maiden) is the object of the quest.

The object of search might be a cure for blindness or sickness. In a number of stories cures for feigned blindness or illness serve as stimuli for action. Frequently, as a result of the successful completion of this task, the new ruler is selected.

Magical Source (*Stories 20–22*). The source of magic must have been a topic of much speculation among the simple folk. The frequency with which this motif appears in the Detroit collection would seem to indicate that people actually believed in the possibility of obtaining supernatural powers if they learned the source of magic. Whereas most folk thought that magic objects served as the magical source, some believed that the possession of a person's name gave one control over his actions. Others thought that with magic-word formulas magic spells could be cast. These basic beliefs gave rise to the name-and-word magic motifs which appear in the Detroit stories.

Among the sources of magic in these stories are: two strands of hair from a monster, genie, or a horse's tail, or feathers from a bird. Where feathers or hair appear in this collection, the hero is told only to rub them together to call forth magical help. This is in contrast to the stories from other Armenian collections in which the hero must burn the hairs or feathers to receive help. Since the friction created by rubbing can create heat and even bring forth a fire, the intent or purpose is still the same. The Armenians, as did many others, believed that fire protected men and scared away bad spirits, especially during the night when the evil spirits who were everywhere could not exist in fire.*

---

* Although the *toneer* [sunken fireplace] does not appear in these stories, it might be considered here because it is associated with ancestor spirits, according to Mardiros Ananikian, "Armenian Mythology" in *Mythology of All Races* (Boston, 1925), VII, 54–58 and Abeghian, *op. cit.*, pp. 67–70. The belief that the hearth fire symbolizes the family's longevity appears in one of the most cherished Armenian blessings even today: "May your hearth (light) not be extinguished." (See Surmelian, *op. cit.*, p. 98.)

Details of the Fire Festival or the Festival of Mehr were related by several Detroit informants. On the Wednesday morning thirty days after Armenian Christmas (January 6), aromatic branches and twigs were placed in a big heap in the church yard by the young bridegrooms and those men who had been married within the past year. After a religious ceremony, a big

Unusual magical sources are a dead mother's bones, snakes appearing as supernatural helpers, the touching of a human tongue to that of the king of snakes and the possession of the signet under the king's tongue. Other sources of magic are: the magic horn, purse, rug, box, club, ring, saddle, sword, book, sponge, the highest rock on the mountain and two grinding stones. The circle is an element of magic which serves as a charm against evil spirits, while magic words and a magic name call forth supernatural help.

Marriage (*Stories 23–24*). In a land where tradition was as strong as in Armenia, one might well expect to find considerable lore about marriage. In "The Story of Mariam" a turtle must run up a tree before marriage can occur. In others the degree of ripeness of an apple and of a watermelon determines whether a king's daughter is of a marriageable age. In other stories changing the position of a lighted candle from the head to the foot of the bed seems to indicate that a girl has been chosen for marriage; drinking from her cup of sherbet has the same significance. Several stories present the unusual condition that the girl must marry her first suitor, or misfortune will follow. In "Nourie Hadig" a prediction is that the heroine will marry a dead man, and nothing she does permits her to escape this fate.

A number of times in this collection a princess has been given the privilege of selecting her husband which she does by shooting an arrow into a crowd or throwing an apple (often golden) to the man she chooses (see "The Monster's Hairs").

In the Detroit stories are a number of human-animal marriages. Girls are married to snakes, bears, lions, eagles; boys are married to turtles and reindeer. In all but "The Bear Husband" the animal mate is transformed by marriage and becomes human, at least at night.*

Unusual Childbirth (*Stories 25–29*). The stories make it apparent that the Armenian people were much concerned with the

---

fire was lighted, and the young men showed their courage by jumping over it. When the fire burned down, many people lit a candle to rekindle their hearth fire. Others were content with taking home a burnt piece of wood, believing it would bring them good luck.

* In discussing human-animal marriages, C. F. Coxwell, in *Siberian Folk Tales* (London, 1925), p. 252, writes: "The subject of mating with animals has important bearing on that of totem ancestry, which depends on the idea of human descent from animate or even inanimate objects." Consider this in light of the many snake and human marriages which appear in the Detroit stories and the belief in saint snakes by the Armenians.

birth of children and considered them a blessing. No matter in what station in life the characters are cast, kings or poor old couples, their great desire is to produce children. This is vital to the plot, since it serves as introduction for magical events. As a rule, a child conceived from eating magical fruit or drinking magical water has unusual characteristics of one kind or another, usually of appearance. He is either in animal form or of unusual size and strength. Frequently, conditions and agreements are made at the time of birth which, if not fulfilled, have tragic effects on the child's future.

Apples provide cures for barrenness, a frequently repeated motif.[42] While the apple aids fertility in women, the core causes mares to bear young.

The Evil-Doer (*Stories 30–35*). The stepmother and jealous brothers and sisters often serve to motivate and further the development of plot. Although the stories in this motif cycle grouping differ considerably from each other, the evil-doers serve as instigators of plot.

The previous pages have served as introduction and background for the stories which follow. The reader has become acquainted with the community from which the stories were collected and the method of collecting and transcribing these stories. He is familiar with some aspects of Armenian history and geography as well as the major migrations and new settlements through the ages. He is aware of the vitality of the oral tradition in Armenia and the remnants of this storytelling art in the American milieu. The kinds of stories, style and distribution of the stories have been discussed in order to prepare the scene for the Detroit tales. Important motifs have been examined to heighten the understanding of the magical elements and to associate them with facets of Armenian life and belief.

Only one hundred of the stories from the original collection appear in this volume. Numerous variants, however, have been outlined and appear in the Comparative Studies after the main story type which is analyzed; sometimes three and four versions are available in this way and are worth reading.

The Comparative Studies contain the type analysis for each story (when it is possible to designate it), the Bolte-Polívka references, available Armenian variants as well as a number of interesting parallels from collections of other lands. The bibliography for these references appears in Appendix C.

Examining these studies will prove stimulating to the reader. It will place the Armenian oral tradition along with the important traditions of the world. Furthermore, it will provide food for thought: how does one explain these similarities?

Now, to the stories. Good reading!

III

The Folktales

MÄRCHEN

1. The Ogre's Soul

ONCE UPON A TIME there was an old man who had three sons and three daughters. One day when he felt that his death was near, he called his sons together and said, "My sons, when I die, you will be masters of this house. Remember my wishes: your sisters are to be married to whoever asks for them, no matter who it may be." Soon after, he died.

It was a custom in those days to guard the grave of those who had just died. So the first night after the father was buried, the eldest son said that he would guard the grave. A little after midnight he fell asleep, however, and when he awoke the next morning, his father's body was lying on the ground beside him. Ashamed that he had done so poorly, he told a story about a huge *dev* [giant] who had overpowered him. Since no one knew the truth, the eldest brother was admired rather than scorned.

That same morning a little dwarf came to the home of the orphans. "I want to marry your sister," he told the eldest son.

"What are you saying, you dwarf! Marry my sister? Aren't you ashamed to come here with such a request?" the eldest son angrily asked.

"Who are you to ask for our sister?" the second brother shouted.

"But, brothers," the youngest said, "remember our father's last request. He told us to give our sisters to whoever asked for them, no matter who the men were."

"But he didn't mean a dwarf," the eldest objected.

"He said 'whoever,' and this would include a dwarf," the youngest said. So the dwarf took the eldest daughter by the hand and led her away to become his wife.

Later that day another dwarf came with the same request. The arguments were longer this time, but the youngest brother won again. The second daughter became the wife of the second dwarf.

This story was told by Nishan Krikorian.
See Comparative Studies for other versions.

77

That evening a third dwarf came, making the same proposition: he wanted to marry the third sister. Now that there was only the youngest girl left, all three brothers were reluctant to see her go. But remembering their father's dying request, they finally consented to the marriage.

As night drew near, the second son said, "Since our good brother stood guard last night, it is my turn tonight." So that night the second son kept watch over his father's grave. But he, too, fell asleep and went home the next morning to repeat the same story his brother had told.

The third night the youngest brother decided that he would like to try his luck with the monster who was not giving his father's spirit any peace. But before he left for the watch that evening, he slipped a knife and a handful of salt in his pocket.

A little after midnight he became drowsy, and realizing that he might fall asleep, he cut his finger with the knife and put salt on the wound. The pain was so sharp that it was impossible for him to sleep. Soon, he saw a huge seven-headed monster approaching him. He fired, but the monster escaped.

Meanwhile, the youngest son noticed that his candle was nearly extinguished. This was the one thing he had forgotten to provide for: an adequate supply of candles. He knew that he could not sit all night without a light, for how could he guard the grave in pitch darkness? There was only one thing for him to do: go to the village as soon as possible for more candles.

On the road he saw an old man who had two balls of yarn in his hands, one black and the other white. He was drawing the black toward him and lengthening the white one.

"What are you doing here at this time of the night without light, playing with yarn?" the youngest son asked him.

"My boy, it is obvious that you don't know who I am. I am Time. This black yarn represents the night and the white one, the day. I am drawing the black one toward me, that is, I'm shortening the night. It will soon be daybreak."

"Well, father, won't you please make the dark a little longer tonight? I must go to the village, get a light and return to my father's grave before daybreak," the boy pleaded.

"Very well, my son, I will work a little slower tonight," the old man said.

Farther down the road the boy noticed that smoke was rising from a nearby mountain. "Who could be there at this time of night?" he asked himself. He wondered if he might borrow a light and save himself the trip to the village. So he started in the direction of the smoke, which, sad to say, came from the cave of the seven-headed *dev*.

Entering the cave, the boy saw a huge woman baking bread. He reasoned that the woman must be the mother of the cave dweller and decided to gain her favor. He quickly kissed her breasts which, being so enormous, she had tossed over her shoulder, after the manner of giantesses.

The woman was surprised. "What do you want? What are you doing here?" she asked. So he told her his story. "Since you threw yourself upon my breast, you are my child; I cannot harm you. Listen, my son, very shortly my seven *dev* sons will be home. Among them is the seven-headed *dev* whom you nearly killed this evening. If these sons of mine should even suspect that you are here, they would eat you in a minute," she warned him.

"Then what can I do?"

"Here, hide in this closet while I get supper ready," she said, as she tried to lift a huge pan. Seeing that the weight of it was almost too much for her, he ran to her assistance and lifted the enormous pan with one hand. The giantess stood back to look at him in great surprise.

Soon her seven sons came home, and there was much excitement among them. The seven-headed *dev* was telling his brothers of a young boy who had so bravely stood guard by his father's grave. He had no idea, of course, that this same boy was in his mother's closet nearby. Soon one of the giants exclaimed, sniffing the air around him, "Mother, I smell human flesh."

"Yes, I do too," another one added. Soon all of them were gathered about their mother, asking questions.

"My sons, there is no human here," the mother tried to assure them.

"No, you cannot trick us. There is a human being here, and we shall have him for supper tonight with that fresh bread which you have just finished baking," one of them said.

The mother, seeing that there was no other way out, tried to frighten her boys. "My sons, you know what a time we have lifting that huge pan in which I bake. That human being who is hiding here can lift that pan with one hand."

"If this person is so strong, why not have him join us?" one of the giants asked. The others agreed that this would indeed be a good thing. The giantess led the boy out of the closet, and the eldest *dev* said, "We are told that you are an extraordinary human

79

being. If we all set upon you now, even though you are unusually strong, there would be nothing left of you. But there is something that you can do to save yourself: join us in our adventures, and you will be considered one of us."

"But what do you do?"

"We rob and plunder wherever and whoever we can," one of the giants replied. The boy, seeing that there was nothing for him to do except what they suggested, consented to become one of their band.

That night the giants planned to rob the king's palace. The boy became their leader because he not only had strength, but he had brains as well. Surrounding the palace was a huge wall which the robbers needed to climb in order to carry out their plans.

"Brothers, you are all very heavy," the boy told them. "Let me go up first, and if everything looks all right, I'll signal you, and then each of you can come up, one at a time."

The giants thought that this was a very good plan and let him climb the wall first. Seeing that everything was quiet, he signaled them.

As the oldest giant wanted to go up first, the others made way for him. Puffing, he finally reached the top. But as the giant made ready to go down the other side of the wall, the boy swiftly cut off the giant's seven heads at once. Before the body fell inside the palace grounds, the boy quickly cut off one of the giant's ears and placed it in his pocket.

The six brothers, seeing that their brother had successfully gained the top, fought among themselves to see who would be the next one up. As each one went over the wall, the boy cut off his heads and one ear, so that, soon, he had a collection of seven ears.

"Now that my work is done for tonight," he said to himself, "I will go inside this beautiful palace and see what these giants expected to find." He silently opened one door of the palace. Entering the room, he saw a beautiful young girl sleeping with a lighted candle at the head of her bed. He changed the position of the candle and placed it at her feet. Then he slipped a ring on her finger and said, "This is my eldest brother's fiancée."

Opening the next door, he saw an equally beautiful young girl. Again he changed the position of the candle and slipped a ring on her finger, saying, "This is my second brother's fiancée."

He opened a third door and found another beautiful girl

asleep. This one, however, was the most beautiful of all. "This," he said to himself, "is my fiancée." So he changed the position of the candle and slipped a ring on her finger, then escaped without being seen.

He quickly left the palace, climbed the wall and started for the village. On his way, he again saw the old man with the two balls of yarn. "Father, now you can pull the black one in altogether and let the white one out. I have finished my work for tonight."

The next morning he told his brothers of the night's adventures. But they would not believe him, for how could their youngest brother have done all this in one night? Meanwhile, the king's guards found the bodies of the seven giants inside the palace walls. They immediately told the king, who announced that the killer of the giants would receive any reward that he might wish.

The boy went to the king's palace to claim the reward.

"You?" the king asked incredulously. "Can you prove it?" From his pocket, the boy pulled a necklace of giants' ears which he had strung together. When the bodies were examined and the missing ears matched, the king was convinced and asked the boy what he would like to have as a reward.

"Your Majesty, you have three daughters, and I have two brothers. Give permission for my two brothers and myself to marry your daughters."

"You speak like a hero," the king said. "I am happy to give my daughters to mighty men like you." So preparations were made, and the king's followers and the daughters started the journey to the boy's home. When they arrived there, the first brother claimed his fiancée, the second claimed his fiancée, but suddenly they discovered that the third girl was missing. They looked everywhere, but when she was not to be found, the boy realized that some evil demon, seeing the girl's great beauty, must have run off with her. So he took leave of his brothers and set out in search of her.

After many days' travel, he came to the land where his eldest sister lived. She embraced him tenderly and asked what he was doing so far from home. When he had told her his story, he asked if she had seen the beautiful girl.

"I have not seen her, but it is possible that my husband has. However, I am afraid to ask because he has no love for my brothers, and since you are in his house, he may eat you in anger."

Just then they heard the dwarf approaching. The sister quickly hid her brother and greeted her husband with, "Husband, do you know what I dreamt last night?"

"How am I to know what human beings dream about?"

"I dreamt that my brothers were visiting me," she said.

"What! Your brothers! They had better not be, for I would eat them for my supper," the dwarf angrily replied.

"But, husband, my youngest brother was kind to you. You have no reason to dislike him."

"Yes, that is right. Your youngest brother would find welcome here," the dwarf agreed.

"Then, husband, we have a guest. Brother, come out!"

True to his word, the dwarf treated the youngest brother well and answered his questions about the missing fiancée: "Yes, I saw a demon carrying a beautiful young girl away. He passed through this part of the country early this morning."

After a little rest the youngest brother started toward his second sister's country. The dwarf-husband welcomed him because he, too, remembered that the boy was the one who had first consented to his sister's marriage. "Yes, I saw that demon, but he passed here early this afternoon," the dwarf replied after the boy told him the reason for his visit.

The youngest brother quickly said good-bye and started for the country of his third sister. Here again he was well received. "Yes, I saw a demon pass through our country with a beautiful young girl, but that was late in the afternoon. It is impossible for you to find them. That demon lives in the sea," the dwarf explained.

The youngest brother was greatly discouraged, but thanking his sister and brother-in-law, he went on. When he came to a large shady tree, he sat down to rest, and being very weary, he soon fell asleep.

Now, in that very same tree, there lived a huge bird—very much like our eagle. Every year a snake would eat all the bird's children while the mother bird was away. Of course, the boy knew nothing of this, and he had been sound asleep when he was awakened by a hissing noise. He jumped up and saw a snake climbing the tree, making straight for the little birds in the nest. In an instant he killed the snake, but still feeling sleepy, he resumed his nap.

The mother bird returned and saw a man sleeping under the tree. Thinking that this was the one who had eaten her children in years past, she began to beat him with her powerful wings. The boy, suddenly awakened from his sleep, had not yet realized what was happening and to his surprise found a bird beating him with her wings. "Now what's wrong? What have I done?" he wondered. The little birds up in their nest, seeing that their mother was hurting their protector, told her in bird language that the boy had saved them from the deadly snake.

"My youth, please forgive me, I did not know the true story," the mother bird exclaimed. "Ask for anything that you wish, and it shall be granted you."

The boy told her the story of the demon who had snatched the beloved girl and taken her into the sea. "I want to follow him into the sea. Can you help me?"

The bird flew with him to the sea, but before she left him there, she gave him two of her feathers and said, "Whenever you need anything, rub these feathers together and ask for it: it shall be yours."

As he explored the regions under the sea, he heard the strains of violin music and drifted toward the place where the music seemed to come from. There he saw the demon trying to bewitch his fiancée with lovely music. But soon the demon left, and the youngest son revealed himself to his fiancée.

"My love, do you know me?" he asked.

"Yes, I know you, and I knew you would come for me," she said.

"Tell me about the demon."

"There is not much to say except that he does not keep his soul in his body," she answered.

"Well, then," the boy said, "here is your first task. We must learn where he keeps his soul so that we can kill him."

When the demon returned that evening, the girl was attentive and tried to tickle his beard.* "Oh, my dear," she said, "I love you so much, but you say your soul is not in your body. Tell me where it is so that I can make a beautiful piece of embroidery and lay it over your soul."

"How sweet you are," the demon said. "My soul is in that broom."

The next morning when the demon left, the youth and his beloved pulled the broom apart but could not find the soul. They put it together again, and the girl tied many ribbons on it.

* A popular Armenian expression which refers to humoring a person or attempting to gain favor. Apple polishing is similar in meaning.

When the demon returned that evening, she showed him the ribbons on the broom. "Fool, how can there be a soul in a broom?" the demon laughed.

"Well, then, dearest one, tell me where it is."

"How much you must love me," the demon said, and he was most flattered. "To tell the truth, my soul is in the stomach of the lion who lives in a cave on Mt. Ararat."

The next morning the girl told her fiancé about the lion. He quickly rubbed the feathers together, and soon he was on Mt. Ararat. He found the lion's cave and killed the beast. He tore the stomach apart and found a glass cage with three little birds in it. These he knew were the three souls of the demon. He killed the first bird. The demon, who was out of the sea, quickly flew home and got into bed.

"What is the matter, dear one?" the girl inquired.

"I feel shaky, that's all. It will soon pass," the demon said.

The next morning the boy killed the second bird, and the demon, who was still in bed, turned very pale.

The boy rubbed the feathers together and went into the sea once again. "Demon, I have killed your two souls, and I have your third one in my hand now. As soon as I destroy it, you will die," he said.

"Let me see what my soul looks like," the demon asked weakly.

"So that you may grab it out of my hand? No! And now, here is your other soul," the boy said, squeezing the third bird. The demon breathed once more and died.

The youngest son and his fiancée embraced. He rubbed the feathers together, and they found themselves home with their brothers and sisters where they all lived very happily.

2. Nourie Hadig

There was once a rich man who had a very beautiful wife and a beautiful daughter known as Nourie Hadig [tiny piece of pomegranate]. Every month when the moon appeared in the sky, the wife asked: "New moon, am I the most beautiful or are you?" And every month the moon replied, "You are the most beautiful."

But when Nourie Hadig came to be fourteen years of age,

This story was told by Mrs. Akabi Mooradian.
See Comparative Studies for other versions.

she was so much more beautiful than her mother that the moon was forced to change her answer. One day when the mother asked the moon her constant question, the moon answered: "I am not the most beautiful nor are you. The father's and mother's only child, Nourie Hadig, is the most beautiful of all." Nourie Hadig was ideally named because her skin was perfectly white and she had rosy cheeks. And if you have ever seen a pomegranate, you know that it has red pulpy seeds with a red skin which has a pure white lining.

The mother was very jealous—so jealous, in fact, that she fell sick and went to bed. When Nourie Hadig returned from school that day, her mother refused to see her or speak to her. "My mother is very sick today," Nourie Hadig said to herself. When her father returned home, she told him that her mother was sick and refused to speak to her. The father went to see his wife and asked kindly, "What is the matter, wife? What ails you?"

"Something has happened which is so important that I must tell you immediately. Who is more necessary to you, your child or myself? You cannot have both of us."

"How can you speak in this way?" he asked her. "You are not a stepmother. How can you say such things about your own flesh and blood? How can I get rid of my own child?"

"I don't care what you do," the woman said. "You must get rid of her so that I will never see her again. Kill her and bring me her bloody shirt."

"She is your child as much as she is mine. But if you say I must kill her, then she will be killed," the father sadly answered. Then he went to his daughter and said, "Come, Nourie Hadig, we are going for a visit. Take some of your clothes and come with me."

The two of them went far away until finally it began to get dark. "You wait here while I go down to the brook to get some water for us to drink with our lunch," the father told his daughter.

Nourie Hadig waited and waited for her father to return, but he did not return. Not knowing what to do, she cried and walked through the woods trying to find a shelter. At last she saw a light in the distance, and approaching it, she came upon a large house. "Perhaps these people will take me in tonight," she said to herself. But as she put her hand on the door, it opened by itself, and as she passed inside, the door closed behind her immediately. She tried opening it again, but it would not open.

She walked through the house and saw many treasures. One

room was full of gold; another was full of silver; one was full of fur; one was full of bird feathers; one was full of chicken feathers; one was full of pearls; and one was full of rugs. She opened the door to another room and found a handsome youth sleeping. She called out to him, but he did not answer.

Suddenly she heard a voice tell her that she must look after this boy and prepare his food. She must place the food by his bedside and then leave; when she returned, the food would be gone. She was to do this for seven years for the youth was under a spell for that length of time. So, every day she cooked and took care of the boy. At the first new moon after Nourie Hadig had left home, her mother asked, "New moon, am I the most beautiful or are you?"

"I am not the most beautiful and neither are you," the new moon replied. "The father's and mother's only child, Nourie Hadig, is the most beautiful of all."

"Oh, that means that my husband has not killed her after all," the wicked woman said to herself. She was so angry that she went to bed again and pretended to be sick. "What did you do to our beautiful child?" she asked her husband. "What ever did you do to her?"

"You told me to get rid of her. So I got rid of her. You asked me to bring you her bloody shirt, and I did," her husband answered.

"When I told you that, I was ill. I didn't know what I was saying," his wife said. "Now I am sorry about it and plan to turn you over to the authorities as the murderer of your own child."

"Wife, what are you saying? You were the one who told me what to do, and now you want to hand me over to the authorities?"

"You must tell me what you did with our child!" the wife cried. Although the husband did not want to tell his wife that he had not killed their daughter, he was compelled to do so to save himself. "I did not kill her, wife. I killed a bird instead and dipped Nourie Hadig's shirt in its blood."

"You must bring her back, or you know what will happen to you," the wife threatened.

"I left her in the forest, but I don't know what happened to her after that."

"Very well, then, I will find her," the wife said. She traveled to distant places but could not find Nourie Hadig. Every new moon she asked her question and was assured that Nourie Hadig was the most beautiful of all. So on she went, searching for her daughter.

One day when Nourie Hadig had been at the bewitched house for four years, she looked out the window and saw a group of gypsies camping nearby. "I am lonely up here. Can you send up a pretty girl of about my own age?" she called to them. When they agreed to do so, she ran to the golden room and took a handful of gold pieces. These she threw down to the gypsies who, in turn, threw up the end of a rope to her. Then a girl started climbing at the other end of the rope and quickly reached her new mistress.

Nourie Hadig and the gypsy soon became good friends and decided to share the burden of taking care of the sleeping boy. One day, one would serve him; and the next day, the other would serve him. They continued in this way for three years. One warm summer day the gypsy was fanning the youth when he suddenly awoke. As he thought that the gypsy had served him for the entire seven years, he said to her: "I am a prince, and you are to be my princess for having cared for me such a long time." The gypsy said, "If you say it, so shall it be."

Nourie Hadig, who had heard what was said by the two, felt very bitter. She had been in the house alone for four years before the gypsy came and had served three years with her friend, and yet the other girl was to marry the handsome prince. Neither girl told the prince the truth about the arrangement.

Everything was being prepared for the wedding, and the prince was making arrangements to go to town and buy the bridal dress. Before he left, however, he told Nourie Hadig: "You must have served me a little while at least. Tell me what you would like me to bring back for you."

"Bring me a *saber dashee*,"* Nourie Hadig answered.

"What else do you want?" he asked, surprised at the modest request.

"Your happiness."

The prince went into town and purchased the bridal gown, then went to a stonecutter and asked for a *saber dashee*.

"Who is this for?" the stonecutter asked.

"For my servant," the prince replied.

"This is a stone of patience," the stonecutter said. "If one has great troubles and tells it to this *saber dashee*, certain changes

---

* A Turkish phrase, pronounced sah-bur dah-shee, meaning stone of patience.

will occur. If one's troubles are great, so great that the *saber dashee* cannot bear the sorrow, it will swell and burst. If, on the other hand, one makes much of only slight grievances, the *saber dashee* will not swell, but the speaker will. And if there is no one there to save this person, he will burst. So listen outside your servant's door. Not everyone knows of the *saber dashee,* and your servant, who is a very unusual person, must have a valuable story to tell. Be ready to run in and save her from bursting if she is in danger of doing so."

When the prince reached home, he gave his betrothed the dress and gave Nourie Hadig the *saber dashee.* That night the prince listened outside Nourie Hadig's door. The beautiful girl placed the *saber dashee* before her and started telling her story:

"*Saber dashee,*" she said, "I was the only child of a well-to-do family. My mother was very beautiful, but it was my misfortune to be even more beautiful than she. At every new moon my mother asked who was the most beautiful one in the world. And the new moon always answered that my mother was the most beautiful. One day my mother asked again, and the moon told her that Nourie Hadig was the most beautiful one in the whole world. My mother became very jealous and told my father to take me somewhere, to kill me and bring her my bloody shirt. My father could not do this, so he permitted me to go free," Nourie Hadig said. "Tell me, *saber dashee,* am I more patient or are you?"

The *saber dashee* began to swell.

The girl continued. "When my father left me, I walked until I saw this house in the distance. I walked toward it, and when I touched the door, it opened magically by itself. Once I was inside, the door closed behind me and never opened again until seven years later. Inside I found a handsome youth. A voice told me to prepare his food and take care of him. I did this for four years, day after day, night after night, living alone in a strange place, with no one to hear my voice. *Saber dashee,* tell me, am I more patient or are you?"

The *saber dashee* swelled a little more.

"One day a group of gypsies camped right beneath my window. As I had been lonely all these years, I bought a gypsy girl and pulled her up on a rope to the place where I was confined. Now, she and I took turns in serving the young boy who was under a magic spell. One day she cooked for him; and the next day I cooked for him. One day, three years later, while the gypsy was fanning him, the youth awoke and saw her. He thought that she had served him through all those years and took her as his betrothed. And the gypsy, whom I had bought and considered my friend, did not say one word to him about me. *Saber dashee*, tell me, am I more patient or are you?"

The *saber dashee* swelled and swelled and swelled. The prince, meanwhile, had heard this most unusual story and rushed in to keep the girl from bursting. But just as he stepped into the room, it was the *saber dashee* which burst.

"Nourie Hadig," the prince said, "it is not my fault that I chose the gypsy for my wife instead of you. I didn't know the whole story. You are to be my wife, and the gypsy will be your servant."

"No, since you are betrothed to her and all the preparations for the wedding are made, you must marry the gypsy," Nourie Hadig said.

"That will not do. You must be my wife and her mistress." So Nourie Hadig and the prince were married.

Nourie Hadig's mother, in the meanwhile, had never stopped searching for her daughter. One day she again asked the new moon the question, "New moon, am I the most beautiful or are you?"

"I am not the most beautiful nor are you. The princess of Adana* is the most beautiful of all," the new moon said. The mother knew immediately that Nourie Hadig was now married and lived in Adana. So she had a very beautiful ring made, so beautiful and brilliant that no one could resist it. But she put a potion in the ring that would make the wearer sleep. When she had finished her work, she called an old witch who traveled on a broomstick. "Witch, if you will take this ring and give it to the princess of Adana as a gift from her devoted mother, I will grant you your heart's desire."

So the mother gave the ring to the witch who set out for Adana immediately. The prince was not home when the witch arrived, and she was able to talk to Nourie Hadig and the gypsy alone. Said the witch, "Princess, this beautiful ring is a gift from your devoted mother. She was ill at the time you left home and said some angry words, but your father should not have paid attention to her since she was suffering from such pain." So she left the ring with Nourie Hadig and departed.

"My mother does not want me to be happy. Why should she

* Informant chose this town arbitrarily.

send me such a beautiful ring?" Nourie Hadig asked the gypsy.

"What harm can a ring do?" the gypsy asked.

So Nourie Hadig slipped the ring on her finger. No sooner was it on her finger than she became unconscious. The gypsy put her in bed but could do nothing further.

Soon the prince came home and found his wife in a deep sleep. No matter how much they shook her, she would not awaken; yet she had a pleasant smile on her face, and anyone who looked at her could not believe that she was in a trance. She was breathing, yet she did not open her eyes. No one was successful in awakening her.

"Nourie Hadig, you took care of me all those long years," the prince said. "Now I will look after you. I will not let them bury you. You are always to lie here, and the gypsy will guard you by night while I guard you by day," he said. So the prince stayed with her by day, and the gypsy guarded her by night. Nourie Hadig did not open her eyes once in three years. Healer after healer came and went, but none could help the beautiful girl.

One day the prince brought another healer to see Nourie Hadig, and although he could not help her in the least, he did not want to say so. When he was alone with the enchanted girl, he noticed her beautiful ring. "She is wearing so many rings and necklaces that no one will notice if I take this ring to my wife," he said to himself. As he slipped the ring off her finger, she opened her eyes and sat up. The healer immediately returned the ring to her finger. "Aha! I have discovered the secret!"

The next day he exacted many promises of wealth from the prince for his wife's cure. "I will give you anything you want if you can cure my wife," the prince said.

The healer, the prince and the gypsy went to the side of Nourie Hadig. "What are all those necklaces and ornaments? Is it fitting that a sick woman should wear such finery? Quick," he said to the gypsy, "remove them!" The gypsy removed all the jewelry except the ring. "Take that ring off, too," the healer ordered.

"But that ring was sent to her by her mother, and it is a dear remembrance," the gypsy said.

"What do you say? When did her mother send her a ring?" asked the prince. Before the gypsy could answer him, the healer took the ring off Nourie Hadig's finger. The princess immediately sat up and began to talk. They were all very happy: the healer, the prince, the princess and the gypsy who was now a real friend of Nourie Hadig.

Meanwhile, during all these years, whenever the mother had asked the moon her eternal question, it had replied, "You are the most beautiful!" But when Nourie Hadig was well again, the moon said, "I am not the most beautiful, neither are you. The father's and mother's only daughter, Nourie Hadig, the princess of Adana, is the most beautiful of all." The mother was so surprised and so angry that her daughter was alive that she died of rage there and then.

From the sky fell three apples: one to me, one to the storyteller and one to the person who has entertained you.

3. The Fairy Child

At one time there was a king who had three daughters. One day he overheard the youngest of his daughters say, "What is man when his wife is absent? It is the woman who is important and not her husband!" When the king heard this, he became angry and decided to marry his first two daughters to rich and noble men and his youngest daughter to a poor man to see what she would do. So he gave her to a man who was so poor that he barely earned enough money to buy a piece of stale bread to eat and who, at night, crept into the coal bins of other people to keep from freezing.

The princess did not mind the fact that her husband was poor, but she was unhappy because he was lazy. One day she said to him, "Go to the woods and bring me three pieces of wood." Her husband was surprised at such a request, but he did as she asked. When she got the wood, she hit him with it, and understandably, he became frightened of a woman who would hit her husband.

Several days later she said to him, "Go to the mountain and bring down a bundle of wood." He did not want to do this, but he was afraid that his wife would beat him, so he obeyed her. While he was up in the mountain, he looked here and there and under a stone, saw a pile of gold. He was too lazy to carry it down the mountain, so he took a few coins, and without getting the wood that his wife had asked for, he returned home. "Husband, where is the wood that I sent you for?" she said to him.

This story was told by Mrs. Katoon Mouradian.

"I didn't bring any down," the husband answered, "but I found these up there instead!"

The wife was angry, but when she saw the gold pieces, she asked the lazy man, "Did you see others like these up there?" He nodded his head. "Come with me then," she said, pushing him along. They climbed the mountain, and her husband led her to the stone under which he found the gold. They gathered all the gold that they could find, which amounted to a large sum of money. As they descended the mountain, the princess was already making plans for the future.

With the great treasure in her hands, she built a magnificent palace across from that of her father, and there she lived with her lazy husband. The king was amazed at this. How could his daughter, who was so poor that she could not find bread, bring together enough money to build such a palace?

As time went by, the princess was about to bear a child. Knowing that the child was to be born soon, she told her husband to find her a midwife. But her husband was so lazy that he did not know where to find a midwife, and neither did he care. So it seemed that the princess would bear her child alone, unaided. Suddenly the door opened, and five angels appeared who helped the princess in her labor.* She gave birth to a beautiful little girl, and the angels were overjoyed at the sight of her. The first one said, "I am going to put this necklace on your throat, my child. If it is taken off, you will die. If it is replaced, you will live again."

The second angel said, "When you bathe, your bath water will become golden, little girl, and so will your hair."

The third angel said, "When you cry, pearls will fall from your eyes, little girl."

"And when you laugh, red roses will bloom in your cheeks," the fourth angel added.

* Abeghian, *op. cit.*, p. 120, describes the supernatural help which sometimes occurs at childbirth: two virgin sisters, the spirits of Tuesday and Thursday, take the newborn, bathe it and sometimes present it with a gift and even a name. Their brother, the spirit of Saturday evening, stands ready to run errands. If a woman has not spent Tuesday, Thursday and Saturday evenings with her husband, thus respecting these virgin spirits, this magical aid will be hers. But if the mother has broken the taboo, these spirits can make labor difficult, even causing injury or death to the child.

Some people believe that fairies serve the function of the spirits described by Abeghian. Tcheraz, *op. cit.*, p. 249, says that Armenians believed (at the end of the nineteenth century) that each person had his fairy. If a person is well endowed with beauty and brains, people say, *"Peris shad sehretz kehz"* [the fairies liked you well].

"Whoever your first suitor is, that man you must marry," the fifth angel said, and together the five of them disappeared.

The years went by, and the little girl grew up. Each time she bathed, the bath water became golden. Each time she cried, pearls fell from her eyes, and when she laughed, roses bloomed in her cheeks.

The prince of a neighboring country dreamt about this beautiful girl and fell in love with her, even though he had seen her only in a dream. He decided that he would go from town to town, and village to village until he found her. This he did and after much travel, succeeded in finding the girl of his dream. The girl, seeing how handsome the prince was, returned his love, and a marriage was planned. Since the wedding was to be in eight days' time in the country of the prince, the youth quickly returned home to make preparations. Meanwhile, the family of the beautiful girl was making ready for the long journey to the prince's country.

As the years had passed, the two older sisters of the princess had become extremely jealous of their younger sister. They saw that she had the best home of any of them, the most money, the most beautiful daughter, and now, she would have an ideal son-in-law. But the youngest princess did not know of these things. She thought that her sisters were as sincere toward her as she was toward them. Therefore, who could be more faithful companions to her daughter on her wedding trip than her own sisters? So she asked them, "Dear sisters, will you take my daughter to the country of the prince? I trust you, whereas I wouldn't anyone else."

The sisters were happy for this was just the occasion they had been waiting for, and they promised to take the best care of their niece. "We will treat her as we would our own daughter," they reassured the mother. So a large caravan with many camels carrying rich and costly gifts was made ready. Finally, the beautiful girl, accompanied by her two aunts and a cousin her own age, started on the long journey.

On the way the girl became very thirsty and asked her aunts for a drink of water. "You will have water only if you give us one of your eyes," the aunts said. And the girl did not ask again until she was so thirsty that she knew she would die if she didn't have a drink of water. So she gave one of her eyes to her aunts and in turn received a small drink of water. Days passed by, and one day the girl could not endure her thirst any longer. When she asked for another drink of water, the evil aunts gouged out her other eye and abandoned the blind girl on the road. With the help of the second sister, the mother fixed the homely daughter to resemble somewhat the beautiful girl so that she could marry her to the prince.

Meanwhile, the blinded girl lay on the road and cried and cried. "My eyes! my eyes!" she called. And her tears which poured down quickly turned into pearls. An old man passing by saw the wealth of pearls on the ground and, tracing the source of it, found the beautiful blind girl weeping pearls. His heart melted when he saw her pitiful state, and he took her home to his old wife. When the girl saw that she was in friendly hands, she told them to bathe her; when they did so, the bath water turned into pure gold, and they had enough money to buy everything they needed.

However, the beautiful girl was always sad and tried to think of some way to get her eyes back. One day when the old man returned home, he told them that the prince of their country had refused, for some unknown reason, to marry the girl who had been sent to him from a distant land. The girl knew immediately that this bride was her cousin. She said to the old man, "I will smile, and roses will bloom in my cheeks. I will give you these roses. You go to the palace and sell them to the guests from the foreign country. But do not take money; ask only for an eye."

So she smiled, and roses bloomed in her cheeks. She picked them and made a bouquet which she gave to the old man to take to her aunts. The roses in her cheeks were unlike any others, and the prince had refused to marry the cousin because she could not produce these roses when she smiled. When the old man went to the palace, the aunt was happy to get the roses, even when she was told that the bouquet would cost an eye. So the old man was given an eye and returned with it to the girl who fitted it carefully into her right eye socket.

When the prince returned that night, the cousin took the roses to him and said, "See, these roses bloomed in my cheeks today, but you were not here to see them." The prince looked at them and knew that these were the roses that bloomed in the cheeks of the one he loved. Yet he could not believe that this girl was the woman he had chosen.

The following day the girl with only one eye smiled again, and the roses bloomed in her cheeks. She picked them and made another bouquet which she gave to the old man, telling him to take it to the palace and trade it for the left eye. This he did and returned with her left eye which she fitted into her eye socket. Now she was whole again; she could see. But she knew that she was not yet rid of her evil aunts and cousin.

When the aunts and the cousin had traded both eyes, they knew that the girl was not dead. So they schemed to get rid of her. They knew that she always wore a necklace which kept the fire of life burning within her. Their plan was to get that necklace. So the cousin lay in bed and cried, "Oh, how sick I am, how sick I am!" The prince and the king were told about her illness and came to see her. "What can we do for you?" the prince asked, for although he had not married her, he felt sorry for anyone who was in pain.

"Get me the necklace of life. I know it is somewhere near this palace," the cousin said.

So the guards were sent to all parts of the country and were instructed to look at all the necklaces to find the necklace of life. Meanwhile, the girl knew what was going to happen, and she told the old couple, "I have a necklace which is very beautiful and very important to me. However, the king's guards will take it away from me. When this happens, I will fall down and seem to be dead, but do not bury me for I shall not be really dead. When that necklace is again placed on my neck, I will open my eyes and continue the work which I was doing when I fell. Promise me that you will look after me and will not let me be buried. Put me at the top of the mountain so that the little birds will take care of me," she begged them. And the old couple so promised.

Soon the guards entered the old man's house and searching all about, finally found the necklace of life which they removed from the beautiful girl. As they did so, the girl fell to the ground as if she were dead. The old man and his wife took her to the top of the mountain and laid her there. The two took turns looking after her every moment, from the spring to the fall of that year.

Meanwhile, when the cousin saw the necklace of life, she became well again, for she thought that the girl no longer lived.

One day when the prince was hunting in the mountains, his dog ran off, and he set out to find it. The old woman who was sitting nearby combing her hair saw the prince hesitate to cross the river. She struck the river with her hair, and the water divided so that the prince could cross in safety. Surprised at this show of magic, the youth wondered how she was able to do this. Although no one knew it, the old woman and her husband who took care of the beautiful girl were both giants and possessed magical powers.

The old woman said to the prince, "I know you are looking for your dog. It is up there," pointing to the summit of the mountain. So the prince thanked her and started up the mountain. When he reached the top, he found his dog standing beside his beloved who was peaceful in a death-like sleep.

What could he do to bring her back to life? He thought about this as he descended the mountain. He remembered the necklace of life which had been found with such great difficulty for the sick fiancée. Surely, he thought, it must have some life-giving quality or why would it be called the necklace of life.

During the night he found the necklace at the palace and returned with it to the mountain top the following morning. When he placed the necklace about her neck, the girl sat up and smiled at her fiancé. Then, together, they descended the mountain, but not before the girl put her arms about the two old people and said to them, "My parents, again and again, you have given me hope and have seen me through difficult times. I owe my life to you."

On the way to the palace the prince asked her to tell him her story, and this she did. She told about the treachery of her aunts and cousin and of the help of the old couple. The aunts and cousin were tied to the tails of wild jackasses which raced over rough mountainous roads so that the bodies of the women were torn to pieces.

The prince and the girl celebrated a big wedding, and everyone from far and wide came and danced and sang. The old man and his wife were there, too, but no one could see them except the girl. Even to her, they looked just like you or me. But when they left the palace, they became large giants.

4. Clever Daniel

There was, once upon a time, a king who had three sons and one daughter. One day the king died, leaving behind his wife and children. Some time later the queen felt that she was about to die, too, so she called her children to her side and said to them, "Always remember this: whenever you leave the house to visit or

This story was told by Kasar Bogosian.

hunt, take your father's great sword, go into the garden and strike it on the marble slab. If you do so, nothing evil will happen to you. If you fail to do this, misfortune will come to you." Not long after that, she died.

One day the first prince decided to go hunting but did not do as his mother had instructed. He sat on his horse and rode until he came to a big, black mountain. There he saw a reindeer and decided to shoot it. He chased it and almost caught it many times, but it managed to escape. Finally, he saw that it entered the opening of a cave, and he followed it.

A huge giant welcomed him and said, "Come in and take your reindeer." The prince walked in cautiously. The giant said, "You are a nobleman; I must not walk ahead of you. Here, you walk before me." So the prince, flattered to be spoken to like this, walked boldly ahead. The giant lifted his sword and cut off the prince's head.

After some time, seeing that his brother did not return, the second prince decided to go and find him. But he, too, forgot to do as his mother had instructed. In time he also saw the reindeer his brother had seen and in search of it, came to the cave which the giant invited him to enter. "You are truly a man of noble birth; you must walk before me," the giant said. And the prince, very happy that he had been so honored, walked boldly ahead. The giant lifted his sword and cut off the prince's head.

When after three days neither brother had returned, the youngest prince decided to go and search for them. As he was about to leave, his sister happened to remember their mother's instructions and told her brother to strike the marble slab with the king's great sword. The boy was very grateful for this reminder, and when he did as his mother had directed, the marble slab broke in two. Then, he sat on his horse and rode forth. He hadn't gone far when he saw the same reindeer his brothers had seen and started on its trail which finally led to the cave.

The giant invited the prince to enter. The prince hesitated until he saw the horses of his two brothers. "Ah! my brothers are here too. Tell me, what have you done to them?" the prince asked the giant.

"Your brothers are inside. Come in, come in," the giant urged. "You are truly a noble person; you must walk ahead of me." The prince, suspecting trickery, said, "I will not walk before you but behind you." When the boy entered the cave, he saw the bodies of his two brothers and became so angry that he ran his sword through the giant's body. The giant fell but didn't die, as the prince thought he had.

The prince left the cave and when he reached home, said to his sister, "Dear sister, our two brothers are dead, and we are left alone. I have destroyed the giant who killed our brothers. His home is a very beautiful cave; let us go there to live." When the two decided to do this, the prince returned to the cave and put the giant's body in a room and closed the door on it.

"Sister, we will have a comfortable life in our new home," the prince told his sister, "but you must not open the last door. If you do, we will become very sad." She promised to do as he asked.

So, every day the prince took his bow and arrows and hunted for game, while his sister stayed in the cave and cooked for him. One day she became very tired of having so little to do and began to wonder what was in that forbidden room. "I will take only a little peek," she said to herself.

The giant, hearing this, cried out from the room, "If you will take care of me, I will become the world's most handsome man and will marry you." When the girl heard this, she was very happy. Now she would have something to do and not only would she have a husband, but the most handsome one in the world! So she opened the door and took care of the giant. When she cooked the meals, she always made more than she and her brother needed and secretly took the giant the best of everything.

Time passed and the sister became pregnant with the giant's child. "Husband, husband, kill that brother of mine, get rid of him. What is to become of us? How shall I bear my child?" she said to him continually. So the giant changed himself to a snake and crawled above the doorway where he waited for the hunter. But when the snake struck at the man, he was unsuccessful, and the prince was not hurt.

One day when the prince was hunting, the sister bore her child. But what was she to do with it? She quickly gave it some milk, wrapped it up and took it to her husband's room. "Husband, husband, what shall we do with this child?" she asked him.

"Throw him in your brother's path, and he will find it and bring it home," the giant said. So the sister took the baby and threw him in the path which she knew her brother would take. That evening when the prince was returning home, he saw the bundle and was so happy to find a child that he took it home with him and told his sister to bring it up as her own.

Three days later they baptized the child and named it Daniel. Every day the prince would leave the house early and return home late. This continued until the boy was almost six years old. For some time little Daniel had noticed that the best food was not eaten by his uncle or by his mother. Then where did it go? He decided to find out. One day he saw the giant eating and his mother speaking to him. He hid himself and listened to what they were saying.

"You must get rid of my brother," the mother was saying. "My child is old enough now to understand what is happening, and no one knows what he might tell his uncle for he loves him very much. You must do something."

"All right, then," the giant said, "I'll make myself into a snake and hide under the doorway. When your brother enters the cave tonight, I will bite his heel."

Daniel, although he was only six years old, was a giant's son; therefore, he was very great and powerful. That night when he saw his uncle nearing the cave, he ran toward him and said, "Uncle, you must let me carry you on my shoulders," and he insisted so much that the hunter did as the boy asked.

The giant, seeing that it was the heel of his own son that he would bite if he did as he had planned, did not bite. The next day when Daniel heard his parents speaking again, he listened and heard the giant say, "I'll coil myself above the entrance of the doorway. When your brother enters tonight, I'll strangle him."

That night when Daniel saw his uncle returning, he ran out and greeted him. "Uncle, you must carry me on your shoulders tonight. I carried you yesterday, and now you must carry me today," he said.

The uncle was puzzled by this behavior, but he loved the little boy so much that he did not want to disappoint him. So he placed Daniel on his shoulders and carried him inside the cave. The giant, seeing that he might hurt his own son, did not do as he had planned.

The following day Daniel heard his parents planning again. His mother said, "We must get rid of him; there is no other way."

"Go to bed and pretend that you are very sick," the giant advised. "Tell your brother that the only thing which will cure you is the meat of the big black bird on the top of the black mountain. Ask him to get it for you. This is very difficult to do, and he will probably die in the attempt. But, if he should return with the bird, you must kill it, boil it and drink the water in which the bird is boiled. That night, we must eat the meat, for it will be truly delicious. In the head of this bird, there are two drams of poison. Make three *gatah* [coffee rolls], one for you, one for Daniel and one for your brother. In your brother's *gatah* put the poison so that when he eats the *gatah*, he will die immediately," the giant said.

That day Daniel's mother went to bed and moaned and groaned. Daniel, meanwhile, was sitting near her side, playing with the knucklebone of one of the animals that his uncle had captured. She said to him, "Son, when your uncle comes home, tell him that I am very sick and that the only cure is the meat of the big black bird on the top of the black mountain."

So when his uncle returned, Daniel told him just what his mother had instructed him to say. "Ah! that is too bad," the prince said. "Tomorrow morning I will set out and capture this valuable bird and return with it."

True to his word, the prince, with great difficulty, captured the bird and returned to the cave with it. His sister thanked him and said, "Now I know that you love me. Now I know that you are a real brother."

The next morning when the prince left the cave, the sister quickly got out of bed. She killed the bird, cooked the meat, drank the stock, shared the meat with her husband and carefully saved the poison. Then she started making three *gatah*. She put the poison in one *gatah* and marked it so that she could tell which one it was. Daniel, who was sitting nearby and playing with the knucklebone, saw this, but his mother didn't know that he was watching.

That day when his uncle was to return home, Daniel ran out to meet him. "Uncle, my mother is well again," he said. The prince was happy to hear this and with Daniel, entered the cave.

"Brother, because you love me so much and because I am again well, I have made you a *gatah* today," she said. They all sat down, and when they were about to eat their *gatah*, Daniel noticed that the *gatah* before his uncle was marked, and he knew that it contained the poison.

"Uncle, do not eat your *gatah* until I run out to urinate," Daniel said, and having secured his uncle's promise, he went outside. But quickly he ran in and said, "Mother, uncle, soldiers are coming toward our house. What shall we do?"

"What is this? Soldiers? Here?" both of them cried and ran

out together. Daniel quickly put his uncle's *gatah* in front of his mother and his mother's *gatah* in front of his uncle.

In a few moments both uncle and mother returned, angry at Daniel because there were no soldiers outside. "Now let us eat our *gatah*," Daniel said. The mother, seeing that she had the poisoned *gatah*, did not want to eat it. But not to betray her secret, she ate it and two hours later, died.

They buried her with her two brothers. The prince wept bitterly, for he did not know the cause of her sudden death. "Uncle, uncle, you do not know what is happening around you," Daniel said, and he told his uncle about the giant in the next room and about the poisoned *gatah*. "Strike him only once," Daniel said, "for if you hit a giant more than once, he will regain all his strength."

So the prince, seeing that the giant was sleeping, drew his sword and cut off his head. The giant cried out, "If you are strong, show your courage and hit me again." But the prince answered, "If I am strong, I need to hit you only once." So the giant died, and the prince and Daniel took some of the gold concealed in the cave and left.

As they traveled, each took his turn keeping watch during the night. One stayed up one night, and the other, the following night. One night as Daniel was watching over his uncle, the light of his candle grew dim. He looked about and seeing a light in the distance, decided to go to it and relight his candle.

The trail led into the mountain, where he saw forty giants seated in a circle, waiting for a huge kettle of *kavoorma* [small pieces of meat] to cook. While they were waiting, they were playing with an apple. Daniel quietly lifted the huge kettle, lighted his candle, put the kettle back on the fire and started back to his uncle without saying a word.

But the giants had seen him and were most surprised. They could not lift the kettle unless all forty helped, and here this little boy had lifted it all by himself! Seeing that the boy was so powerful, they wanted him to be their friend. They called after him and told him that they wanted him to become a member of their robber band. They said, "The king has three very beautiful daughters, but they are locked in a palace of gold and silver which has no doors. If you can open this palace, you can have the youngest princess for yourself while we have the older two. Will you do it?"

So Daniel decided to try. He went to the palace, and found

that there was no door visible. But after searching for a while, he discovered a secret panel. Inside he found three girls sleeping, each with a ripe apple near her bed. He went back and told the giants to climb the high wall one by one, being careful not to arouse the sleeping guards. As each one climbed the wall and started descending the other side, Daniel cut off his head and kept his ears. When all forty of them were dead, he again entered the palace, took the apple of the youngest princess and with it returned to his sleeping uncle.

The next morning the two decided to go into the town nearby and spend the day there. As they entered, they saw a great commotion and asked the cause of it. They learned that forty dead giants had been found within the palace walls and that the apple of the youngest princess was missing.

"Oh, that's nothing," Daniel said, "I killed the forty giants, and here are their ears to prove it." He was taken before the king who was so pleased with him that he wanted to give him much money, but Daniel would have none of it. The youngest princess, seeing that the youth was very handsome and brave, said to her father, "Father, this boy took my apple—therefore he should marry me." So Daniel married the youngest princess; his uncle married the second princess; and they all lived in the palace the rest of their lives.

5. The Giant-Slayer

There was once a king who had three beautiful daughters. The girls were so beautiful that every day a red-haired giant secretly took the eldest princess to his palace, a big blond-haired giant took the second oldest princess to his palace, and an ugly black-haired giant took the youngest princess to his palace.

In another country there was a king who had three sons. This king had a younger brother who, because he had tried to gain control of the throne, was forced to hang on a rope from the ceiling in the throne room. At all times it was necessary for either the king or one of his three sons to sit on the royal throne. If they should leave the throne unoccupied and the rope swinging from the ceiling should break, the brother would take possession of the throne and would become king.

One day when the king felt that his end was near, he called

This story was told by Mrs. Katoon Mouradian.

his three sons to his bedside and said to them, "My sons, I am about to die. Receive my blessing, and may God give you many good and peaceful days. Since I will not be here to remind you of your duties, you must always remember that one of you must sit on the throne. Do not leave it empty even for a moment. If you should do so and the rope by which your uncle is hanging should break, he will occupy the throne and will make himself king. Then he will harm you. Remember also to stay away from the sea, the black mountain, the green grass and the old mill. Now pray for my sinful soul, my sons."

The king died, and the three princes took turns sitting on the royal throne for a while. But, as time went on, the two older brothers did not want to sit there while their friends were enjoying themselves. So they did not go into the royal throne room. The youngest prince continually told his brothers that they should do their part in occupying the throne, but as they did not, he sat on it day and night.

One day the youngest prince became angry. "My brothers enjoy themselves while they do not for one instant think of me. Why should I spend my life sitting on the throne day in and day out?" The very next morning he took his bow and arrows and started out to hunt.

The uncle, seeing that the throne was vacant, swayed back and forth many times until, finally, the rope broke, and he fell to the floor. Quickly he seated himself on the throne and established himself as king. When the three brothers returned home, the new king ordered that they be taken to the woods and killed and that their bloody shirts be brought to him.

So the guards took the three princes to the woods and were about to kill them when they suddenly felt very sorry for the unfortunate youths. "If we don't kill you, will you promise to stay away from this country?" they asked. When the brothers promised that they would, the guards asked for their royal shirts. Then they killed three crows which were nearby, dipped the shirts in the blood of the birds and permitted the princes to leave. The guards took the royal shirts back to the king who was happy in the thought that now he would not have to fear the young princes.

The three brothers, after they left the guards, walked until they came to an old mill. "Let us stop here and rest for the night," the older brothers said.

"Brothers, brothers, how can you think of staying here?

Don't you remember that our father told us to stay away from an old mill? We should not disobey him," the youngest prince said.

His brothers answered, "You may go on if you like; we will stay here tonight." Finally the youngest prince, although he did not think well of it, decided to remain with his brothers. The three princes went inside the mill where they made themselves comfortable and lay down to sleep. The youngest brother, however, was so troubled that he could not fall asleep and sat up to wait for the dawn. Near morning a huge giant entered the mill and approached the sleeping youths. The youngest prince, seeing him, aimed an arrow and killed the monster. The prince cut off half of the giant's ear, put it in his pocket and then went to sleep without waking his brothers and telling them what he had done.

The following day the three brothers started out again. They walked until sunset, and then, as they were very tired, they stopped to rest. "Let us spend the night on this nice green grass," the two brothers said.

"Brothers, we must not stay here. Our father told us to keep away from the green grass. Remember his words and do as he advised," the youngest brother begged.

"You said the same last night, and nothing happened. We will stay here. If you like, you can go on," the two older brothers said. But as before, the youngest prince decided to stay with them. The two older princes fell fast asleep, but again the youngest prince sat up with his arrows ready for whatever should come. After midnight a huge giant appeared and walked toward the sleeping youths. But the youngest prince, quick as thought, shot his arrow, and the giant fell dead. The youth then cut away the thick heavy skin from the middle of the giant's body and put it in his pocket along with the ear of the first giant. And in the morning he did not tell his brothers what had happened the night before.

The three brothers set out again. They walked until sunset, and being very tired, they stopped to rest. "Let us spend the night on this cool beach," the older brothers said.

"Brothers," the youngest prince said, "don't you remember what our father said before he died? He told us not to go near the sea. Come, let's move on."

"Enough of your talking!" the two brothers said. "You said that about the mill and the green grass and you say it again now. Nothing happened in those places, what could happen now? If you like, go on, but we will stay here tonight."

The youngest prince thought best to stay with his brothers so the three lay down to sleep by the seashore. But the youngest brother kept his arrows ready in case he should have need of them. And he was glad that he did so, for, after midnight, an ugly slimy creature slipped out of the water and moved toward the sleeping youths. Again the young prince shot an arrow and killed him. Then he cut off the animal's tail and put it in his pocket along with the giant's ear and the second giant's skin. The next morning he did not tell his brothers what had happened during the night.

That day the three brothers continued walking until they came to a large red building. "Brothers, let me go inside and see what kind of place this is," the youngest prince said as he entered. Inside he found a beautiful maiden seated, doing embroidery. "Youth, turn back, or the red-haired giant will come and eat you," she said. "Hurry! He will be home anytime now; I can hear his footsteps already." So the boy hid himself, and when the giant entered, even before he could greet the beautiful maiden, the prince shot him and cut off his ugly head. Then he left the building and without telling his brothers what he had done, went on with them.

They walked until they came to a white building. Here again, the young prince told his brothers to wait until he went inside to see who lived there. He saw another beautiful maiden seated and working on an embroidery. This girl was even more beautiful than the first one. When the maiden saw the boy, she cried out, "Youth, turn back and go home, or the blond-haired giant will come and eat you."

"When will he return?" the prince asked her.

"He'll be home any moment now; I can hear his footsteps already." So the prince hid himself with his weapons ready for use. When the giant entered, the boy aimed his arrow, killed the monster and cut off his head. And again he returned to his brothers without telling them what he had done.

Together they walked until they came to a black building. The prince asked his brothers to wait until he went in to see who was there. Inside he saw a third beautiful maiden, the most beautiful of the three, seated and doing embroidery. When she saw him, she begged, "Youth, go back, or the giant will come and eat you. He will be home soon for I can hear his footsteps already." So again the prince hid himself, ready to shoot. When the black-haired giant entered, the youth aimed his arrow, killed the ugly monster, cut off his head and returned to his brothers without telling them what had happened.

The three continued walking until they came to a high black mountain which the two older brothers decided to climb, and the youngest brother went with them. So they climbed the mountain for some distance and then settled down for the night. In the village below there was a great commotion, but the brothers did not know the cause of it. The two older brothers were hungry and sent their younger brother to the village to get some food. He climbed down the mountain, and on the road to the village he saw seven giants with huge millstones tied around their feet. They asked him where he was going. "My brothers and I are very hungry, and I came down to the village to buy some food," he answered.

"You will get food only if you deserve it," the giants said. "We'll tie one of these millstones around your leg and see if you can still walk." So they tied one of the heavy millstones around the prince's leg, but the youth was so strong that the stone split in half and fell off. When the giants saw this, they were both surprised and afraid. They gave the prince some food and told him, "We are seven brothers, and we want to marry the daughters of the king. The king had seven daughters, but, as four of them are married, there are only three left. You must go into the palace and bring us these princesses, and you must arrange it so that we can enter the palace walls and rob the palace."

The boy climbed the high wall that night and entered the palace. He went into the king's room where he saw a snake sliding toward the sleeping king. He immediately killed it, cut it into small pieces with his knife, put the pieces under the king's bed and stuck the snake's head into his pocket. Then he left the room and went into the rooms of the girls. He saw that each of the three princesses had a ripe apple placed at the head of her bed, signifying that she was ready for marriage. At the foot of each bed stood a lighted candle. The youth changed the position of the candles by moving them to the head of the beds. Then he put the apple of the first princess on the table of the second princess, the apple of the second princess on the table of the third princess and the apple of the third princess on the table of the first princess. He placed a ring on the finger of each of the girls and left the palace.

He climbed the wall and told the giants to come up one at a time and he would help them over the wall. As the first giant swung over the wall, the boy cut off his head and took the giant's bow and arrows. Soon all the seven giants who had climbed the wall one at a time were dead.

The next morning the king awoke to find the bodies of the seven giants within the palace wall. He wanted to know who had done this. That same day they found the pieces of the headless snake under the king's bed. "It must mean that this snake was about to kill me when someone killed it. It is likely that the person who killed this snake also killed the giants," the king said to himself. So he announced that anyone who could produce the head of the snake could have anything he wished.

When the youngest prince heard this, he went to the king and showed him the snake's head. "Youth, you have saved my life and the lives of my family. Ask for your reward: you will receive anything you wish," the king said.

"Your Majesty, I need no money, nor do I seek office. My only wish is to marry your youngest daughter and to have your other two daughters marry my two brothers," the boy said.

So the king ordered that arrangements be made for the royal weddings. The prince returned to the mountain for his brothers and brought them back to the village with him. There was a big wedding for the three couples, and everyone was made welcome and happy.

Two days after the wedding, however, the youngest of the brides said to her husband, "Why did I marry you? I don't love you. I'm not going to sleep with you."

"Why?" the husband asked, much surprised.

"I don't love you, I love the giant with seven heads," she replied.

The two older brothers reported that their wives had said the very same things to them. "What kind of girls have we married, I wonder?" the youngest prince asked himself. He decided to go away for forty days and went to his wife to say good-bye to her.

"Where are you going?" she asked.

"I am going to find this giant who is ruining my honor."

"Ha, ha," she laughed, "you can never hurt him. He lives at the top of Mt. Massis which is far from here, and even if you got there, it would be impossible to kill him."

That was all the prince wanted to know. He wore old clothes and started out on his search. After walking for a long time, he reached Mt. Massis and came upon a cave. He thought, "Ah! this must be where the seven-headed giant lives." As there was no one at home, he cleaned the house and the garden, prepared a good meal, then hid himself and awaited the owner's return.

When the giant returned, he was so pleased that he said, "Whoever you are who has cleaned my house and cooked my supper, show yourself, and I promise not to harm you." So the prince appeared in his old clothes, hunched up and acting like an old man. "Ah! it is you, old man. Well, I like your work, and if you don't get in my way, I will let you stay and work for me," the giant said.

So the prince stayed on. But the giant, who was not sure that his servant was really an old helpless man, said, "Old man, my sword is hanging from that tree there. Bring it to me."

The prince went to the tree and tried to lift the sword but pretended that it was much too heavy. "Ah! you fool, can't you even lift a sword? Are you so powerless?" the giant asked. But when he saw the terrified look on the prince's face, he burst out in laughter. "Ha, ha, it will be all right, I have nothing to fear," he thought, "if this man can't even lift my sword, surely he cannot harm me."

So the prince stayed with the giant and cooked and took care of the house and garden. Every night the prince saw that three birds flew into the giant's garden, took off their feathers and became beautiful girls. They entered the large pool nearby, and later they each took turns sleeping with the giant. One night the prince hid in the bushes beside the pool, and when the girls disrobed, he recognized his wife and his two sisters-in-law. "Ah! so this is their story!" he said to himself. He continued watching them for a whole week and saw that every night, at a certain time, they came to the giant's garden.

One day the giant asked the prince to take down his heavy sword from the tree. When the prince again pretended that he could not do it, the giant went to the tree and proceeded to show him how. "There, you see, like this!" he said. Content that he had shown his great strength, he lay down beneath the tree and fell sound asleep. The prince quietly neared the tree, quickly took down the sword and cut off the largest, biggest head of the giant. He dipped the sword in the blood of the giant, and when he burned the blood, the giant died. The prince dragged the giant's body into a cave and set a great stone at the entrance of it.

When it was about time for the three girls to visit, he returned to the giant's house. He arranged the bed so that it appeared that the giant was asleep. Then he hid himself and waited to see what would happen. The first princess went to bed, but found no giant there. Quickly she realized that something was wrong, so she flew away. The same thing happened to the second and third princesses but not before the prince had cut away part of their clothing.

The next morning he started for home. As he came to the red, white and black buildings, he told each girl that he would return in a week to take her away.

When he reached home, he told the king, his father-in-law, about the seven-headed giant and the princesses. "I will not believe what you say," the angry king replied. "How am I to know that you are speaking the truth?"

From his pocket the prince took the pieces which he had torn from the clothing of the three princesses and showed them to the king. "Here, my King, see if these do not belong to your daughters," the prince said. The king immediately recognized the cloth and ordered that his daughters be killed.

"You have suffered, my sons," the king told the brothers, "and for that, you shall be rewarded."

The three brothers went to the red, the white, and the black buildings and returned with the girls. The oldest brother married the maiden in the red building; the second brother married the maiden in the white building; and the youngest brother married the youngest maiden in the black building.

The oldest brother received the kingdom of his first father-in-law, the father of the three bad princesses; the second prince received the kingdom of the three giants. Meanwhile, the evil uncle, who formerly hung on a rope from the ceiling in the throne room, heard of the adventures of the three princes, and fearing that he would be attacked, he threw himself into the sea and died. And so the youngest prince became king of his own country, the land of his father.

6. Wisely Spent

Once upon a time there was a king who had three daughters. This king liked to disguise himself and walk through the town, listening to what the people had to say about him and the conditions under which they lived.

This story was told by Mrs. Mariam Serabian.
See Comparative Studies for another version.

The three princesses slept in one room, and on this particular night they had their window open, their lamp burning, and they were talking. The king, seeing the light, drew near and decided to listen to what they were saying.

"If my father gives me to a prince, I would make such a rug that all my father's soldiers could sit on it and half of it would still be unused," the first princess said.

"If my father gives me to a merchant, I would bake such a loaf of bread that all my father's soldiers could eat it and half of it would still be unused," the second princess said.

"The one who builds or pulls down the house is the wife," the third princess said. "I do not care to whom my father gives me."

"*Vhy!* [What!] How can that daughter of mine speak in such a way! I will teach her something! I will give her to a very poor man and see if it is really the woman who is the builder of the house," the king said to himself. So he called a hamal and gave this third princess to him. "Take her home with you. She is now your wife."

Of course, the hamal was much pleased to have such a beautiful lady for his wife. But he was very poor and already supported both his mother and his sister. So he took the princess to his house and returned to his work. Several days later the princess noticed that if her husband earned fifty *para* [Turkish coin], he spent all fifty that day, not saving a single *para*. So she took it upon herself to correct him.

"Husband, if you make twenty *para*, let's save ten *para* and spend ten. Let's do that for a whole week, and we shall see what happens," she said.

So each day of that week they saved some money. At the end of the week she gave her husband these instructions: "Go to the marketplace and bring me one spool of this thread and one spool of that thread—." The hamal went to the marketplace and bought the thread that his wife had asked for. She drew some original designs and began to embroider. As she was a princess and did unusual needlework, her embroidery was very beautiful. She made ten small pieces and gave them to her husband to sell for one-half gold piece each.

The husband sold the embroidery very quickly and with the money was ready to return home. Just as he was about to leave the marketplace, he heard a dervish saying, "For one piece of gold, I have one saying. For one piece of gold, I have one saying."

"I wonder what this dervish has to say that is so valuable. I will give him a gold piece and listen," the hamal said.

The dervish pocketed the money and said, "Do not leave this evening's work until tomorrow morning."

The hamal went home and told his wife of his success in selling her work. "But husband, the money is short. Where is the rest of it?"

"As I was leaving the marketplace, I saw a dervish who was crying that he had one saying to sell in exchange for one gold piece. I wanted to learn what this saying was, so I gave him one piece of gold," the hamal said.

"What did he say?"

"He said not to leave this evening's work until tomorrow morning," the husband replied.

"Ach! [Alas!] The dervish was just looking for someone simple like you. He gave you two silly words, and you gave him a gold piece. Never do such a foolish thing again."

However, she continued making beautiful embroideries, and her husband continued to take them to the marketplace and sell them at a good price. One day as he was returning home, he saw the dervish again at the entrance of the stalls. "For one gold piece, I'll give you one saying. For one gold piece, I'll give you one saying."

"I wonder what he has to say this time that is worth one gold piece," the hamal said to himself. So he gave the dervish a gold piece and heard, "Wherever you are called, don't be afraid, but go; if you aren't called, don't go."

When the boy returned home, he told his wife of the dervish's saying. Again she was angry and asked him to stop spending money foolishly.

The third time that he went to the market with her embroideries, he met the dervish again. "I'll give you one saying for one piece of gold, one saying for one piece of gold," he said.

Again the boy was interested to learn what it could be that would be worth a gold piece to hear. So he gave him a piece of gold and heard, "Your heart's desire is the most beautiful. The one whom your heart desires is the most beautiful. Remember these sayings."

When the hamal returned home, his wife was angry at him for wasting money and threatened to stop making needlework if he insisted on throwing the money away. The hamal knew that she was right, so he said nothing. However, the following morning he met the dervish again as he was leaving the marketplace. "For one piece of gold, I'll tell you one saying, for one piece of gold, I have one saying," he said.

So again the boy gave the old dervish a gold piece and heard, "Remember, patience is life."

When he returned home, his patient wife became angry, and the two began quarreling. So he decided to leave his home and seek his fortune. "Wife, I am going to seek my fortune," he told her.

"When?" she asked with some concern because she was expecting her child.

"Tonight," the boy said, remembering the dervish's first saying. So that very night he left his home and loved ones. He walked along and saw that a large crowd was gathering. He wanted to join them but suddenly remembered the dervish's words—not to go where he was not called. So he did not go. And fortunate it was that he hadn't gone, for the giants who were causing the commotion would certainly have eaten him as they did the others who were part of this crowd.

He continued walking until finally he came to a well. As he was very thirsty, he lowered his water pouch to get some water. But the well was almost dry, and he had to climb down to scoop some water. When he reached the bottom of the well, he saw a huge giantess whose one lip reached the sky and the other one, the earth. Her right breast was thrown over her left shoulder and her left breast over her right shoulder. Beside the giantess sat two women: one was a very beautiful golden girl, and the other was an ugly dark one.

"Which of these is the more beautiful?" the giantess asked the hamal. He began to think. If he should say that the golden girl was more beautiful, he would most certainly be punished. If he should say that the dark girl was more beautiful, he would be lying. So, remembering the dervish's words, he said: "The most beautiful is the one whom the heart desires." And it was a very good answer, too, for if he had said anything else, he would have been eaten by the giantess. Again the huge woman asked, "Which is the most beautiful?"

For a second time the boy replied, "The most beautiful is the one whom the heart desires."

The giantess asked her question a third time, and a third time, the boy gave the same answer.

The giantess was much pleased with the boy's answer and gave him three pomegranates full of jewels. The boy did not realize this, however, and thinking that they were only to be eaten, sent the pomegranates to his wife because she was with child. Meanwhile, when his wife opened one of the pomegranates and found all the precious stones, she built a beautiful palace and lived in it with her newborn son. They waited and looked forward to the husband's return.

The hamal moved on, working where he could and saving his money. After fifteen or sixteen years he decided to return home and live on his savings for the rest of his years. But when he reached the place where his home had been, he found a beautiful palace. He wondered where his wife was, where his old home was. He looked in a window to discover who could be living here. To his great surprise, he saw his wife lying beside a handsome young man. He became very angry to think that during all his hard lonely years, his wife had not been faithful to him.

He lifted his bow and arrow to shoot the youth when suddenly he remembered the dervish's words, "Patience is life." So he decided to wait and learn the truth of this.

"Who is that sleeping with you?" he sang outside the window.

"It is my son. Who are you, and why do you ask?" the woman said, not realizing that she was speaking to her husband. Then the hamal smiled and entered the door. He embraced his wife and his son whom he was seeing for the first time.

"How did you build such a beautiful palace?" he asked her.

"With some of the precious stones that I found in the pomegranates you sent me many years ago," she said. It was only then that he realized that the pomegranates were not ordinary fruits. The hamal then asked about his mother and sister.

"*Ach!* [Alas!] God rest their souls!" she said, telling her husband about their deaths years ago.

However, the boy, his wife and their son lived happily ever after. Their wish was realized, and ours will be, too. The story is ended.

From the sky fell three apples: one to me, one to the storyteller and one to the person who has entertained you.

7. The Seven Giant Brothers

There was once a giantess who was highly skilled in magic. She had seven grown sons and a baby daughter, all of whom

This story was told by Mrs. Katoon Mouradian.

were giants. One day the first son decided to seek his fortune and left home. Since he did not return, the second brother went to look for him. When the second brother failed to return, the third brother went after him, until finally, all seven brothers had left their mother.

As she grew up, the young sister could not remember her brothers and thought that she was an only child. One day she was attending a gathering with others of her age. In the center of the room there was a large red apple around which the people were dancing in a circle. Suddenly someone stole the apple, and everyone began to search for it.

When the guests were asked if they had taken it, each swore by the members of his family that he had not. But when the girl's turn came, she said, "I swear by my little white goat that I did not take it."

They said to her, "Why swear by your little goat? You have seven handsome young brothers. Why not swear by them?" The girl was very much troubled, for she had never been told about her brothers. When she returned home, she asked her mother if she really had seven brothers, so her mother told her the story of how they left home.

"Well, then," the girl said, "I must set out and find them." But where were they? How was she to find them? When her mother saw that she was very much in earnest, she said, "Daughter, I will make you a donkey out of clay which will take you where your brothers are. But you must not say 'Whoa, donkey.' If you do, the donkey will crumble to pieces. Otherwise, it will travel along until it reaches the place where your brothers are, and there it will fall apart."

So the giantess mother made a donkey for her daughter out of clay. The girl sat upon it and rode away. On the road she saw a large diamond, and she said to the donkey, forgetting her mother's instructions, "Whoa, donkey!" At those words the clay donkey crumbled to pieces. The girl picked up the diamond and started out on foot to return home. After months of travel she reached her mother's house and asked for a second donkey. Her mother made her another donkey out of clay, and the girl set out again.

She rode for months, over all kinds of roads and through many lands, until finally the donkey crumbled to pieces near a beautiful palace which was built on the highest peak of a mountain. "This must be my brothers' home," the girl said. She entered and saw that the people who lived there were undoubtedly hunters who were away for the day. She cleaned the house, made the beds, cooked the supper, and when it was time for her brothers to return, she hid herself inside a rug that had been rolled in a corner.

Soon her youngest brother returned to prepare the supper for his brothers but saw that the house was neat and clean and that the supper was cooked. "Who could have done this?" he asked himself. He looked about but was unable to find anyone. "I won't tell my brothers anything about this today. We'll wait and see what happens tomorrow."

The next day when he returned, again he saw that the house was clean and neat and that the supper was cooked. Then he told his brothers, and they were greatly puzzled. "Stay home tomorrow and pretend that you are sick. Learn who this person is," the brothers said.

When the six brothers left the next morning, the seventh brother stayed in bed and pretended he was sick. The sister, not knowing that the boy had stayed home, came out of the rolled rug and began to clean the house. The youngest brother jumped out of bed and caught her. "Who are you, and what are you doing here?" he asked.

"I am your sister, and I have come to keep house for you," the girl said.

The brother was indeed very happy, and when the six hunters returned that night, they, too, were happy to learn that this beautiful girl was their young sister.

Every day she found two raisins in the palace. She was instructed to eat one herself and to give the other to the kitten. One day she was unable to find the kitten, so she ate both raisins herself. The kitten returned as the girl was stringing rubies and became angry because he did not have a raisin to eat that day. He went to the fireplace and urinated there, putting out the fire. The girl knew that her brothers would be angry with her if they returned and saw that the fire was out. She went outside and saw smoke from a mountain nearby. "I will go there and ask for a light," she decided.

She took the form of a gust of wind and went to the mountain where she saw seven giantess sisters cooking *hadig* [a whole grain pilaff]. She asked them for some fire, and they gave her some which she gathered up in her skirt. Then she returned to the palace of her brothers.

When she reached home, a seven-headed giant appeared outside the palace and said to her, "Give me your little finger to suck your blood. If you refuse me, I will eat you up." The girl, afraid of the huge creature, did as he asked. She stuck her finger through the door, and the giant sucked her blood. The giant appeared several times a day and sucked her finger. Meanwhile, the brothers saw that their sister was becoming more and more pale. She grew very quiet and lost the bloom of youth. The youngest brother asked her one day what was troubling her. So she told him about the seven-headed giant who visited her.

"I'll stay home tomorrow, and when he asks you to stick out your finger, refuse to do so, and leave the rest to me," her brother said.

This she did. When the giant came the following morning and asked her to stick out her finger, she refused to do so, and the giant threatened to come in and eat her. "Come in, if you will, but I will not let you suck my blood any longer," the sister said. So the giant flung the door open and entered, but the brother was ready for him and killed him immediately.

Some time later she told her brothers about the fire she had borrowed from the nearby mountain. The brothers were surprised that anyone was living nearby.

"There were seven beautiful giantesses there who befriended me," their sister replied. So the seven brothers went to that mountain and brought back the seven sisters for their brides. The seven giantess sisters pretended to like their sister-in-law very much, but secretly, they were jealous of the brothers' love for their sister and they planned a way to get rid of her.

The sister was a good *gatah*-maker [coffee-roll-maker]. One day the eldest of the seven giantess sisters asked the girl to make them some *gatah*, and the girl gladly did so. While she was not looking, the giantess put a little snake in the *gatah* and after it was baked, had the girl eat it. The sister did not know she had eaten a snake but knew that she had eaten something which did not belong in the *gatah*. She asked for her handkerchief, but the giantess said that it could not be found.*

In time the snake in the girl's stomach grew larger and larger, and the girl became paler and paler. The brothers thought that their sister had been unfaithful and had become pregnant. They called their youngest brother to them and told him, "You

---

* Informant added that if the handkerchief could have been found, no harm would have come to the girl.

were the one to find our sister; now you must be the one to get rid of her. No matter how you do it, this must be done." So the youngest brother asked his sister to take a walk with him. The two walked and walked and walked until the sister became very tired and asked her brother if she could stop by the brook and rest a bit.

The brother put his arm under her head to serve as a pillow, and the girl fell sound asleep. Then the brother cut off his arm and left her alone. By magic another arm grew to the younger brother in place of the one which was left under the head of the girl.

In a field nearby a farmer was plowing and witnessed the scene between the girl and her brother. "I wonder who this girl is?" he thought, noticing her condition and watching her to see what would happen when she awakened. Soon the snakes in the region decided that it was time to go to the brook for a drink. When the huge snake in her stomach smelled other snakes, he stuck his head out of the sleeping girl's mouth and began to talk. "Where are you going?" he asked.

"We are going to drink," the snakes answered. "Come with us."

"Oh, I cannot do that," the snake said, "I have a nice home here because whatever this girl eats, I eat."

"That is nothing," the other snakes said, "we can eat anything we wish out here. You can only eat what the girl eats. Come out!"

The snake thought for a while, then decided that perhaps the other snakes were right, so he writhed his long body through the sleeping girl's mouth and came out. The plower, who was witnessing all this quickly killed the snake and cut it into many pieces. Then he returned to his work and waited for the girl to awaken.

Soon the girl woke up and seeing that she had been tricked by her brother, cursed, "May a thorn pierce his foot, and may he travel throughout all the world for a cure. Finally, may he return to me, when, with the touch of my little finger, I will cure him." At this very moment a thorn pierced the youngest brother's foot, and all the healers of the world could not help him remove it. He wandered from town to town in hope that someone, somewhere, would know a cure.

Meanwhile, the plower took the sister home to his old wife and said, "My girl, you have been left alone, but that does not matter. Stay with us, for although we have wanted children all our lives, we have never had one. Stay with us and be our daughter."

The girl, seeing that these people were good, decided to stay with them and help them. "I know that you have wanted children for many years. There is a mountain known as the Black Mountain. If you go there, you will see that there is nothing on this mountain but a beautiful white bird, a sheep dog and a brook. If you bathe in that brook, you will have a son."

The plower thought a minute and said, "But there is no Black Mountain near us. Why do you claim that there is?"

"Come with me, and I will show you," the girl said, taking the old couple to a mountain which was indeed black and just outside the town. They easily found the brook, and the old couple bathed in it. When they stepped out, the woman looked twenty-five years old and her husband, twenty-eight years old. They left the mountain, and when they turned around to make certain that they were not imagining things, they saw it no more: it had disappeared.

Soon after their return home, the woman became pregnant. After a year a son was born, and after the child was born, the mother again became fifty years old, and her husband became as old as he had been formerly.

Meanwhile, the youngest brother was still looking for a cure for the thorn in his foot. He came again to the brook where he had left his sister. "I wonder what happened to her? I wonder which animal ate her, the unfortunate girl."

The plower, seeing the youth, offered to help him. "Tell me, is there a healer in this village?" the youngest brother asked.

"Yes, I know a very good healer in this village," the plower said. "If she can't cure you, no one will be able to." So he took the youngest brother to his home. The moment the sister saw the visitor she recognized him, but he was unable to recognize her.

"If I am to cure this man, you must leave me alone with him," she said. When they were alone, she put her little finger on his sore foot, and the thorn magically fell out.

"How did you do that?" the amazed boy asked.

"Do you recognize me?" she asked him. When he did not, she told him who she was and how the plower had taken her in and given her a home. "Why did you leave me by that brook?"

"You were pregnant," the youngest brother said. "We were ashamed of you."

The sister then called the plower in, and he told the story of the snake and also showed the pieces that he had cut. The brother thanked the plower and with his sister, returned to his six brothers. When he told them the story of their sister, they decided to get rid of their wives who had proven to be wicked women.

The first brother suggested to his wife that they take a walk, and as he had planned, he threw her off a cliff and got rid of her. The other brothers did the same, and in this way, all seven giantess sisters were killed. Then with their young sister, the brothers returned to their mother, and they all lived together again. As it happens, the king of that country had seven daughters and one son. So the seven brothers married the seven daughters, and the daughter married the prince.

From the sky fell three apples: one to the storyteller, one to me and one to the person who has entertained you.

8. Abo Beckeer*

There was once a giantess who had a son known as Abo Beckeer. One day Abo Beckeer—who looked like a human being and not at all like a giant—was thirsty and went to the brook for a drink of water. A very beautiful girl was drawing water at the brook, and when Abo Beckeer saw her, he liked her and wanted to speak to her.

"Nice girl," he said, "give me a drink."

"There is plenty of water in the brook. Take some," the girl answered.

"I like you very much. Please let me drink water drawn with your own hands," he implored. She ignored him and continued with her task. "Who are you? Where do you live?" he asked her.

"Many people have asked to marry me, but my parents have refused all of them," she said, and she started for home. Abo Beckeer, unwilling to lose sight of her, followed her. When she reached her home, she stepped inside, and he did, too.

The parents, being hospitable people, welcomed the stranger and made him comfortable. Soon Abo Beckeer told them the

This story was told by Mrs. Mariam Serabian.
See Comparative Studies for another version of this story.
* This is a non-Armenian name.

purpose of his visit. "I saw your daughter by the brook and liked her very much. I want to marry her."

The girl's mother liked the handsome boy and approved of the way he spoke up. But the girl's father was not so eager. "How do you know who he is? Who are his folks? Are they rich or are they poor?" the father said to his wife.

Abo Beckeer, sensing the father's doubts, assured them that he would provide generously for their daughter and would give her everything she could wish for. The father was not convinced and drew his wife aside. "This boy looks strange to me. I do not approve of him for my daughter."

Abo Beckeer continued, "Parents will give me any girl that I ask for, but I don't want any of them. I only want your daughter for my wife."

After some time the parents consented to the marriage. They gave their daughter a fine wedding, and when the festivities were over, the boy took his bride to his mother's home. When they reached their destination, Abo Beckeer told his wife to take the broom and sweep the rooms carefully. When this was done, he instructed his wife to prepare his mother's favorite dish, a lumpy porridge. "Get it ready at once because my mother will be home soon."

When the giantess arrived, she cried out, "I smell human flesh," and looked all about the house. "Who is it that has cleaned my house and prepared my favorite food?" she asked. "Whoever it is, come forward."

Abo Beckeer and his wife, who were hidden in the stable, did not appear at the giantess' command. The next morning after the mother had left, Abo Beckeer said, "Wife, clean the house and prepare my mother's favorite porridge."

When it was time for the giantess to return, Abo Beckeer changed his wife into a broom and put it in a corner. When the giantess came home she searched the house, again crying, "I smell human flesh." When she was unable to find anyone, she said, "Whoever you are come out, come out. I know that this is the work of Abo Beckeer; only he could trick me."

The third day, when the giantess left the house, Abo Beckeer changed his wife to her normal shape and told her, "Clean the house and prepare my mother's favorite porridge. She will be home soon." When the girl had done as he instructed, he changed her into a dustpan and stuck it in a corner. When the giantess came in, she again smelled human flesh. She beat her hands on her knees and cried, "This is Abo Beckeer's work. Whoever you are, come into my sight. By the sun of my only child, Abo Beckeer, I promise that I will do you no harm."

When Abo Beckeer heard his mother's solemn oath, he changed his wife to her original form, and the giantess saw a beautiful girl standing before her. The saliva ran down her chin as she looked at the delicious mouthful of food, but she had made an oath which she could not break. "I have made this terrible oath," she said to herself, "but my sister is under no such obligation." To the girl she said, "You just stay here for a few moments, and I will call my sister to see you. She will be anxious to know who it is that Abo Beckeer has married."

"My mother plans to have my aunt eat my wife since she is under oath not to do so," Abo Beckeer said to himself. "Truly, I am afraid." The girl, sensing what difficulties were upon her, began to cry. "Dry your tears, don't cry," Abo Beckeer said to her. "Come, let us run away from here."

When his mother and aunt returned, they found the young people gone. "Sister, sister, hurry after them. Abo Beckeer is trying to run away with the girl. Catch up with them and eat her."

Abo Beckeer and his wife ran and ran, but when Abo Beckeer turned around to check on his pursuers, he saw that his aunt was fast on their trail. As they were passing a brook, Abo Beckeer changed his wife into a wooden cup, threw it in the brook and hid himself in a mist.

The aunt was puzzled; the young people had disappeared before her very eyes. What should she do? How could she chase someone when there was no one there to be chased? So she turned around toward home.

Meanwhile, Abo Beckeer picked up the wooden cup from the brook, and at his wish, the girl regained her original shape. They started running quickly, but the aunt looked back and saw them. She changed her direction and began pursuing them a second time.

When Abo Beckeer saw that his aunt was gaining on them, he took out his pocket knife and threw it behind him on the ground. Immediately the ground became covered with small sharp stones, just as sharp as the knife. The aunt, of course, had a difficult time getting across the stones, but she continued her pursuit.

When Abo Beckeer turned around again, he saw that his aunt was still on their trail. So he transformed his wife into the trunk of a fruit tree, stuck it in the ground and wrapped himself in a mist. The aunt suddenly discovered that the young couple had again disappeared. "Where did they go?" she asked herself, looking on all sides. But when she failed to see them, she turned back.

Abo Beckeer pulled the tree trunk out of the ground and gave his wife her human form. But the aunt looked behind her and saw the two running. She once again reversed her direction and gave them chase. When Abo Beckeer saw that the giantess was catching up with them, he made a big black cloud like a pillar reaching from the ground to the sky, and he and his wife hid inside it.

When the aunt saw the huge black pillar, she became frightened. Abo Beckeer played on her fears and caused strange things to appear and disappear within the pillar, frightening her so that she turned back and went to her sister's home.

"Sister, such things happened! Such things happened!" she moaned.

"Did you catch them?" the mother asked. "Did you eat the girl?"

"No, first I would see them, then they would disappear. Again I'd see them, then they would vanish," the exhausted giantess reported.

"Did you see anything on the road?" the mother asked.

"What is there on the road to see?" the aunt replied. "There was a brook and a wooden cup alongside it for people to drink with."

"You should have brought along that cup! That was the girl!" the mother exclaimed. "What else was there?"

"There was a little trunk of a fruit tree."

"You should have pulled it out of the ground! That was the girl! What else did you see?"

"There was a big black cloud like a pillar, and there were things in it that frightened me. I could not bear to get near it, so I turned back."

The furious mother hit her knees with her hands and cursed, "Until I hit my knees with my hands again and say 'Vhy [Alas], Abo Beckeer,' her child shall not be born!"

Meanwhile Abo Beckeer and his wife returned to the girl's parents. In time his wife was with child, but no matter what was done, the child would not be born. Abo Beckeer knew that this was his mother's curse and only trickery would remove it.

So with his wife, he returned to his mother's house, and they hid in the stables.

Abo Beckeer wrote a letter, supposedly from his wife's parents, saying Abo Beckeer had died. Then he left the letter on the table where his mother would see it.

When the giantess came home, she read the letter and started crying, "Vhy, Abo Beckeer," and hit her knees with her hands. "Vhy, Abo Beckeer, my one and only son is dead!"

As soon as she had spoken these words, the child was born. It began crying, and the giantess heard its cry. "Oh, I have been tricked!" she exclaimed, pulling her hair. "I have been tricked!"

"Abo Beckeer, my son," she cried as her son appeared, "here is my hand. I promise you that I will not harm either your wife or your child," and she held out her hand to her son. "Give me your hand," the mother said to Abo Beckeer's wife when she saw her. When she had the hand, she began pulling it toward her. Although she had promised and although she did not want to harm the wife, her craving for human flesh overpowered her.

Abo Beckeer, seeing that his mother was about to eat his wife, changed the girl into an apple and threw it to the ceiling. "Ah! Abo Beckeer, you have done all this to me, but I couldn't do anything to you. No, I will never touch her again," the giantess said.

"Mother, I will bring my wife down from the ceiling, but if you try to harm her, I will kill you," Abo Beckeer said.

When the giantess saw the girl, she started shuddering and could not keep still. As much as she did not want to harm her daughter-in-law, she was unable to control herself. "Abo Beckeer, kill me, I forgive you for it beforehand. I cannot control myself."

"How can a mother kill her child? How can a child kill his mother? My wife is your child; you cannot harm her just as I cannot harm you," Abo Beckeer said.

Beneath the ground there were giant voices and screams. "Abo Beckeer, be careful, I am going," the mother cried.

"Where are you going, mother?"

"I am going—they are coming after me. I will never return," the giantess said, and she disappeared. The young people were afraid that she would come back in a few days to harm the boy's wife. However, a week passed, and she did not return.

A week later the aunt came looking for her sister. "Abo Beckeer, where is my sister?"

"I don't know where she is," the boy replied.

"Abo Beckeer, who is this?" the aunt asked as she saw the boy's wife. Abo Beckeer quickly changed his wife into an apple and threw it to the ceiling. "Just as I made my mother go under the ground, I will make you go, too," he said to his aunt.

"Abo Beckeer, be careful of what you say, or I'll eat you, too," the aunt threatened.

"Are you going home, or are you going to stay here?" Abo Beckeer asked his aunt.

"I am going to eat you, your wife and your child."

"Go ahead," Abo Beckeer said as he brought his wife down from the ceiling. "Come, eat us!"

Again they heard great noises under the ground—terrible screams and yells. The aunt put one hand on Abo Beckeer and the other hand on his wife. Just then the ground ripped open, the aunt fell into the crack and the ground closed above her. Both sisters were now under the ground where all giants went when they died.

Abo Beckeer, his wife and their child went to the home of the wife's parents. The old people had been so worried about their daughter that they were sick. When they saw her, Abo Beckeer and the beautiful baby, they recovered and gave a great feast of thanksgiving. When the girl's father died several years later, all his wealth went to Abo Beckeer. So he stayed with his wife and child in the quiet town and lived happily ever after.

From the sky fell three apples: one to me, one to the story-teller and one to the person who has entertained you.

9. The Giantess Leader

At one time there was a king who had three sons. The first son set out to see the world and did not return. The second prince wanted to see the world, too, so he set out, but like his brother, he did not return. The king was so grief stricken that he died. Because of this triple tragedy, the youngest prince decided to give a *Hokeh-Hankeest.**

After the prince had done this, he decided to go in search of his brothers. He walked and walked until he passed a moun-

This story was told by Mrs. Katoon Mouradian.
* Literally: "Soul Rest." Special prayers are sung in church for departed ones and special gifts of food or money given to the poor on behalf of the departed.

tain where he saw a beautiful palace. As he approached it, he saw forty powerful horsewomen enter, but none came out. As both the leader and her followers were very beautiful, the prince was greatly interested and decided to wait and see what would happen next.

In the morning the beautiful leader with her thirty-nine followers left the palace. During the day rich and well-dressed men entered the palace, but none left. At night, again the beautiful women returned.

The next morning after the women had left, the prince entered the palace. Inside he saw a man, the lower half of whose body was stuck in the ground. "Friend, what happened to you?" the prince asked the man.

"The giantess leader yelled, I heard her scream, and this is what happened," the man replied."

As the prince went along, he found many men who, just like the first one, were stuck in the ground up to their waist. At the far end of the palace he saw an old man who said to the prince, "Son, stuff cotton in your ears and hide so that you will not become fixed like us." So the boy followed this advice: he put cotton in his ears and hid.

When the giantess leader and her thirty-nine followers returned that evening, she yelled for half an hour. All the men who had entered the palace during the day were stuck half-way in the ground except the prince who, having his ears blocked, did not hear the cry.

As the giantess leader was walking around to see whom she had caught that day, she found the prince unharmed. "Tell me what you did to save your life," she asked.

When he told her, she said, "Brave youth! you have saved your life; therefore, I will marry you." So the two were married and went on a long journey together. They traveled until they came to a lonely palace built on the sea. When someone stepped inside the door, the floor split open, and he fell into the sea. The prince knew well enough that this was what had happened to his brothers. So he told his wife, "You must go inside and bring my brothers back to life." She did this, and the three brothers and the beautiful woman started back home together.

As they traveled, the news of the woman's beauty spread throughout the land. The king of the country through which they were passing decided that he wanted the beauty for his own and had her stolen away.

The oldest prince was on his way to town to buy some bread when this happened. A white dove flew down in front of him and the prince gave it chase. It led him to an old hut in the mountains which was the home of a giantess. When he knocked on the door, a very old woman answered and admitted him inside. When the prince asked about the dove, the old woman answered, "Yes, your dove is here, but before we cut it open and eat it, let us play a game of cards." So the oldest prince sat down and played a game of cards with the old giantess. But try as he did, the prince could not win the game. At the end the old woman threw both him and his horse down the stairs.

When the second prince saw that his brother did not return, he went to the town, and he, too, saw the dove and followed it. It led him to the home of the giantess. And after she played cards with him and won, she threw him down the stairs as she had done with his brother.

When the youngest prince saw that his brothers did not return, he set out for the town to find them. On his way he saw the white dove and following it, was led to the home of the giantess in the mountains. When she began playing cards with him, the prince knew well enough that she was the cause of his brothers' absence. As he was an expert at cards, he won the game. Then the giantess said, "Here, here, let me kill this bird, and we will eat it!"

But the boy said, "No, you must leave the bird alone!" When she refused, he cut off one of her hands and tied the other so that she could not use it. "Tell me where my brothers are!" he ordered, and she told him that they were below. He went down the stairs and found them and they told him that the king had stolen away his beautiful wife. After the three brothers came up, the youngest prince said to the old giantess, "If you find my wife, I will set you free. I will untie your hand and give you my ring."

"Put me into a barrel and throw me into the sea. But make certain that you break this blue string on the wall so that I can act," the giantess replied.

So the prince untied her hand and put her into a huge barrel and threw her into the sea. Then he broke the blue string on the wall. The barrel was tossed along by the waves, and the fishermen found it with the old giantess inside. Disguised as an old beggar, she entered the palace and went to see the prince's wife. She learned that the young girl had not yet married the king.

"You must return to your husband," the old beggar said to the beauty, "for if you do not, he will kill me."

That night, with magic words, the old giantess put the girl into the barrel and pushed it into the sea. Finally the barrel reached the shore, and when it was found and opened, the girl saw her husband waiting for her. After the brothers had killed the doves of the old giantess, the youths became as wise as the wife of the youngest prince.

With this knowledge of magic they changed the old giantess into a sheep. Then they returned to the palace of their father where they remained. The two older brothers married two other beautiful princesses.

10. The Miller and the Fox

There was once a miller who owed a man sixty *para* [Turkish coin]. Day after day his creditor came and asked for his money, but the miller was so poor that he kept giving him one excuse after another.

One day his creditor had been very angry and had embarrassed the sensitive miller. So the miller sat by his mill and began to think of what he could do to pay his debt that very day and be rid of the man. Meanwhile, a fox that was in the neighborhood decided to eat the only two chickens which the miller had and silently crept near the mill. But there he saw the unhappy miller who sat thinking away. "I wonder what this man is thinking about?" the fox asked himself. He waited a bit longer, and still the miller did not move or speak, but sat thinking. "Friend miller," the fox said, "what are you worrying about?"

"Friend fox," the miller replied, "if I do not worry, who should worry?"

"But, friend miller, what is your grief? Tell me, and perhaps I can help you."

"How can you help me?" But the fox gave him no quiet until the miller told him about his debt of sixty *para* and his impatient creditor. "Well, if that is all, then worry no longer. This is nothing," the fox said. "If you put me on your back and carry me up that hill, I will give you the sixty *para*."

The miller did not want to do this for he feared that someone would see him. But thinking of the sixty *para* he would earn

This story was told by Hovhannes Kaprelian.

and of his impatient creditor, he placed the fox on his back and quickly went up the hill. "Now, fox, give me the sixty *para* that you promised," the miller said as they reached the top of the hill.

"No, not today," the fox said, "but if you take me up again tomorrow, I will give the money then."

So the next day the miller carried the fox up the hill and again asked for his money. "No, not today," the fox said, "but if you take me up tomorrow, I will then give you the sixty *para*."

So the miller carried the fox up the hill a third time, and this time he was paid. He quickly paid his creditor and returned to his mill, a happy man.

But the fox, who was a good judge of human nature, saw that the poor miller was a sincere and simple person. So he decided to help him. One day he returned to the miller and said, "What is your name, friend miller?"

The miller answered, "Tozoglan."

"Well, henceforth, you will be known as Tozleebeg."* When the miller protested that he was no "*beg*," the fox said, "If you complain, you must give back the sixty *para* I gave you."

And as the miller did not have the money, he kept quiet. "Friend miller," the fox continued, "I am going to see that you marry the princess."

"But, fox," the miller cried, "what are you saying? Who am I to marry the princess? I am so poor that I cannot even marry one of the village girls."

The fox threatened to demand his money back, so the poor miller again kept quiet. The fox went to the king's palace and said, "Your Majesty, my master, Tozleebeg, has sent me here to ask if he may borrow your bushel which measures nickel pieces."†

The king was surprised at such a request but readily gave his permission, and the bushel was given to the fox. He returned to the miller and placed a few nickel coins in several cracks of the bushel and a day or so later, returned with it to the palace and thanked the king for the use of the measure. As he was about to leave, the king was notified that there were several nickel pieces left in the measure. "I am told that there are a few nickel pieces in the measure," the king said. "Collect them on your way out."

"Oh, that is nothing! My master Tozleebeg has so many of

* According to informant, *oglan* is a Turkish suffix which denotes a poor commoner; *beg* is a suffix used to denote rich and powerful men.
† Informant used these monetary classifications only to make the story fit the American background.

those pieces that I am sure he will not miss a few," the fox said and gave the impression that this master was indeed very rich.

Some time passed and the fox went to the palace and asked for the dime measure. When he returned it, he purposely left a few dimes in it. The king was told; the fox, recalled, said, "Oh, that is nothing! My master, Tozleebeg, is so rich that I am sure he will not miss a few small coins."

Next he borrowed the quarter measure, later the dollar measure, and finally the gold measure. The king was beginning to believe that this Tozleebeg, whoever he was, was indeed a very rich man.

One day the fox went to the king's palace and said to the king, "Your Majesty, my master, Tozleebeg, wants to marry your daughter."

"Tell your master that we shall see about it," the king told the fox, happy at the thought of such a rich son-in-law. "Bring him to the palace so that we can see what kind of a man he is."

So the fox went to the miller and said, "Come, miller, we are going to the king's palace. If the king approves of you, he will allow you to marry the princess."

"But, fox," the miller implored, "I cannot go to the palace in these rags. What shall I say? How shall I act?"

"If you do not do as I say, you must return my money," the fox threatened. And as the miller did not have the money, he became quiet and went along with the fox.

As they neared the palace, they came to a stream which they had to cross. The fox said to the miller, "You stay here, and when I return with many men, act as if a great assault had been committed against you. Remember, if you are not here when I return, my friend the king will cut off your head." And the miller, afraid of both the fox and the king, stayed just where he was.

Meanwhile, the fox went to the palace and said, "Your Majesty, Your Majesty, while my master, Tozleebeg, and his men were coming to your palace, a band of robbers attacked us and stole all the gifts we were bringing for the princess and everything else that had any value. In fact, they even took away my master's beautiful golden clothes and left him in rags. What shall I do? What shall I do?"

The fox so completely tricked the king that the ruler sent men to bring the great Tozleebeg to the palace. Once he was there, the king ordered that a suit of clothes be given to the visitor. When the miller looked at his sleeve and saw the beautiful gold and silk embroidery, he smiled, thinking to himself, "Is this really me? Am I really wearing the king's clothes?"

The king, seeing the visitor smiling, asked the fox what was the cause of it. "Oh, Your Majesty, my master is smiling because the suit he is now wearing is nothing compared to what he wears at home," the fox said.

And the king, embarrassed at this, ordered that his own suit which he wore on special occasions be given to the visitor. When the miller saw his reflection in a mirror, again he smiled, thinking, "Yesterday at this time what was I doing—and what am I doing today!"

The king, seeing that his visitor was smiling again, asked the fox, "What is Tozleebeg smiling at now?"

"Oh, Your Majesty," the fox said, "this suit he is wearing now is nothing compared to what he has at home."

The king, very much embarrassed and angered, ordered that his newest and most elaborate suit of clothes be given to the visitor. When the fox was dressing his master, he whispered, "Miller, listen to what I say. If you smile this time, I will expose your trick, and besides, I will make you pay me the sixty *para* which I gave you."

So this time the miller did not smile. The king said to the fox, "How does our Tozleebeg like this suit of clothes?"

"Well, Your Majesty," the fox said, "this suit is almost as good as his own." The king began to think that this visitor was indeed a very rich person, for how else could he have such beautiful and elaborate clothes for such ordinary occasions?

Meanwhile, great preparations were being made for the feast which was always given to important visitors. The fox whispered to the miller, "You must not eat any more than I do. If you disobey me, I will expose your trick and will ask for my sixty *para*, too."

So the miller promised not to eat any more than the fox. They were led to the great tables laden with food. The fox ate very little. The miller followed his example but remained very, very hungry. He said to himself, "At least, when I was a miller, I could eat at night. As Tozleebeg, I must remain hungry. Alas!" The king, who was watching Tozleebeg, saw that this man was indeed well educated, for he ate very little.

That night when all were in bed, the miller quietly got up and decided to go to the kitchen to steal something to eat. As it was dark and he could not see where he was going, he fell into a large kettle full of water. This made such a noise that everyone awoke and ran to see what had happened. The fox cried out, "Oh, my master, Tozleebeg, are you hurt?"

"What were you doing?" the people began to ask.

The miller, for shame, could not answer. But the fox, sensing the truth, said, "My master, on his way to make his toilet, fell into this kettle of water."

So all was forgotten, and people returned to their beds. But again the miller could not sleep. "Tomorrow, as is the rule, I will have to take the king and his noblemen to my palace to feast, for I have been entertained at the king's palace today. But how can I do this? I have no palace, and only dry, stale bread for myself. What shall I do?"

The next morning the fox started out ahead of the king and his court, saying, "I will go ahead and make preparations."

As he went along, he saw some shepherds taking care of a large herd of cows and horses. He stopped and said to them, "My friends, you look like hard-working men, and I do not want evil to come to you. Let me tell you a secret, but do not tell anyone who told it to you. Our king is at war, and he will take all the animals for his army. But when you are asked to whom these animals belong, answer, 'To Tozleebeg,' and he will not take them because Tozleebeg is his favorite. If you do this, your herd will be safe."

The shepherds, thankful of this good advice, blessed him many times. He left them behind and went on. Soon he saw a few shepherds taking care of their large flocks of sheep. He repeated to them what he had said to the first shepherds, and they, being very thankful, blessed him many times.

He went on and saw a huge palace in which lived forty giants. "My friends," he told the giants, "the king is very sick, and the only cure for him is giants' fat. We'll leave this crippled giant here, but the rest of you hide in the bushes outside. If someone is to die, there is no need to harm good, healthy giants like you. I know that the king is on his way, for he was just a little behind me."

The giants, believing that the fox was telling the truth, quickly hid in the bushes. Then the fox burned the bushes and the giants with them. With the help of the crippled giant, the fox made pilaff and roasted meat, set the tables and waited for the king's party.

Meanwhile, the king and his court rode along until they

came to the herd of cows and horses. "Good men, whose are these herds?" the king asked.

The shepherds, remembering what the fox had told them, replied, "These herds belong to Tozleebeg."

The king bit his lip in amazement, nodded his head and went on. Soon they came to the flocks of sheep. The king asked the shepherds, "Good men, whose are these sheep?"

And the shepherds, remembering what the fox had said, replied, "These sheep belong to Tozleebeg." The king again was so surprised that he bit his lip and thought that this Tozleebeg was certainly a wealthy man.

They rode along and finally reached the beautiful palace where the fox invited them inside to the feast which was prepared. The king saw that this palace was indeed much better than his own and decided to have the rich man for his son-in-law.

But the fox said to the miller before the marriage, "Friend miller, see how much I have helped you. You are soon to marry the princess. I have done all this for you, and I ask only one thing in return. Promise me that when I die you will bury me in a golden coffin."

The miller answered, "Friend fox, if that is all that you want, rest assured, for I will see that a golden coffin is made for you."

So the fox felt much better and made preparations for the royal wedding. The miller married the princess, but at night instead of sleeping beside her, he slept on the floor. The princess could not learn the cause of this, and after a few nights she told her father. Soon the fox heard that his master did not sleep with his wife but, instead, slept on the floor. He called the miller to one side and said, "Miller, you had better learn to sleep on a soft bed beside your nice soft wife, or I will tell the king all about you and I will have you return the sixty *para* that I gave you." And the miller, afraid of the fox, began to learn to sleep on a soft bed beside his soft, pretty wife.

So the years went by, and the fox began to think that perhaps the miller had forgotten his promise to bury him in a golden coffin. "I will test him and see," the fox said. So one day when the miller was hunting, the fox fell to the floor and pretended that he was dead.

When the miller returned to the palace, his good wife told him that their friend, the fox, had died. "Died? Good! throw him out into the road!" the miller exclaimed.

But the fox, who heard this, jumped up and said, "So, friend and master, this is how you keep your word, is it?" And the miller cried, "Oh, do not listen to what I just said, for I was only joking." But the feelings of the fox were hurt, and he did not often speak with the miller after that.

When several years had passed, the fox really died. The miller was told about it; this time, fearing that perhaps the fox was only pretending again, he ordered a golden coffin to be made and put the body of the fox into it. But, alas! the fox was really dead and did not know that his friend, the miller, had really kept his promise.

11. The Work of the Genii

There was once a king who had only one daughter. Another king had only one son. The second king told his son that it was time for him to marry and raise a family. The prince, however, did not want this, so the king had him thrown into a prison on a lonely island. Every day guards took him food and then left him alone.

As it happened, the first king wanted his daughter to get married. But when the girl told him that she was not ready yet, he became angry and scolded her. But whatever he did, she would not obey her father's will.

Without their knowing it, each of these two young people who did not know each other, had a guardian genie. The prince had a male genie, and the princess had a female genie. These genii looked very much like humans, but they could not be seen by the human eye. One day the genii met and began discussing their masters. "Oh, my prince is so handsome, but alas! he has been locked up in that prison for seven years!" the male genie said.

"My princess is so very beautiful that if just a drop of her blood were applied to one's face, that face would become most beautiful."

"Well, if she is that beautiful, I would like my prince to see her."

"And if your prince is so handsome and steadfast, I would like my princess to see him." So the two decided to get the young people together. When the princess had fallen asleep that night, the genie put a scented flower to her nostrils, and the princess

This story was told by Mrs. Katoon Mouradian.

slept on soundly. Meanwhile, the male genie had done the same to the prince, and soon both prince and princess, though far apart, were sound asleep and would not awaken until the genii willed it so.

The male and the female genii quickly built a beautiful palace at the crossroads between the prince's country and the princess' country. When this was finished, as it soon was, the genii brought the two young people and laid them side by side in the same room and then awakened the princess. She, of course, could not see the genii watching her. When she saw the man beside her and noticed his great beauty and the manliness, she was happy. She took off his ring and put it on her finger. Then the genii put her to sleep again.

Next they awakened the prince. He saw the beautiful princess beside him, and he was very happy for he knew that the years of waiting which he had spent in prison had not been wasted. He took off her ring and put it on his finger. Then the genii put the prince to sleep. And thus they left them until dawn. Then the female genie quickly carried the princess to her father's palace, and the male genie carried the prince to his prison on the lonely island.

The following morning the prince awoke to find himself in his prison again. "How strange!" he said to himself. "I thought surely that I was not dreaming last night!" He looked about but saw that he was still in his prison. He looked at his hands and saw the girl's ring on his finger instead of his own. He quickly took it off and read the name inside it. When he realized that the girl he had slept with the preceding night was flesh and blood, he fell sick because of his great love for her. The king was notified that the prince was very ill, and he ordered that his son be taken to the palace and treated by the best healers in the country. But, alas! no cure could be found for the prince.

Meanwhile, when the princess awoke the following morning, she found herself in her father's palace. "What a strange thing," she said, "I was certain that it was not a dream!" When she looked at her hands, she found the boy's ring with his name written inside. She, too, fell sick because her love for the prince was so great. All the healers in the country were called, but no one could help her.

The princess' father had adopted a little orphan boy years ago and had sent him to school so that the boy had developed great wisdom. The adopted son was very much like a brother to the princess, and so the king instructed him to learn the cause of the girl's sadness. "Brother, I don't have much to say," the princess said to the adopted son, "only take this ring and find its owner."

The adopted son knew what the cause of her sickness was, but he said nothing and decided that he would do all he could to make his sister happy. Disguised as a healer, he walked from one town to another, asking for the prince's name to compare it with the one which was written on the ring. Finally he came to the prince's town but learned that he was very sick and no cure was possible. The adopted son went to the palace and said that he was a healer and would try to cure the prince.

When the two were left alone, the adopted son played with the ring on his finger until it caught the prince's eye. "Where did you get that ring?"

"Get well, and I will tell you about this ring," the healer told him. "It is from the person whose ring you have." These words acted like magic on the youth, and he quickly got better. Everyone was surprised at the great change which occurred in the sick prince. When he was well, the prince said to his father, "Father, permit me to walk a little today with my friend." And the king, grateful to the healer for the cure which he had produced, readily agreed to this. So the two started walking, but they did not plan to return to the palace.

They walked and walked until finally they came to the sea. As they stood wondering how they were to cross it, a giant, perhaps it was the prince's genie in disguise, appeared before them and asked them if they wanted to get across. "Yes, we must," the two answered. So the giant told them to close their eyes, which they did, and they crossed over immediately.

They continued their journey and soon reached the country where the beautiful princess still lay very sick. The adopted son went to see her and told her what had happened and said, "I will send the prince here dressed as a healer." So he returned to the prince and told him to wear the healer's clothes which he himself had previously worn. And thus the prince entered the palace and went to see the princess. She soon became very well from his repeated visits. They went to the king and asked to get married. The king was happy to see that his daughter would marry such a handsome man, so he readily consented. A great royal wedding was held for forty days and forty nights, and everyone came and sang and drank with the new couple. After all the guests had departed, the prince and his wife left for his father's country.

The princess had a locket which contained a magic inscription. This locket was wrapped in leather, and she carried it with her always. Some time after her arrival at her new home, she was strolling with her husband in the royal gardens. An eagle swooped down, snatched her locket and flew away with it. She cried and begged her husband to follow the bird and return the locket to her. The prince quickly started to do as she requested, but the eagle flew out of sight. Soon the prince found himself in a land where there were few people. He walked about and finally saw an old hut. He knocked on the door, and a very old man opened it and admitted him inside.

The following morning the prince looked out and saw two birds having a fight. One bird killed the other, and the prince, curious about the affair, cut open the bird's stomach and, to his surprise and happiness, found the locket which his wife had lost.

As it happened, the old man was not really an old man at all but a giant. He said to the prince, "In our garden there is a very big tree which prevents the sun from warming the earth. Cut it down so that the garden will be green." When the prince did this, he found much gold under the roots of the tree, and he quickly told the old man about it. The old man, seeing that the prince was so honest, gave him the gold and had the prince promise that he would bury him when he died. The prince promised to do this and sent the gold to his father's country by boat.

Meanwhile, the princess, seeing that her husband did not return, did not want her people to think that he had deserted them. So she put her hair back, wore her husband's clothes, and as she looked very much like him, she took his place. The princess of a nearby country saw the disguised princess and thought that she was a boy. Noticing the beauty of the youth, she decided to marry him. The prince's wife didn't want this, for how could two women marry? Yet she could not tell the truth to anyone. Try as she would, she could do nothing to stop the affair, so she was married to the princess. That night she placed a sword between the two of them, and the bride was greatly puzzled and insulted. "Perhaps he does not want me, for why else would he put that sword between us?" she wondered.

The next morning the prince's wife took off her disguise and told her bride that she was not a man but a princess like herself. "Wait until my brave and handsome husband returns, and he will marry you, too, and we will be real sisters." What could the bride do but keep still and wait for the prince's return?

About this time the gold which the prince had sent to his country arrived and was taken to the palace. The princess said to the men who brought it, "Tell the person who sent this that he is needed and must return immediately." The men promised to do so.

Meanwhile, the prince was waiting for the old man to die so that he could fulfill his promise and bury him before he returned home. And soon this came to pass, too. So the prince boarded the ship and returned to his country. There he saw his wife again, and when she told him about the promise she had made to the other bride, the prince married her too—and all lived happily together.

12. The Magic Bird-Heart

At one time, there was and there was not, there were a man, his two sons and his second wife. Although this second wife was a stepmother to the children, she treated them well. However, the family was very poor, and they considered themselves fortunate to find their daily bread.

One day the two brothers were walking through the mountains when they saw a very beautiful bird fly away from her nest. The boys went over to look into the nest and saw two pretty eggs. Each brother took an egg, and they decided to go to the marketplace to sell them. At the market a Jew saw the eggs and wanted to buy them.

"Boys, how much do you want for those eggs?" he asked them.

The boys did not know how much to ask for them, so they did not reply. The Jew, misunderstanding their silence, said, "I'll give you two *medgzeh* [Turkish coin]."

The brothers were surprised, for how could just two eggs be worth two *medgzeh?* They immediately sensed that there was something here that didn't meet the eye, so they didn't give the eggs to the Jew for that price. The Jew, on the other hand, thinking that the boys knew the secret of the eggs, was willing to pay almost any price to get them. Finally, he offered five gold pieces

This story was told by Nishan Krikorian.

for the two eggs, and the boys sold them to him and took the money home to their father.

When the father asked them how they had earned the money, they told him. And the father was very happy, of course. The next day, the two brothers again went to the mountain to the bird's nest, but this time they found only one egg. They took it to the Jew and asked for five gold pieces. "But I gave you five gold pieces for two eggs yesterday; why should I give you five gold pieces for just one egg today?" he asked.

"If you don't want it, others will," the boys replied, making a move to leave. But the Jew called them back and paid for the egg, asking them to bring him any others like it which they might find.

One day the Jew said, "If you find the bird whose eggs you have been bringing me, I'll give you hundreds of gold pieces." So the next day when the two brothers went up to the mountain, they took along a large sack. They threw the sack over the bird and caught her. But instead of taking the bird to the Jew, they decided to keep it home, feed it and sell the eggs to the Jew one at a time. Meanwhile, the Jew had been paying the boys so generously that the family had become well-to-do.

One day the Jew asked the boys if they had tried to catch the bird yet, and they told him that they had done so and had it safely at home.

"Why don't you bring it to me? I'll pay you well," the Jew said. But the boys answered that they did not intend to sell it.

After asking several times and always receiving the same answer, the Jew asked whether he might visit them someday. The boys promised to ask their parents.

"Let him come! Let him come! After all, he's our benefactor, isn't he? If it had not been for him, we would still be hungry today," their parents said. So the Jew was invited to their house. The stepmother was dressed very nicely, and when she saw the Jew, she liked him. He, on the other hand, gave her much attention in order to gain her favor.

Soon the Jew and the stepmother were carrying on a love affair. One day the Jew said, "Unless you have that bird killed and save the heart and the head for you and me, I will see you no more."

"But why should I have the bird killed?" the woman asked.

"I don't know. That's all I have to say. You must have it

killed and save the heart and the head for me, or I will never see you again," he said.

"How can I do this?"

"Just pretend that you are very sick and that you will die unless you have some of the bird's meat; then they will kill it for your sake."

So the stepmother pretended that she was very sick and kept asking for the bird's meat. Finally, her husband killed the bird, but she saved the heart and the head so that she could eat them with the Jew. She placed them aside, cooked and ready to eat.

The boys, who had been playing, became hungry and came in to see what they could find. When they found the heart and the head of the bird, they decided to eat them. The younger brother ate the heart of the bird, and the older brother ate the head. That same day the Jew came to see the stepmother. "Do you have the heart and the head ready?" he asked her.

"Yes, they're in the kitchen," she said and took him by the hand and lead him there. But when they reached the kitchen, they saw that the heart and the head had disappeared.

"Where are they?" the Jew demanded.

"I put them here, but the boys must have eaten them."

The Jew was very angry. After all the planning he had done, the boys had eaten what he most wanted. He could not endure to see them with so much good fortune! "If you love me, if you want to be my friend, you must get rid of your two sons," he demanded.

"But why should I do that? They have always been good to me," she said.

"I don't know. Either they go or I go."

As the woman loved the Jew and did not want him to leave her, she promised to get rid of her stepsons. She said to her husband the next day, "Either you get rid of your sons or I will leave you. Decide! Either they go or I go!"

The man did not answer her. But she kept after him until finally, to stop her nagging, he took his sons by the hand and started out. They traveled all day, until at nightfall they entered a forest. The two boys were very sleepy, so their father told them to go to sleep under the trees and he would watch over them. But just as soon as they were asleep, the father started back home.

In the morning when the boys awakened and found their father missing, they began crying. Finally, they decided that it was best to separate and each seek his own fortune. One brother went one way, and the other went the other way. The older brother walked and walked until he finally came to a town where he saw all the people gathered in one place. He asked a man why the crowd was gathered. "Our king is dead, and we are going to choose a new king," the man replied.

"How will you do that?"

"Do you see the pigeon? They are going to let it fly and the man on whose head it alights will be the next king," the man replied.

The bird was set free to perch on any head he wished. It circled the whole crowd several times and then alighted on the older brother's head. "No! No! He is only a poor, ragged boy. We cannot accept him for our king," the people cried. So the bird was set free a second time, and again it alighted on the same boy's head. Again, protests were heard on all sides. So a third time the bird was set free, and for a third time it alighted on the boy's head. So the people accepted their fate and made the poor boy their king.

Meanwhile, the younger brother walked and walked until he came to a poor hut owned by a blacksmith. There he knocked on the door and asked for work. "My son, I cannot give you work because I am a poor man," the smith said.

"Let me work for a crust of bread and a place to sleep," the boy begged. Seeing the eagerness of the boy, the blacksmith consented and prepared a bed of twigs in one corner of the barn where the boy could sleep. After several days the smith told the boy that he could no longer give him even bread and asked him to move on. So the boy went on his way. "Wife, clean out those twigs so that I can have more room for my work," the smith told his wife.

While the wife was cleaning away the twigs, she found handfuls of gold where the boy had rested his head. She quickly called her husband and showed it to him. As the two of them realized the meaning of this discovery, the smith ran after the boy. "Son, come back, I'll arrange for you to stay," he shouted.

"No, I've decided to go farther," the boy replied, and he continued walking.

The smith asked again and again, but the boy said that he was determined to seek his fortune. So the smith gave the boy five pieces of gold and turned back. The boy, much surprised, walked and walked until he saw a big tree. He arranged a rock under it to serve as a pillow and went to sleep. In the morning when he awakened, he pushed the rock away with his foot and to his great surprise, found a handful of gold.

"Ah! Now I see why the smith was so anxious to have me return," the boy said to himself, putting the gold into his pocket. He soon discovered that each time he laid his head down, no matter whether it was morning, noon or night, he would find a handful of gold on his pillow. Very soon, of course, he became wealthy. He told everyone that he came from another land and that his parents were wealthy. He had a good reputation and he always gave to the poor.

One day, he was walking toward the forest when he saw three giants fighting one another. The boy became frightened and tried to hide, but the giants had already seen him and called him to come near.

"What do you want of me?" the boy asked them.

"We are three brothers," one of the giants said, "and we own three things between us. But we are going to part and we do not know which object should go to each of us."

"The rug belongs to me," one of the giants said.

"No, it belongs to me," another said, and the two began fighting.

"Is that all that's troubling you?" the boy asked.

"Yes," the giants replied.

"If you bring me a small piece of wood, I'll solve your problem," the boy offered. The wood was brought, and the boy gave his instructions to the giants. "Before I can decide anything, I should know what these things can do. Tell me, what is the power of this rug?"

"It is a magic rug. If one sits on it and gives the name of the place where he wants to go, he will be there immediately," one of the giants said.

"Very well," the boy replied, "now, what is the power of this club?"

"If one takes this club in hand and says certain words, then touches another person with the club, that person will become a donkey. With certain other words, accompanied by the touch of the club, that donkey can become a man again," the second giant said.

"That's very interesting. But tell me, how is this sheepskin cap used?" the boy asked.

"If one wears the sheepskin cap, he will become invisible," the giants told him.

"All right, I know just what to do now," the boy said. "I am going to throw this piece of wood I have in my hand just as far as I can throw it. The three of you are to run after it and try to find it. The one who finds the wood the soonest will get the rug, the second to find the wood will get the club and the third will get the sheepskin cap. Will this do?"

"Why, that's very good! Why didn't we think of it ourselves?" the giants asked. The boy took the piece of wood and threw it just as far as he could. The giants began to run after it.

When the boy saw that the giants were quite a distance from him, he took the club and the sheepskin cap and sat on the rug and flew away, leaving the giants behind.

One day, as he was walking through a town, he saw a man throwing gold beneath the palace window. "I wonder what this man is doing," the boy said to himself. Asking someone standing nearby, he learned that the man was trying to see Duenia Gezeley [Turkish: World Beauty], the princess of the town. "To marry her one must throw gold at her feet until she is tired of standing. Now, you see, that man has been throwing his gold for hours, and all he can see of her is her little finger. No one has been able to see more than that," the bystander explained.

"No one?" the boy asked himself. "Well, then I shall!"

During the next day or two, he slept and got up, slept and got up, until finally he thought he had enough money to go to the princess. He continued throwing his gold for hours until the princess began to tire but still all she showed was her little finger. Finally the princess said to her maid, "Go down and see if he has much more gold. I am getting tired."

The maid did as she was told and saw that there was much gold. When she told her mistress about this, the princess sighed and said, "Tell the youth to come to me."

The boy entered the palace, and the two ate and drank and had a happy time. "Dear one, I am yours and you are mine. Tell me, how did you get all this gold?" she asked.

"You see my rug? This is my secret," the boy said, not telling her the truth. When the boy fell asleep, she took his rug away from him and had him thrown out into the road. In the morning the boy awoke to find himself in a pitiful condition. After a while he remembered what had happened to him and was very angry at the princess. He slept and awoke, slept and awoke until he had more money than on the preceding day.

For the second time, he went to the palace and began throwing money below the window of the princess. The maid saw him and ran to tell her mistress that the man who had been there the day before was there again. "Tell him to come in," the princess ordered.

The boy went to the princess. "Since I cannot get rid of you, let us marry," she said, hoping that by this means she would learn his secret.

A big feast was prepared and all the nobles were present. There was a great deal to eat and drink, but the boy ate very little and didn't drink at all. When the celebration was at its peak, the boy went into a quiet corner, put on his sheepskin cap and immediately became invisible. Then he touched everyone with his club, causing all of them to become donkeys. The room suddenly became full of three or four hundred donkeys. The boy, however, knew which one had been the princess. Looking out of the palace window, he saw a donkey-dealer passing by. He called the man in and said, "Friend, how would you like to have these donkeys if I gave them to you free?"

"I would like that very much!" the surprised man said.

"Well, then, I will give them to you, but you must listen to my one condition. Do you see this little donkey? You must never take her pack-sack off. If ever I see her without her pack-sack, I will take all the donkeys away from you. Remember, you must never take the pack-sack off this one."

The dealer listened and then answered, "If you give me all these donkeys with only one condition, of course I will respect that condition." So the dealer took the donkeys, put their pack-sacks on and loaded heavy goods on their backs. From town to town, the donkeys went, always carrying heavy loads. And true to his word, the dealer never took the pack-sack off the princess.

Every time they passed the palace of the king of a neighboring country, however, the princess would separate herself from the rest of the donkeys and stop underneath the palace window. There she would linger a while, then return to her fold. The king finally took notice of the donkey's action. "This is unusual. I wonder why this donkey behaves in such a manner," he asked himself. One day he called the dealer and asked why that one donkey separated herself from all the others and stopped in front of the palace window.

"I don't know why she does that, Your Majesty. But the man who gave me all these donkeys told me that I must never remove her pack-sack," the dealer said.

"Why is that?" the king asked.

"He told me that I might have all these donkeys without paying for them if only I would not take the pack-sack off this one."

"Who is the owner of these donkeys?" the king asked.

"He is the great merchant in ————," the dealer answered.

So the king had the rich man brought before him. "Tell me, why did you instruct this good man not to take the pack-sack off this one donkey?" the king asked.

"Your Majesty, that is a long story, but I will tell you all of it," the merchant said and told his story beginning in his early childhood and ending with the trickery and transformation of the princess.

"Now listen to my story," the king said after he had very attentively listened to the merchant, and he told him his story from the very beginning to the time he became king.

"That means that we are brothers!" the youngest exclaimed when the king became silent. The two embraced and cried for joy.

"Your story is very interesting, brother, but you must do one thing for my sake," the king said after a while. "You must change all these donkeys back into men, and you must make the princess her lovely self again."

"I will transform the other donkeys back to human beings, but not the donkey that was the princess!" the brother said. But when the older brother insisted, the boy relented and changed all the donkeys, including the princess back to their original forms.

Several days later, the king said, "Brother, we have an old father whom we haven't seen for years. I am going to send my soldiers to bring him here."

"Brother, that's unnecessary. All I need to do is to sit on my magic carpet, and I am in our old home!" No sooner said than done, and the boy was at his father's home. He saw a great many people going in and out of the house, but he didn't know what had happened. He went inside the house and found his father, bent, crying. He learned that his stepmother had just died. "Father, your wife has died, but may your days be long."

"Thank you, son," the old man said, "I am not crying for my wife! I am crying for my two sons that this wife of mine made me lose years ago."

The younger brother smiled to himself. "Well, father, may I

stay with you overnight?" he asked. The old man welcomed him
to stay and showed him every courtesy.

The next morning, the two of them talked and ate. "Let us
pack a little lunch and go under those trees and eat there," the
boy suggested, and the old man agreed to do so. When they
were about to sit down, the boy said, "Wait, let me put this rug
down so that we won't get our clothes dirty." He put the magic
rug down. When both father and son were seated on it, the boy
said a few words, and the rug began flying through the air.

"What's this? What's happening?" the old man cried.

"Don't be afraid, nothing is happening. I am your younger
son, and your older son is a king. I am taking you to him now."

"My sons? Is it possible that you were not killed by the wild
animals that night in the forest?" the father asked.

"Yes, and I am a rich merchant while my brother is a big
and powerful king," the boy repeated. The old man was overjoyed.

When the guards at the palace caught sight of the flying
rug on which the boy and the old man were seated, they immediately told the king. The king, attended by great crowds, met
his father and brother, and the three embraced again and again.

"Now, everything is settled, except one," the king said.

"What is that?" the brother asked.

"I haven't completed the plans for your wedding." The
younger brother looked puzzled, so the king continued, "You will
marry the World's Most Beautiful, Duenia Gezeley, for I know
that she has captured your heart."

The younger brother could not say anything, because in spite
of her deceptive ways, he loved the girl. So the wedding was
celebrated, and it lasted for forty days and forty nights. They
all lived happily ever after.

They reached their goal, and so shall we reach ours. Our
story is ended. From the sky fell three apples: one to me, one
to the storyteller and one to the person who has entertained you.

13. The Magic Figs

Once upon a time there was a very wealthy man who had
a wife and a son. He hired teachers to educate his son, and the
boy became very wise. One day the father, who was an old man

This story was told by Nishan Krikorian.

and had not many years to live, called his son to him and gave him a piece of good advice: "Know your friends, my son, always remember this. Know the difference between true friends and your so-called friends. If you remember this, you will find the world a much easier place to live in."

Not long after, the father died. As he had been a rich and important person, people from many great distances came to his funeral. A group of rich and idle young men decided to go to the youth and tell him how sorry they felt about his father's death. "Your father is dead, but may your days be long," they said. The boy thanked them for their sympathy. "Why not become one of us? Come with us and we will keep you from thinking. We will help you forget your worries."

The young men gave the boy *raki* [potent raisin brandy], and he forgot his worries and told them that he felt happier. "If you want to join us, meet us each day at this place," they said and left. So, each day he met these young men at the specified place. They ate and drank *raki*, and when they were ready to leave, the boy paid for all the expenses.

This continued for some time until one day the boy found that he had no more money. When his friends discovered this, they dropped him from their group. After a time the boy became poor; his clothes were thin and worn. "I'll go to my mother. She will give me a few *para* [Turkish coin]," the boy said to himself. When he reached her home, the mother refused to give him anything. "You threw your money away. If you do without any for a while, you will appreciate its worth," she said.

But the mother's maid had brought up the boy and felt sorry for him. "Give him a *para*," she said to her mistress. So the boy's mother gave him a *para*. The boy didn't have any pockets and didn't want to carry the money in his hand. "Mother, won't you give me an old purse so that I can put this *para* in it?" he asked.

The maid looked on the shelves and found an old purse and gave it to the boy. He put his *para* in the purse and started toward town. When he reached his destination, he opened his purse and found a gold piece instead. So the boy knew immediately that there was magic connected with the purse.

He had the gold piece changed to *para*. When he reached home, he found that all the *para* had turned to gold pieces. He changed the gold pieces to *para* again and put them into the purse, and they again turned to gold pieces. "Now I have nothing to worry about," the boy said to himself. "But I must get into some neater clothes." And he went to the best tailor in town and soon was dressed as richly as ever before. "Now I need a horse," the boy said to himself, and he selected the best steed he could buy. "Well, I am ready to travel, but first let me bid my mother good-bye."

Of course, his mother was very much surprised to see her son looking so prosperous when only a few days before he had been begging for even one *para*. But she did not ask anything. "Mother, I am setting out to see the world," he said.

"Then good-bye, my son; may God make your journey a good one," his mother answered.

So the next morning he started out on his journey. After traveling many weary miles, he saw a horse and rider coming toward him. "Ah, I shall have company," the boy said to himself. When the rider came up to him, the boy said, "Good day to you. How are you? Where are you going? Where are you coming from? May God make your journey a good one."

"You are young; don't ask me where I've come from," the rider said. But the boy's curiosity was aroused, and he begged to hear. The rider, seeing that there was no other way out, was forced to tell him. "The king of Adana* has a beautiful daughter, the most beautiful in the world, known as Duenia Gezeley [Turkish: World Beauty]. If a man wants to marry her, he must throw gold pieces at her feet until she is satisfied and will agree to marry him."

"Well, then, that's where I must go," the boy said to the man, and he rode on.

When he reached Adana, he found lodging. He sent his horse to the stables and took a room. He called the landlord to him and said, "I want two million little purses made." And the landlord had them made. The boy changed all his gold pieces to *para* and put these *para* into the magic purse. When they had all turned to gold, he put them in the other purses which had been made for him. He kept this up until all the two million purses were filled, then he had the purses carried under the princess' window. The pile was so great that it resembled a mountain.

Now the rule was that the princess must remain standing until the suitor had offered all his gold. But the boy had so much of it that the princess became tired and asked for a chair to sit

* Town arbitrarily selected by informant.

down. Soon she was so tired of sitting down that she sent her maid out to see if there was much more to come.

The maid went outside and saw a pile of purses as tall as a high mountain. She went back to her mistress and said, "You can't believe the treasure he has!"

The princess felt hopeless. "Go tell the man that I will see him." The boy came to her and saw her great beauty. "All the world came and couldn't even see my little finger. But now you behold my true self," she told him. The boy, of course, was overjoyed. The princess wanted to know his secret, so she put a potion in his drink. "You are mine, and I am yours. Tell me, sweet one, where did you find all that money?"

The boy took out his purse and shook it before her eyes. "Do you see this? This is my secret." Soon he fell into a deep sleep. The princess took the lucky purse away from the boy and had him thrown out into the road. To make sure that he wouldn't trouble her again, she had a big rock put on his stomach.

In the morning when he awoke, he found himself on the road behind the palace. Then he felt the heavy rock on his stomach and pushed it off. Gradually he remembered what had happened and could not forgive himself for having been such a fool. However, there was nothing he could do, so he went back to his lodging, took out his horse and started back for his mother's house. He did not tell her of his misfortune. Instead, he told her that he was engaged to marry a most beautiful princess and that he would bring her home with him soon.

That night when both his mother and her maid were asleep, he slipped out of bed and looked about the house, hoping to find another magic purse. This time he was not so fortunate, but on the shelf he found a man's shirt, and knowing that no one at the house had use for it, he took it and put it among his clothes. The next morning he bid his mother farewell and started back to the town of the beautiful princess.

When he reached his destination, he returned to his old lodging, cleaned up from his trip and put on his new shirt. To his amazement, he discovered that he had suddenly become invisible! He decided to visit the princess and look at her as much as he wished since now no one could see him.

So he entered her room, gazed at her fondly, approached her, tickled her here and tickled her there and finally slept beside her. The girl knew that something was happening but couldn't see anyone in the room. "Show yourself to me, whoever you are, and let me see who has tricked me," she said.

The boy pulled the shirt over his head and showed himself to her. "Ah! It is you! I should have known that no one else could have done this!" she said tenderly. Again, she put a potion in his drink. She gave it to the boy, and when he was asleep, she quietly removed the shirt from under his pillow and again had him thrown out into the road.

In the morning the boy awoke and found himself in an unhappy condition. He knew immediately what had happened, but what could he do now? He pushed the rock off his stomach, returned to his lodging, sat on his horse and started back for his mother's house.

And again his mother was happy to see him. "Come with goodness, my son," she said, and she made him comfortable. He told her once again that he was to marry the princess but had returned only to see if all preparations for her arrival were completed. "Bring her when you will, my son, we will not be black-faced [embarrassed]. Even a king's daughter will be impressed with our preparations."

That night when both his mother and her maid were asleep, the boy slipped out of bed and again looked through the shelves to see if he could find another magic object. While he was searching, he saw a horn lying there, so he picked it up and placed it to his lips. No sooner had he done so than an enormous slave appeared before him. "I am at your command," the slave said.

"You may go now, but wait for my further orders," the surprised boy replied.

The next morning he bade his mother good-bye, telling her that he was going to get his fiancée and bring her back. He made sure to take the horn along with him.

When he reached Adana, he found lodging, took his horse to the stable and went to his room. Then he blew on the horn, and the slave appeared.

"I want all this town surrounded with soldiers, cannons and fortifications. I want a huge rainbow-colored tent placed opposite the king's palace and two rows of warriors assigned from my tent to the palace," the boy ordered.

"As you say," answered the slave, and he disappeared.

In the morning the boy saw that his every wish had been fulfilled. He went into the rainbow-colored tent and waited. The people were afraid of the soldiers and ran to the king's palace and told him what had happened, begging for his protection.

The king was much surprised at this new development. How could such a thing happen overnight? He called several of his men and gave them the following orders: "I want you to go to the chieftain who is most probably in that rainbow-colored tent across from the palace. Tell him that whatever he asks for, he shall have, if he will only spare my people."

Whoever went to perform this task died of fright on the way when he saw the double row of soldiers. Finally the king said: "Whoever goes to deliver my message to the chieftain will receive a great reward."

So an old hag with one foot lame and one eye blind volunteered to deliver the message. She walked through the double row of soldiers and went inside the rainbow-colored tent. "Oh, great chief, my king says that anything you wish for will be yours if you will not harm his people," she said.

"I want the princess, and if the king does not give her to me, I will burn the town," the boy answered.

"I will deliver your answer to the king."

When she returned to the palace, she told the king of the boy's answer and claimed her reward. "You have done well, mother," the king said, giving orders for the fulfillment of her promised reward. "Call my daughter to me," the king continued, and the princess was brought before him. "My daughter, we are in great danger, and you are the only one who can save us. The chieftain in that rainbow-colored tent has said that unless you marry him, he will burn the town. You must go, my child."

The princess with two of her attendants went to the rainbow-colored tent and recognized the boy. "Oh, my love, where have you been all this time?" the princess said, falling on his neck and weeping. The boy was caught off guard by her expression of love. She was so beautiful that she was able to do anything, and he could not help but forgive her. Again she put a potion in his drink and said, "Now you have no reason to doubt me. Tell me, are we not one? What great power you must have to do all this!"

"Your hair is long, but your brains are short,"* the boy answered, pointing to his magic horn.

Soon he fell into deep sleep. The princess put her lips to

* A popular masculine remark made about women.

the horn, and the slave appeared before her. "I am at your command."

"See that all these soldiers are removed and that this tent is also removed," the princess said. "Take this foolish boy into a cave on ——— island."

The next morning, the boy awoke to find himself on a strange uninhabited island. Soon he remembered what had happened and was very angry for having been tricked again. "Well, I know that I can never get off this island. I may as well look around and see what I can find," the boy said. Looking about him, he saw some large fig trees. "At least I will not be hungry," the boy said, reaching up for a huge fig. As soon as he had eaten it, he became a buffalo. "Well, now that I am a buffalo," the boy thought to himself (because he could not speak aloud), "let me see what else there is here."

Soon he came across a small, delicate fig tree. "I can't be in a much worse condition than I am. I will eat one of these figs, too," he thought. So he reached up and picked one. And no sooner had he eaten the small fig than he resumed his normal form. "Now I have a way of fighting that princess if I can only get off this island," the boy said to himself. So he built a secure raft and picked three big figs and three small figs. He tied these in his handkerchief and slipped it beneath his shirt.

After many adventurous days, he reached Armenia. He walked to Adana where he found lodging. He washed, changed his clothes, put the three large figs on a dish and walked right under the king's window at the palace. "Figs, figs, beautiful figs. Figs, figs, beautiful figs."

"What? Figs at this time of the year?" the king asked. And he was assured that there was a man selling large fresh figs just outside. "Bring him here," the king said. They called the boy in. "How much do you want for your figs?"

"If you buy one, you must buy all three of them," the boy said. "I will sell all three of them for fifty pieces of gold."

"Very well, such royal fruit is worth that price," the king said, paying him for the figs.

That day the king, the queen and the princess ate the figs. But no sooner had they eaten them than they became buffaloes. The noblemen and soldiers were amazed. What had happened? What could have caused this sudden transformation? They did not know, of course, that it was due to the figs; and neither the king, the queen nor the princess could speak. They just nodded their heads this way or that way, but could not say a word. All the world's best healers came to cure them, but, of course, it was useless. Finally, when the boy thought that they had suffered enough, he dressed as a healer, took the three little figs, put them in a suitcase and went through the streets announcing his profession as a healer.

People heard him and ran to the palace to tell the king's chief adviser about the strange doctor who was announcing his profession in the streets, saying that he could cure anyone of anything. "Bring him to the palace," the adviser said. The boy was brought to the palace. "Can you cure our royal family?" the king's adviser asked, after telling him of their condition.

"If I can see the king alone, I will assure you that he will be cured," the boy said. The boy was left alone with the king. "If I cure you, will you give me your daughter?" the boy asked the king.

The king, not being able to speak, nodded his head up and down. Then the boy opened his case, took out one of the figs and gave it to the king. No sooner had the king eaten it than he resumed his normal form again. Then the boy went to the queen and gave her the second small fig, and she resumed her normal form, too.

Then he went to the princess. "Now, if I cure you and make you the same beautiful girl that you were before, will you marry me?" he asked. The princess nodded her head in consent. "Where have you put my magic purse?" the boy asked her. The princess, not being able to speak, nodded toward the place where she had hidden it. The boy went and found it and put it in his pocket.

"Now tell me where you have put my magic shirt and my horn." The princess once again nodded toward the place where she had hidden them. The boy went and found them, too.

"Tell me once more, if I cure you, will you marry me?" the boy asked.

The princess slowly nodded her head. Then the boy gave her the last fig. No sooner had she eaten it than she became the beautiful princess she had always been. The princess wanted to stay with her parents, but the boy wanted to move on, so she had to go along. With great riches, they started toward his mother's house. The mother, by one means or another, had heard of her son's glorious return and welcomed the young people with music and large crowds. And a beautiful wedding was celebrated for forty days and forty nights.

Their hopes were realized, and so shall ours be. The story is ended. From the sky fell three apples: one to me, one to the storyteller and one to the person who has entertained you.

14. The Magic Horse

There was once an old widow who had a young son. When the lad was old enough to enjoy the pleasures of the world, he was poor, and no one would even look at him.

One day he asked, "Mother, who has fed and taken care of us since my father's death?"

"My son, God has looked after us all these years."

"Well, who is going to take care of us now?" he asked.

"Now it is time for you to find work somewhere, my son, and support us," the mother answered. And this the youth did, but no matter how hard he tried, he could not find any kind of work which he liked.

One day he asked his mother, "Mother, what kind of work did my father do? Why haven't you spoken about him to me?"

"Go into the barn, my son, and you will see for yourself," the old woman said. The boy went into the barn and looked around but saw nothing. "I have been in this barn every day of my life, and I have seen nothing which suggests what my father did. Why did my mother send me here?" he asked himself angrily. As he looked about further, he became more and more angry. Finally, he was so enraged that he kicked the walls. Suddenly the wall parted, and he saw a room which he had never before seen.

"Ah!" the youth said, "why haven't I seen this before?" He went inside and saw a bony horse standing in one corner. The boy led the horse out and for weeks fed it and cared for it. One day when the boy thought that the horse was well, he put a saddle on it and decided to see how it rode. But the moment he sat on the animal, he no longer remembered what happened! He realized only that the horse was flying and that he was sitting breathlessly on his saddle.

When they stopped, the youth found himself near a fountain in a wilderness. While the horse and rider were resting, the boy

This story was told by Kasar Bogosian.
See Comparative Studies for other versions.

saw a beautiful feather on the ground and picked it up. He marveled at its beauty, then threw it down again. Suddenly the horse said, "If you take this feather with you, you will be sorry; if you leave it behind, you will be sorry, too."

The boy was surprised to hear his horse speak. But he thought that since he would be sorry in either case, he might as well take the feather with him. So he put the feather in his hair, sat on his horse and rode off. Unknown to the youth, a great light sparkled from the feather in his hair, and people on all sides were spellbound by its beauty.

The boy and his horse entered a town, and the people were so excited about the unusual feather that the king heard about it. He ordered his guards to bring the youth before him. When the boy saw that the powerful king liked the feather so much, he presented it to him as a gift.

The king's vizier, seeing that the ruler spent his days and nights marveling at the beautiful feather, said, "My King, if just one feather is so beautiful, think how beautiful the entire bird must be."

"True, true, but where is this beautiful bird to be found?" the king asked.

"Surely, the person who can find just one feather will have no difficulty finding the whole bird," the vizier said. So the king ordered the youth to be brought before him and said, "You must bring me the bird to whom this feather belongs. If you fail, you will lose your head."

The sad youth left the palace and went to the stable to talk to his horse and tell him what the king had ordered. The horse said, "Don't worry—just ask the king for enough wheat so that when you are crouched in it, you will not be seen. Take this wheat near the fountain where you found the feather and hide amongst the wheat. At this time of the year, all the birds of the world come to this fountain to drink. When the bird with the beautiful feathers alights, you will see it through the wheat stalks. You must seize the bird's wings so that it cannot fly away. I will be waiting nearby, and you will immediately mount me and we will quickly return to the king."

So the boy asked for a good quantity of wheat and returned near the fountain where he had found the unusual feather. He piled the wheat just as the horse had instructed him to do and hid among it. When the beautiful bird alighted, the boy seized it by its wings, jumped on his horse and quickly returned to the king. The bird was so beautiful that the whole country was bathed in light day and night. Indeed, it was believed that the bird was the sun itself.

The bird was not only very beautiful, it also spoke day and night. But sad to say, no one in the kingdom could understand what it was saying. So the vizier said to the ruler one day, "My King, you have this beautiful bird, but you do not know what it says. You need an interpreter."

"But where can I find such an interpreter?" the king asked.

"Surely, the person who found the bird can find its interpreter," the vizier said. So the king had the boy brought before him. "You must bring me the interpreter for this bird. If you fail to do so, I'll cut off your head."

The boy went slowly to the stable and told his horse what the king had ordered. The horse said, "I knew that this would happen, but now that it is done, let us see what we can do about it. Come, sit on my back and stay on until I stop. Then dismount, and I will tell you what to do next." So the youth sat on the horse, and they started out. They rode for some time, and finally the horse stopped at the highest peak of a mountain. The boy dismounted and waited for instructions.

"Walk straight down this path," the horse said, "and you will see a fountain from which pus flows. Take some to your lips and say 'How good this tastes, how nice it looks.' Continue on the path until you come to a field which is full of mud as high as your knees. Walk through the mud and say 'What a nice soft path.' In the center of this field there stands a palace with seven doors. The first door is open, the second is closed, the third open, the fourth is closed, and so on. When you enter through the doors which are closed, leave them open. Inside the palace you will see steps which you must climb. On these steps there are sharp nails which will tear your flesh. Instead of complaining, you must say 'How soft you are, how nice you look.' Upstairs you will see seven giants sleeping. You must be very careful not to touch their clothing as you pass between them. Beyond that room there is another room in which a girl with a ring on her finger lies sleeping. You must remove the ring without touching her finger. Then throw the girl over your shoulder, carefully pass the giants without touching their clothing, praise the nails as you walk down, pass through the open doors and then come to me."

The boy did as he was told. He went straight down the path and came to the fountain of pus. He tasted it and praised it. He went on to the muddy field and praised the nice soft path. He entered the palace with seven doors, leaving the closed doors open. He climbed the stairs studded with sharp nails which tore his feet, and said, "How soft you are, how nice you look!" Finally he came upon the giants, and without touching their clothing, he passed to the inner room. He removed the girl's ring without touching her finger, threw her over his shoulder, carefully passed the giants, praised the steps as he descended, went through the door, climbed the mountain, sat on his horse and flew away.

He took the beautiful girl to the king's palace, and when the ruler saw her, he wanted to marry her. She said, however, "I am tired, I have had a long journey. I must bathe and rest, and only then will I marry you."

The king ordered that a bath be prepared for her, but she laughed at him and said, "Foolish man, do you think that I can take a bath as easily as that? I must have my soap, my comb and my towel."

"But where will I find your soap, your comb and your towel?" the distraught king asked.

"Surely, he who brought me here can also bring my soap, my comb and my towel," the girl said. So the king ordered the boy to be brought before him and told him that he must set forth and return with the girl's comb, towel and soap or lose his head.

The boy went to the stable and told his horse of the king's new demands. The horse said, "Listen now: those giants have looked all over for us and have been unable to find us. They are now very tired and having put their heads together, are fast asleep. I will take you to that same mountain: you must taste the pus from the fountain, you must praise the muddy field, you must leave the closed doors open, you must praise the nails on the steps, you must carefully pass the giants, you must enter the room where the girl had been sleeping and find her comb, her soap and her towel. But you must not put these three things together— they must not rub one another. If you fail in this, it will be your end."

So the horse again took the boy to the mountain top. He went down the path and tasted the pus from the fountain and said, "How nice it looks, how good it tastes!" Then he passed on and reached the muddy field. He walked through the mud to his knees and said, "How soft you are, how soft!" He walked on until he came to the palace with seven doors. He entered through one door after another and did not close any behind him. Inside, as he climbed the stairs, he said to the nails, "How nice you are, how soft!" Upstairs he was careful not to touch the clothing of the giants. He entered the room where the girl had been sleeping and found her comb, her soap and her towel and prepared to carry each so that it would not touch either of the others. Carefully, he passed by the giants and again praised the nails on the stairs, passed through the open doors, climbed the mountain where the horse was waiting for him and quickly returned to the king's palace.

With her magical accessories, the girl took her bath and became even more beautiful than before. The king said, "Now we will be married." The youth, meanwhile, seeing the girl's great beauty, had fallen in love with her.

"You old fool!" the girl said to the king. "See how beautiful and young I am? Why should I marry an old man like yourself?"

"But you must marry me for you are my slave!"

"I will marry you only if you are young again," the girl said.

"But how is that possible?"

"In my garden there is a magic apple which can make you young again," the girl said. "If you cut the apple in many pieces and drop it into your bath water, when you emerge from your bath, you will become as young and beautiful as I am."

"But how can I get this magical apple? Where will I find your garden?" the king asked.

"Surely, the youth who brought me here and later brought my soap, my comb and my towel to you can bring a mere apple from my garden," the girl said.

So the boy was called before the king again and was told that he must find an apple from the girl's garden. If he failed in this mission, he would lose his head.

The boy went to his horse and told him about the king's order. The wise horse said, "I will take you to a place where two mountains have come together, forming a wall through which no one can pass. But at certain times these mountains part from each other so that the wall of stone opens. We must watch until the mountains begin to part and only then can we pass through." So the boy mounted, and the horse took him to the two mountains which formed a huge rocky wall.

The horse said, "Now listen carefully: you must hit me so hard that the milk which I drank as a child will come through my nostrils, causing me to jump right through that small opening to the country on the other side. Do not spare me, but hit with all your strength." When the mountains began to part, the youth hit his good horse so hard that the milk he had drunk in his childhood gushed through his nostrils and he jumped so powerfully that both horse and rider found themselves on the other side of the mountain, in the midst of a beautiful garden.

The horse said, "This is the apple tree you are seeking. You must pick three apples, but be very careful that they do not rub against each other. Place them in different places on your body. Be careful, too, not to touch any of the branches. If you do, all the giants in the world will appear before us, and we will surely be destroyed."

So the youth carefully took the three apples and placed them in different pockets and returned to his horse. The horse said, "You have done very well so far, but you must continue to do just as I tell you. When those mountains begin to part, you must hit me so hard that I will jump clear across and both of us will land safely on the other side."

But the boy, thinking that it was a pity to hurt such a good horse, did not strike him as hard as was necessary when the mountains began to part. Therefore, the horse could not get across fast enough, and his hind legs were caught in the mountainous wall. The horse pulled himself up from the ground where he had fallen, but his hind legs remained behind. The maimed horse looked sorrowfully at the boy, then disappeared.

Magically, the horse flew to the fountain of youth and in moments returned to his master. The boy was surprised indeed when he saw his good horse with four legs and looking more youthful and beautiful than ever before. He mounted, and, together, horse and rider returned to the king's palace. The youth gave the three magical apples to the king.

That night when he was asleep in the stable near his horse, the boy dreamt that he should go to the fountain where he knew the king would bathe and lie there in wait for the ruler. The king would cut the apple into small pieces, then take off his clothes in preparation to bathe. The boy knew that the king, being old, would be slow in his movements. The boy was told in the dream to step into the fountain quickly, bathe himself, then hide before the king could see him. Indeed, the dream was so interesting and unusual that the youth decided to do as it advised.

The next morning at sunrise, the horse poked his master and awoke him. The boy went to the royal garden and saw that the king had just finished cutting the apple into small pieces and was putting the pieces into the fountain. While the old man was slowly removing his clothes, the boy tore off his own few things and quickly stepped into the water without being seen by the king and just as quickly stepped out again. Finally, the king was ready to take his bath. But when he stepped into the water, he vanished completely, and in his place, there remained only a handful of sea foam. The boy, however, who had bathed first, was even younger and more handsome than before.

The boy put on the king's robes and returned to the palace. And everyone, thinking that this was the king who had been rejuvenated, honored him as their ruler. The youth married the beautiful girl who, through her magical powers, knew that he was the brave hero who had brought her to this land. So there was a royal wedding for seven days and seven nights, and everyone ate and drank and made merry. The boy, his beautiful wife, the illuminating bird and the magic horse lived together happily forever after.

15. The Huntsman

Once upon a time there was a poor widow whose only son was a very good huntsman. Every day he would go into the woods and hunt birds and deer to support his aged mother.

One day while he was hunting, he saw a bird which dazzled him with its beauty, but he did not shoot it because it was so beautiful. Instead, he turned in another direction and tried not to think about it. But the bird came toward him as though asking him to shoot it. The huntsman once more turned aside and started in still another direction. But again he saw the same bird approaching him and felt sure that God had directed it to him. So he took careful aim and brought down the bird which he had so greatly admired.

When he took it home, the sight of the beautiful feathers, the vivid colors and the noble appearance of the bird made him sorry for what he had done. He handled the bird with great care so that he could stuff it. When he had done this, it looked almost as beautiful as the original had been, and the huntsman was very proud.

That evening when both mother and son were asleep, there appeared a bright light in the house which awakened them. The

This story was told by Nishan Krikorian.

mother asked her son if he had left the candle burning. When the boy assured her that he had not, they got up to investigate. To their amazement, they found that there was no candle burning but that the great beauty of the bird was filling the room with light.

"What shall we do, mother?" the boy asked.

"This is too great a thing to keep in our humble home, son. You must take it to the king tomorrow," the mother replied.

Early the next morning the huntsman carefully wrapped the stuffed bird, presented himself at the palace and told the guard that he had a gift for the king.

"What a beautiful bird!" said the king when he was shown the huntsman's gift. Then he ordered his vizier to give the hunter three pieces of gold. The vizier led the boy to another room and took three pieces of gold from a box. But because he was very greedy, he gave the boy only two of these pieces and kept one for himself.

The king was so proud of the bird that he had it placed in the throne room. When the vizier saw it there, he said to the king, "This bird is truly beautiful, Your Majesty, but if the throne room were made of ivory, how much more beautiful the bird would appear!"

"But how can we get ivory?" the king asked. "We have none in this kingdom, and it is very costly to buy."

"But surely, Your Majesty, the person who could get such a beautiful bird can easily succeed in getting any amount of ivory that you may wish!" the vizier replied.

"Perhaps you are right, my friend. Send two of my guards to bring the huntsman to my palace at once!"

A short time later the boy was brought before the king. "I am sending you to find ivory with which to decorate this room. If you succeed, well and good; if you fail, you will lose your head."

"But, my King, how can I get ivory for your throne room? You know it is very difficult to find."

"You have heard my command!"

The huntsman returned home and told his mother of the king's order. He took some food along and wearily set out. He knew that it was an almost impossible task that the king had asked him to perform.

For months he roamed and saw many foreign lands. He was soon out of food and was living on herbs and game. One afternoon as he was resting against a large rock and looking at a dirty little stream, he saw a herd of elephants coming toward the stream to drink. He hid himself behind a rock and watched them. The next afternoon he hid again behind the same rock to see if the elephants would return. And soon they arrived—forty of them. He followed the same plan the following day and came to the conclusion that these elephants were in the habit of coming to the stream every day at this time.

With happiness he picked his way back to his homeland. He went to the palace where he said to the king, "Your Majesty, if you will give me forty mules, forty men and forty jugs of wine, you will have the ivory."

"Very well, you may have all that you ask for," said the king who gave orders to his vizier.

After the huntsman had seen his mother and rested, he started out with the caravan. The journey was pleasant, and there was plenty to eat and drink. Soon they reached the stream where the boy had seen the elephants. As it was early in the day, he had the men drain all the water from the stream and pour the wine in its place.

At the usual time the elephants came toward the pond but noticed the strange odor and wouldn't taste the water. After some time, however, their thirst was so great that they tried to drink. Immediately they liked the wine and drank to their hearts' content. It was not very long before every one of them was drunk and lay down to sleep. The huntsman and his men went up to the unconscious beasts, cut off the ivory tusks and rode back to the king. "Your Majesty, your wish is fulfilled," the huntsman said as he presented the ivory to the king.

"Very well, now the bird will be even more beautiful in an ivory setting. Vizier, give this good man three pieces of gold," the king ordered.

The vizier went into another room followed by the huntsman. He took three pieces of gold from the coin box but, as before, gave only two pieces of gold to the youth and kept one for himself. The huntsman went home to share his wealth with his mother.

"Well, my vizier, how do you like the throne room now that it is paneled with ivory? Don't you think the bird looks lovelier than before?"

"Your Majesty, it is indeed very beautiful. But it lacks only one thing," the cunning man replied. "You have a beautiful bird and an ivory throne room, but you lack a beautiful queen. I have heard that the daughter of the king of Fairyland is the most beautiful and the wisest woman in the world. It is only right that she be your queen."

"Yes, the princess of Fairyland is the only one who can share with me the beauty of this room. But how can this be arranged since no one knows where Fairyland is?" asked the king.

"Why, surely, Your Majesty, the person who could get such a beautiful bird and who could succeed in finding enough ivory for your throne room would be able to find the princess of Fairyland," the vizier told the king.

"Yes, yes, you are right! Send two guards after that huntsman and have him come before me at once!" the king ordered.

Again the youth stood before the king. "I have heard that the princess of Fairyland is very beautiful," the king told him. "You are to bring her here to be my queen. If you fail to do so, your head will be cut off."

"But Your Majesty, how am I to find Fairyland? No man has ever seen it. The people in it fly around with wings. Your request is impossible for me to fulfill," the poor boy said.

"Go!"

The huntsman felt that this time he was going to die. It made no difference that he was in the prime of youth. When he reached his home, he told his mother of the king's command, packed some food and set out on the journey.

After months of travel he was disheartened, tired and hungry. But one day as he was going along, he saw a curious thing—a man was kneeling down with his ear to the ground. "Friend, what are you doing?" the boy asked.

"Seven years ago I let a crippled fly escape. I have been waiting for him all this time, but he hasn't returned. I can hear him buzzing around, and someday soon he will come back to me," the man replied.

"But what a thing to do!" the huntsman said in disbelief.

"Why, isn't it possible? I have heard of a man who has found enough ivory to decorate the throne room of the king's palace."

"I am that man! I found the ivory for the king's palace."

"Well, if that is so, let me join you in your travels."

"Come along," the boy said. On the road the huntsman explained to the listener the purpose of his journey.

After some time the huntsman and his companion came upon a man with a huge millstone tied around his foot. This man had two rabbits in his hands. He let one rabbit go, ran after it and caught it; then he let the other rabbit go, ran after it and caught it. The huntsman and the listener were amazed at such speed. How could this man run faster than the rabbits even though he had a millstone weighing almost two thousand pounds tied to his foot?

Finally, they stopped the man and asked him how he could perform such feats. "Why, this is nothing. I have heard of a man who has found enough ivory to decorate the throne room of the king's palace," the man told the travelers.

"I am that man. I found the ivory for the king's throne room," the huntsman said.

"If that is so, let me join you in your travels," the runner said.

"Come along," said the huntsman. Then he told the man what his mission was, and they became good friends. Now they were three instead of two. A few weeks of travel brought them to an enormous man who was sitting on a large rock, looking up into the sky.

"What are you doing, friend?" the huntsman asked the big fellow.

"Fourteen years ago, I threw an iron ball straight up into the sky. I have been waiting here for it to return ever since, but it hasn't come down yet," the man told the amazed huntsman.

"But could such a thing be possible?"

"Why couldn't it be possible? I have heard of a man who has found enough ivory to decorate the king's throne room."

"I am that man. I found the ivory for the king's throne room," the boy said.

"Well, I am proud to know you. May I join you in your travels?" the thrower asked the huntsman.

"Come along," said the huntsman. On the road the boy explained the purpose of his trip to the thrower. The four of them traveled together until they saw a man kneeling by the mouth of a mill, eating all the flour seven combined mills produced.

"Is this possible? How can you do this?" the amazed huntsman asked.

"Why, there is nothing to this. I have heard of a man who has found enough ivory to decorate the throne room of the king's palace. That is truly something."

"I am the man who found the ivory for the king's throne room."

"Oh, I am proud to know you," the man said. "May I join you in your travels?"

"Come along," said the huntsman. One by one, the other men introduced themselves to the eater. And finally the five of them reached the country of Fairyland. There they were taken to the palace as guests of the king. When the king asked them the purpose of their visit, the huntsman told his mission. "Very well, your king may have my daughter if you can fulfill three of my requirements. If you are successful, you will have a new queen; if you are not successful, all of you will die."

The next morning the king told the huntsman and his companions the first task. "Go to a certain field and bring me a bunch of grapes from that vineyard. You must return before my daughter does because she will be sent on the same mission."

When they were alone, the huntsman asked his friends how they were going to do this since they all knew that the princess had wings and could fly through the air at great speed. "Oh, do not give this thing another thought," the runner told his friends. "You saw how fast I ran after my rabbits; surely I can outrun this fairy princess." So it was decided that this task would fall to the runner.

The next morning the runner started on the journey. He could not see the princess who was far behind him. Although the princess was invisible, she could see the runner ahead of her and was alarmed. The runner reached the field, picked a bunch of grapes and was starting back when he heard the sweet voice of the princess. "You are truly wonderful. See, you have your grapes before I have even reached the field. Come, now, put your tired head on my lap and take a short rest before returning. There is no need to hurry: you are way ahead of me anyway."

Now, as we said before, the princess was very beautiful and had a lovely musical voice. The runner was so taken by her charms that he complied with her request. The princess lulled him to sleep, and when she was sure that he would not wake, she softly slipped his head from her knee to a nearby rock and raced toward the field to get the grapes. The runner, unaware of what had happened, was still in a sound sleep.

The huntsman and his companions were waiting for the runner to come back when all of a sudden, the listener turned to the boy and said, "I'll just put my ear to the ground and see how our friend the runner is faring." The men waited anxiously. "The runner is sound asleep, and the princess will reach the palace within a half hour," the listener said.

"Never mind, let the princess come. I, who could throw a

ball into the sky so far that I had to wait fourteen years for its return, can throw this princess such a distance that she will have to fly her course all over again because she will have lost her grapes," the thrower told his friends.

True to the listener's prediction, the princess was circling around the palace within half an hour. The thrower took her and hurled her upward with such force that the runner, who was sleeping peacefully, woke up with a start to behold the princess hurtling through the sky. Suddenly he saw through her trick and realized how he had been fooled. Immediately he started for the palace with his grapes and ran as he had never run before.

The first requirement was fulfilled to the king's satisfaction. "Very well, you have succeeded in the first task. Now here is the second one," the king told the men. He ordered his cook to prepare four barrels of meat (each barrel holding at least one thousand pounds) for the five visitors. "You must eat until all these barrels are empty or have your heads cut off," he ordered.

The huntsman looked at his friends and thought that this time his death order was signed. "But Your Majesty, four thousand pounds of meat fried in oil is too much for five men to eat—it is impossible!" he told the king. But his pleading fell on deaf ears.

"My dear huntsman, why do you worry?" the eater asked. "I have an enormous appetite, for I have not had enough to eat for some weeks now. Let me get at that meat, and I will finish the whole by myself." The eater, thus saying, threw himself upon the food.

When the eater had finished the first barrel, he ordered the second one to be brought before him. He made short work of the second and started on the third. Then the huntsman and his friends intervened and joined in finishing the last barrel.

The king looked at the five men as if he had witnessed a miracle. But he controlled himself and said, "Very well, my friends, you have fulfilled the second requirement. Now if you can be as successful in executing my last wish as you have been in fulfilling my two previous ones, my daughter will be your queen. All five of you are to take a shower in one of my specially constructed shower rooms. If you come out alive, the order will be fulfilled."

The huntsman and his friends knew that this task would be the most difficult. However, they let themselves be led into the room where they were to take a steam bath. At first they enjoyed it very much, but little by little the room became hotter, and the steam began to burn their bodies. They were in a bad situation, for they knew that they were locked in the room.

The listener put his ear to the ground and heard the fairy princess saying to her maid, "I have left my golden comb in the bath where my father is testing the men today. If they find the comb and take it in their hands, the steam will be shut off, and the room will be cooled."

"But, Your Majesty, you have hidden it in a safe place, haven't you?" asked the maid.

"Yes, they will never be able to find it because it is behind the soap in the closet," the princess replied.

The listener told the huntsman about the conversation he had just heard, and all of them searched the closet and found the comb. They took it in their hands, and as the princess had said, soon the steam was shut off, and they were able to breathe comfortably.

The next morning the king ordered several of his servants to remove the carcasses of the five men. When the servants went to carry out the command, they found all the imprisoned men alive and well. The king, upon hearing the news, thought there was a mistake and went to look for himself, but sure enough, he found the five men in a sound, peaceful sleep! The huntsman was awakened, and the king admitted that all his requirements had been fulfilled and that now his daughter could become their queen.

A few days later the huntsman, the fairy princess and the four friends started homeward. Soon the eater came to his mill and asked if he could stop there and return to his work; the huntsman consented. Then the thrower came to the place where he had thrown the ball fourteen years earlier, and he, too, asked to be excused from going on. When the listener and the runner had dropped out, the huntsman and the princess found themselves alone. Neither of them spoke until they reached their destination.

Then the princess said to the huntsman, "You stay here and be ready at an instant's notice. When I call you, rush up the palace steps." With that remark, she went into the palace alone. "I am the princess of Fairyland, Your Majesty," the princess said to the king. "I am ready to be your queen. There is one thing, however, that I would like to understand. Call your vizier here."

The king called the vizier. "Your Majesty, tell me: when

that huntsman brought you that beautiful bird and furnished your room with ivory, how much gold did you give him?" the princess asked the king.

"Why, three pieces of gold. Ask my vizier here; he received my instructions," the king said.

Then the princess turned to the vizier and said, "Tell the king how many pieces of gold you gave the huntsman."

"Your Majesty, I gave him two pieces of gold and kept one for myself," the man was forced to admit.

"Very well. Now, Your Majesty, you have ruled for a long time, but because you have been so cruel to the huntsman, you shall rule no more." With that, the princess said a few magic words, and both the king and the vizier became little birds and flew through the window to the mountains.

"Huntsman, huntsman, come here!" the princess called. The youth, when he heard her summons, rushed in and found the princess safe. She told him the whole story and asked him, "Would you like to be the new king? And would you like to have the princess of Fairyland as your queen?"

The huntsman threw himself on his knees before her. Thus, a poor boy, who never for a moment forgot the welfare of his mother, won a most beautiful, royal wife, became king of his country and, for many, many years, ruled fairly and wisely.

16. The Dreamer and His Dream

Once upon a time a young man had a strange dream and overslept. His mother called him and said, "Get up, the sun is already up!" But the boy did not pay any attention to her. He kept on sleeping. Then the father said, "Son, son, get up! There is much work to be done, and I am an old man!"

Finally, the boy awoke and said, "I was having such a nice dream! I wonder what it means."

"What did you dream?" his mother asked.

But the boy would not tell her.

"What did you dream, son?" the father asked.

But the boy would not tell him. "If you had a dream, we have a right to know what it was," the angry father said. "Tell us about it!"

This story was told by Hovhannes Kaprelian.

But the boy would not tell them. "Well then, if you will not tell us, leave our house!" the father shouted, and so the boy left his home behind and started out to seek his fortune.

He walked and walked—I don't know if it was far or near— but he finally reached a country which was ruled by a king. The people, seeing a stranger, asked where he was coming from, where he was going and why he was traveling. He replied to them, "I had a dream, and I would not tell about it to my mother or father, and they made me leave home."

"Well, what was your dream?" they asked him.

But he would not tell them. The people became curious and began talking about the strange youth who would tell no one about his dream. Finally, the king of the land heard about the boy and asked that he be brought to the palace.

"Son, you are a visitor in our land. Why have you come here?"

"I left my home behind and started out to see the world because I wouldn't tell my parents about a dream that I had," the youth replied.

"Well, what was your dream?"

But the boy would not tell the king, and the ruler became angry with the boy and put him in prison. Three times each day the king went to the prison and asked the boy about his dream. And each time the boy refused to tell him.

One day as the princess was passing by, she saw the handsome boy and motioned to him to build a tunnel leading from his prison to her room. And he did this. He spent his days with the beautiful princess, and when it was time for the king's visits, he quickly returned to his prison.

Time went by, and one day the king received a beautiful highly polished stick from a distant king with instructions to indicate which end of the stick had grown nearer the earth and which end had grown nearer the sky. If the king failed to distinguish this, the distant ruler would wage war against his land. But the king could not make this choice because both ends of the stick were identical.

The princess, seeing that her father was sad, asked him what was troubling him, and he told her his problem. She also became very sad, and the boy, seeing her so, asked what was troubling her. When she told him, he laughed and said, "Don't worry. This is an easy matter. When the sea is very quiet, dip the stick into it. Whichever end goes into the water deeper than the other has grown nearer the earth. Whichever end points to the sky has grown closer to the sky."

The princess told the king, who did just that and sent the stick and his answer back with a messenger. The other king was truly amazed, for he could not see how anyone could have answered his question correctly.

So by the same messenger he sent eight horses who had neither hair nor teeth. They were all the same size and the same color. "Tell your king," the ruler said, "to choose which is the mother and which are her children."

The messenger took the horses back to his king and told him what the other king had instructed. Again the king was very sad as he sat down to think about what he was to do. The princess, seeing her father sad, asked him what was troubling him. He told her, and she also became very sad. When the youth saw her, he asked the cause of her sadness.

She told him, and he laughed, saying, "If that is all, do not worry. Tie these horses separately in the stables. Give them plenty of grain but no water at all. When you untie them, the colts will go quickly to suckle their mother."

The princess told her father who did just as the boy had instructed, and it became an easy matter to find the mother. The king sent the eight horses and his answer back to the other king.

This time the king sent an iron arrow and an iron shield with instructions that the arrow must pierce the shield. When the princess' father was told of this, he became very sad and did not know how it was to be done. The princess, seeing the unhappiness of her father, asked what troubled him. He told her, and she, too, became sad. When the youth saw her sadness, he asked her the reason for it. She told him about the task which had been given to her father. "Tell your father that no one must be out in the streets tomorrow. Insist that all the doors and windows be locked and the iron shield and arrow be placed in the palace garden. I will do the rest."

So the following day all houses and doors were locked, and no one was out in the streets. The youth went to the palace garden and pierced the shield with the iron arrow. The king was very happy and returned the shield and arrow to the king who had sent it. This king was much surprised and asked to see the man who had done this marvelous feat. When the princess was asked who advised her, she told about the boy in prison. So the king arranged a royal wedding and married his daughter to the wise boy. After forty days the boy set out for the country of the king who had asked for him. His wife said, "Husband, whoever asks to join you on the way, take him along for my sake." And the boy promised to do this.

So he rode along until he met a man with such large ears that he used one for a mattress and the other for a quilt.* This man was bending, and his ears were near the earth. "What are you doing?" the boy asked.

"I am known as Hearer of the Lower World," the man said. "There is a war in the world below ours, and I want to know which side is winning and which side is losing."

"Could such a thing be possible?" the boy asked in amazement.

"Why not?" Hearer of the Lower World asked. "I have heard of the son-in-law of such-and-such a king who pierced an iron shield with an iron arrow. What is more amazing?"

"Oh, that was nothing," the boy said. "I am that son-in-law."

"If you are this brave hero, let me go along with you," the hearer said. So together, they went along until they met a man with a hill in each hand, elevating one and lowering the other. The boy stood in amazement. "What are you doing?" he asked.

"I am known as Weigher of Hills," the man said. "This hill is a bit heavier than the other one."

"That seems impossible!" the boy said.

"Why should it be impossible?" the man asked. "I have heard of the son-in-law of such-and-such a king who pierced an iron shield with an iron arrow. What is more amazing?"

"Oh, that was nothing!" the boy said. "I am that son-in-law."

"If that is so, let me join you and go wherever you go." So together, the boy, Hearer of the Lower World and Weigher of Hills started out. They traveled until they saw a man who, when he shot an arrow, made the hill level. The boy stood there in amazement and watched the man. "What are you doing?" he asked.

"I am known as Leveler of Hills, and with one arrow I can make a hill level," the man answered.

"But is such a thing possible?" the boy asked.

"Oh, this is nothing," Leveler of Hills replied. "I have heard of the son-in-law of such-and-such a king who has pierced an iron shield with an iron arrow. That is truly remarkable."

"That is nothing," the boy said. "I am that son-in-law."

* According to informant: expression of vastness.

"If that is so, brave hero, let me go along with you and your men," Leveler of Hills said. So together, the boy, Hearer of the Lower World, Weigher of Hills and Leveler of Hills started out. They walked along until they saw a man who jumped from one hill to another. His speed was so great that they could barely see him. "Friend, what are you doing?" the boy called.

"I am known as Catcher of Deer because I am a fast runner," the man replied.

"But such speed is impossible!" the boy said.

"This is nothing, my friend," Catcher of Deer said. "I have heard of the son-in-law of such-and-such a king who has pierced an iron shield with an iron arrow. That is truly remarkable."

"That is nothing," the boy said. "I am that son-in-law."

"If that is so, let me join you and your men," Catcher of Deer said. So together, the boy, Hearer of the Lower World, Weigher of Hills, Leveler of Hills and Catcher of Deer started out. They walked along until they saw a man lying down, his large mouth wide open, sucking in the water from the river. On one side of him there was much water; on the other side it was completely dry. The boy stood there for a minute and tried to understand what was happening. Finally he asked, "Friend, what are you doing?"

"I am known as Swallower of the River," the man answered. "I have drunk all the water of this river to my left, and now I am starting on the river to my right."

"How can anyone hold so much water?" the amazed boy asked.

"Oh, this is nothing," Swallower of the River answered. "I have heard of the son-in-law of such-and-such a king who has pierced an iron shield with an iron arrow. That is truly remarkable!"

"That is nothing," the boy replied. "I am that man."

"If that is so, let me join you and your men," Swallower of the River said.

"But, friend, how can I supply you with all the water you need and want?"

"Don't worry about that," the drinker said, "for I can live a whole month without water if I need to." So Hearer of the Lower World, Weigher of Hills, Leveler of Hills, Catcher of Deer and Swallower of the River started out together. They walked along until they came to a place where there were seven ovens, all baking bread. One man was running from one oven to another, eating all the bread that was baked. The boy stood and watched the eater in great surprise. "Friend, what are you doing?" he asked the eater.

"My name is Eat-Much," the eater said, "and I eat all the bread that these ovens bake."

"That seems impossible," the boy said. "You are such a small man!"

"Oh, this is nothing," Eat-Much said. "I have heard of the son-in-law of such-and-such a king who pierced an iron shield with an iron arrow. That is truly remarkable!"

"That is nothing," the boy said. "I am that son-in-law!"

"Let me join you and your men and see the world," the eater asked.

"How can I ever satisfy your hunger?" the boy asked.

"Don't worry about me," the eater said. "I can live without eating for a whole month if I need to." So the boy, Hearer of the Lower World, Weigher of Hills, Leveler of Hills, Catcher of Deer, Swallower of the River and Eat-Much started out together. They walked along until they came to the country of their destination. They went to the palace and were taken before the king.

"Did you pierce the iron shield with the iron arrow?" the king asked. When the boy assured him that he did, the king said, "I am going to give you and your men three tasks to fulfill. If you can do them, you will be rewarded, but if you cannot fulfill them, you will die." The boy agreed to enter this contest. "First, your fastest runner must run a race against my fastest runner. They must go to this certain apple tree, pick an apple and bring it back to the palace. Whichever one returns first will be the winner of the race."

"Well, friend," the boy said to the Catcher of Deer, "this is your work. Set out and return with the apple."

So Catcher of Deer started out and quickly reached the apple tree. He looked about and saw that the other runner was far behind him. "I'll just take a little nap until he gets here," the runner thought, so he went to sleep right beneath the apple tree. The king's runner reached the tree, snatched an apple and started back for the palace.

The boy and his men saw that the king's runner was on his way back, but Catcher of Deer was nowhere to be seen. "Friend," the boy said to the hearer, "put your ear to the ground and see what is happening to our friend the runner." Hearer of the Lower

World put his ear to the ground and heard Catcher of Deer snoring.

"What are we to do now?" the boy asked. "Leveler of Hills, shoot an arrow toward that apple tree and awaken our friend the runner."

Leveler of Hills shot an arrow near the apple tree which made such a noise that the runner jumped out of his sound sleep, grabbed an apple and with two steps reached the palace before the king's runner. So the boy and his men fulfilled the first task.

"Now," the king said, "my cook will prepare forty kettles of pilaff. If even one grain is left in any of the kettles, you will die."

But the bread eater, Eat-Much, sat down and ate thirty-nine kettles of pilaff before the others had even finished a half of the fortieth kettle. He helped them with that, too, and soon every last grain of pilaff had vanished. And they had fulfilled the second requirement.

"Very well," the king said, "now you will be taken to a forty-acre field which is full of water. If there is one drop of water left in that field tomorrow morning, you will die."

When they were taken to the field, Swallower of the River said to his friends, "Do not worry. I am very thirsty and I'll make short work of this." And true to his word, in a few hours all the water had disappeared. In fact, the earth was so dry that it became cracked. So that task was fulfilled, too.

"The last thing that I will ask you to do," the king said, "is to take your men and climb that hill and wage war against my men. If you win, you will have fulfilled all my tasks." When the boy and his friends left the room, the king called his men and instructed them to bury dynamite under the hill on which the boy and his men were to fight.

But the boy, suspecting a trick, told Hearer of the Lower World to put his ear to the ground and hear what he could hear. The hearer told the boy about the hidden dynamite.

"Well, friend," the boy said to Weigher of Hills, "let us see what you can do. Change the position of these hills so that we will fight on their hill and they will fight on ours." And Weigher of Hills quickly did so.

The next morning the boy and his friends stood on their hill and faced an army of several hundred. Leveler of Hills shot an arrow which divided the hill in half and caused the dynamite to start its action. All the men from the king's army were killed, yet not a single hair of the boy or his friends was hurt. And the last task had been fulfilled.

The king called the boy to the palace and said, "My son, you have done well all that I have asked you to do. Now I ask you to claim a reward."

"Your Majesty," the boy said, "I am married to the princess of such-and-such a country. Sad to say, my father-in-law and you are always at war with each other. By marrying your daughter, too, I would be son-in-law to both of you. This would stop the blood from flowing between the two countries. Then perhaps you will both act like one man, and when one is attacked, the other will only want to help him."

So the boy married the princess of this country, too, and after a royal wedding of forty days and forty nights, the boy, his new bride and his friends started out again. When the bread eater, Eat-Much, saw all the bread which had piled up during his travels, he decided to stay there and eat. So he stayed with his ovens.

As they went along, the drinker, Swallower of the River, saw that the river was quite high and decided to stay behind and drink it dry. Soon Catcher of Deer saw his deer running about and decided to stay and run after them. The rest went along until Leveler of Hills saw his hills and decided to stay behind and shoot his arrows. The others continued on their way until Weigher of Hills saw the tall hills and began to wonder which was heavier. He decided to stay there and weigh them again. They traveled on until Hearer of the Lower World decided that he wanted to remain behind to learn which side was winning the war in the world below. So he stayed there, and the boy and his new bride went ahead.

When he reached the palace of his first bride, a great wedding took place for both women which lasted for forty days and forty nights. Several days later the boy again had the same dream which he had had several years ago. He got up in the morning and said, "Wives, I had an unusual dream last night."

"May good come of it! Tell us about it," his first bride said.

"Well, this is the same dream which I dreamt several years ago," the boy said, "but because no one said, 'May it be good,' I would not tell them about it. I dreamt that the sun was sitting on my one knee and the moon was sitting on the other. This is a strange dream, isn't it?"

"I am the sun," the first princess said, "and your other wife is the moon. Your dream has come true!"

17. The Patient Suitor

There was once a poor family who had one son. One day, the boy said to his mother, "Go to Toros Beg and ask for his daughter."

"But, my son," the mother answered, "Toros Beg is the town's richest man, and we are the town's poorest people. How can you suggest that I ask for his daughter?"

"You just go," the boy said. He asked his mother day after day and week after week for a whole month. Finally the poor mother could not bear to see her son's unhappiness any longer and decided to do as he requested. She went to the rich man's house and said, "I am going to ask a great favor of you. I hope that you may see fit to grant it, though I am ashamed to ask such a thing."

"What is it that you want?" the man said.

"My son wants to marry your daughter."

"All right," the rich man answered, "tell your son to come and see me."

Amazed, the mother went home and told her son what the rich man had said. So the boy went to the rich man's house. "My boy, I will let you marry my daughter if you will go to Van* and learn the story of the man whose business it is to wash clothes from dawn to sunset and yet he cannot even finish washing a single handkerchief," the rich man said.

So the boy set out for Van, and there he saw a man by the brook, about to wash a handkerchief which he held in his right hand. This man looked up at the flat steeple on a nearby church, ran up there, looked about and ran down again. Just as he was about to dip the handkerchief in the brook, he looked up at the steeple again, ran up, looked about and ran down again. He did this from dawn to sunset and could not wash even a small handkerchief.

"Friend," the boy asked, running alongside him, "why do you

This story was told by Hovhannes Kaprelian.
See Comparative Studies for another version.
*The towns mentioned in this story were picked arbitrarily by the storyteller.

continually run up and down? Why don't you stay here and wash your handkerchief?"

"I cannot answer your question until you go to Moush, and there, before the church, you will find a blind beggar. He is asking for alms, yet when people give him anything, he says, 'Take this away and slap me instead.' If you can discover the sense of this, then I will tell you my story," the washer said.

The boy left the washer and started for the town of the blind beggar. After some time he came to the church and found the blind man there, just as the washer had said. Whenever someone took pity on him and gave him a few coins, he said, "Please take this back, and slap my face instead." When the boy had watched the blind man for some time, he asked him, "Why do you refuse to take alms and instead ask people to slap you? If you will tell me this, the washer at Van will tell me his secret, and then I can go back home and marry the girl of my choice."

"In Erevan there is a very wealthy merchant. When he goes with his caravans, he is gone for six years and brings back many rare and precious things. Immediately upon his return, he goes to a place where he has set two huge rocks and knocks himself first against one of them, then against the other. If you can learn why he does this, return to me, and I will tell you my story," the blind beggar said.

So the boy went to Erevan. He asked here and there and learned that the merchant had left on one of his long trips only the week before and would not return for six years. What was he to do? Since he was now here and since Toros Beg's daughter was so beautiful, he decided to stay and wait for the merchant.

Six years later the merchant returned with great riches from all parts of the world. The boy thought, "He is too tired today. I will wait until tomorrow to ask him any questions."

But early the next day the merchant went to the spot where he had placed the two rocks and knocked himself first against one rock then against the other. He did this until he was bleeding and fell down to the ground in a faint. Then he was quickly taken home, and the healers stood ready to anoint his bruised body.

Several days later when he was better, the boy went to him and said, "You are a wealthy and successful man. Tell me, why do you knock yourself against those two rocks and hurt yourself? If you will tell me this, the beggar in Moush will tell me his story; then the washer in Van will tell me his story; and then I can return home and marry the girl of my choice. I have been waiting for your return for over six years."

"My son, if you had enough patience to wait for me six years, I will tell you the story of my life. When I was young, I decided to seek my fortune; so I left my wife and went my way. At that time my wife was pregnant. I roamed about, bought and traded, and after twenty years, became a rich man and decided to return home. When I reached my village, I peeped into the window of my house to see if anyone was at home and saw my wife lying beside a handsome youth. Thinking that she had been unfaithful to me, I took my bow and arrow and shot both my wife and the man. Then I went and slept at the tavern. The next morning I heard that someone had killed my wife and my young son. If only I had had enough patience, this would not have happened. So now I must repent, and that is why I knock myself against those two rocks to punish myself," the merchant said.

"Thank you," the boy said. "Now I can go back to the beggar, and he will tell me his story." So the boy started back to the church where the blind man was begging. "I have seen the merchant, and he told me his story. Now, will you tell me yours?" the boy said.

"What did he say?" the blind man asked.

The boy told him the story of the penitent merchant. "Now tell me your story," he added, "so that I can return to the washer for him to tell me his story. Then I will be able to return home to marry Toros Beg's daughter."

"Well, then, here is my story," the blind man said. "At one time I was a camel driver and took loads from one town to another. One day a dervish came to me and asked me what I was doing.

" 'I am looking for a load,' I told him.

" 'I have a load that I want transferred to Kharput. I will load forty camels with gold. You are to transfer thirty-nine of them and keep the last one for yourself. Do you agree to this?' the dervish asked.

" 'Oh, yes, yes, that will be very good,' I answered happily. So we went to a cave, and after the dervish had said a few words, the cave opened, and we went inside. There was a little box on the shelf which he removed and put into his pocket. We loaded forty camels with gold and left the cave. He said again, 'Take any one of these camels for yourself—that will be your own. The

177

other thirty-nine take to Kharput.' Thus we parted; he went one way and I another.

"But I began to think. One camel was good, but how much better it would be if I had ten camels. How much more gold I would have! So I called after the dervish and said, 'Dervish, I want nine more camels of gold or I won't take your load.' So the dervish said that I could have nine more. This meant that I had ten camels carrying gold.

"As I went on, I decided that ten camels weren't enough, so again I called to the dervish and said, 'Dervish, give me ten more camels so that you can have twenty and I can have twenty.' And the dervish said that I could have ten more camels.

"I went a little way, then I decided that twenty camels weren't enough; and again I called to the dervish and said, 'Dervish, I want ten more camels to make my number thirty.' And the dervish said that I could have ten more camels.

"I went along a bit further and decided that thirty camels weren't enough. Again I called to the dervish and said, 'Dervish, I want ten more camels.' And the dervish said that I could have ten more camels.

"Now I had forty camels loaded with gold, but still I was not satisfied. I remembered that the dervish had put a little box in his pocket, and I wondered what was in that box. Probably he had something even more valuable than this gold, I thought. So I called to the dervish and said, 'Dervish, what do you have in your box? Bring it to me and let me see!'

"The dervish answered, 'Man, I have given you my forty camels loaded with gold, and I have not complained. But the box contains magic for dervishes like me. What would you do with it?'

"But I wanted to know what there was in that box, so I cried out, 'Give me that box!'

"So the dervish said, 'In this box there is a medicine. If it is applied to one eye, it enables a person to see what there is beneath this earth of ours. He is able to know the location of oil wells and buried treasures. But if the medicine is applied to both eyes, the person will become blind. Here, since you insist, take the box, but be careful of its use.'

"So I took the medicine and put it on one of my eyes, and I was able to see the oil wells and buried treasures beneath the earth. But I still wasn't satisfied. 'If I can see all this with one eye, just imagine what I could see if I had this medicine on both eyes!' I said to myself. So I put the medicine on my other eye and immediately became blind. I called to the dervish for help, and he came and saw my condition, 'You are too selfish ever to enjoy life.* Therefore, remain as you are and repent,' the dervish said, slapping my face and taking all the forty camels and the box along with him. This is my story, my son," the blind man concluded.

"Thank you, thank you," the boy said. "Now I can go to the washer and hear his story." So the boy went to the washer and said, "I have heard the stories of the blind man and of the merchant. Now tell me yours."

"What is the blind man's story?" the washer said. So the boy told him the story of the greedy camel driver. "Now what is your story?" he asked again.

"Well, many years ago I was a poor washerman on this very same road, and I washed clothes for the passersby. One day when I returned to my hut just off the road, I saw that it was not a hut any longer, but a beautiful palace. I was surprised and stopped to see if I had made a mistake or if there was a mist before my eyes. But the door opened, and a very beautiful woman, like an angel, stood before me. She said, 'Come in, come in, this is your home, and this is your family.' She took me into a room which was full of the world's most precious gems. The curtains and rugs were made of pure silk, and the throne in the center of the room was so beautiful that there was none like it in the world. In the room were thirty-nine other women just as beautiful as the one who had opened the door for me.

" 'We are all here to live with you. You can eat and sleep with any and all of us. But there is one condition. You must never express dissatisfaction, for if you should do so three times, you will be just as poor as you ever were,' the most beautiful of the women said.

"So I stayed with them and ate and slept with them. In fact, one of them even bore me a child. Everything was plentiful, and I led an easy life. One day, however, it was very misty, and I said, 'Why is it so misty today? Why isn't the weather pleasant sometimes?'

"The most beautiful woman said to me, 'Be careful, you have complained once. You have only two more chances now.'

* In speaking of greediness, Armenians use the expression: "His eye has a hole."

179

"So months went by until one day, when it was very rainy, I said, 'Is there a hole in the sky? Is that why it is so rainy?'

"The leader of the beautiful women said to me, 'Be careful, you have complained twice. You have only one more chance now.'

"Months passed until one day it was very, very hot. It was so hot that I could hardly breathe, so I said, 'What a hot day! I can hardly breathe!' No sooner had I said this than everything I had disappeared, and I found myself in my old broken-down hut.

"Now, when I begin to do the washing, I look up at the steeple and see my wife and my child. But when I run up to speak to them, they are gone. When I come down, again I see them. But when I run up to them, again they are gone. That is why I cannot wash even a handkerchief from dawn to sunset," the washer said.

"Thank you, thank you," the boy said. "Now I can return home and marry Toros Beg's daughter." When he returned to the rich man, he told each of these three stories which he had spent years to hear.

"My son, since you showed such patience in learning these stories, you are the right man to marry my daughter." And so the boy married the beautiful girl.

18. The Country of the Beautiful Gardens

Once there was, or there was not, there was a king who had a very wise son. This boy was so intelligent that he could speak the languages of all the birds and animals. The king was getting old and wanted his son to rule in his place. But the boy, who knew the headaches and heartaches of leaders, did not want to become king.

A neighboring king, who had even greater power than the boy's father, wanted the boy for his son-in-law. But the boy did not want to marry the king's daughter, and he did not want to leave his homeland. Since this king was most powerful, however, the prince was commanded to go to the neighboring kingdom. But the boy decided that once there, he would not speak a word: he would become speechless. Surely, he thought, they would not choose a speechless bridegroom for the princess. On the journey, he did not say a word. When he reached the palace, he would

This story was told by Mrs. Mariam Serabian.

not talk, and no one knew what had caused this speechlessness. Indeed, everyone began to wonder if the youth had ever spoken.

The king sent messengers to the boy's father, telling him of the boy's inability to talk. When the boy's father heard the news, he became very ill and soon died. The messengers returned and told the king that the boy's father had died of grief. The king thought that at last this was his chance to hear the boy speak. "My son, I have heard from my messengers that your father has died," the king said.

The boy wanted to ask how and why his father had died, but remembering his plan, he did not say a word. Instead, he merely shrugged his shoulders. The king was disappointed: his plan had not worked.

"I will put this boy in my loveliest garden, and perhaps he will speak to one of the beautiful bushes or birds. I will have my men hidden everywhere, and if one of them hears him say a word, he will let me know immediately. I must know whether or not this boy can speak," the king said to himself. So he had the boy taken to one of his loveliest gardens and left him there with men hidden all around. The boy stayed in the garden for several years without saying a word, merely admiring the beauty around him.

One day he saw three very beautiful, colorful birds alight near the pool. He was hidden, so they were unable to see him. Each of the birds took off her feathers and as a fair maiden, plunged into the water to bathe. The boy saw that the first maid was beautiful and the second maid even more beautiful, but the third maid was so beautiful that she could say to the sun, "Sun, sun, go away, for I will shine on the earth today." The boy immediately fell in love with the youngest maid, and when the girls were bathing, he quietly went up to the edge of the pool, and stole the feathers of the beauty.

When they had finished their swim, the three maidens started to put on their feathers, but the youngest could not find hers. Her sisters flew up into a tree while the third sister, still searching for her feathers, looked up at them from the ground. "Sisters, sisters, where are my feathers?"

"Who knows what you have done with them?" they said. "Hurry and find them, or we will not wait for you."

The girl knew that someone else must be nearby. As she looked around, she saw the boy. "Youth, I know you have my feathers. Please give them to me so that I may fly away with my sisters!"

"I will not give them to you," the boy answered, and this was the first time he had spoken in many years. The men who were stationed around the garden heard him speak and ran to tell the king. The boy did not care whether or not the king knew about it now. He had found his beloved, and the king could do little to stop their marriage. However, when the king was told of the boy's speech, he became angry. "That means that all these years, he was able to speak; call him before me," the king ordered. When the boy was brought before the king, he asked: "Tell me, why didn't you speak when you were brought here many years ago?"

"Why should I speak? You wanted me to marry your daughter, and I did not want to marry her. Now I have found my mate, and you must let me depart to my country with my future bride."

When the king saw that it would be useless to argue with the youth, he gave him permission to return home with the girl. The boy knew that his father was dead, but thought that perhaps his mother was still living. He went to his town where he recognized his home. He knocked on the door, and his mother opened it. But she had been crying so much that she was almost blind and did not recognize her son.

"Mother, may we stay here?" he asked.

"No, my son, I have no room for you," she said.

When the boy slipped a handful of gold into her hand, she said, "Enter and be comfortable, my son."

"Mother, will you marry this girl to me in your house?" the boy asked.

"My son, I am the wife of a great king. I have my reputation to think of; I cannot marry strange men and women in my home."

"But, mother, I am not a stranger; I am your son!" the boy said. The woman looked at him and suddenly realized that he was speaking the truth, that he was her son. Tears of joy came to her eyes. She announced to all the return of her son and the event of his coming marriage. Everyone came to the prince's wedding, for they were anxious to see the chosen girl. She was even more beautiful than ever before, and she said to the sun, "Sun, sun, go away, for I will shine on the earth today."

The prince, his wife and his mother lived happily together, without trouble from the outside world. The boy gave the girl's feathers to his mother to keep and begged her never to let his wife have them.

One day they received news that the powerful king, in whose palace the boy had spent so much time, was giving a big wedding for his daughter and that they were invited to attend. So, mother, wife and prince started for the wedding. They had a happy time there, but everyone was jealous of the great beauty of the princess, and everyone planned to harm her. When the wedding was almost over, the mother gave the feathers to her daughter-in-law and told her that it might be safer for her to fly home. The princess took the feathers, and although she did not use them, she kept them without telling her husband. The morning after they reached home, the princess put on her feathers and flew to a little tree standing in front of the house. Then she began calling, "Mother, mother!" Her mother-in-law ran outside and looked around for the girl but could not find her. "Daughter, daughter, where are you?" she asked.

"Mother, I'm up here, up here," the princess said.

The mother looked up, and there she saw a beautiful bird. She suddenly realized what this meant, but there was nothing that she could do now. "Come down, come down," the mother-in-law urged.

"No, I will not come down, but I'm going to leave a message with you for your son. Tell him that he is too good to waste his life trying to find me, so tell him not to try. I am going home now, to the Country of the Beautiful Gardens, and even if he wore out shoes of iron and an iron staff in an attempt to find me, he would never be able to do so," the bird said and flew away.

That evening when the prince came home, there was no wife to run forth and meet him; there was no wife to take the saddle off his horse, to feed and refresh the beast. He was surprised but did these things himself and went inside the house. "Mother, mother, where is your daughter-in-law?" he asked when he saw that his wife was nowhere in sight.

"Son, forgive me, I didn't mean to do this to you," she began.

"Tell me, is she here?"

"When the wedding was almost over, I gave her the feathers so that she could fly home quickly. But although she decided to return with us, this morning she put on her feathers and flew away," the mother said, crying.

"Mother! Mother! What are you saying?"

"Son, son, forgive me, I didn't intend to do you harm," the

woman said. "She asked me to tell you to spare yourself and not to waste your life in pursuit of her. She is returning to the Country of the Beautiful Gardens, and even if you wore out iron shoes and an iron staff, you could not find her."

"Obviously you are trying to get rid of us; you are tired of having us live with you. This is why you have done as you have. Farewell! I shall stay here no longer; I shall try to find my wife," the son answered. He put on iron shoes, took an iron staff, kissed his horse on both cheeks and begged the kind beast to help him find his beloved wife.

They traveled for a long time and finally reached the land of the dogs. The dogs growled and were about to attack the traveler when the boy said in dog language, "Take me to your leader." The dogs stopped and thought: Here was a man, but he could talk their language, and he had enough sense to ask for their leader! They were sure that he was not an ordinary man, so they took him to their leader.

"Leader, I am looking for the Country of the Beautiful Gardens. Can you help me?" the boy asked. The leader counted the number of dogs, and when he was sure that all were present, he put the question to them. None of the dogs was able to give any information, so the prince thanked them and went on to the next kingdom, that of the wolves.

When the wolves saw him, they rushed toward him and were about to tear him to pieces, until the boy asked for their leader. Then the wolves stopped and began to think: "No, this is not an ordinary man since he can speak our language, and he has enough sense to ask for our leader." So they took him to their leader.

"Leader, I am looking for the Country of the Beautiful Gardens. Can you help me?" he asked. The leader counted the number of wolves and when he was sure that all were present, he put the question to them. None of the wolves was able to give any information, so the prince thanked them and went on to the next kingdom, that of the sheep; then he went to the kingdoms of the bears, the tigers, the lions, the foxes, the elephants, always asking the same question and always receiving the same answer.

When all the animals had failed to help him, he began with the birds. He went to the kingdoms of the doves, the gulls, the crows, the pigeons, the nightingales, always asking the same question and always receiving the same answer. Finally, he came to the kingdom of the peacocks, and the leader of the peacocks said to him, "Friend, if you have come this far, it means that you have passed every animal and bird kingdom except one, and that one is the kingdom of the eagles. If the eagles cannot help you, no one can. Good luck to you."

The boy thanked the leader and started out for the kingdom of the eagles. The eagles swept down low to attack him, but the boy asked for their leader. The eagles were so surprised that a man was able to speak their language that they immediately took him to their leader.

"Leader, I am looking for the Country of the Beautiful Gardens. Can you help me?" he asked. The leader counted the number of eagles but discovered that there was one missing. "Friend, we have one eagle missing; he is a lame eagle, and it is either because of his lameness that he is late or because he has been caught by some human. Wait and we will learn which it is," the leader said.

Not long after, the lame eagle came hobbling in. Then, when the leader again made sure that all were present, he put the question to the great birds. None of the eagles was able to help the prince except the lame eagle. "Yes, I know where the Country of the Beautiful Gardens is," he said. "I know because I have just now returned from there. It is a great distance from here, and it is very difficult to get there; but if this is where you must go, I will help you." The birds gave the boy a feather cloak which made him invisible, yet in which he could either walk or fly. With two other birds who carried meat, the lame bird and the boy started on their journey to the Country of the Beautiful Gardens. In his haste to seek his wife, however, the boy forgot to remove the saddle and bridle from his horse which he had to leave with the eagles. So the horse was unable to get his own food or to eat the food which the eagles gave him.

Whenever the lame bird became hungry, he said, "Meat," and the boy gave him some of the meat which the other two birds were carrying. They went up, up and over the clouds, then came swiftly down until they reached the Country of the Beautiful Gardens.

The boy looked around and saw an old man plowing. "Father, father, what country is this?" he asked. The old man, upon looking around and seeing no one because the boy had on his invisible cloak, paid no attention but kept right on working.

"Father, father, what country is this?" the boy repeated.

The old man looked around again and not seeing anyone,

thought that it was a small boy playing pranks with him. "Son of a dog, this is the Country of the Beautiful Gardens!" the old man shouted.

"Aha! I have reached my destination," the boy said to himself. Looking around, he saw a little lake not far away. He wanted to know what lake it was. "Father, father, what is that water?" he asked the old man.

The old man did not answer the first time.

"Father, father, what is that water?" the boy asked again.

"Son of a dog, it is the water around the palace of the youngest princess! As if you didn't know that there are three princesses in this kingdom and that the two older ones have married, but the youngest one locks herself in that palace and won't let anyone see her."

"Why does she do that?"

"Don't you know that she once flew to earth and was captured by an earth man who made her his wife? Now she will not marry anyone else and continually talks about her earth husband," the old man said.

The boy was beside himself for joy! He went toward the palace, found and entered his wife's room without being seen. She looked even more beautiful than before! She, of course, didn't know of the presence of her husband. When her meal was served, the boy ate whatever food he wanted, and the princess remained hungry.

"If it were not for the love of my earth husband, I would eat you up!" she screamed to her serving woman. "Why are you bringing me such a little bit of food?"

The serving woman insisted that she was innocent of this. The boy, meanwhile, silently laughed as he watched her. The same scene was repeated the next day and the day after. Finally, the servant informed the king and the queen of the unusual behavior of the princess.

"Ah! She is again in one of those black moods! Most likely she is remembering her earth husband. Well, don't take any food to her at all for a day or two; that will take care of her," the king ordered.

When the boy saw that the servant did not bring food, he disclosed himself to his wife. She was very happy to see him and shed tears of joy. "How did you get here? How did you get here?"

"I wore out iron shoes and an iron cane," the boy said smiling at her. The wife and husband embraced, and such happiness as they experienced is too great for a person like me to tell. That night the boy slept with his wife, and in the morning he put on his feathers and became invisible to the servant, who had returned.

"Girl, I am very hungry. Bring me twice as much food as you have been bringing me," the princess asked.

The servant, seeing that this was not a passing fancy, brought more food for her mistress. Then the boy and his wife both had enough to eat.

The couple lived in this manner for some time until one day the father of the princess entered into war with a neighboring country. The boy heard of the condition of his father-in-law's army and decided to help. That afternoon, he took off his feathers, mounted a handsome horse and went straight to the battlefield. He took out his sword and cut off heads right and left. With each swing of his sword a few more heads flew off. In the struggle, however, he cut his little finger, and the king tied it with his royal handkerchief. Seeing that most of the enemy had fallen, the boy again mounted his horse and rode away.

The king and his men were surprised because they had never seen the boy before and thought they would never see him again. But the king was also angry. "That daughter of mine! Ah! that daughter of mine! She sighs and moans all day and talks about her earth husband. Now, why couldn't she marry a man like that? Why can't she marry a person that we would be proud of?" the king said to himself.

The boy, however, went to his wife's palace and was so tired that he fell asleep on the couch, without wearing his feather cloak. When the queen came to visit her daughter, she said, "Daughter, daughter, your father is so angry with you! There was such a boy, such a boy, at the battlefield today, that all the heads flew off as he swung his sword. Your father is saying that you should marry someone like him and forget your earth husband."

"Mother, you recognize my father's royal handkerchief, don't you?" the girl asked. When the queen assured her that she did, the princess took her mother into the next room and showed her husband asleep on the couch, his finger tied with the handkerchief.

"Oh, daughter, why have you been keeping this a secret from us?" The girl then told her mother about how her earth husband had searched for her. The queen ran to call her husband, who was shown the young man asleep on the couch with his little finger tied in the royal handkerchief.

Although her parents were anxious to awaken the boy and talk to him, the princess insisted that he continue to rest. When he awakened, the girl told him about the visit of her parents. He was taken before them, and they liked him even more than they had when they saw him asleep. They accepted him as their son-in-law and made him stay in the Country of the Beautiful Gardens for many months.

Finally, one day the boy said to the king, "Your Majesty, I have enjoyed being here with you, and I love your country; but I cannot stay here any longer because I have an old mother on earth, and I must return to her. Therefore, give me permission to leave with my wife."

The king did not want to let them go, but when they insisted, he gave them a small flock of birds to accompany them. Each bird was carrying some valuable or other for the home of the royal couple. The boy wore his invisible feathers and flew with his wife.

High up over the clouds they went and flew swiftly down to the kingdom of the eagles. The boy thanked the eagles for their help, and especially the lame eagle for his leadership. As he was about to leave, he saw his horse standing on a rock. Needless to say, the horse was not a pretty sight; he was all skin and bones and had a bad skin disease all over his back. Quickly the boy went to his horse and took off the bridle and saddle. The horse sighed and said, "This is gratitude for you!" The boy knew that he had been at fault, but there was nothing he could do now. He and his wife continued flying, with the horse slowly following them on foot.

As they reached the lands of the different birds and animals which the prince had visited while in search of his wife, he thanked them, passed on and finally reached home.

He knocked on the door of his mother's house, and his mother opened the door; but she had been crying so much that she was almost blind and was unable to recognize her son and her daughter-in-law.

"Mother, mother, do you know me?" the boy asked.

"Mother, mother, I have come back!" the princess said.

Then the mother realized that they were her children! She embraced them and wept tears of joy. How happy she was, reunited with them again! After a few days they saw the horse drag himself to the house. Then and there the princess made a vow that she would wash the horse with rose water every day until he was entirely cured and well again, and she kept her vow. Every day she washed the horse with rose water and fed him with her own hands. Finally, he was entirely well and forgave the boy for his inhuman treatment.

The three lived happily together, with few worries and in good health. They reached their goal, and may God grant that we reach ours.

From the sky fell three apples: one for me, one for the story-teller and one for the person who has entertained you.

19. The Riddles

There were once a king and a queen who had one son. The king lost his throne, and the family became poor. When the son grew old enough to seek his fortune, he wanted to go out into the world, but he had no clothes, no horse and no money. Finally, he went to a king and presented himself. "Your Majesty, I have a male slave and a female slave. How much will you give me for them?" he asked.

"They are your slaves; name your price," the king said, feeling that the prince was going to offer for sale his father and his mother, former rulers.

"I want a good horse for my male slave and a bag of gold for my female slave," the youth said.

"Very well, you shall have them."

The young man went back to his parents. "Come with me," he told them. The parents may have suspected what he had on his mind, but if they did, they said nothing and went along with him. He sold his parents and in their stead received a horse and a bag of gold. With the gold he purchased some new clothes, mounted his horse and set out to seek his fortune. On his travels he heard of a princess who was very beautiful, rich and wise, and decided to seek her out and make her his wife. Finally one day, very tired, he reached a little cottage and knocked on the door. "Good morning, what do you want?" an old woman said, sticking out her head.

"Mother, won't you give my horse a place?" the youth asked.

"Dear me, how can I give your horse a place when I don't

This story was told by Mrs. Mariam Serabian.

have a place for myself?" the old woman replied. But when the boy pressed a gold piece in her hand, the old woman quickly found room for both the boy and his horse.

During the night the boy awoke from sleep to see a very bright light in the sky not far away. In the morning he asked, "Mother, what was that light in the sky last night?"

"Son, don't ask me about that," the old woman said. "I would tell you if I weren't afraid of what might happen to you." When the boy urged her on, she said, "That light belongs to a princess who is very wise. She has a collection of ninety-nine heads of young men who have failed to answer the questions she has put to them. If a youth cannot solve the riddles which she asks for three days, she cuts off his head. But if he can answer her riddles for three days, she will marry him."

"Thank you, kind mother, don't you worry. Mine won't be the hundredth head in her collection," the boy said, and early the next morning he went to the palace. When he told the guards that he wanted to match skills with the princess, they took him before the king.

"Well, my son, I hear that you want to try your wits against my daughter's," the king said.

"Yes, Your Majesty," the boy replied.

"Consider, my son, and consider again. If you should lose, you know the penalty," the king warned. But the boy would not be turned back. So the king sent his messengers to the princess and told her of the boy. "Let the youth in," the princess replied. Thereupon the boy was led into a large and beautiful room. The princess was seated behind a heavy screen so that the two could not see each other.

"Good morning, young man," the princess said.

"Good morning, Your Highness," the youth replied.

"I am going to ask you questions which you must answer correctly, or I will have your head cut off. If you can answer correctly for three days, I will become your wife," the princess said.

"Very well," the youth agreed.

"What is it that is silver on the outside and gold on the inside?" the princess asked.

"An egg," came the boy's reply.

"That is a little child's riddle," the princess said. "Now answer this one: what part of man's body is it that has no hair?"

"The middle of the palm," the young man replied.

"That's enough for today. You can go now, but we shall see

what tomorrow will bring," the princess said, dismissing the boy.

The old woman with whom he was staying was much surprised to see him when he walked into her house that night. The second day he left early again, and the princess started the questioning. "What is it that doesn't have a pillar?" she asked.

"The ocean," was the boy's reply.

The princess was becoming worried. This boy knew all the answers! "What was the name of the animal whose chewing bone was used by one man in killing another man?" the princess asked.

"It was with a donkey's jawbone that a man killed his brother," the youth answered.

"That is enough for today, but tomorrow is another day. I'll have your head in my collection yet!" the princess said.

The third day, the young man again left early for the palace. "What is it that is long and narrow and yet has no shadow?" the princess asked.

She was very happy to hear the youth say, "I'm going to have some difficulty answering that one. But since you have been asking me riddles for three days, will you let me ask you one while I am thinking of the answer to this one? If you can give the correct answer, go ahead and kill me," the young man said.

Since the king and others of his family thought that the boy's request was quite fair, the youth proceeded with his question: "What was it that I wore, what was it that I rode?"

The princess could not answer him but promised that she would do so on the following day. The youth, very happy, returned to the home of the old woman and went to bed early.

The princess, meanwhile, had other plans. She and two other girls, as pretty as she was, dressed themselves in beautiful feather costumes. They prepared many delicacies, and taking along some seven-year-old *raki* [potent raisin brandy] to drink, they started for the lodging of the youth.

The boy heard a knocking on the door and opened it to find three lovely creatures in beautiful feather costumes standing before him. "Won't you invite us in?" the princess asked.

"Please come in, come in, but I'm not prepared for you," the amazed youth said.

"Oh, we have brought all the preparations for a banquet along with us," the princess said coyly.

The youth was very happy. Such a beautiful creature! And he was sure that she would be his tomorrow! The princess made him drink the mellow *raki* and eat the rich food until soon he was feeling fine indeed.

"My dear one, tomorrow I'll be yours," the princess said.

"Yes, how fortunate I am," the youth answered, very happy.

"But you know that I am yours now, don't you? Tell me, what did your question mean?" the princess asked, embracing the young man as she spoke.

"You'll learn that tomorrow."

"Why not now, dear? I didn't wait until tomorrow to become yours; why wait until tomorrow to tell me what I want to know?"

"I'm afraid that you will add my head to your collection," the youth said.

"How could you think of such a thing? We are now one. How could I do such a thing to my chosen mate?"

"Oh, sweet one, then I will tell you," the boy said, bewitched by the beautiful princess. "The clothes I wore I received by selling my mother, and the horse I rode I received by selling my father." Soon after the girls had heard this secret, they slipped out, and the youth fell into a heavy sleep.

The next morning he awakened to find the house in disorder. After a time he recalled the girls' visit and was very sad because he knew that he would lose his head. He looked around for his hat and found the princess' feather dress which she had carelessly left behind. "Luck is with us," the youth said, folding the dress and slipping it underneath his shirt as he set out for the palace.

When he arrived, the princess greeted him with: "I can give the answer to your riddle now: you bought the clothes you wore by selling your mother and the horse you rode by selling your father."

All applauded the princess with exclamations of surprise.

"Against that one, I'll give you another riddle, and then you can kill me," the youth said. "What was it that came to me as one of three birds, that ate, drank, made love to me and went away leaving its feathers behind?"

"No, I can't answer that question," the princess said, fearing that the youth would expose her immoral behavior. "I'll marry you."

Thereupon everybody was happy. They had a wedding that lasted for forty days and forty nights. Then the youth took his wife and went to the king to whom he had sold his father and mother as slaves. He bought his parents back, and they all moved into a beautiful palace where they lived happily ever after.

From the sky fell three apples: one to me, one to the story-teller and one to her who has entertained you.

20. The Magic Ring

There were once a mother and a son who were very poor. The boy was in the woods one day with a group of his friends when he saw a snake. The other boys wanted to kill it, but the boy took pity on the snake and said, "No, we should not kill it."

So the snake was not killed. The boy took it home with him, put it in a large bowl and fed it sand. For three days the boy fed the snake. On the third day the snake said to the boy, "Take me back where you found me and you will get your reward."

The boy was surprised, for how could a snake speak? When they had reached the place where the boy had first seen the snake, it said: "I am the prince of snakes and my father is the king of snakes. When I tell him that you have saved my life, he will ask you what you want. Tell him that you want nothing. When he insists on your answer, ask for the ring which he keeps under his tongue. Also, ask him for the kitten and the puppy who are very wise and useful animals and from whom you will receive excellent advice. Now, when we go in the cave, there will be snakes all over the ground. Do not be afraid. As long as you are with me, you may step on their backs." And it was so: when they came to the cave, the boy saw that all available space was covered with snakes! But the boy was with the prince, and they crossed over together.

The prince told his father how the boy had saved his life and how he had taken care of him. "You have saved my son's life, and I owe you very much. Tell me, what do you wish?" the king asked.

"I wish for nothing but your happiness."

"Come, what do you wish?" the king asked for the second time.

"I wish for your happiness."

"You must have some other wish, tell me," the king asked for the third time. "After all, what is my happiness to you?"

"I wish for the ring which you keep under your tongue," the

This story was told by Nishan Krikorian.
See Comparative Studies for other versions of this story.

boy finally answered, "and I would like to have the kitten and the puppy, too."

"Very well, they are yours," the king said, taking the ring from underneath his tongue and handing it to the boy. After the king had given the boy the kitten and the puppy, the boy and the prince walked out of the cave together. When they were outside, they parted, and the boy went homeward.

When he reached home, he licked the ring and wished for food, and a tray with delicious food soon appeared before him. He and his mother ate a hearty meal.

"Son, tell me, how did we get such food?" the mother asked.

"How do I know? God gives and God takes," the boy answered.

When she turned around, he licked the ring and the food disappeared.

"Son, where did the food go? There was still so much food left," the poor mother mourned.

"Mother, God gives and God takes," the boy repeated.

Every day the boy licked his ring and the mother and son found abundant food. One day the boy decided that he would like to marry the princess. "Mother, go to the king and ask for the princess."

"Son, we are lucky if we find our daily bread. How can we look after a princess?"

"I don't know; but trust me for I know what I am doing. You do as I ask and go to the king." So the poor woman set off for the palace and was permitted to see the king. "My King, my son has sent me here to ask for your daughter."

The king was surprised, knowing that the woman and her son were poor, but not to refuse directly, he said, "I will give her to your son if he can build a palace across from mine which is larger and more beautiful than my own."

The mother went home and told her son what the king had asked. "But how can we build a palace larger and more beautiful than the king's palace? Look how poor we are," she added.

"Don't worry, mother, leave everything to God," the son replied.

That night before going to sleep, the boy licked the ring and commanded that a palace, more beautiful and larger than that of the king, be built. In the morning such a palace stood across from the king's. The palace was so large that its shade fell across the king's palace and kept out the sun. And so this morning the king and his nobles slept very late because the sun did not awaken them. When they looked to see why the sun had not risen, they found directly across from them a beautiful palace, even more beautiful than that of the king.

That morning the boy told his mother to go to the king and again ask if he could marry the princess. She did so. "My son has built the palace you wanted. Now will you give us your daughter?"

"Yes, the palace is built, and it is beautiful. But now your son must build an identical palace directly behind mine so that my palace will be between the two. And on the pathways to both palaces, he must sprinkle gold."

The mother went home and told her son what the king had said. That evening before going to bed, the boy licked his ring and made his wish. In the morning the king and his noblemen found another palace, as beautiful as the first, standing on the other side of the king's palace, and the pathways joining the three palaces were sprinkled with all the gold pieces that one could imagine. The boy sent his mother to the king again. As the king now did not have any reason for refusing the boy, he consented to the marriage. So the princess and the boy were married, and a wedding was celebrated which lasted for forty days and forty nights.

Now the king's adviser, who at one time had loved the princess, knew that he still had her favor. He also knew that palaces did not appear overnight without the use of magic. He asked the princess to learn her husband's secret so that the two could run away together. Since the princess did love him, as he had thought, she agreed to help him.

The following night she treated her new husband so much nicer than she had before that he did not know how to reward her or what to say and she was finally able to learn his secret. When he fell asleep, she stole the ring and, before dawn, gave it to the adviser. Immediately the adviser licked the ring and wished that a beautiful palace be built on a lonely island. He wished it to be furnished lavishly with rugs and other valuables and that he and the princess be transported there. A few minutes later the princess and the adviser found themselves together on a lonely island in a beautiful palace.

When the boy awoke in the morning, he found that both his bride and his ring were gone. What was left for him to do? His kitten and puppy, seeing his sadness, wondered what caused it. One day the kitten asked the boy why he was so sad. The boy was much surprised to hear the animal speak but replied, "If I am not sad, then who should be sad? My new bride has stolen my ring and run away."

The animals decided to help their master by bringing the ring back for him and started for the lonely island. The kitten sat on the puppy's shoulders as the puppy swam across the water. When they reached the palace wall, it was so high that the puppy could not climb it, so the task of recovering the ring fell to the kitten. Finally, with patience, the kitten reached the palace, and opening door after door, she finally found the princess. But next to the princess lay the adviser, with the ring held firmly in his mouth.

"How can I get the ring away from that man?" the kitten asked herself. She tickled the end of the adviser's nose with her tail until he sneezed and the ring flew out of his mouth. The kitten seized the ring and climbed down the wall to the puppy. "Quick, let's return home," she said as the two ran off. "But friend, since you have to swim across this river, let me carry the ring to insure its safe return. If you keep it in your mouth, it will fall out as soon as you breathe."

"Nothing of the kind," replied the puppy. "Here I work, carrying you across and back, and I should let you get all the credit by giving our master the ring?"

"But when we get on dry land, I promise I will give the ring to you. Let me keep it now so that you won't lose it when you are swimming," the kitten said. The two argued back and forth until the puppy finally declared: "If you don't give me the ring, I will not take you across."

"*Ach!* [Alas!] What more can I say but be careful at least. Don't open your mouth too wide," the kitten warned as she gave the puppy the ring.

The puppy took the ring in his mouth and with the kitten on his back, started for the shore. But on the way he took a deep breath, and the ring fell into the water.

"Now, see what you have done!" the kitten exclaimed. But what was done was done, and the two animals knew that they could never find the ring in all that water.

When they reached the shore, they saw a fisherman hauling in his nets. The two suddenly realized that they were very hungry, so they silently crept up and stole a fish for their supper. As they were eating it, they came upon their master's ring in the fish's stomach. They were overjoyed and started back for the palace immediately. The puppy made the kitten carry the ring this time because he was afraid of losing it again. The boy was very thankful to have such good friends and put the magic ring safely away. Meanwhile, the king had been asking the boy about his daughter. But since the boy did not know where she was, he could not tell her father. When the animals told him their story, he told it to the king.

"Do you mean that my daughter could have acted so dishonorably? Bring her and my adviser here," the king asked, knowing now about the powers of the ring.

The boy licked the ring as he made his wish, and immediately the princess and the adviser appeared before them. The king ordered that two wild jackasses be brought to him and tied his daughter and the adviser to the tails of the animals. He had the jackasses whipped over mountainous trails and the bodies of the princess and the adviser were so torn that the largest pieces of them ever found were their ears.

Their wish was fulfilled, and so shall ours be. The story is ended. From the sky fell three apples: one to me, one to the storyteller and one to the person who has entertained you.

21. Hagop's Wish

Hagop was the son of a wealthy man in Armenia. His father spent much money so that the boy could learn many things. But Hagop did not learn to use his hands, he did not know a trade. When his father died, Hagop spent his money, never thinking about tomorrow. Soon all the money was gone, and Hagop was without either money or friends.

A friend of his father saw that the proud boy was hungry and did not know which way to turn. "Hagop," he said, "take this book and go some little distance from the town. Draw a circle around you and begin to read. While you are reading, you will hear many voices. You will hear 'Kill him!' 'Stick a knife in him!' and other terrifying commands. You are not to pay any attention to them but continue reading. Don't be frightened, but listen for names. The people who are shouting have names just as you and I have. Listen to those names carefully, and make sure you re-

This story was told by Hovhannes Kaprelian.

member one of the names you have heard when the voices are gone."*

Hagop took the book, went out of the town, found a place and sat down. He drew a circle around him and began to read. Soon he heard the voices shouting "Kill him!" "Stick a knife in him!" "Hold him!" Hagop did not look up but kept on reading. He remembered the name "Levon."

When the voices became silent, Hagop closed the book, put it in his pocket and looked about him, hoping to find a purse of gold. There was no gold; there was nothing. So Hagop returned to town and told his father's friend that his condition was unchanged.

"Of all the shouting that you heard, do you remember a single name now?" the friend asked. When Hagop assured him that he did, the friend said, "Go home and call this name. In answer to it, a huge slave will appear and bring you anything you may wish."

When Hagop did as he had been told and called out, "Levon," an enormous slave appeared before him. "I am hungry," Hagop said, and immediately a grand dinner was set before him.

"Call me and ask for anything you want and it shall be yours. If you need me when you are with others, repeat my name to yourself. If you call my name in the hearing of others, I shall never be able to help you again," Levon said and disappeared.

Several days later Hagop decided to see if Levon really could do all that he had promised. He called him and asked for a sum of money, let us say one hundred dollars. Straightaway the money was his, and Hagop, happy that he had no need to save for the future, hurried out to buy new clothes because he looked so ragged.

---

* At one time, Armenians apparently believed that a book of magic really existed. Tcheraz, *op. cit.*, p. 244, speaks of the Armenian patriarch of Constantinople, the legendary Hagop Aswodzapan who assembled all the copies of the magic *Vetzazarya* (6000) over 226 years ago and threw them in the fire, thereby making it almost impossible to find a copy of this book today.

Reading only the *Rahmaniye*, the divine part of the *Vetzazarya*, enables one to cure all illnesses. Those reading the *Cheytaniye* are capable of bringing about all bad things and have a recourse to the intervention of the damned. First-time readers of this section believe that they see terrible dervishes and Arabs, hear the noises of windows and doors opening and closing without interruption. If they are brave enough to continue, they gain knowledge and wealth. If they are afraid and stop, they become paralyzed and die.

The next day he called for Levon again and asked him for a larger sum of money, let us say one thousand dollars. Immediately the money was in his hands. The following day he asked for an even larger sum, let us say one million dollars. Again, the money was his the moment he asked for it.

So Hagop took his money and went to a beautiful part of the town. He hired scores of artisans to build him a palace and insisted that the finest of materials be used for it. Whenever he needed more money, he called on Levon.

Soon the palace was finished. Hagop asked Levon for beautiful rugs on the ceiling, walls and floor. The next morning the entire palace sparkled with rugs, mirrors, furnishings and everything that a palace should have. Outside, a beautiful garden flourished where a day ago there was nothing but weeds and dirt.

As Hagop walked through the magnificent palace, he thought, "Now I have everything but a wife." He called Levon and said, "I want the king's daughter to be brought here tonight." That evening when the princess arrived, Hagop quietly told Levon to bring food and drink. After Hagop had shown the princess through his palace, they ate leisurely, and later Hagop directed the slave to take the beautiful girl back to her father's palace.

When the princess awoke in the morning to find herself in her room, she thought that she had been either dreaming or sleepwalking.

The next evening Hagop gave Levon the same order, and the princess was again brought to the palace. This continued for a long time until finally the princess was convinced that her visits to the mysterious palace were very real and she told her mother so. At first the queen doubted the truth of this, but when the girl told the same story morning after morning, the queen decided to consult her husband.

The king was furious. "Who would dare take the princess out of her room?" he cried. Then he ordered guards all around the palace and stationed two of them outside the door of the princess. But still, the next morning the princess told the same story. The following evening the king ordered all his troops to stand guard. But again the princess reported that she visited Hagop that evening, as usual.

The king was in despair. He called his servant and said: "Paint the hands of the princess with red paint so that when she leaves tonight, she will place her hand on the door of the house she visits and the wet paint will rub off. Tomorrow morning we will search everywhere, and whoever lives in the house which shows marks of fresh red paint will suffer."

The servant carried out the king's order, and that evening the princess left a red mark on Hagop's door as she entered. Levon noticed this, however, and taking a can of red paint, he painted the same mark on every house in the country. The next morning when the king sent his soldiers to find the house with the red mark, he was told that each house in the kingdom was decorated with a red paint mark.

The king was dumbfounded and did not know which way to turn. He asked his daughter again and again to describe the mysterious young man, the house, the interiors. The princess remarked that to her the most amazing thing was that, although the owner of the palace appeared to have no servants, everything was done exactly as it should be. It seemed that the food was cooked and served by invisible hands.

Meanwhile, the king's son, and brother of the princess, had noticed that a young man, living not far from the king's palace, lived alone in a large palace without servants. Thinking this most unusual, he purposely started a friendship with the youth.

One day the prince invited Hagop—for the new palace was none other's but his—to eat at the king's table. Hagop accepted the hospitality offered him and, in turn, invited the prince to lunch with him at an inn.

"You insult me by asking me to an inn when you have a home of your own," replied the prince. "If you invite me to your home, I will accept. If you insist on this insult, our friendship must come to an end."

Hagop had no choice but to take the prince to his palace. As the prince saw more of the palace, he became convinced that it was the one his sister had described. While Hagop was showing the prince about, he softly ordered Levon to prepare a beautiful banquet. Soon the prince saw before him a feast fit for a king. He was more than amazed. How could such delicious food have been prepared in such a short time, and by whom? There were no servants to be seen.

"Hagop, let us have some wine," the prince suggested.

Hagop silently asked Levon to supply wine lavishly, and, before their very eyes, jugs of delicious wine appeared. The prince was convinced that there was magic here and set himself to discover its sources. He decided to get Hagop drunk, so he hid jugs of wine beneath the table, meanwhile calling for all the more. When Hagop was completely drunk, the prince asked angrily, "What kind of front are you putting up? You don't have enough wine to satisfy me!"

Hagop, who was not too drunk to feel insulted, commanded Levon to bring all the wine that he had. But when he gave his order, he forgot himself and called for Levon in a loud voice. Of course, Levon's power vanished, and the prince learned the secret which he had planned to discover.

"Now I have you, you villain! You are the father of my sister's unborn child! Come, we will take care of you at the palace!" the prince said, and he dragged Hagop along.

Hagop was taken to prison and whipped soundly. Then it was decided that he was to be hanged the next morning. In the middle of the night he awakened from his stupor and found himself in prison. He called for Levon, but no Levon appeared. He tearfully begged Levon to rescue him, but Levon turned a deaf ear to his cries.

However, Hagop's lamentations were so heartfelt that the chief of the slaves heard his cries. "Where is this Levon who does not answer his master?" he asked. Levon was brought before the chief, and he told the story of Hagop's betrayal.

"Everyone makes a mistake," the chief of slaves said. "Your master has made one and finds himself in real trouble. Go to his assistance at once. But if he should do wrong again, you must forsake him."

The next time Hagop called for Levon, the slave appeared. "Quick, get me out of here and put the prince in my place."

The next morning the guards dragged out the prisoner and started whipping him. "Stop! Stop! I am your prince!" the prisoner cried. The guards were outraged, and the more the prisoner protested, the more he was beaten.

Finally the leader said, "Listen, men, what if he really is the prince? The best thing to do is for one of us to go to the king and find out whether the prince is in his room. If he is not, then this is truly the prince." They carried out the leader's advice and discovered that the prisoner was indeed the prince and that Hagop had disappeared.

A few days later Hagop asked Levon to bring the princess to his palace again. The following morning when the princess told her mother that she had been at the young man's palace, the king fell deep in thought. He ordered Hagop to be brought before him and asked, "Do you love my daughter?" And Hagop did indeed.

The king asked his daughter if she would like to marry the boy. When she said that she would, the king gave orders for a large wedding which lasted for forty days and forty nights. And they lived happily ever after.

22. The Monster's Hairs

There was once a country that had one huge pool of spring water, no rivers. All the inhabitants of the country were dependent on that pool for water. But there was a huge monster who came to the pool and who, every so often, demanded that a young girl be thrown in the water for his supper. If he were denied the victim, he would poison the water.

At the time of our story, the monster had been asking for a girl every day. Soon all the girls in the kingdom had been sacrificed except the princess. Then the monster cried out that unless he received a young girl for supper the following day, he would poison the water. Now, the king loved his one and only daughter very much and didn't want to see her eaten alive. So he told his subjects that whoever killed the monster would receive half of his kingdom.

In that same country, there lived three brothers, the eldest of whom boasted to the other two, "I will kill the monster and get half of the kingdom." That evening, he ate his supper and went to keep guard by the pool. Nothing stirred; everything was so quiet, and he had eaten so much that very shortly he fell asleep.

The next morning the monster repeated his demand. The people went without water that day so that the princess would not have to be sacrificed. And the king renewed his offer of the preceding day.

This time the second brother decided to trap the monster and get half of the kingdom. That evening he went to the pool and waited for the creature to reappear. But everything was so peaceful that, like his brother, he, too, fell asleep.

The next morning the monster repeated his demand, but the people again went without water. Again the king renewed his offer.

This story was told by Mrs. Mariam Serabian.

"I will try to capture the monster," the youngest boy told his brothers.

"You? Are you laughing at us? Why, if we were unable to catch it, how can you expect to do it?"

"You tried your best and I should have a chance, too."

That night, the youngest brother ate a light supper, slipped a handful of salt and a sharp knife into his pocket and set out to the watch. When he became sleepy, he cut his finger and put salt on the wound. The pain was so sharp that he could not sleep. In the middle of the night, he saw the monster climbing into the pool. He quickly fired a shot at him. Taken by surprise, the monster begged, "Please do not kill me."

"I must kill you so that my people will not die of thirst," the youth replied.

"If you don't kill me, I'll do anything you ask."

"Then get out of the pool and swear never to enter it again."

"Just as you say," answered the monster, swearing that he would not return. "But for your kindness to me, I will give you two hairs from my head. Whenever you need anything, rub them together, and you will receive whatever you want."

The youngest brother put the two hairs in his pocket and forgot all about them. The next morning when the people went to the well and saw that the monster was not there and the water was clear, they ran to the king and told him the good news. The king called all his people together. "As you know, the monster has left the pool. Whoever has forced him to do this, come forward now and claim your reward," the king commanded.

The youngest brother went to the king reluctantly.

"My son, name whatever you want and you shall have it," the king said.

Realizing that his two brothers were jealous of him, the youngest brother wanted to avoid the glory and praise which would be his, and replied, "Your Majesty, I am perfectly happy with life as it is."

"This will never do, my boy. I must give you something. Guards, bring this young boy two *deegs* [measures] of gold," the king ordered.

The youngest brother accepted the gold, but when he arrived home, he gave the entire reward to his brothers. Still he could see that they were not satisfied, so fearing for his own safety, he ran away from home.

Since he was a very handsome youth, he wanted to avoid inviting attention to himself and decided to look as ugly as possible. So he cut off his hair and covered his head with a cap made of sheepskin. He changed his clothes and wore rags and walked like an old man.

He walked until he came to a beautiful country where he decided to stay for a while. There, still keeping his disguise, he found work as assistant gardener to the king. The boy looked ugly indeed and acted stupidly. The chief gardener would be at the end of his patience before his orders were understood.

One day the youth, finding himself alone in the garden, wanted to see if the monster's hairs would really work. So he rubbed them together and asked for a white horse and a suit of clothes. His wish was immediately realized. He changed his clothes, took off his sheepskin cap (by this time, his hair had grown long) and rode up and down, trampling the garden.

The youngest princess, in the meantime, finding herself alone, had taken some needlework and decided to sit by the window looking out into the garden. To her surprise, she saw a very handsome youth, beautifully dressed, riding on a snow-white steed who was trampling and wrecking the whole garden. Her first impulse was to open the window and call for him to stop. But on second thought, she wondered who this person could be. Where did he come from? If she were to call, he would probably disappear, and she would never see him again. So she quietly watched the scene, waiting to learn who the man was.

The boy, hearing footsteps, quickly rubbed the hairs together, and the horse and the new clothes disappeared. He assumed his old disguise, sat down under a tree, and began to cry. When the chief gardener saw his garden ruined, he ran to the youth and cried, "Tell me what happened! What does this mean?"

"Oh, sir, a big man on a white horse came into the garden and hit me on the head! Then he rode up and down, ruining everything."

"Why, you good-for-nothing! After all the hard months of work we have put into this garden, look what we have to show for it!" the chief gardener said, whipping the boy.

The youngest princess, having discovered the identity of the rider, quickly leaned out of the window and said, "He is speaking the truth, gardener. A big man on a white horse came into the garden and hit him on the head and then ruined everything."

At this note of authority, the chief gardener stopped the whipping and turned away.

For three days the boy rode his horse and ruined the garden. For three days the chief gardener whipped him, and for three days the princess took the boy's part. The following day the youngest princess instructed the gardener to send the ragged boy to her with a basket of fruits. The chief obeyed the order, and the princess filled the empty basket with gold and sent it back. The boy should have kept the gold, according to the custom of servants, but showing his ignorance, he gave it to his master. The chief gardener was delighted, of course, and more convinced than ever that this man was not in his right mind.

Now the king of the land had three daughters. But since one must be rich to marry a king's daughter and such wealth was not easy to find, none of the princesses were married. The first princess was getting old, the second was a little younger, but the third was in her prime.

One day, the king fell sick and called in his healer who advised, "It is wise to get your daughters married so that when you die there will be someone to rule the country. You know that you are an old man."

"It is not that I want to keep my daughters with me," the king replied, "but as of today, no one has asked to marry any of the three."

"Gardener, bring me three watermelons from the garden," the healer asked. The gardener brought the watermelons to the healer. He cut the first watermelon with a knife. It was nearly spoiled and had a yellow color. "You see, this is your eldest daughter. She is old, and if she is ever to marry, she had better do it soon."

Then he cut the second watermelon. It was neither very good nor very bad. "This, Your Majesty, is your second daughter. It is not too late for her to marry," the healer said.

Then he cut the third watermelon. It was bright red and tempting. "This is your third daughter. She is exactly at the right age for marriage."

The next day, the king asked all the young men of the country—poor, rich, all of them—to come to his palace. The king called his daughters together and said, "Daughters, I am going to give each of you a bow and arrow to shoot into that crowd of young men. Whichever one you select will be your bridegroom."

The two elder daughters quickly took their bows and arrows

and ran out on the balcony. The youngest, however, went out slowly, looking around for the ragged boy with the sheepskin cap. The youth was sleeping under a tree in the garden when he felt someone kicking him. "What has happened? What is the matter?" he asked, jumping up.

"Wake up! Wake up! Don't you know that the king has asked that all the young men—poor, rich, blind, crippled, and even crazy like you—should appear before the palace today?" the chief gardener asked.

"What does the king want from me?"

"I don't know what he wants, but you must be there," the chief said, pushing him along.

Meanwhile, the two older princesses had already picked their husbands. The youngest would not shoot. Her sisters begged, her father commanded, but she seemed to be waiting for someone. Finally, she saw the boy with his sheepskin cap approaching the palace. She took careful aim and shot at him.

"But, my daughter, you are the youngest: you should have the very best man here. Instead, you have selected a dumb boy with a sheepskin cap. No, this will never do, you must shoot again tomorrow," the king said.

The next day, she shot at the same boy again. "No, this is impossible! I give you one more chance to shoot tomorrow," the angry king shouted.

The next day, she again shot at the young gardener. The king became very angry. "For my other daughters, I will give a wedding that will last for forty days and forty nights, but for you—nothing! My real daughters will live in the palace with me, but you—you and your husband will live in my barn!"

So the youngest princess and her husband lived in the king's barn. Not once during all that time did the youth take off his cap. Not once did he tell his young wife the truth. He kept acting so dumb that even she thought she might have been mistaken.

One day, the king became very ill. The healer decided that the only remedy for his sickness was drinking lion's milk. "There is nothing easier to find than that," the king said. "Call my sons-in-law here, and they will get it for me." The two sons-in-law were summoned. "My sons, as you know, I am very ill, and the only cure for me is to drink lion's milk. You must get it for me as soon as possible." Both of the men readily agreed to find the cure for their king and father, and before their departure, they were feasted and dressed in beautiful clothing. Appetizing foods were prepared for them to take along on their trip and they set out.

"Your great and honorable father has given his other sons beautiful horses to help them find the lion's milk. If he gave them horses, let him give me a lame donkey, and I will attempt to find some lion's milk, too," the boy told his wife.

So the youngest princess went to her father. "What are you doing here?" the king asked her. "Did I not forbid you entrance into the palace?"

"Oh, father, I have come to inquire about your health. Have you had word from your other sons-in-law yet?" she asked.

"No, not yet," the king answered. "Do you think that it is easy to find lion's milk?"

"Father, you gave your other sons-in-law beautiful horses. Why not give my husband at least a lame donkey? He may find success where the others do not."

"What! that dumb, good-for-nothing gardener! Get out of here!"

"Please, father, if you have ever loved me, please give my husband a lame donkey and give him permission to search for lion's milk for you," she begged.

The king was unable to resist her flood of tears and words and gave orders that his third son-in-law should receive a lame donkey. The youngest princess went home and told her husband what the king had said. The next morning he started out on his lame donkey to succeed where the others might fail.

As soon as he left the town, he took out the monster's hairs and rubbed them together, wishing for a white horse and a beautiful suit. Straightaway, the horse and clothing appeared. He took off his old clothes and tied them on the donkey which he concealed behind a tree. He was altogether a new person when he started out on his fine steed. He very shortly caught up with his brothers-in-law who were sitting under a big shady tree. They did not recognize him, of course, when he stopped to speak to them.

He had no sooner resumed his journey than his horse turned around and asked him, "Where are you going?"

"I am going to find lion's milk," the boy answered, most surprised.

"Go behind this hill, and you will find sleeping there a lioness with a very sore udder. Take an arrow, throw it at her udder and run away." When the boy did as the horse directed, the lioness began to howl. When the pressure was released and the great distress lifted, the beast said, "What do you want? Tell me and it shall be granted!"

"I want a small jug of lion's milk and a small jug of cow's milk," the boy answered. The lioness gave him both kinds of milk and was happy to get rid of him so easily.

The boy sat on his horse, hid the lion's milk carefully in his pocket and rode back. As he returned, he saw his brothers-in-law sitting in the same position.

"My friends, you told me that you were looking for lion's milk. What would you say if I should give it to you?" he asked.

"If you have lion's milk, we will give you anything you ask," they answered.

"I don't want very much. I only ask that you let me brand your buttocks with my horse's hoof. If you agree to this, the lion's milk will be yours."

"Very well, go ahead and brand us. Who will see our buttocks, anyway?" they said to themselves.

The boy branded them, then gave them what they thought to be lion's milk but was really cow's milk. They hurriedly mounted their horses and returned to the palace. "Your Majesty, we have gone through much danger to find this lion's milk for you," they said, giving him the jug. But when the king's healer examined the milk, he exclaimed, "This is not lion's milk! It is only cow's milk!"

In the meantime, the boy was on his way to the palace. Just before entering the town, he rubbed the monster's hairs together, and the white horse and the fine clothes disappeared. He again put on his rags, sat on the lame donkey and rode to his barn behind the palace. "Here, take this to your father," he told his wife as he handed her the small jug of real lion's milk. She took the milk to the king. "Here, father, your third son-in-law sends this to you," she said as she gave the king the jug of milk.

"Who knows what is in this?" the king said, and he ordered his healer to examine the milk. When he determined that it was real lion's milk, the king drank it and became strong again.

However, before the king was completely well, war broke out. The two favored sons-in-law rode off as heroes but were unsuccessful at the battle front.

The youngest bridegroom rubbed the hairs together, mounted his white horse and wore his fine clothes and armor. Then he went off to war, and no one recognized him. Alone he fought the whole enemy and returned home. For three days, he continued in this way. The third day, he finally conquered the enemy but cut his finger in the battle. The king stopped the bleeding by tying his own royal handerchief around the finger. After the battle, the boy dismissed his horse and returned home on his lame donkey.

As he was tired and wounded, he stretched out in one corner of the barn and was soon sound asleep. His wife, coming near him, saw her father's handkerchief tied around his little finger. Just at that moment, the queen came to visit her youngest daughter to tell her about the hero of the day. "Now, why didn't you marry such a brave hero instead of that dumb, good-for-nothing gardener?" she asked.

"Mother, come with me," the princess said, leading her mother to where the boy was sleeping. "You said that my father, the king, bound his handkerchief around the hero's little finger. Do you recognize the royal mark?" she asked as she pointed to the embroidery on the handkerchief.

The queen was most astonished when she saw the handsome young man asleep, his little finger bound with the king's handkerchief. The princess quickly explained to her mother why she had married the dumb gardener from amongst all the men.

Upon hearing this, the queen immediately summoned the king. When he arrived, the king was surprised to find the hero of the day asleep in the royal barn. Beads of perspiration stood on the boy's forehead, and the king took out his royal handkerchief and wiped them away. Now, when the king discovered the true identity of the hero, he gave a spectacular wedding feast.

During the feast, the third son-in-law turned to the king, "Your Majesty, don't a man's servants stand behind him and serve him on such an occasion as this?"

"Why, yes, of course," the king answered.

"Mine are not doing that."

"I didn't know that you had servants," the king replied with much astonishment.

"I have two, and what's more, I have branded them on the buttocks with my horse's hoof. They are sitting at this very table with us; they are your two sons-in-law." Then the youth told the story of the search for lion's milk. "And my brothers-in-law still bear the brand of my horse's hoof."

"We will see if your story is true," the king said, and he ordered his two older sons-in-law to undress immediately. The brands were there for everyone to see. "You are no sons-in-law of mine," the king said. "Take your wives and go!"

The two sons-in-law, without a word, walked out of the wedding with their wives. Only then did the king realize the worth of his third son-in-law. "Such courage should not go unrewarded," he said. "At my death, you shall be king of this land."

So the third son-in-law and his beloved wife lived very happily ever after.

23. The Turtle Skin

There was once a poor man who had a wife, a son and a daughter. When the man died, it fell to the son, who was a nail-cutter by trade, to support his mother and sister with his meager earnings.

One day one of the boy's best friends was married, and the boy wanted to get married, too. "Mother, I want to get married," he said.

"You can't get married. If you do, who will support us? How will we live?" the mother and sister said, jumping on him and hitting him.

The boy started crying and went out of the house. He walked and walked and soon came to a pond. As he sat and watched, a very pretty turtle climbed out of the water and approached him. The creature walked slowly around him and then went back into the water.

"My, what a pretty turtle!" the boy said. And the turtle was really beautiful, for it had the brightest colors imaginable and very pretty rosy cheeks. The boy sat there for a little while then started for home. When he got there, his mother and sister quarreled with him as usual.

The next day the boy went to the pond to admire the turtle again. This time when the creature climbed out and walked around the boy slowly, he picked it up and began to stroke it. "You are too beautiful to remain here," the boy said. "You must come home with me." It seemed as though something inside him was saying, "Pick her up and take her home, pick her up and take her home." So the boy took the turtle home with him.

This story was told by Mrs. Mariam Serabian.
See Comparative Studies for another version.

"Why did you bring that thing with you?" the mother and sister exclaimed, striking him.

"Since you won't let me marry anyone else, I'm going to marry this turtle," the boy answered.

His mother and sister complained, but what could they do? They had to accept his decision. A little later the boy went out and left instructions for his mother and sister not to touch his wife. When he walked by the pond where he had first seen the turtle, he saw that the water was churning up and down. But he didn't know and couldn't understand what was happening. In truth, the commotion was caused by the turtle's mother who was looking for her daughter.

The boy went home to the turtle and found her on a pillow, just where he had left her. When he kissed her, the turtle stuck out her head and started to lick his face. He put her on his chest and went to sleep. In the morning the boy was awakened by the turtle licking his face. Without a word, he kissed her and started for work. And so they lived.

"Isn't it a pity that he married a turtle?" the mother asked her daughter over and over again.

One day it was announced that the prince was to be married and everyone in the land was invited to the wedding celebration. The mother and sister wore their best clothes and prepared to go. "If you were not a turtle, you could come with us," they said, hitting the turtle twice on the back.

After they had gone, the turtle quickly slipped out of the house and went to the water's edge. "Mother, give me three gowns," the turtle begged. Her mother put three beautiful gowns in a walnut shell and handed the shell to her daughter.

As soon as the turtle reached home, she took off her turtle skin and cleverly hid it. Then, in the form of a lovely girl, she opened the walnut shell and took out a blue gown which she put on, and she went to the wedding. There she sat right next to her mother-in-law and sister-in-law. She looked so very beautiful, with clear white skin, golden hair, black eyes and brows that she attracted the admiration of everybody. Her mother-in-law and sister-in-law were duly impressed by her beauty. "*Aman, aman* [my, my], what a beautiful girl you are! Whose bride are you?" they asked her.

She didn't answer them.

They asked her a second time.

Again she didn't answer.

When they asked for the third time, she said, "I am a bride in a family where they hit me with a burnt piece of wood." If the two women had been wise, they would immediately have known that the girl was their bride, but they didn't even remember hitting their turtle daughter-in-law with a burnt stick before leaving.

When the wedding was almost over, the beautiful girl slipped out of the palace and went home. She quickly took off the blue gown and put it away in the nutshell. Then she wore her turtle skin and sat quietly on her pillow.

Soon the mother-in-law and her daughter came home. "May you be blind! Why did you have to marry my son?" the mother asked. "There was such a beautiful, beautiful bride at the wedding tonight; you should have seen her!" She hit the turtle twice on the back and left the poor thing sitting on the pillow.

When the rest of the family ate, the turtle did not join them; she was never hungry. During the night when everyone was asleep, she slipped out of her turtle skin, put on her gown and slept by her husband's side. That night the boy awakened before dawn and found her beside him. She was so lovely that he said to her, "If you love God, don't wear that turtle skin again." She told him that it would be some time before she could stop wearing the skin. "But," she said, "do not worry, I'll put it aside one day, soon. Meanwhile we must let your family think that I am really a turtle."

So in the morning she put on the turtle skin again. The boy kissed her and left. The boy's mother and sister hit the turtle and cursed her. "May you be blind for marrying my son," the mother said.

"May you be blind for marrying my brother," the sister repeated.

That evening mother and daughter wore their best clothes to attend the wedding feast which was to last for many days. But before they left the house, they hit the turtle twice with a stick.

When she was alone, the turtle removed her skin and put on the second gown. Again she sat by her mother-in-law and sister-in-law. They were very much pleased to be so honored and asked once more whose daughter-in-law she was. After they repeated their question three times, she gave them the same answer that she had given them the preceding night. But they still did not realize that she was their turtle.

Meanwhile, the king heard of this great beauty who had appeared at the ball, so he ordered all his men to watch her and follow her. But before the night was over, the girl slipped out of the palace, unnoticed, and went home. She removed her gown, laid it in the nutshell, put on her turtle skin and sat on the pillow.

When her mother-in-law and sister-in-law came home, they were excited about the beauty who had sat near them. "Oh, may you be blind for marrying my son!" the mother exclaimed.

"May you be blind for marrying my brother," the sister echoed. They hit her twice on the back and went to bed.

When everyone was asleep, the girl removed her turtle skin, put on one of her gowns and slipped into her husband's bed. The turtle didn't mind the abuses of her mother-in-law and sister-in-law. "There is still time," she said to her husband.

The third day, the boy kissed the turtle, and as usual, she licked his face. Then he left for work. The mother-in-law and sister-in-law beat her once more and went to the wedding. The turtle-girl took off her turtle skin, put on her third gown and went to the palace. Again, she sat right near her mother-in-law and sister-in-law. "Whose bride are you?" they asked, dazzled by her beauty. When they had repeated this question three times, she answered, "I am the bride of a family where they hit me with a burnt piece of wood." And again, the mother and daughter failed to understand the meaning of these words.

The king, who had been very angry with his men because they had let the girl escape the preceding night, ordered them not to let her out of their sight again for a minute. That evening, when the party was almost over, the girl slipped away, but this time she was not unobserved. The men trailed her home and returned to tell the king.

Meanwhile, her husband, who had come home from work early that night, had found his wife's turtle skin and decided to burn it. When the girl entered the house, she smelled the skin burning and screamed in anger and fright. "My dear, you should not remain in concealment," her husband said, embracing her.

In the midst of all this the mother and daughter returned. And what did they see but the same beautiful girl who had been sitting near them at the party! And they smelled skin burning. "This is our turtle, and she is crying because I burned her skin," the young husband said.

"Don't cry, don't cry, why should you cry?" the women asked, kissing her and trying to soothe her.

The next morning the king sent for the master of the house,

so the boy went before the king. "I want you to get me such a carpet that all my soldiers can sit on it and half of it will still remain unused," the king told the boy.

"But, Your Majesty, how can I get such a huge carpet?" the boy asked.

"That is your affair. If you cannot bring me such a carpet within three days, your head will be cut off."

The boy went home very much worried. He was sure that he would lose his head. "What are you worrying about?" his wife asked him when he reached home.

"Why shouldn't I worry? If I don't worry, who should worry? The king has given me three days' time to get him such a carpet that, when all his soldiers sit on it, half of it will still be unused."

"Don't worry about it; you have three days. God will open many doors by then,"* his wife told him. On the third morning she called her husband to her. "Go to the pool where you found me and repeat what I shall now say to you. 'Janyat Kanum [Turkish: Lady of Paradise], give me the Paradise's great rug.' "

The husband went to the edge of the pool where, following his wife's directions, he said "Janyat Kanum, give me the Paradise's great rug." In reply, he was given a tiny piece of rolled cloth and returned home discouraged.

"Did you get the rug?" his wife asked.

"They gave me this little piece of cloth."

"That is all you need; take it to the king."

The boy took the cloth to the king. The king opened it, and it started unfolding and unfolding and unfolding. He called for more help, so many people helped to unfold the rug. It seemed that the more they unfolded it, the larger it grew. When it was finally spread out, all the king's soldiers sat on it, and there was more than half of it still unused. "Very well, go home now; I'll call you later," the king told the boy.

So the boy, very happy, returned home. The next morning the king summoned him again and ordered: "Get me such a loaf of bread that, after all my soldiers have eaten, there will still be half of it left."

"But, Your Majesty, you have several thousand soldiers. How can I get such a loaf of bread?"

"Nevertheless, that is what you are to do in three days' time, or you'll have your head cut off." Of course, the king's purpose

* An expression of faith commonly used by Armenians.

in giving the boy these impossible tasks was to get rid of him so that he could marry his beautiful wife.

The boy went home very discouraged. "Well, husband, what are you worrying about?" his wife asked.

"If I don't worry, who should worry? The king has given me an impossible task to perform," the boy said sadly. "Within three days' time I must obtain such a loaf of bread that, after all his soldiers have eaten, there will still be half of it left."

"Don't worry about it now. God will show us a way."

On the third morning she called her husband to her and said, "Go to the pool where you first found me and say, 'Janyat Kanum, give me the Paradise's big bread!'"

Following his wife's directions, the boy went to the pool and said, "Janyat Kanum, give me the Paradise's big bread." Immediately he was given a piece of bread which was folded over four times. He took this and returned home to his wife.

"Did they give it to you?" his wife asked.

"They gave me this little scrap of bread," replied the boy.

"That is all you need; take it to the king."

The boy took the scrap of bread to the king. When the small piece was unfolded, it grew bigger and bigger, and the king called for more help until finally many people were helping to unfold it. All the king's soldiers ate bread and more bread, and still there was more than half unused.

The king was afraid of this man. How could he accomplish the impossible? He said to himself, "I'll give him such a task that he will never be able to succeed." But to the boy he said, "Go home now and return in the morning for your third task."

The next morning when the boy arrived at the palace, the king called him in and ordered, "I want you to make me ten hundred thousand nails."*

"But, Your Majesty, if all the people in the world worked day and night, they could not produce that many nails in seven years," the boy said.

"If you can't make that number of nails in three days, your head will be cut off," the king replied.

The boy walked slowly home. He knew that although he was a good nail-cutter, he could not even begin to fill the king's order.

"What are you worrying about?" his wife asked.

"The king demands that I make ten hundred thousand nails

* This number was selected arbitrarily by the informant.

in three days. If everyone in the world worked day and night for seven years, they could not make that number of nails," the boy replied.

"Well, don't worry. When God closes one door, He opens another," she said.

And that was how it happened. At midnight the young people heard a knock on their door. The boy opened the door, and there stood the king's messenger. "The king has died, and we need nails for his coffin. When can you get them ready?" the messenger said.

"I'll work quickly," the boy promised the messenger. To his wife he said, "That man wanted to get rid of me, but God took him instead."

After the death of the king everyone was happy, especially the boy and his wife. And so they remained ever after.

24. The Golden Box

At one time there was a wealthy man who had a very beautiful wife and a young daughter. As it happened, the wife became very sick and was about to die. She said to her husband, "Do not marry anyone who is less beautiful than I." So when she died, the wealthy man set out to find a woman as beautiful as his former wife.

He looked everywhere but did not find her equal. What was he to do? He had money, a beautiful house, but he wanted a wife. One day he noticed the beauty of his daughter and saw that she was even more beautiful than his wife had been. "I will marry her!" the man decided. "Who says that I shall be without a wife at my age?"

When he suggested this to his daughter, she would not listen to him, for she could not believe that he meant to do what he said. But after repeated requests, she finally decided that he was serious. "Give me a dress of pure gold," she said, and her father had a dress of pure gold made for her. When this was done, she said, "Give me a pair of golden slippers." And again her father had golden slippers made just for her.

Then, when her first two requests were fulfilled, she said, "I want a large box made of pure gold, and the key must lock from inside." So the father had a box made large enough for her to

This story was told by Mrs. Katoon Mouradian.

get inside and which locked as she wanted. "Now, I will marry you," she told him.

The day before the wedding, she had the golden box secretly taken to the waterfront. She climbed inside and shoved herself in the water. She floated until a fisherman saw the golden box and took it ashore. Try as he might, he could not open it, so he took it to the king as a gift. When the king and all his craftsmen could not open it, the king presented the box to the prince. The prince was so pleased with it that he put it in his room and took great delight in just looking at it.

Each night the beautiful girl quietly opened the golden box and ate the food which was left out for the prince. Meanwhile, the prince wondered what was happening to his food. So one night he did not go to sleep, but instead watched to see what would happen. Soon he saw a very beautiful girl open the box, quickly climb out and eat the food left out for him. When she started to enter the box, he caught her and would not let her close the lid.

"Tell me why you hide in here," the prince said. So the girl told about her father's strange request and what she had done to get away from him. The prince, seeing her great beauty, married her, and they celebrated a great wedding for forty days and forty nights.

After several years the girl suggested that they take a journey. With the prince, she visited one place and another and finally came to the home of her wealthy father. He did not recognize his daughter. The girl said, "This man seems to be a bad person. It is best that he be killed before he harms someone." The prince agreed with her and ordered that the wealthy man be killed. When this was done, the girl told her husband that the man who had just been killed was the father who had wanted to marry her years before.

25. The Magic Box

Once upon a time there was an old couple who very much wanted to have a child. After many years of waiting, the old man decided to seek God and ask Him for a child. "Good-bye, wife, I am going to find God and ask Him for a child," he said one day and he set forth.

This story was told by Mrs. Katoon Mouradian.

As he went along, he met a young girl on the road. "Where are you going, father?" she asked him.

"I am going to find God and ask Him for a child," the old man answered.

"Father, when you see Him, ask Him why my luck is not open.* I am a young and pretty girl, yet none of the young men court me. When am I going to be married? Ask God this for me," she said.

"Very well, daughter. When I see God, I'll ask Him why you cannot get married."

He left the girl behind and went on until he came to a stream. The stream asked, "Where are you going?"

"Stream," the old man said, "I am going to find God and ask Him for a child."

"Father, when you find God, ask Him why my water is not sweet. Ask Him why He has made my water bitter so that none will drink of it."

"Very well, stream. When I find God, I'll ask Him why your water is bitter."

He left the stream behind and walked on until he came to a big apple tree. The tree said, "Old man, where are you going?"

"I am going to find God and ask Him for a child."

"When you find God," the apple tree said, "ask Him why my apples are not sweet so that people can eat them."

"Very well, tree, when I find God, I will ask Him why your apples are not sweet."

He left the tree behind and walked for a long time until he came to an aged dervish. "Where are you going, old man?" the dervish asked.

"I am going to find God and ask Him for a child," the traveler replied.

"Here, old man," the dervish said, "take this apple and give half to your wife and eat the other half yourself. Then you will have a child."

The old man took the apple, but he did not believe that this would bring a child to him and his wife. "Old man, is that all you wanted of God?" the dervish asked.

"There is a big apple tree on the road that wants to know why its apples are not sweet," the old man said.

"The apples on that tree are not sweet because buried beneath the roots of that tree is a chest of gold. When the gold

* An Armenian expression indicating a lack of luck.

is removed, the apples will be sweet. Is there anything else that you want to know?"

"Yes, farther down the road there is a stream that wants to know why its water is bitter."

"The water of that stream will become sweet only after it has taken a man's life. When it asks you what it must do, wait until you have left it far enough behind to be safe. Then turn around and tell it to take the life of a man. Is that all you want of God?" the dervish asked.

"No," the old man replied, "a girl I met on the road wants to know why her luck is closed. She wants to know why she has no suitors."

"She has no suitors because when she cleans the house in the morning, she shakes the dust into the face of the sun. And the sun, you know, does not like dust. He will not permit her to have any suitors until she cleans her house before the sun comes up."

"Thank you, dervish father, now I can return home."

The old man walked and walked until he again saw the apple tree. "Old man, old man, did you see God? Did He tell you what I should do?"

"Yes, I saw God," the old man said, thinking that the dervish was God, "and God says that the reason your fruit is not sweet is that beneath your roots there is a chest of gold. If this gold is removed, your apples will become sweet."

"Old man, old man, be good enough to dig this chest out for me," the tree asked.

"But I am too old, I cannot do such heavy work."

"I will draw myself up," the tree said, "and you pull the chest from under my roots." So the tree drew itself up, and the old man pulled out the chest.

"What shall I do with this gold?" the old man asked.

"Keep it, keep it. What can I do with it?" the tree answered.

So the old man took the gold, said good-bye to the tree and went on. When he came to the stream, it cried, "Old man, old man, did you see God? Did He tell you what I should do?"

The old man did not answer but passed quickly by. "Old man—old man—old man," the stream wailed. When the old man was a safe distance away from the stream, he turned back and cried, "Yes, I saw God, and He said that your water will become sweet only when you have taken a man's life."

"Come back then, come back."

But the old man was far enough away, and the stream could not harm him. He went on until he came to the young girl who had no suitors. "Old man, old man, did you see God? Did He tell you what I should do?"

"Yes," the old man answered, "I saw God, and He said that you have no suitors because you shake the dust into the face of the sun every morning. Since the sun does not like this, he will not permit you to have a suitor. Clean the house before the sun rises."

"Thank you, father, thank you."

The old man walked on and began wondering about the apple in his pocket. "What good is an apple?" he said. "I wanted a child, and God gave me an apple. If I take this apple home, my good wife will laugh at me. I am hungry right now; I think that I shall eat it." So he ate the apple as he walked along.

When he reached his home, his wife asked, "Husband, did you see God? What did He say?"

"Yes, I saw God, but He did nothing except to give me an apple which I was to divide with you. But I became very hungry and ate all of the apple myself. After all, what good is an apple when I asked Him for a child?"

He returned to his plowing and lived life as he had before. But after forty days and forty hours, he felt something in his throat and out of his mouth came a small box. He did not know what it meant, so he put the box upon the windowsill, and there it stayed for twenty years. At the end of that time, one day when the old woman was in the house alone, she heard a voice say, "Go to the king and ask for the princess." She looked around, and when she could see no one, she became frightened and ran out of the house and stayed away until nightfall when her husband returned.

"Wife, what are you doing here?" the old man asked when he found his wife waiting for him outside.

"Husband, husband, such a strange thing happened today!" she cried as she greeted him. "I heard a voice in the house say, 'Go to the king and ask for the princess!' When I looked around, I did not see anyone. I am afraid to go inside alone."

"Do not be frightened, wife, but tomorrow, if you should hear this voice, try to see where it comes from and who it belongs to." So the two went into the house, ate their supper and went to sleep.

The next day again the wife heard the voice say, "Go to the

king and ask him for the princess." But instead of running out as she had done the day before, she looked about and discovered that the voice came from the little box on the windowsill.

That night when her husband returned from work, she said, "Husband, the voice came from that box. It told me to go to the king and ask for the princess." It was indeed strange for a box to speak, but they did not question the matter further. The next day the old woman went directly to the palace and asked for the princess.

The king was surprised that this poor woman wanted his daughter. "Old woman, if your son can build a palace better than mine with beautiful birds and gardens, precious trees and flowers, if he can provide seven kinds of soldiers to guard the palace, then he can marry my daughter."

When the old woman returned home, the box asked her what the king had answered. "The king said that if my son can build a palace better than his own, if he can produce gardens and birds, precious trees and flowers, and seven kinds of soldiers to guard the palace, he will give us his daughter."

That night, when the old man returned from the fields, the box said, "Go to the top of the mountain and hit the highest rock. A big Arab will appear and ask you what his master wants. You will ask for the palace, gardens, birds, flowers, trees and the seven kinds of soldiers required by the king."

So the old man did as he was told, and the big Arab appeared, as the box had predicted. "What does my master wish?" he asked. The old man told him of the king's request, and the Arab answered, "Return home; your request will be fulfilled."

When the old man reached home, he saw a palace standing across from that of the king and surpassing it in beauty. He saw gardens, birds, trees and flowers—so beautiful that one could not look at them with unprotected eyes. The next morning the seven kinds of soldiers began arriving at the humble home of the old couple. They bowed before the little box and said, "We have come, master." Then they went to the new palace.

The king, astonished that all his requirements were fulfilled, began to make arrangements for the royal wedding. The princess was taken to the old couple's house and left there. The old people cried and cried, saying, "What shall we do? Why have they brought this beautiful princess here? We have no son to marry her."

They led the princess to the room where the box was, told

her that the box was her husband and left her there. The poor
girl did not know what to do. But suddenly the box opened, and
out stepped a tall, handsome youth, dressed in a black robe. He
took off the robe and put it back into the box. "I am your husband," he said. "Twenty years ago my parents wanted a child
very much, but they could not have one. So my father set out to
seek God and ask Him for a child. After he had traveled a long
time, he met a dervish who gave him an apple and told him to
share it with his wife and they would have a son. But my father,
doubting that this was possible, ate the apple by himself. After
forty days and forty hours a box fell from his mouth. Not knowing what else to do with it, he put the box on the windowsill, and
there it remained for twenty years. I was in that box. My parents don't know that they have a son; they have never seen me.
This is my secret. Never betray me, for if you do, I will turn
into a bird and fly so far away that you will have to wear out
iron shoes and an iron cane to find me. Never tell anyone where
I came from. Now go call my parents in; let them see their son."

When the princess called in the parents to meet their son,
they ran in, and seeing the handsome youth, they embraced him,
crying, "Our child! Our child!"

So the youth and the princess were married, and they lived
together with the old man and wife, happily, day after day, never
tiring of one another. One day the queen decided to visit her
daughter and see how she liked her new home. The husband,
anticipating the visit of his mother-in-law, reminded his wife not
to betray his secret.

When the queen saw the handsome youth, she began to
wonder why she had not seen him before. The daughter tried to
reassure her mother that there was nothing unusual. But the
queen was very curious and constantly asked about the boy. Finally, on the seventh day the youth knew that his secret was
going to be revealed. He sat next to his wife and drank Turkish
coffee, but he was not happy. The girl was so weary, so angry
with her mother that, when the queen again questioned her about
her husband, the girl said, "There, from that box! That is where
he came from!"

At that very moment the coffee was upset, and the youth
disappeared, and as it seemed, in his place a bird flew out the
window. "Alas, alas!" the princess cried, "He has gone!" And
truly, she could not find him anywhere.

She had a pair of iron shoes and an iron cane made. Then, bidding the old folks good-bye, she set forth. She walked and walked until one day, she noticed that her shoes were getting worn. She remembered that her husband had told her these shoes must wear out before she could find him. For another four years she walked, and her hair became pure white. Then one day she noticed that there was a small hole in her shoe. "Aha! This means that he is near!"

As she walked on, she met a farmer who asked her where she was bound. "Many years ago my husband became a bird and flew away, and I must wear out iron shoes and an iron cane to find him. Now that there are holes in my shoes and my cane is worn down, I feel that he must be near."

"It is very likely," the old man said, "for nearby there is a pool where all the birds of the world come to bathe. I have seen one bird take off his feathers and become a man. Perhaps he is the one you seek. Come, you can stay with my wife and me tonight and watch for the birds tomorrow." So the princess went with him to his home.

The next morning the girl went to the pool to watch the birds. As she watched, one of the birds took off his feathers, and she recognized her husband. While he was bathing, the girl stole his feathers and hid them. When the youth came out of the water, he could not find his feathers. "Whoever has my feathers, return them to me!" he pleaded.

"I have them, but I will not return them to you. You will become a bird again and fly away from me once more."

"So it is you?" the husband said. "What do you want?"

"I want you to forgive me and to return home with me to your old parents." After chiding her for betraying his secret, the youth went with his wife to the farmer's house where they stayed that night. The next morning they started back home.

When they arrived, the old parents were very happy to see their children. The king, hearing that his daughter had returned, went to see her. The princess told him her story, and he became very angry. "And you say that this all happened because your mother urged you to reveal your husband's secret? Then we must punish your mother for her curiosity which made you suffer so much." So the queen was exiled from home and country as long as she lived. The youth forgave his wife and returned her former youth and beauty to her.

26. The King of Snakes

There was once an old couple who were neither poor nor rich. Their only wish was for a child, but they never could have one. "We have enough to eat, thank God, we have a place to live, but we don't even have a child to enjoy our wealth after our death," the woman said. She continually prayed to God for a child, "Dear God, give us a child, be it cat, dog or donkey."

One day God heard her voice and gave her a snake for a child. When the child was born, all saw that it was a snake. "Thank you, God, you have heard my voice and have finally given me a child," the woman said. "People cannot say now that I never bore anything."

The snake grew bigger until it was a yard long. He would coil himself and sit on his tail before his mother. The parents brought sand and put it in front of him, and the snake would eat the sand and grow. "Vhy, vhy, vhy, vhy [Alas], what am I going to do?" the mother asked. "If my son were a human child, I would send him to school."

The snake, hearing this, looked hard at his mother. The woman shuddered because she knew that she should not have said that. "God, you know, I would like to have him go to school and learn a language, but this cannot be done. So I will have to get someone who knows his language."

The snake sat up and listened to his mother. "What do you want, son, what do you want?" The snake stuck out his tongue and then drew it in. He did this several times. He bowed to his mother, then climbed up the wall and finally reached the ceiling, where he had made a hole, and disappeared. The mother did not know where her son had gone. But, in truth, the baby snake had gone where the other snakes were so that they would teach him the snake language. This snake was by no means a mere snake: he was the king of snakes.

Every morning the snake would bow to his mother and go to school. In the evenings, when he was ready to go to sleep, he would bow to her again and then go to bed.

One day he went before his mother and sat down, coiling his tail around and around.

"What do you want, my son?" his mother asked. But the snake kept winding his tail around and around. "Very well, son, whatever it is that you want, go ahead and do it. I don't know

This story was told by Mrs. Mariam Serabian.

what you mean." The snake son, who was the king of snakes, as we said before, silently ordered his subjects to bring two grinding stones before him. His order was immediately fulfilled, much to his mother's surprise. The snake began turning these stones with his tail, and the most delicious food appeared. No matter what was wanted, by turning the magic grinding stones, it appeared.

"What's this?" the mother asked. "How fortunate we are that our son is so smart." When the snake finished showing his mother how to use the grinding stones, he sat on his tail, bowed to his mother, climbed the wall and disappeared into the ceiling.

Each morning when he got up, it became his habit to bow to his parents and then leave. One morning, however, he bowed neither to his mother nor to his father. They were surprised that he left them without a sign. In the evening he went to bed without bowing. For four days he did not bow to his parents.

"What have we done to him that he does not bow to us anymore?" the mother asked her husband. But he could not tell her what it was because he did not know. "Oh, my God, what have we done that our child will not speak to us?"

"Maybe he wants to get married, wife," her husband suggested.

"Son, what do you want?" the mother asked. In reply the snake stuck out his tongue. "Do you want clothes?" Her son did not answer. "Do you want food?" Again her son did not answer. "Husband, go get the grinding stones and give him some food," she said.

The father went and brought the grinding stones. When they put the food before him, he did not touch it. "Son, do you want me to find you a wife?" the mother asked.

Her son nodded his head and left through the ceiling.

"How shall we ever find a girl for him? Who will have a snake for a husband?" the wife asked her husband. In desperation they went to a very poor man and asked for one of his daughters. Although they were poor, the girls were very pretty. The man consented to the marriage, and the snake and the girl were engaged.

When the wedding ceremony was to be performed, the snake stood up on his tail before the altar, and everyone knew that he was not an ordinary snake. But they did not know what he was, for he most surely was not a man.

Like the wedding of a king's son, this one lasted for forty

days and forty nights. There was plenty of food because the grinding stones produced as much as they needed.

The snake insisted on sleeping with his wife. He would lick her face until she was unconscious and fell asleep. When he was certain that she was asleep, he would get out of bed, take off his snake skin and put it under the pillow. Then he would get back into bed again. This was repeated night after night, and the bride never knew what happened.

After a long time, when the bride was to have a child, her mother took her home for a short visit. All her friends and neighbors visited her. "If your husband is a snake, how could you be with child?" they asked her.

The girl could not answer them because she did not understand this either. "When you go to bed, cut your finger and put salt on the wound so that you don't fall asleep. See exactly what happens during the night," they advised her.

When she returned to her husband's home, she cut her finger one night and put salt on the wound. She went to bed as usual but did not fall asleep. The snake got in beside her and licked and licked her face. When the snake finally thought that she was asleep, he got out of bed, took off his snake skin and became a very handsome young man. Then he climbed back into bed. He did not realize that his wife had witnessed his transformation.

In the morning the young wife saw her husband get out of bed, take the snake skin from under the pillow and put it on. Then, bowing to his parents and his wife, he left through the ceiling.

That morning when the bride tried to tell her mother-in-law what she had seen, she started to shake so violently that she could hardly speak. "My heart is breaking because of my happiness," she said.

"What is it? Tell me," the mother-in-law said, kindly.

"Last night," the bride started to say and then began crying. She cried too much for words to tell.

"Husband, come here," the mother-in-law said. "I am your mother, and my husband is your father. Tell us what you have on your mind," the poor woman said. "Your husband is a snake; our son is a snake. We cannot help that for it is God's work. It has been written on our forehead that we should live thus."

"Father, mother, I am going to tell you something," she said. "Go, open the doors, and pass out money to the rich and poor alike for three days. Don't ask me why; I will tell you later."

The father went to the grinding stones and asked for money. He took this money and passed it out to rich and poor alike for three days.

During the following nights the girl again did not sleep but watched her husband until she was thoroughly convinced that he was a human being.

After the third day she fell on her knees before her mother- and father-in-law and kissed their hands. "That will be enough, father, you don't need to give away any more money," she said. She kissed their hands again and began crying. The snake's parents thought that their daughter-in-law was going to leave them and began crying because they had come to love her. "Father, what is your son? Mother, what is your son? As you bore him, you must know. What is he?"

"Don't you know that he is a snake? I asked God for a child, and He gave me a snake," the mother replied.

"No, mother, he is not a snake," the girl said.

"Daughter, what are you saying?"

"Don't cry, and I will tell you about it," she told them. "I began thinking that if my husband were a snake, how could I be with child? I decided not to sleep and to learn what I could. So one night I cut my finger and put salt on the wound. Your son, in the form of a snake, crawled beside me and licked and licked my face until he thought that I was unconscious. But I had decided not to fall asleep, and I didn't. When he was quite certain that I was sleeping, he got out of bed, took off his snake skin and became the most handsome man you ever set eyes on. In the morning before the rest of us were up, he left me and slipped into the snake skin again."

The father and mother took the bride in their arms and kissed her again and again. Their joy was beyond imagination. The three of them hugged each other and began crying. "What are we going to do about it?" the father asked.

"I don't know. You are to tell me," the bride said.

"Don't sleep again tonight," the parents-in-law said. "When your husband licks your face, let him think that you are asleep. When he takes his skin off, puts it under the pillow and goes to sleep, quietly take the skin from the hiding place and burn it. We won't sleep either and will come immediately to help you."

So great was their emotion that they joined hands and stood together like statues. When the snake came home and found them like that, he knew that something unusual had happened, but he did not know what it was. He bowed and sat down.

"Son, tell me the truth," his mother said. The snake looked at them but did not, or could not, speak. He was waiting until his child was born before destroying his snake skin. "It is a pity, son, that you do not take off that shirt of yours and be one of us," the mother said.

The snake shook his head to mean "no." He stuck out his tongue and drew it back, stuck it out and drew it back.

Finally, when they were ready to go to sleep that night, the parents quietly reminded their bride not to fall asleep.

The snake got into bed with his wife and, as usual, licked and licked her face until he thought she was unconscious. But the girl was not sleeping. Finally, the husband took off his snake skin, put it under his pillow and soon was in a deep sleep. The girl very quietly took the skin from beneath the pillow, got out of bed and started to burn the skin, but she was in such a hurry to do so that she burned her hands. When the parents, who were just outside the door, smelled the skin burning, they rushed in to help her and treated her hands as best they could.

The snake, meanwhile, awakening and smelling his skin burning, gave a terrifying scream. His parents fell on his neck, crying and embracing him while his bride cried with happiness. The neighbors, thinking that there was a death in the family, all rushed in to see what the screaming was about. Instead of death, they found great happiness. "Who is this man? What is he doing here? Is he having an affair with your daughter-in-law? Where is the snake?" everyone asked on all sides.

"My friends, this is the snake, my son. Our daughter burned his skin, and he is angry about it," the mother said. The neighbors, much relieved, wished them happiness and left.

"Mother, you waited this long, couldn't you have waited three more months? When my child was born, I would have burned my snake skin voluntarily." But how were they to know what his plans had been?

"Son, we will give you another wedding when your child is born," the parents said. When the child was born—and a beautiful boy it was!—another wedding, forty days and forty nights long, was celebrated.

With the grinding stones, the boy collected expensive rugs and many other rare things and became a rich merchant. His wife had only that one child. The merchant lived with his parents and his family peacefully ever after.

From the sky fell three apples, one to me, one to the story-teller and one to the person who has entertained you.

27. The Nine-Seeded Apple

There was once a king who had no children. He was very sad about this but could do nothing to change matters. One day he and his vizier went for a walk and met a dervish. "Hello, Your Majesty," the dervish said. The king was very much surprised for he was in disguise and thought that no one could recognize him. "How did you know that I was the king?" he asked.

"Oh, I know that you are the king and that you are very sad because you don't have children," the dervish replied. "Perhaps I can help you. In this apple there are nine seeds. Give three seeds to your wife, and she will have three sons; give three seeds to your favorite mare, and she will have three colts; plant the other three in front of your palace, and three trees will grow, one for each son. I will do all this for you, but when your youngest son is seven years old, I will come to the palace and will ask you to give me one of your sons. If you promise me this, I will give you this magic apple."

The king thought that this was a good bargain, so he accepted the apple and with his vizier started back to his palace. He cut open the apple and gave three seeds to his wife, three seeds to his favorite mare, and planted the other three seeds. Soon three sons were born to the queen, three colts were born to the favorite mare, and three trees appeared in front of the palace. The king did not tell his wife about his meeting with the dervish, and the queen did not know of the bargain her husband had made.

When the first son was fifteen years old, the second son ten years old and the youngest son seven years old, the trees had grown proportionally. Whenever the boys did not feel well, the trees looked sickly too. One day the dervish came to the palace and asked to see the king. "Your Majesty, I said that when your youngest son was seven years old, I would come to claim one of your boys. I am here now, and you must do as you promised."

The king was very sad, but what could he do? He could not

This story was told by Mrs. Katoon Mouradian.

break his promise. So he went to his wife and told her about the bargain he had made many years ago. She, too, became very sad. "What shall we do? Which of the boys shall we give?"

"Oh, surely, not our eldest!" the queen said.

"No, not our eldest."

"Nor our second son," the queen said.

"No, not our second son, either."

"Not our youngest! He is so young!"

"But he is the only one left. We must give him to the dervish!" the king said. So the young seven-year-old prince was given to the dervish.

The dervish took the boy, and together they started out. When they were quite a distance from the palace, the dervish beat the boy and knocked him down. Then he sat on his horse and rode on.

The little colt which the prince had left at home, sensing that his master was in danger, had left the stable and was following the boy. When he saw his master on the ground, he licked his face, and helped him to get up. Then the boy sat on the colt's back, and they started out again, following the cruel dervish. On the road, the boy met another dervish who was a good one. He said to the young prince, "My son, for fifteen years your master, the dervish, will put you to studying, and he will imprison your colt. After many years he will ask you to bring him a big book. But don't go after it. Finally, he will become angry and will get it himself. When this happens, hit the door through which he passes, and the knife which is above it will fall down on him and kill him."

The youth thanked the good dervish and told his colt to go where they must. The colt took him to a cave where he knew the dervish was waiting for them. The big rock at the mouth of the cave rolled away, and the colt and rider entered. The dervish was inside. To the colt he said, "Go to your place!" and the colt quietly went to one corner and stood there. To the boy he said, "You will stay in this cave and study and learn for fifteen years. After that time I will return." Meanwhile, in the palace garden the smallest tree looked sickly indeed!

After fifteen years the dervish returned. He stayed at the cave for several days; then, one day, he asked the young prince to bring him the big book. The boy remembered what the good dervish had told him many years before, so he replied, "Which big book? I don't know which one you want!"

"That one, that one there!" the dervish said, pointing to the book he wanted.

"That one?" the youth asked, and he purposely went to the wrong one.

The dervish became angry and went to get the book himself. At that moment the prince quickly hit the door through which the dervish had passed, and a big knife fell down and killed him. The prince then decided to move one of the rocks on the floor to see what was underneath, and he saw a great river with many dead bodies floating in it. He knew that if he had not killed the dervish, his body would have been in this river one day, too.

The boy went among the rocks forming the outer part of the cave and found many keys as well as silver and gold pieces. Nearby he saw a golden river which led to a lower world. When he reached that world, he washed his face and hands in the water for he had not washed for fifteen years. But when he did this, his whole body became golden! He looked about and finally found and freed his colt. He washed the animal in the golden water also. Taking along a large sack of gold, he mounted his horse, and together they climbed to the world above.

Meanwhile, the oldest prince, seeing that the tree of his youngest brother was bent and sickly, decided to set out and help him. Soon the tree of the first brother became bent, too. Then the second brother set out to find his two brothers. And soon his tree was also bent. But when the youngest brother reached the world above, the third tree straightened up, and his parents knew that he, at least, was safe again.

Finally the two brothers found their younger brother, and they were all happy. But while they were on their way back to the palace, a cruel giant suddenly appeared in front of them and said, "I will not let you pass unless you do as I ask. A very strong man has taken my wife to that mountain, and I am afraid to go there for he is stronger than I am. If one of you will go up the mountain, kill the man and bring my wife down, I will let you go free."

So the youngest brother went up to the mountain, killed the strong man and returned with the giant's wife, who was not his wife at all but a beautiful princess. Then the youngest prince killed the giant, too, and with his brothers went to the giant's cave and took all of his gold. The youngest brother liked the princess and decided to marry her. But just then he discovered that his little colt had disappeared.

The colt returned to the palace, and when the king saw it, he knew that his youngest son could not be far away. The colt, meanwhile, went directly to the stable to tell the other horses about their masters. Then he led the way to where the three brothers and the princess were waiting. They all sat on their horses and returned home. After that the trees always stood straight and tall.

28. Tanzara and Dyeer

One afternoon a rich government official, his subordinate and their wives were taking a walk together. Neither of these couples had children, but, as our story starts, they were on their way to visit a healer to learn from him how they could change this condition.

They had not gone far before they met a seer, a wise man, who stopped them and said, "I know why you are troubled, and I know how to help you. Yes, I know how you can have children." He took an apple from his pocket, cut it in two and gave half to each man, telling him to share it with his wife and give the peel to his horse. "Remember this: one of these children will be a girl and the other, a boy. When they are grown, they must marry each other. If they do not, if someone interferes, their lives will be tragic."

His words came true. Both women gave birth, one to a boy who was named Dyeer, and the other to a girl who was given the name Tanzara and who was the child of the richer man.* Each of the mares of the two families, which up to this time had never borne young, now gave birth to colts.

The children grew up together and became childhood sweethearts. At school they could not be parted from each other. The government official, however, did not want his daughter to marry the son of his subordinate, so he tried to part the young people. As he was unsuccessful in this, he decided to get rid of Dyeer.

Tanzara's father had a large box made, which was much like a coffin. He ordered his guards to put Dyeer in this box and throw it into the river which flowed nearby. For eight days the

This story was told by Mrs. Mariam Serabian.
* Both names are non-Armenian.

box floated in the water until finally it was caught fast in a mill wheel. The miller found the box, pulled it apart and discovered Dyeer who, by the grace of God, was not dead.

Dyeer worked in the mill for a year, knowing that he was not very far from Tanzara's house. During this time he built a tunnel under the water which led to her room. When Dyeer went to visit Tanzara, she received him in her room, but they were very careful not to arouse the suspicions of anyone.

However, there was a big Arab who was also in love with Tanzara and always followed her around, noting everything that she did and reporting it to her father. When the Arab saw Dyeer in Tanzara's room, he told her father about it. The father sentenced Dyeer to seven years of exile in Merdi, a town about four hundred miles away from the city of his birth. Before he left, the boy made Tanzara promise that she would not marry anyone else while he was away.

In Merdi, Dyeer made his living as an *ashough* [wandering minstrel]. Near the completion of the seven years the Arab went to Tanzara's father and threatened to tell everyone the cause of Dyeer's exile if Tanzara did not marry him. Ashamed of his daughter's conduct, the father consented to the marriage, and Tanzara was promised to the Arab.

Tanzara went to a fountain which had a top shaped like a faucet, and met two travelers who had stopped to refresh their horses. "Good travelers, are you going in the direction of Merdi?" Tanzara asked them. When they told her that they were, she said, "Will you take a message for me?"

As the travelers promised that they would take the message, Tanzara ran home and brought back a golden cup, Dyeer's favorite cup. She wrote a letter and gave both letter and cup to the travelers. "When you get to Merdi, give everyone a drink of water from this cup. If a person with the name of Dyeer should want to know whose cup it is, give him my letter."

The travelers did as Tanzara instructed and found Dyeer. They gave him both cup and letter and then went on their way. Dyeer read the letter which said: "Whether you get this at night or in the daytime, set off immediately! My father is marrying me to the Arab."

Dyeer lost no time in preparations and rode three days and three nights until he finally reached the one he loved. He entered her room and embraced her. But the Arab, who was outside the door, heard Dyeer's voice, and he went to his future father-in-law to tell him that Dyeer had returned.

Tanzara's father was very angry with the young people. "Guards, bring Dyeer here!" he ordered.

When Dyeer was brought, the father said, "Dyeer, if you are able to repeat three times without error the phrase which I give you now, Tanzara will be your bride; but if you do not, your head will be cut off."

Dyeer consented. Twice he repeated the phrase without error. Tanzara, hearing that she was about to be free to marry her loved one, appeared in her golden slippers on the balcony directly across from Dyeer. The youth was repeating the phrase for the third time when suddenly he looked up and saw Tanzara. Dazzled by her beauty, he uttered her name and thus failed to word the phrase correctly. It was decided that Dyeer must be killed. Tanzara fainted. Dyeer was dragged out to be beheaded.

Instead of waiting to kill him at the specified place, however, his captors killed him on the way there. Meanwhile, Tanzara recovered and begged her father to spare her lover. Finally he relented and sent word that Dyeer be freed. But the pardon was too late: Dyeer was already dead.

Tanzara shut herself from the world to mourn the death of Dyeer. Finally Tanzara's father thought that by giving his daughter some of Dyeer's flesh, she would forget her sorrow. So he ordered that some of Dyeer's flesh be prepared for her supper. But when the flesh was served, Tanzara said, "Is there famine in this land that we must eat the flesh of the dead?" And she refused to touch it.

Then her father thought that by letting her weep over Dyeer's body, she would recover from her sorrow. Tanzara was happy to hear of her father's decision. Before setting out with her guards, she slipped a razor in her beautiful, long hair. As she walked along, she took her golden slippers off and dropped them on the road. The guards who were with her lingered behind as she had hoped they would, to pick up the valuable slippers. Tanzara went alone to Dyeer. She threw herself upon the body of her beloved and cut her throat with the razor which she had hidden in her hair. When the guards came, they found her dead, just as she had wished to be.

The seer had said, "The two must marry each other, else ill fortune will come to both," and his words came true.

29. Mundig

Once upon a time in a peaceful village in Armenia there lived an old couple. Though these people very much wanted to have children, their wish had not been granted.

One day the woman was sitting outside her home when a dervish went by. "I wonder if this dervish can tell me what I must do to have children," the woman said to herself. "Dervish *Aga* [lord], won't you come here?" she asked him.

"What is it you want, woman?" the dervish said, coming close.

"Dervish *Aga*, I don't have a child, and I want one very much. What can I do?"

The dervish did not answer but began writing and writing and finally turned to her: "If you get a handful of *sissair* [chick-peas] and sit on it, you will have a child."

The woman was very happy for now at last she would have a child, her very own. She took a handful of *sissair* and did as the dervish had said. And sure enough! a whole bunch of babies, about as big as your thumb, were scattered all through the room! "Oh, what shall I do with all these little things?" the poor woman said, hitting her hands on her knees, pulling her hair and crying. "What shall I do with all these tiny things?"

In the midst of all this she remembered suddenly that she had to prepare her husband's lunch. So she hurriedly heated the oven and started to bake the bread. "I know what to do! I'll put all these little babies in the oven right now and get rid of them!"

After she had baked the bread, she took all the babies and put them into the hot oven. Of course, they all died immediately. "Oh, dear me, what have I done? I should have saved at least one of them to take lunch to his father!" the woman exclaimed.

But, contrary to what she thought, not all the babies had died: one had slipped through her fingers and escaped. When the baby heard his mother's words, he called out, "Mama, I'm here."

"Where are you, my child?" the mother asked.

"I'm up here," the baby said as he climbed up the wall.

"Come down, Mundig [Tiny], and take your father's lunch to him," the mother said. So the child became known as Mundig.

The mother prepared the lunch and tied it to Mundig's back. But needless to say, the lunch was bigger than the little boy. "You wait here, Mundig, while I go and get the donkey out," his

This story was told by Mrs. Mariam Serabian.

mother said. She got the donkey out and seated Mundig right on his back. But what do you think Mundig did? He crawled from the donkey's back and hopped right into the donkey's ear! Oh! he liked it there.

Mundig and the donkey reached a field where there was a man plowing. "That must be my father," Mundig said to himself. "Father, father, come and get your lunch," Mundig called out from the donkey's ear.

The father looked up and saw the donkey without a rider. "When did this donkey of ours begin speaking and calling me father? I imagined it, no doubt," the man said to himself and returned to his plowing.

But no sooner had he resumed his work than he heard the voice saying, "Father, father, come and get your lunch."

"This is very strange," the man said. "I wonder who this is for I surely can't see anyone on that donkey. Child, child, where are you?" the father called out.

"I am in the donkey's ear," Mundig said.

The father took his baby and his lunch out of the donkey's ear. "What is your name?" he asked.

"My name is Mundig. Let me plow while you eat, father."

"No, my son, you will fall under the oxen's manure." But when the boy continued to beg, the father said, "All right, Mundig, but be careful. Don't walk directly behind the oxen."

Mundig was very happy. He started to plow a while, but he was not careful and soon fell under the oxen's manure. "Father, father, come help me! I'm under the oxen's manure," Mundig yelled.

"Didn't I tell you to be careful?" his father said, pulling the tiny boy out. "Oh, Mundig, you are so dirty! Come, I'll take you to the brook and wash you."

Mundig knew what it meant not to listen to his father, so he went along quietly. Soon they reached the brook, and his father began bathing him. "Mundig, don't look up," he said.

"Why, father?"

"There is an apple tree above us."

Mundig glanced upward and saw a beautiful tree heavy with juicy ripe apples. "Oh, if I could only get up there," Mundig said to himself. Presently, when Mundig's father had loosened his hold on him, Mundig jumped right up into the apple tree! It happened so quickly that the father could not stop him. "These apples are so good!" Mundig said, eating one apple after another.

"Mundig, come down," his father ordered.

"I'm going to eat these apples."

"Mundig, come down or you'll fall," his father repeated. But when Mundig did not answer him, he said, "All right then, if you aren't coming down, at least give me an apple."

Now Mundig knew what his father meant to do. He knew that if he should bend over to give the apple to his father, he would be caught and forced to come down. So instead of handing down the apple as he should have done, he threw it down.

"That Mundig is really a smart boy," his father said under his breath. "Come, Mundig, give me another apple," he called out.

And again, Mundig threw the apple down.

"Mundig, come down, come down," the father asked. But when Mundig continued to sit in the tree and eat apples, the father left him and returned to his plowing. When Mundig had eaten all the apples he wanted, he began to think of what to do next. "Where shall I go? Home? No! I know what: I'll try to find my aunt's house." So off he went, running and playing, to find his aunt's house.

However, his father had seen him running away. "I'd better go home and tell my wife about it," he said and started for home. "Wife, our son has run away," he told her.

"Our little Mundig? Oh, what shall we do!" his wife said, crying and hitting her hands on her knees. Mundig's father went back to the fields, and his mother sat at home crying.

Mundig, meanwhile, found his aunt's house. "Aunty, I am here," he called.

"Mundig, is that you? Come in," she said. She had heard of him but had not yet seen him.

So Mundig went inside the house.

"Oh, Mundig, does your mother know that you are here?" his aunt asked. When Mundig avoided answering her, she said, "All right, Mundig, you stay here while I go and tell your mother not to worry."

Mundig noticed that his aunt was preparing supper. "I wonder what she is making," Mundig said, lifting the cover of the pan. And what a delicious treat did he see: his favorite food— lamb, cut into small pieces and roasted until tender and tasty. "Let me just taste a piece," Mundig said to himself, taking first one piece, then a second, then a third, until finally the very last piece of meat was gone.

"What shall I do now? I've eaten all the meat, and if my aunt finds out, she'll hit me!" Mundig said to himself. He looked around and saw his baby cousin in her cradle. "I know what to do!" he said. "I'll put my cousin in the pan, and they will never know the difference."

So he took his little cousin, put her in the pan and put the pan on the stove. Just as he finished doing this, he heard footsteps coming near. "Oh, I'll have to hide somewhere, or my aunt will hit me for eating all the meat," Mundig said. He looked around and noticed that there was nowhere he could hide. "Oh, the ceiling! She can never get me there!" Mundig said, quickly scaling the wall and getting up to the ceiling.

His aunt and mother walked into the house. They looked around for Mundig but could not find him. "Mundig, where are you, Mundig?" they called. But no Mundig was to be found. "Well, sister, come let's eat something first and then go out to look for him," the aunt said.

They poured some of the contents of the pan into two dishes and sat down to eat. The aunt put her spoon in and drew out an earring. "What is my baby's earring doing here?" she asked. "Where is my baby?" she cried, running to the cradle. Of course, she could not find the baby in the cradle. "Oh, that Mundig! He ate the meat and put his cousin in the pan. What shall I do? My beautiful baby!"

In this excitement Mundig escaped through the window.

Both mother and aunt ran outside looking for Mundig. "If I catch him, I'll do the same thing to him that he did to my baby," the aunt said, weeping.

Mundig walked and walked until he met a man playing a fiddle. Mundig took the fiddle away from the man, and the man was so frightened that he ran away. Mundig took the fiddle and started to sing:

"Oof, my fiddle, oof my fiddle,
My mother wanted a baby and couldn't have one.
She asked a passing dervish what she could do;
He told her to sit on a handful of *sissair*,
She did, and a lot of small babies were born.

" 'What shall I do with all these tiny babies?' my mother asked herself;
She put them all in the oven and killed them, but I escaped.
'Oh, what did I do, what did I do!' my mother said.

'I didn't even leave one so that he could carry his father's lunch.'
I was on the wall and said, 'Mother, I'm here'.
'Where are you, son?' she asked.
'Right here on the wall,' I said.

" 'Come down, Mundig, and take your father's lunch,' she said.
She tied the lunch to my back and put me on the donkey's back.
I slipped from the donkey's back into his ear.
I took my father's lunch.
I wanted to plow, but my father wouldn't let me.

"Finally I plowed, but I fell under the oxen's manure.
My father picked me out and took me to the brook to wash me.
There was a big apple tree right above us, and when my father
    loosened his grip on me,
I jumped up the apple tree and began eating.
'Come down, Mundig, come down,' my father said.
'No, I won't come down,' I said.
'Come, Mundig, or you'll fall,' my father said.
'No, I won't come down,' I said.

" 'All right, then, give me an apple,' my father said.
I was too smart to give him an apple so I threw him one.
Finally, my father went home and told my mother that I had run
    away.
I went to my aunt's house.
My aunt went to tell my mother not to worry about me.
When she was away, I ate all the supper.

"I put my little cousin in the pan and put it on the stove.
My aunt and mother came home and couldn't find me.
I was watching from the ceiling.
They sat down to eat a little before looking for me.
My aunt put her spoon in the meat and found an earring.
'Whose earring is this?' she asked.
She ran to her baby's cradle and found her baby missing.
'Mundig ate all the supper and put my little baby in the pan in-
    stead!' my aunt cried.
They went out to find me, but I escaped.

"I walked and walked and saw a man playing a fiddle.
I took his fiddle away from him, and he was frightened and ran
    away.
Now I'm playing and singing.
Oof, my fiddle, I'm playing and singing."

Just then Mundig saw his mother and aunt coming toward him. He took his fiddle and ran away again. He walked and walked until he saw three musicians playing different instruments. "I think I'll join these men," Mundig said, playing on his fiddle. He jumped from one musician's lap to another's, playing on his fiddle all the while.

Mundig looked down the road and again saw his mother and aunt approaching. Holding tightly to his fiddle, he ran and ran and jumped in the river.

And no one has ever seen Mundig since.

30. Cinderella

At one time there lived an old couple who had three daughters. When the father died, he left them a little money, but, as we all know, money which is not added to but always taken from will soon disappear. So it was now, and the sisters and their mother were soon left penniless.

The two elder sisters continually reminded their mother that they were poor and had nothing to eat, but the youngest sister never complained.

"Let us go out and get food, no matter what we must do," the elder sisters said.

"No, don't do that," the mother said, "I would prefer that you kill me and eat me rather than bring dishonor to this home."

"No! No! I will never let them do that!" the youngest sister said, crying.

For ten days the two sisters told their mother that they were hungry, and for ten days the mother gave them the same answer. So on the tenth day the sisters decided to kill their mother.

"Oh! Mother, I will not let them do this!" the youngest daughter cried and threw herself on her mother's neck.

When the older girls were away, the mother took her youngest child aside and said, "Don't cry, my child. They will kill me, I know this: nothing can be done. Let them eat as much as they want, but don't you eat. After they have finished, take my bones and bury them behind the house. Whenever you need anything— whether it be food, clothes, money—just come to my grave and ask for it, and it shall be yours. When you no longer need it, dig

This story was told by Mrs. Mariam Serabian.

the ground a little and stick it in. But don't ever let your sisters know this," the mother said.

And so it happened. The cruel sisters killed their mother and sat down to eat her. "Come, eat!" the two sisters urged, but the youngest girl refused, saying, "I will not eat my mother's flesh." The older sisters did not worry at all since now they had all the more to eat.

When the two sisters had finished and left the house, the youngest sister took her mother's bones and buried them behind the house. Meanwhile, in the days following, the youngest girl reminded her sisters over and over that they had killed their mother and eaten her.

One day the king announced to all his people, rich and poor alike, that his one and only son was to be married, and everyone was invited to the wedding feast. The two sisters were much excited, and when they were both dressed in their best finery, they asked their youngest sister why she was not ready.

"Why should I go with you? You killed my mother and ate her," she said, crying. They gave her a blow on the head and left.

When the sisters were gone, the youngest sister went to her mother's grave where she asked for a beautiful blue dress. Immediately on the ground before her appeared a lovely blue gown. The young girl combed her hair and put on the lovely dress. Such beauty as hers was not for human eyes! At the feast everyone noticed the beautiful girl, but no one could learn her name. When the youngest sister saw that it was getting late, she slipped out unnoticed and returned home. She changed her clothes and hid the dress as she had been told to do.

When the sisters returned, they said, "You should have been there today! There was such a beautiful girl, but no one knew who she was!"

"Why should I go with you? You killed my mother and ate her," the youngest said.

The two sisters, angered by this reminder, gave her another blow and went to bed. The next evening the two again prepared to go to the wedding feast and asked their youngest sister to go with them.

"Why should I go with you? You killed my mother and ate her," the youngest sister said. Again the sisters hit her and started on their way. The youngest sister went behind the house and asked for a second dress. When it appeared, she washed, combed her hair, put on her dress and started for the palace.

Again everyone marveled at her beauty and wondered who she was. The king, too, became curious and ordered his men to follow her.

But on the second evening, as on the first, the youngest sister slipped out of the palace without being discovered. She hurriedly went home, changed, hid her dress and was ready for her sisters' return.

"Oh! You should have come with us tonight! The beautiful girl was there again! She sparkled like a jewel!" the two sisters said.

"Why should I go with you? You killed my mother and ate her," the youngest sister said. Again the sisters grew angry, beat their youngest sister and went to bed.

The third day of the wedding the two sisters put on their best dresses and asked their youngest sister if she would go with them.

"No, why should I go with you? You killed my mother and ate her," the youngest sister answered. The cruel sisters hit her again and left.

When the youngest sister found herself alone, she went behind the house and asked her mother for a third dress. When it appeared, she washed, combed her hair, put on the dress and went to the palace. Now the king had heard such descriptions of the beautiful creature who came to the ball every night that he decided to see for himself how true this talk was. He hid himself so that he could see the people without being seen. How true! She was as lovely as they had said and even lovelier! Who was she? He called some of his men together and ordered them not to let her pass out of their sight for even one moment. The youngest sister saw that she was surrounded with men all that evening but did not know why. Again she slipped out of the palace without being noticed. The king was furious and told his men that they would be punished if they did not catch her the next night.

The youngest sister went home, changed her clothes, concealed her dress and sat down to wait for her sisters. When they returned, they spoke of the beautiful girl and asked their youngest sister why she did not go with them.

"Why should I go with you? You killed my mother and ate her," the youngest sister said, whereupon the two older sisters beat her and went to bed.

The fourth day the two sisters again made ready for the wedding feast. Again they asked their youngest sister to go with them. "Why should I go with you? You killed and ate my mother," the youngest said. The two sisters beat her once more and left for the wedding. When the girl was alone, she went behind the house to her mother's grave and asked for a beautiful dress. She washed, combed her hair, put on the dress and started out.

The king, not wishing to take a chance of losing her, disguised himself and with his men surrounded her constantly. When she saw that it was getting late, she slipped out of the palace, but this time she did not go unnoticed. The king and several of his men followed her and saw her enter a house. They knocked on the door and said to her, "What are you doing here? Come, the king wants to see you."

"This is where I live, why else would I be here?" the girl answered. "What does the king want with me?"

"Aren't you proud that the king wants to see you?" they asked.

"I can't go to the king now; I have two sisters who are at the wedding."

"Well, let them stay behind," the guards said.

"No, they killed my mother and ate her," the girl said, beginning to cry.

"What is this?" the men asked in surprise.

So the youngest sister told them the story of her mother's death. "When my mother knew that my sisters were going to kill her, she told me to save her bones and bury them in the back of the house. She told me whenever I needed anything—money, food, dresses—to go to her grave and ask for it, and I would receive it. And after I had finished using it, I was to bury it in the ground," the girl said.

"What! Is such a thing possible?" the king (who was in disguise among his men) asked. "Show me how you do this."

The youngest sister took the men behind the house. She asked for a dress, and a dress appeared through the ground. The king told his men to dig into the ground and see what else was beneath it. The men found dishes, clothes, slippers and everything a girl would want. The king was astonished.

While they were puzzling over this, the two older sisters returned home. "All you do is sit home and cry all the time. You should have been with us to see the beautiful girl today. Now you will never see her because today was the last day of the wedding," the sisters said.

"Why should I go with you? You killed and ate my mother,"

she answered. The two older sisters gave her a good beating and then went to bed.

The next morning a troop of soldiers came to the door and took the two elder girls before the king. "Since you killed your mother, you are to be put in prison," he ruled. The two sisters tried in every way they knew to deny this deed, but, of course, they could not change matters. So they were put in prison.

The same day the king went to the girl's house and carried off the youngest sister. They celebrated a big wedding for forty days and forty nights. Meanwhile, the two sisters, who were in prison, did not know what had happened to their youngest sister.

One day the king told his wife, "I will build a church where your mother's home stood and have a beautiful statue placed where her bones are buried." So a beautiful church was built, and a tall statue with the mother's name written on it was set over the mother's grave. "Now you can go every morning to this church and pray," the king told his wife, hoping that this would ease her sorrow.

However, the king was still angry about the cruel deed of the sisters and wanted them killed. But the youngest sister, pleaded and finally convinced him to free them instead. Because the king loved his wife dearly, he set the two sisters free. They returned home to find that their house did not exist, but in its place there now stood a beautiful church. Near it they saw a large statue of their mother. They were much surprised, because, of course, they didn't know that their youngest sister had brought this about. They asked their neighbors about this but no one would tell them what had happened.

One morning when the youngest sister was leaving this church, she saw her two sisters walking in the churchyard. She ran and fell at their feet. The two sisters were much surprised. Who were they that such a noble lady should fall at their feet?

"Don't you recognize me, sisters?" the queen asked.

When the two heard this rich and beautifully dressed lady call them "sisters," they looked again and recognized their youngest sister. The two older sisters started crying, and the youngest joined them. After a while they forgave one another. The two sisters left the town, and the youngest sister went back to the palace. When she reached home, she told the king about her meeting, and he was happy that the sisters had forgiven one another.

The king and queen lived happily ever after.

31. The Golden-Haired Twins

There was once a king who had three daughters. This king had a habit of disguising himself in the evening so that no one could recognize him and of walking among his people.

One warm summer evening as he walked underneath the windows of the princesses' room, he heard them laughing and whispering. "Ah! I am in luck! Now I will be able to hear what my daughters really think and do," the king said to himself. He heard his first daughter say, "If my father gave me to a prince, I would make such a carpet that all of my father's guards could sit on it and there would still be half of it unused."

"If my father gave me to a rich merchant, I would make such a loaf of bread that all of my father's soldiers could eat it and half of it would be left over," the second daughter said.

"I don't care whom I marry. I will bear a pair of twins, a boy and a girl, with golden hair, each with a golden cane in his hand and a little bag of gold on his pillow every morning," the youngest daughter said.

"Very well, I will do what they ask and see whether each will keep her word," the king said to himself. He married his oldest daughter to a prince but reminded her, "Don't forget: you are to make such a carpet that when all my guards sit on it, there will still be half of it unused."

He married his second daughter to a wealthy merchant and reminded her, "Don't forget: you are to make such a loaf of bread that all my soldiers will eat of it and half will be left over."

He gave his third daughter to a middle-class man and reminded her, "Don't forget: you are to have a pair of twins, a boy and a girl, with golden hair, each with a golden cane in his hand and a little bag of gold on his pillow every morning."

After a few weeks the first son-in-law reminded his wife of her promise: "You must start making the carpet soon."

"I, the daughter of a king, the wife of a prince, I should make a carpet! Aren't you ashamed for even suggesting such a thing?" the angry woman asked. The prince was so frightened by her anger that he said no more.

The second son-in-law reminded his wife of her promise: "You must start baking the bread soon."

"I am a king's daughter, a rich and successful merchant's

This story was told by Mrs. Mariam Serabian.

wife. Aren't you ashamed for even suggesting that I put my hands in dough?" the second daughter said. The merchant was so afraid of his wife that he did not say another word.

The king went to his third daughter. He was disappointed by his first two and was very angry. "Well, when are you going to keep your promise?" he asked.

"If God find us worthy of such an honor, we are always ready," the youngest daughter said.

"Very well, that is what you say now. But remember, if you don't have a pair of twins, one boy and one girl with golden hair, and each with a golden cane in his hand and a little bag of gold on his pillow every morning, I will cut off your head."

In those days there were no doctors, only midwives to help at birth. When it was almost time for the babies to be born, the two older sisters called a midwife and pressed a gold piece in her hand. "If you do as we say, there will be many more gold pieces," they whispered to her. "We are taking you to a woman who is going to have a child very soon. [You know, don't you, that the youngest princess was the woman?] If she has a pair of twins, a boy and a girl, with golden hair, each with a golden cane in his hand and a little bag of gold on his pillow, choke these children, and in their places put two little blind newborn puppies which we will bring to you. If you do this, you will not regret it."

The midwife agreed to do as they asked. Meanwhile, the two sisters sent men throughout the town looking for newborn blind puppies. At last they found a pair of them, put them in a little basket and gave the basket to the midwife to take along with her.

Meanwhile, the third princess' husband was much excited and told the king that the children were to be born soon. Both husband and king anxiously awaited the birth. And the children were born, just as the princess had said that they would be. The twins, a boy and a girl, had golden hair, each held a golden cane in his hand and a tiny bag of gold was tied around his little finger. The midwife took the children before the mother was able to see them, placed them in a basket and put the blind puppies in place of the children.

When the midwife finished her work, the king and the third princess' husband rushed in to see the golden-haired twins. But, instead of the beautiful twins, they saw two newborn blind puppies. The king was very angry and the husband, very much embarrassed. The king shouted, "She is no daughter of mine! Quick, get her dressed in her oldest clothes." The midwife and the two sisters smiled secretly to themselves as they dressed the third princess in her oldest clothes.

The king ordered his carpenters to come to him. "Make a long, narrow box," he commanded. The carpenters hurriedly made the box as requested. The king then put his daughter into this box and left a hole at the top of it through which she could be given food and water. He had this box taken to a busy corner, and he ordered that everyone who passed by should spit at her and hit her with a stick which he provided right next to the box. Those who failed to obey the king's command were to be punished.

Meanwhile, the two sisters took the twins, put them in a basket and threw the basket into the river. The sisters were jealous of their younger sister because they had promised their father to do certain things and they had not kept their promise, while their younger sister had promised her father that she would have a pair of twins with golden hair and she had kept her promise.

The basket was tossed about by the waves until a part of it broke, but by the will of God, the children were not drowned. Soon the basket reached shore and was hidden among the weeds.

In that place there was an old woman who had a goat which was tended by a village boy. This boy took the villagers' goats and sheep out to pasture during the day and brought them back at night. Every evening when the goat was brought back, the old woman would milk her.

One day this goat got away from the boy and went to the river where she found the basket. When she saw the young children in the basket, she suckled them. That night when the old woman milked her goat and there was little milk, she wondered what had happened.

On the second day the goat got away from the boy once more, went to the shore and again suckled the golden-haired twins. That evening, too, the goat did not give her usual amount of milk, and the old woman was quite puzzled.

The next day the same thing happened again. The woman thought that the herd boy had milked the goat before bringing her home. "Why do you take my goat's milk? Why don't you take the milk of some other goats?" she asked him.

"Don't accuse me of such a thing, for I have not done it. Come early tomorrow and see what happens. Your goat always leaves early, and I think she comes straight home. Come tomorrow and follow her," the boy said.

The next morning the old woman did as the boy suggested and kept a watchful eye on her goat. In the middle of the afternoon she noticed that her goat slipped away from the others and started on the road to the river.

"Now, I wonder where that goat could be going?" the woman said to herself as she started following her. She saw that the goat went by the tall weeds near the river and bent over a basket. "What is she doing?" the old woman said as she went to investigate. And what do you think she saw? Huddled together in the broken basket were two beautiful babies with golden hair, each with a golden cane in his hand and many bags of gold on his tiny pillow. "Oh! What beautiful babies! I will take them home and raise them as my own," the kind-hearted woman said. So she took the golden-haired twins home with her. She looked after them until they grew to be about eight years old, and never told them that she was not their mother.

One day, however, when the boy was playing, his comrades called out in singsong, "Motherless, fatherless, motherless, fatherless."

The little boy came running inside the house, very angry. "Mother, don't I have a mother and a father?"

"I am your mother and your father, son," the old woman said. "Why do you ask?"

"The boys called me 'Motherless, fatherless' while I was playing."

"Don't listen to them for they are bad boys," the old woman said. But when the boy begged for the truth, she told him how she had found the two babies in a little basket by the shore when her goat was suckling them. The boy decided that he and his sister should leave and search for their real parents. The old woman pleaded with him to stay, but he refused. So he took his sister, and they started out.

After many days they came to another land and found an out-of-the-way cave in which they lived. Because each of them had a bag of gold every morning on his pillow, they did not have to worry about money. Each morning for eight days the boy took one of the bags of gold and went to a neighboring village to do the marketing.

By chance, the cave where the twins had found shelter was near their birthplace where their aunts still lived. One day the sisters heard of a beautiful young boy with golden hair and a golden cane in his hand who visited the market every day.

Now, as we have said, the twins' mother had been put in a box which was set on a busy corner. The king had ordered that everyone who passed by must spit at her and hit her with a stick. The golden-haired boy, although he didn't know that she was his mother, felt sorry for the woman. Instead of hitting her, he would slip her a piece of bread or a little fruit and take his punishment.

One day the two sisters purposely went to the market to see if this boy could, by chance, be their nephew. And to their surprise they saw that he was! They hurried to the midwife and said, "What shall we do now, the boy is still alive!"

The midwife asked, "Are you sure of what you say?"

"Oh, yes, we saw him ourselves. He was in the market, but he has finished his marketing by now and is going home. You can trail him and see where he lives," the sisters said. So the midwife trailed the boy and saw that he went into the cave. Then she turned back and returned home.

The next morning when the boy had gone marketing, the midwife entered the cave and found the sister alone. "Sweet girl, how can you live here alone?" she asked.

"I have a brother, but he has gone to the market to bring us something to eat," the innocent girl replied.

"Living alone is not good; tell your brother to get you a Hazaran Bulbul," the midwife said, and she left. When the brother returned home, the girl would not speak to him. "What is the matter, sweet sister, that you will not speak to me?" he asked.

"Why won't you get me a Hazaran Bulbul to keep me company?"

Now, a Hazaran Bulbul was a very rare bird which had the gift of human speech. This was not only very difficult to find, but it was well known that the man who set out to find one rarely returned alive. The brother realized all this, but since it was his sister's wish, he resolved to find the rare bird for her. The next morning he went to the marketplace and bought a horse. He thought that it was just an ordinary horse, but, in reality, he had bought a magic horse. He went to the cave, embraced his sister and started out to find the Hazaran Bulbul.

The boy began the search not knowing where he was to go. As he sat wondering what direction he should take, he heard a voice say, "Where are you going?"

The boy looked around but saw no one. "Who is speaking?" he asked.

"It is your horse," the animal said.

The boy was very much surprised. "My sister wants me to find a Hazaran Bulbul, and that is what I am setting out to do now."

"Do you think that Hazaran Bulbuls are so common that you can find one anywhere?" the horse asked in a mocking tone.

After they had gone a little distance, the horse said, "I am taking you to the place where the bird lives, but when we get there, you will hear people yelling and making much noise. You must cry out, 'Tanzara Kanum [Turkish: Lady Tanzara], for the sake of your brother Bedros, give me a Hazaran Bulbul.'"

Meanwhile, the midwife had returned to visit the sister. "Where is your brother today?" she asked the girl.

"He has gone to find the Hazaran Bulbul for me," she answered.

"Good girl, now you will be happy," the midwife said, believing that the boy would surely die in the attempt.

When the golden-haired boy arrived at his destination, he heard terrible cries, but having been warned beforehand, he tried not to pay attention to them. He noticed that there were great black slaves with lips as thick as the sky, guarding the gates. "Tanzara Kanum, for the sake of your brother Bedros, give me the Hazaran Bulbul," the golden-haired boy cried.

Tanzara was a very young and beautiful woman. Her brother had died recently, and his memory was very dear to her. When she heard this human cry, she ran out to see who it was who called her brother's name. "For that, I am going to reward him," she said. When she saw that it was a beautiful golden-haired boy who had called, she told him to follow her. She gave him the Hazaran Bulbul in a cage and said, "Take this and ride on, but never look back for anything. If you do, you will turn to stone!"

The golden-haired boy took the bird, sat on his horse and rode away fast, never once turning around. When he reached home, his sister was very pleased with the beautiful talking bird.

The next morning the boy returned to the market to buy some food for the day. There the aunts saw him again and told the midwife. The midwife waited until the next day when the boy was in town, then she went to visit the sister in the cave. "See, my sweet one, isn't your Hazaran Bulbul a comfort to you? But do you understand the bird's language?" When the girl told her that she did not, the woman said, "Tell your brother to bring you an interpreter." The midwife was sure now that this time the boy would die.

That evening when her brother returned, again the sister would not talk to him. "What is the matter, sister? What have I done to offend you?"

"Why don't you get me an interpreter for this bird? I can't understand what it is saying."

"Sister, wait, you are going to eat my head yet,"* the brother said. Sadly, he embraced her, mounted his horse and rode away to fulfill her request.

Again he talked to Tanzara who invited him in and gave him a beautiful girl who was to serve as interpreter. Again Tanzara warned him not to look back. The boy obeyed her and reached home safely with the girl. His sister was happy now, and so was the brother when he saw his sister in such good spirits.

The next morning the golden-haired boy went to the market, and the aunts saw him and again told the midwife. The following morning the midwife paid the sister another visit. "Aren't you happy? He did bring her!" she said, seeing the interpreter. When she left, the interpreter said to the girl, "You have come across a bad person. Tell your brother to go to the place where he found me and get the other girl who is there. Together we can protect you so that no one can do you harm."

When the sister told her brother about this, he mounted his horse and again went to Tanzara's land. "For the sake of your brother Bedros, give me the other girl that you have here," the boy begged. Tanzara invited him in and gave him the other girl. "You must ride very fast, and you must never look behind until you are safely away, or you will turn to stone," she warned him.

The boy thanked Tanzara and set out. But after riding half-way home, he turned around by mistake. And immediately the horse, the girl and the golden-haired boy all turned to stone. Tanzara knew what had happened, however, so she ran, took a magic sword and hit the statues, whereupon they became alive again. Tanzara, knowing what was in store for the boy, went along with him to give him added protection.

When they reached the cave, the sister was happy to see her brother and the other two girls. The boy left them together and went to the market. Tanzara said, "We must be careful! Someone will be here to visit us soon." No sooner had she said these words than the midwife entered the cave. Since the golden-haired boy

* An Armenian expression similar in meaning to: "You are going to bring about my death."

had gone to the market, the midwife found only four very beautiful young maidens.

"My dear," the midwife said to the golden-haired girl, "see how happy you are now! That is because you have such good company!" But Tanzara told the midwife to leave the cave and never to return. She knew the evil woman planned only to hurt the two young people.

While the boy was in town, the king saw the beautiful youth and decided to follow him. When the golden-haired boy reached the cave, Tanzara told him that they were going to have a royal guest but that they should not be afraid of him.

"In the middle of town there is a large box in which a woman is imprisoned. Have you ever struck this woman?" Tanzara asked the golden-haired boy. He told her that he had felt great pity for the poor woman and had never hit her. "Good, for this box is very important to you," she said.

Just then the king walked into the cave and found four very beautiful girls and the handsome, golden-haired boy. "What do you want? Tell me, and I will answer you," Tanzara said to the king. Seeing that the king did not answer, Tanzara asked, "Who is this boy, and who is this girl? Where is their mother? Why did you put her in a box in the middle of town?"

The king bit his lip. "What are you saying?"

"These are your grandchildren, the golden-haired twins. Each of them has a golden cane and wakes up in the morning with a purse of gold."

The king almost lost his mind.

"Quick! Get that poor woman out of that box!" Tanzara said.

The king ordered that his daughter be taken out of the box and given a hot bath, warm clothing and food. Tanzara, the other girls and the golden-haired twins went to the king's palace. Tanzara sent the twins to their mother, and the three of them cried with happiness for being together again!

"I am going to give my eldest sister to you, Your Majesty; my second sister, I will give to your vizier; and I will marry the golden-haired boy," Tanzara said.

The king was very pleased with this arrangement, but he added, "I have something else I must do first." He ordered three wild jackasses and had his two older daughters and the midwife tied to them. Then he had these jackasses whipped and driven over mountainous roads. Of course, the bodies of the two sisters and the midwife were dashed to pieces.

The weddings took place, and all led a happy life thereafter.

From the sky fell three apples: one to me, one to the storyteller and one to the person who has entertained you.

32. The Story of Mariam

There was once a widower who had only one daughter named Mariam. When Mariam was old enough to go to school, she had a strict, unreasonable teacher who wanted to marry her father. "Mariam, go home and tell your father to marry me," the teacher told her.

And Mariam, too young to understand, went home and told her father that she wanted her schoolteacher for a mother. But her father said, "No, Mariam, I will not marry her."

When Mariam told this to her schoolteacher, she said, "Never mind, ask again. Cry and say that he must marry me."

When Mariam tried again, her father said, "When the turtle climbs the tree, I will marry your teacher."

So the teacher gave a turtle to Mariam and said, "Put this turtle on the tree, then call your father and show him the turtle. Then he will have to marry me." Finally, Mariam's father married the schoolteacher. Mariam was only six years old at the time.

One day when Mariam's father was away from home, her stepmother beat her and cut off one of her hands. When Mariam's father came home, he saw that his daughter was crying and that one of her hands had been cut off. "Wife, what is this? What has happened to Mariam?" he asked.

"That child of yours is very bad! She has turned this house upside down!"

"Never do a thing like that again, hear me, no matter what she does," the father said.

The next day when he came home he saw that the child's other hand was cut off. The father was very sad but didn't know what to do. He could not sit down and see his child forever crippled. Finally he decided to carry her off to the forest and leave her there for the animals to eat so that she wouldn't have to go through life without hands.

This he did, and Mariam was left alone deep in the forest. In due time the wolves, tigers, lions and all the wild animals came to her, but none touched her. Instead they brought her food and watched over her.

One day the prince was hunting in these woods when he saw

This story was told by Mrs. Mariam Serabian.

many animals grouped together. In the middle of the group he saw a little girl with no hands. The prince was very young, not yet fifteen, but he understood that God intended that this poor child should become his wife when they were old enough to marry. So he took her home with him.

There she was treated like a princess. When she grew to be eighteen, the prince made her his wife. She was very beautiful, but because she was without hands, she was unable to do anything for herself.

Mariam was expecting her child when a war started. As the prince left for the battle, he told his mother to let him know immediately when his child was born. Not long after this, a little boy was born to Mariam, and the queen sent a messenger to the prince.

While on his long journey to find the prince, the messenger grew tired. He saw a house in the woods and asked if he might rest there for the night. As it happened, this was the house of Mariam's parents, but, of course, the messenger did not know this. During the evening he told the old couple about his prince's wife who was so beautiful except that she had no hands. They knew immediately that the princess was their Mariam.

Later in the evening the stepmother and her husband succeeded in getting the messenger drunk so that he slept soundly. Then they looked inside the messenger's cap and found the queen's letter telling the prince that he was the father of a beautiful little boy.

The stepmother wrote another letter in which she made no change except that she substituted the word "puppy" for "son." The next morning the messenger, not knowing of this change, went on his way with the letter to the prince. When the prince received the news, he could not understand it.

Finally he wrote a letter to his mother saying, "Puppy or no puppy, do nothing until I get there." That night when the messenger passed the house in which he had been so well entertained, he decided to stop in to see the old couple. The stepmother could ask for nothing better. She invited him to stay the night, got him drunk once more and removed the letter from his cap. She copied this letter exactly except that instead of saying "Do nothing until I get there," she wrote, "I need neither wife nor child. Kill them both before I return."

When the queen received her son's letter, she could do nothing but obey his command. She had the baby tied to Mariam, and both were left in the mountains to perish. But Moses, by the command of God, went to Mariam and told her to put her wrists in a spring of holy water which he pointed out to her. When Mariam had done this, her hands were returned to her. The baby, who was almost dead because of the severe weather as well as the lack of food, again became well. Angels took them into a cave and supplied them with food and everything else they needed. For seven years Mariam and her son lived in this way. Then, one day the prince returned from the war and asked his mother where his wife was.

"Your wife? Where did you think she would be?" the queen asked her son. "You wrote me that you needed neither wife nor son and to kill them both before your return!"

The prince called the messenger and discovered that he had stopped at a cabin for the night when he took the letter to the prince and that he had stopped there again on his return journey. "Very well then, we must question these people," the prince said, and he ordered that they be brought to him. When the prince learned that they were Mariam's father and stepmother, he had them tied to the tail of a wild jackass and had the jackass driven over rough mountain roads.

One day as the prince was sadly riding through the mountains, he saw a little boy standing outside a cave. When the child saw the stranger, he ran inside. The prince followed him and found the boy clinging to a woman. "What are you doing here, my good woman? Why did this little boy run inside when he saw me?"

"The child has not seen any human being except me since we came here soon after his birth," the woman said.

"Why are you here?" the prince asked.

So Mariam told him her story, and the prince was convinced that he had found his wife and his young son. He straightaway took them from the cave to his palace, and there they lived happily ever after.

33. Yeghnig Aghpar (Stag Brother)

There was once a widower who had a son and a daughter. When he married a second time, his new wife bore him another daughter. However, this woman did not like her stepchildren and treated them cruelly.

This story was told by Mrs. Mariam Serabian.
See Comparative Studies for other versions.

One day the father, who was a farmer, was getting ready to plant corn. He prepared the ground for the grain and with great care planted it in neat rows. He waited and waited, but the corn did not grow. He planted some more and waited again, but nothing grew. "Wife, there is something wrong here. All our neighbors' crops grow, and they work only half as hard as I do," he said to his wife. Little did he dream that she had purposely ground the corn so that it would not sprout.

"I know what prevents your corn from growing," she said.

"If you do, tell me!"

"Your children are evil, and as long as they are in this house, your corn will not grow. Get rid of them and you will have a good crop."

"Nonsense," the father said, "what do my innocent children have to do with my corn crop?" And they left it at that.

Now the second wife's daughter was a very lazy and selfish girl. She would not work, and so Hripega,* the first wife's daughter, had to do the work of both girls.

One day when Hripega had gone to the well, she saw an old woman sitting there, gazing into the water. "Good morning, mother, what are you doing here by yourself?" Hripega—who was always respectful of her elders—asked the woman.

"Come, sweet child, see what is hurting my head so much," the old woman said.

"Oh, what beautiful hair you have. It is just like threads of gold," Hripega said as she picked the lice out of the woman's hair. The child was so innocent that she didn't see anything unpleasant about lice and baldness.

The old woman, sensing the sincerity of Hripega, said, "My child, my eyes are weak. I want you to look into this water, and soon three colors will appear to you. Let the black and white waters pass, but when the gold comes, let me know immediately."

Hripega watched the colors, and when she saw the gold water appear, she told the old woman who picked her up quickly and plunged her in. When she pulled Hripega out, the girl's hair had changed from its original color to gold. Hripega, however, was unaware of the change.

When the water cleared, Hripega dipped her bucket in it and started for home, afraid of what her stepmother had in store for her for being so late. The stepmother, who was standing at

* Name of the informant's daughter and a member of the storytelling audience.

256

the door waiting for her, asked, "Where have you been all this time?" But before the girl could answer, she exclaimed, "What has happened to your hair!"

When Hripega began to cry in fright, the stepmother changed her tone and tried other ways. "Come, Hripega, don't cry. I will not hurt you. Now tell me, what did you do after you left here to get the water?"

Hripega told her all about the meeting with the old woman. After the stepmother had learned all the details of this meeting, she sent Hripega to bed and called her daughter and tried to make her listen.

"Sweet child, child of my soul, listen to what I have to say, and you will never be sorry. You will be beautiful; you will have hair of gold. Tomorrow morning very early I will send you to the well where you will see an old woman. Be nice to her. Imitate Hripega!" The girl grumbled, but the mother continued, "Tell her how pretty her hair is and act happy to be near her. Do this, and you will be very happy."

So the next morning the lazy girl went to the well. "Good morning, grandma, what are you doing up so early? People your age should stay in bed," she said, letting her sharp tongue run off.

Now every woman, no matter how old she may be, does not like to be called old by others. The old woman was annoyed but decided to give the girl a chance to redeem herself. "My child, come comb my hair for me, and we'll see if that helps to stop my headache," the woman said.

The girl, remembering her mother's words, took the comb in her hand and started to comb the woman's hair. "Oh! Grandma, what a mess of lice you have in your hair, and bald spots, too! I don't want my fingers to touch your scalp!" she cried.

The old woman said to herself, "This won't do; first, she reminds me of my age which I am trying to forget, and second, she reminds me that my hair is full of lice and that I am going bald. No, this will never do. I will take care of her." Then aloud she said, "Sweet child, my eyes are weak, and I cannot detect the different colors in the water, but I want you to watch for me. Soon you will see three colors, white, gold and black. Let the white and gold waters go by, but when you see the black water, let me know immediately."

She watched and when the black water appeared, she poked the old woman who plunged her deep into the water and held her there for a long time. When the old woman pulled her out, she looked altogether different. Was she like Hripega? Oh, no, not like Hripega! If you listen very carefully, I will tell you just what happened to this selfish girl. When she got out of the water, her skin was very dark, and her hair was coarse in some spots and fine in others, light in some spots and dark in others. And that is not all. She had, growing right in the middle of her forehead, a soft white horn! The girl felt that there was something heavy on her forehead, but she thought that it was the weight of the gold. So she filled her bucket with clear water and started back.

When the girl arrived home, her mother was waiting at the door and ran toward her, expecting to see a very beautiful creature. But what did she see! "Oh, child, what has happened to you? What is that on your forehead?" the frantic mother asked. "Oh, what have they done to you! How am I ever going to find a husband for you now? What is that thing on your forehead? What is the matter with your hair? Who did this to you, tell me, who did this to you?" the poor woman cried, suspecting that her daughter's sharp tongue had brought her this misfortune. She quickly put the girl to bed and slept a troubled night thinking of a way to punish Hripega as well as to get rid of her daughter's horn.

The next morning when the woman saw the beautiful Hripega cheerfully pursuing her tasks, she became more determined than ever to get rid of her. As we said earlier, this was the corn season, and the crop of Hripega's father was a wretched failure. We know that this was due to his wife's grinding the corn before he planted it. Now, his wife was so very angry that she began grinding the corn even finer than before.

"We will starve this winter, wife. Our corn crop is not even producing weeds," the poor farmer said one day.

"Well, you can easily fix that. Get rid of Hripega and her brother and you will see how good a crop you will have." She continued saying this every day until finally the father was unable to resist and decided to get rid of his children. "Come, children, we are going to the woods to have a picnic today," he told them. And the children, delighted at the thought of the picnic with their father, went with him innocently.

When they were in the heart of the forest, the father seated them under a huge tree and exclaimed, "Children, what a fool I am! I have brought you on a picnic, but I have left the food at home. Now I must go home and bring it here or we will be hungry. I will hang this big pumpkin on the tree, and if I am late, hit it with this stick. As soon as I hear the sound, I will hurry back to you." Saying this, he left his children, with no intention of ever returning to them.

"Well, did you have enough courage to do it?" his wife said when he reached home.

"Yes, I did it. Perhaps it is better for them if the animals devour them," he said.

Meanwhile, Hripega and her brother waited under the tree for their father. Many hours passed, but he did not return. The children became very hungry and frightened. They beat on the pumpkin as their father had told them to do.

All the animals of the forest gathered around the children. But instead of eating them, as their stepmother had hoped they would do, they began to cry for them, so great was their pity. Hripega and her brother stayed on the spot for three days, waiting for the return of their father. Finally, when they were convinced that he was lost, they started out to find him.

The brother became very thirsty, and seeing a little stream, he ran toward it; but Hripega caught up with him and begged him not to drink. "Don't drink from that stream," Hripega said, almost in tears. "That is where the donkeys drink. If you drink here, you, too, will become a donkey." The brother, seeing the distress of his sister, did not drink the water.

On they went, deeper into the forest. When they came across another tiny stream, the brother again wanted to drink. "Brother, if you have any love for me, don't drink from that water. If you do, you will become a calf," Hripega said. The brother, again overwhelmed by his sister's pleadings, did not drink the water.

So they continued walking into the forest. Soon they saw another small stream, and this time the brother fell on his hands and knees before it. "Oh, brother, brother, don't drink that water or you will become a stag," Hripega said.

"Hripega, I cannot endure this thirst any longer. If I don't drink, I will die of thirst. If I drink, I will become a stag. Would you rather that I be dead than to be a stag?" he asked.

Hripega, seeing that there was nothing she could do, began weeping. The brother drank the water, and his form changed into that of a graceful little stag. Hripega clasped his neck and began weeping. "Don't cry, Hripega, don't cry! It is better this way; now I can find food for both of us, and when I was a boy, I couldn't."

The two continued walking until they came to a large stream.

On the shore there was a huge tree. The boy told Hripega to climb the tree while he went in search of food, and not to come down until his return. Hripega climbed the tree and sat on a branch waiting for her brother. He returned shortly with food for both of them. Hripega spent the night in the tree while her brother kept watch from below.

The next day they did the same thing. "Hripega, don't come down the tree for anyone but me," the stag said when he left. But, for one reason or another, he was late in returning. It became dark, and Hripega was frightened, sitting in the tree all by herself, wondering where her brother had gone. Suddenly she saw two figures approaching her. As they came closer, she saw that one was a white colt and the other, a youth of fourteen or fifteen. They stopped right under the tree, and the boy pushed the horse into the stream. "We've had a hard day today; here, take a nice long drink. I wonder where that stag could have gone; he vanished before our very eyes," the young man said.

The horse started greedily for the water but suddenly drew back.

"What's the matter? Come, take a nice long drink," the young man said, urging his horse into the stream.

But the horse drew back again. The young man forced him in a third time, and again he drew back. "Something is wrong here. Why should my tired horse draw back from a stream of water three times? Perhaps the water is dirty. I'll take a look," the young man said. He bent over into the stream and behold! What do you think he saw? A beautiful golden-haired goddess looking at him through the waves!

"How did she get there? She can't possibly be on the water or beneath it. She must be above the surface of the water," the youth said to himself, looking above him. And there was his goddess! Sitting among the branches of the tree was Hripega, crying softly to herself because she thought that her brother had been harmed. "You, up there, what are you doing?" he asked.

Hripega didn't answer but kept on crying.

"What's the matter, why don't you answer me? What is so beautiful a creature doing in these woods?" the young man asked.

No reply from Hripega.

"Dear one, are you crying? Don't cry, I won't hurt you. Come down from the tree; you may slip and fall from your branch. Come down, and I will take you home with me," he said.

Meanwhile, the stag brother had returned and was quietly witnessing this scene.

"I am the prince of all Armenia, and I want to marry you. You are so beautiful that you can say to the sun, 'Sun, go away, I will shine upon the world today.' Come, tell me, what is your name?"

"My name is Hripega, and I won't come down, and neither will I marry you."

The unhappy prince finally decided that no amount of pleading would convince her. So the next day he sought and found an old witch. "Now if you listen to what I have to say, you will find it worth your while," he told her. "Right beside this stream there is a huge tree. In that tree there is a beautiful girl. I want to get her out of the tree and take her home with me, but she is very stubborn and will not come down. You are an old woman, and she will trust you. Here is what you are to do." And he told her his plan. The old woman nodded that she understood the plan, knowing, too, that she would be well paid for her work.

The next morning the witch took a large bowl full of juicy raisins and sat beneath the tree where Hripega was hiding. She threw the raisins into the river and kept only the stems. After some time she heard a sweet childish voice from above: "Mother, what are you doing? Why don't you keep the raisins and throw away the stems?"

"How can I do that? I don't understand," the old woman innocently replied.

"Just keep the raisins in the dish instead of the stems," Hripega directed.

"Won't you show me what you mean?" the woman asked.

Hripega, seeing the helplessness of the old woman, swiftly came down the tree. "See, like this." But she saw a terrible look on the wrinkled old face, and realizing that this was a trick, she quickly climbed the tree again.

The old woman had been unsuccessful. The prince was more than discouraged and more determined than ever to marry the beautiful golden-haired girl.

"We can never capture her this way. I'll have the tree cut down!" he said. That day he found four or five strong men and ordered them to cut down the big tree.

So the next morning the men began cutting the tree. The brother did not know that his sister was in trouble. But Hripega, seeing her danger, began crying and praying that her brother,

Yeghnig Aghpar, would come back so that she might see him before she died. God permitted the stag brother to hear her plea. Swiftly he returned and saw the crew of men cutting down the tree in which his sister was taking refuge. When he saw that the tree was almost ready to fall, he began to pray, "Oh, dear God, send us either a terrible rain or a terrible storm so that these men will have to stop working."

Thereupon a fearful storm arose and everyone left his work with the tree still standing. After the woodchoppers had gone, Yeghnig Aghpar licked and licked the bark of the tree until it grew together again and was even thicker than it had been before it was cut.

The next morning when the men came to work, they were astonished by the miracle. "Say, didn't we have this tree nearly cut down yesterday?" one said to the other. But there, in front of their very eyes, was the tree with not a scar on it! "It's a miracle, nothing less!" When they told the prince what had happened, he was very much disappointed. "Well, then, since God will not have us cut the tree down, there is only one thing that I can do. I must persuade her to come down of her own will," the prince said.

He pleaded with her and promised many gifts. When she continued to refuse him, he asked, "Why do you refuse to marry me? Am I not handsome enough? Am I not rich enough? Am I not humble enough?"

"I will not marry you because you would kill my brother."

"Why should I kill the brother of the one I love?"

"My brother is a stag, and if I marry you, you will kill him, not wishing to have a stag for a brother-in-law." When the prince asked her how this was possible, Hripega told her story from the very start to the end. The prince then promised that he would never harm her brother. Finally convinced, Hripega came down the tree, and she and Yeghnig Aghpar went with the prince to his palace. Everyone there liked Hripega and took good care of her, and the prince kept his promise to her and treated Yeghnig Aghpar as he would his real brother.

When Hripega was old enough, the prince made her his wife. The news of the marriage and the story of the beautiful bride with the golden hair were heard everywhere. They spoke, too, of the little stag who was her brother.

When Hripega's stepmother heard the news, she became convinced that the bride was her stepdaughter. When her husband came in from work that night, she told him the news and said that she planned to go to the palace to visit her daughter.

The next day she put on her best clothes and went to the palace of the prince. "I want to see the princess," she told the guard. "I am her mother." Forgetting the many unpleasant things which her stepmother had done to her, Hripega wished to see the woman, too.

When the stepmother came into the room, she fell on Hripega's neck and began to weep. "Oh, my beautiful child! Where have you been all these years, why didn't you let me know where you were?" Hripega, in her innocence, began weeping too. She asked about her father and told her stepmother how her brother drank the water in the forest and became a stag.

From that time on, the stepmother frequently visited the palace, until one day she learned that Hripega was to have a child. "Now is the time to take revenge," the evil woman said to herself. So she told the prince: "Dear son, my daughter's confinement is almost at hand. Let me take her home, to the familiar scenes of her childhood. She will return to the palace with renewed strength and will bear your son with greater ease." The prince, completely deceived by the stepmother, consented to the visit. And so the stepmother took Hripega home.

The day after their arrival when the stepmother was giving Hripega a bath by the river, she saw to it that the strong soap got into her eyes and mouth. When she looked around and saw that they were alone, she shoved the princess into the water.

Hripega, being in a clumsy condition and having soap in her eyes and her mouth, was quite helpless. A whale which was nearby when the incident occurred, opened his huge mouth and swallowed the princess.

The next day the prince sent for his wife. The stepmother, who had anticipated this, dressed her own ugly daughter in Hripega's clothes and gave her full instructions about what to do. "Don't talk until you are spoken to, and when you do talk, disguise your voice so it sounds like Hripega's. Never get out of bed, and keep moaning. Always wear a thick veil so that the prince cannot see your face. Try to get rid of Yeghnig Aghpar as soon as you can. Don't eat, because if you do, you will have to lift your veil and the prince will see your horn. If you remember these things, you will have a husband, and what a husband he is!"

When the ugly daughter arrived at the palace, she immediately went to bed. As soon as the prince was notified of this, he went in to see her. "Hripega, how do you feel? Did you enjoy your visit?" he asked.

The girl turned her face away from the prince and said, "I feel sick; get away from me." The prince, much surprised at the change in her sweet disposition, left her alone. The ugly girl became hungry, but since she could not eat, she started nibbling on the soft horn which grew on her forehead. But the more she handled the horn, the more it grew.

This continued for some time, and the prince could not understand what had happened to his wife. Not only was the princess not eating or talking, but she refused to finish preparations for the birth of the child. The prince, very worried, asked, "Aren't you hungry? You haven't eaten since you returned two days ago!"

"I'm not exactly hungry," the girl said, "but I crave for some of Yeghnig Aghpar's meat."

"Yeghnig Aghpar's meat? You? I thought you loved your brother dearly. How can you ask me to kill him?"

Finally, the prince decided that if this was what she wanted, he would kill the stag. He ordered seven kettles and seven sharp knives to be prepared. When these were ready, he told Yeghnig Aghpar that because Hripega wanted his flesh, he would have to be killed.

"I understand, prince," Yeghnig Aghpar answered. "You have been a faithful brother to me, and you cannot avoid doing this. Before you have those sharp knives in my flesh, however, let me go for a walk, and I promise you that I will return."

The prince consented. Yeghnig Aghpar knew that Hripega was in the whale's stomach and that it was their stepsister who was at the palace, but he could do nothing. However, he went to the waterfront and sang,

> "Sister, sister, sweet sister,
> They are going to kill me, sister,
> They have prepared seven knives, sister,
> They have prepared seven kettles, sister,
> They are going to kill me, sister."

Hripega, in the whale's stomach, heard the heartrending song of her brother and replied,

> "Brother, brother, sweet brother,
> Let the seven knives be dull,
> Let there be holes in the seven kettles.
> I am in the stomach of a whale,

I have borne a son with golden hair
And a golden cane in his hand,
I am in the stomach of a whale."

Yeghnig Aghpar wept bitterly and went back to the palace. And what do you think he saw when he got there! All the seven knives had grown dull, and there were holes in the seven kettles. The palace cooks had to postpone the slaughter until fresh preparations could be made.

The next day when everything was ready and the cooks were about to kill Yeghnig Aghpar, he asked permission to go to the waterfront again. The permission was granted. When he reached there, he sang,

"Sister, sister, sweet sister,
They are going to kill me, sister,
They have prepared seven knives, sister,
They have prepared seven kettles, sister,
They are going to kill me, sister."

Again, Hripega, in the whale's stomach, replied,

"Brother, brother, sweet brother,
Let the seven knives be dull,
Let there be holes in the seven kettles.
I am in the stomach of a whale,
I have borne a son with golden hair
And a golden cane in his hand,
I am in the stomach of a whale."

Yeghnig Aghpar wept bitterly and returned to the palace. And again the seven knives had become dull and the seven kettles had holes in them. Once more the slaughter had to be postponed.

The third day, when everything was again ready, Yeghnig Aghpar asked permission to go for a little walk. The prince granted him permission but was curious to know where the stag had been going these past days. So he decided to follow him. He saw the stag go to the river and call for someone. He could only hear faintly what was said. When Yeghnig Aghpar was ready to return to the palace, the prince stopped him and asked him to whom he had been talking.

"I was talking to my sister."

"Your sister is at the palace, awaiting the birth of my child. How could you be talking to her?"

"My sister is in the water, in the stomach of a whale, and a beautiful son with golden hair and a golden cane in his hand has been born to her," Yeghnig Aghpar answered.

The prince took a gold piece from his pocket and threw it in the water. "Whale! Disgorge what is in your stomach!" the prince commanded.

By the will of God, the whale came to the surface and disgorged Hripega and her son. The prince quickly took off his cloak and wrapped them up in it. Then he took his wife and son to his room and ordered his servants to bathe and clothe them.

The prince went to his supposed wife. "How are you, my dear?"

"Oh, I feel very sick," she wailed while she continued nibbling on her horn, which was her only form of nourishment. "I want Yeghnig Aghpar's meat."

"My poor sweet one, if you are so ill, let me bring your mother to you," the prince said and sent for the mother and father of the pretender. When they arrived, he made their daughter get out of bed, pulled off her veil, and her true identity was revealed. Next he ordered three wild jackasses to be brought, and he had the three wicked people tied to the tails of these animals. Then he commanded his guards to whip the animals and force them to run madly over treacherous mountain trails. All three victims were dashed to bits, the largest pieces of their bodies which were later found being their ears.

Hripega, her son, the prince and Yeghnig Aghpar lived happily ever after.

34. The World Below

Once upon a time there was a king who had three sons. In the garden of his palace this king had a beautiful pomegranate tree which bore only three pomegranates yearly. However, each year, just as the fruit ripened, a seven-headed *dev* [giant] stole all three pomegranates so that neither the king nor his children had ever tasted a single fruit.

One year when the pomegranates were ripening, the eldest prince announced that he would guard the tree that night and present his father with one of the unusual fruits the next morn-

This story was told by Nishan Krikorian.
See Comparative Studies for other versions.

ing. That night, armed with a bow and arrows, the prince went into the garden, hid himself near a tree and waited. Toward midnight the *dev* came into the garden like a whirlwind, snatched a pomegranate and left. The prince, who was hidden, was so terrified at the sight of the giant that all he could do was to lie flat, face to the ground, to escape the *dev's* attention. Of course, there was no pomegranate for the king the next morning.

The second son promised to guard the tree next. But when the *dev* appeared, picked a pomegranate and left, the young boy was too frightened to do anything. So the king was unable to taste his unusual fruit the second morning.

The youngest prince decided that it was his turn to guard the tree. That night he took his bow and arrows, a knife and some salt and went into the garden. He hid himself and waited. When he became sleepy, he cut his finger with the knife and sprinkled salt on the wound. The sting was so sharp that he forgot all thoughts of sleep.

When the *dev* appeared, the boy was not frightened; he was alert and ready to shoot. Just as the *dev* reached for the third pomegranate, the boy let his arrow fly, aiming at the thief's throat. The *dev*, terrified and wounded, left everything behind and made his escape. The brave prince noticed that the *dev* was leaving a trail of blood and knew that it would be an easy matter to follow him. Putting the pomegranate in his pocket, he went to sleep. In the morning he presented the fruit to his father.

"Brothers, I wounded the *dev* last night," the young prince said, "and in his escape, he left a trail of blood. If we follow that trail, we will surely find him."

Much against their will the two brothers joined the third in his search for the wounded thief. They walked for one day, two days, and finally came to a well where the trail of blood ended. They knew that the *dev* was in the deep well.

"I will go down and kill him," the eldest prince said. But as he went down a short way, he began screaming, "Oh, I'm burning! I'm burning! Pull me up! Pull me up!"

So they brought the first brother up, and the second brother made the descent. He had gone down just a little farther when he, too, began screaming, "Oh, pull me up! Pull me up! I'm burning!"

So the second brother was brought up, and the third boy prepared to descend. "The more I say that I'm burning, the farther down you must drop me." Finally he reached the bottom of the well and opening a door, found a beautiful girl.

"Human being, what are you doing here?" the surprised girl asked. The boy explained his mission and said, "You will be my eldest brother's fiancée." He explored further and in a second room found a second girl. To her he said, "You will be my second brother's fiancée." Opening a third door, he found a third girl, the most beautiful of the three, and told her, "You are mine!"

"What are you doing here?" she asked him. "If the *dev* sees you, he will eat you."

"Where is the *dev?*"

"He is wounded and is lying down," the girl said.

The boy found the giant and struck another blow.

"Courageous boy, hit me once again," the giant begged.

"I was born from my mother only once: I will strike you only once," the prince said, knowing that additional blows would renew the *dev's* life.

First, the boy sent the first girl to the upper world, then the second. When it was time to send up his own fiancée, she refused to go before him. When the boy became suspicious of her motives, she said, "If I go up before you do, your brothers will not bring you up. They will cut the rope and will let you stay down here forever."

The boy refused to believe her and insisted that she leave first. "If you find that your brothers do cut the rope and leave you behind, look around," she said. "You will see a golden dish upon which a dog chases a rabbit yet never catches it, a walnut containing a pair of my slippers and a walnut containing my beautiful gown. Carry these with you always. Every Friday you will find two rams playing at the end of the cave. Try to mount the white one. If you get on the black one, however, you will go to the bottom of the earth."

When the brothers saw the third girl, they were jealous because she was so beautiful. They decided not to pull their brother up so that they could keep this lovely girl for their own. They lowered the rope, and the youngest brother tied it to his waist, but midway up the well, the rope was cut and the boy fell down again. "Ah! she was right. They have tricked me," the prince said sadly. He looked around and saw the dish and the two unusual walnuts. He tucked them under his shirt as the girl had advised. He waited until Friday and tried to mount the white ram, but as luck would have it, he got on the black one which took him to the world below.

The boy walked and walked and becoming tired, fell asleep under a big tree. He was sleeping soundly when the chirping of birds awakened him. He looked up and saw a big snake climbing the tree, so he took out his bow and arrow and killed the snake. Then he went back to sleep again.

These birds, known as Zumroot Kooshey [Turkish: green bird], were not ordinary birds. When the mother came home not long after, she saw the boy sleeping under the tree. "Ah! I have at last found my enemy! For a hundred years I have been having children, and they have all been eaten; this man has done it!" she said, sweeping down toward the prince.

But the little birds spoke to their mother and told her of the boy's deed. She opened her big wings to shade the place so that the boy could sleep a little longer. Finally the prince awoke and found the huge bird above him.

"You have done me a big favor," said the bird. "Ask for your reward."

"I want your happiness," the prince said.

When the great bird asked the question three times, the boy answered her, "I want to go to the world above."

"Akh! [Alas!] You should have come to me in my youth," she said. "But let me see what I can do. Can you bring me forty deegs [measures] of wine and forty whole oxen?"

"I don't know if I can."

"If you bring me the meat and wine, I will take you to the world above," the bird said.

The boy left the bird and her childen and walked along and finally came to a town. Since he was very thirsty, he went to a door and asked the old woman for a drink of water. Even though he repeated his request a number of times, the woman told him that she had no water. Finally, she said, "I'll get you some water." She put some of her own urine in a cup and brought it to the boy. The boy then knew that there was some strange explanation for the old woman's action and decided to discover it. He asked for shelter, and that night he questioned the old woman.

"In this town there is no water," she told him.

"What kind of town is it that has no water?"

"We have a big stream, but there is a snake who enters the water each day. He demands a girl for his supper and says that he will cut off the supply of water if he is denied her. All the girls of the town have been sacrificed, and only the princess is left. And the snake is to eat her tomorrow," the old woman said.

The next day the boy hid himself and watched carefully when the princess was thrown into the water. When the snake approached, the boy aimed his arrow and killed him. The princess immediately dipped her hand in the snake's blood and pressed it on the boy's back, without his knowledge.

The princess returned to her father and said, "Tell our people not to store any more water. The snake has been killed."

In his attempt to reward the unknown hero, the king ordered all the men in his kingdom to appear at the palace. But the princess looked at each of them and could not find her savior. The king then ordered that if any of his subjects knew of a man who had not appeared at the palace, he should report it.

Someone remembered that a boy was staying at the old woman's house at the edge of town, so the boy was summoned to appear at the palace. Although the prince was wearing a sheep-skin cap, the princess recognized him and let the apple she was holding fall on him. The king was happy to find the hero. "You have done this town a great service. We have been without water for many years, and our young girls are all gone. Ask for a reward, and it will be yours."

"My reward is your happiness," the prince replied.

The king repeated his question three times, but three times the prince gave him the same answer. Finally, the prince said, "My only wish is to get to the world above. If you can give me forty whole oxen and forty *deegs* of wine, I can accomplish this."

"If that is all, that is nothing," the king said, ordering the required items to be prepared immediately. So the boy took the meat and wine to the eagle.

"Tie the wine to one of my wings and the meat on the other and sit on my back. When I flap my right wing, put wine into my mouth. When I flap my left wing, put meat into my mouth. I must get nourishment until I reach the earth," the eagle told the boy.

So they started on their journey. Each time the eagle flapped her right wing, the prince put wine into her mouth and each time she flapped her left wing, he put meat into her mouth. This continued until they were almost to earth, and the bird flapped her left wing. The prince saw that there was no meat left, so he cut off part of his thigh and put it into the bird's mouth. The bird immediately noticed the difference in taste and, instead of swallowing the meat, kept it under her tongue.

When they were safely on the ground, the eagle said, "My son, get up now and walk."

"No, you start back; I'll rest for a moment."

But when the bird insisted and the boy started up, his thigh pained him so much that he could not walk. "Here, my son, I knew that you had cut off part of your thigh," the eagle said, licking the boy's thigh and putting the piece of flesh into place. Then she flew away, leaving him alone.

Wearing his sheepskin cap, the boy walked into town. He went to a goldsmith's shop and asked for work. The man felt sorry for the ugly boy and took him in, giving him a crust of bread and a place to sleep.

Meanwhile, the eldest prince wanted to marry the third girl. But the beauty insisted that she would marry the prince only if he could produce a golden dish upon which a dog chased a rabbit. The prince called the goldsmith to him and said, "Smith, I'll give you forty days' time to make me such a dish. If you fail, you will lose your head."

When the smith returned from the palace, he was sad and worried. The boy asked his master why he was so sad. "If I don't worry, who should worry?" the smith answered. "The prince has ordered that I make a golden dish on which a dog is chasing a rabbit. Is such a thing possible? And if I don't succeed in forty days' time, I will have my head cut off!"

"Is that all? Don't worry! Just get me a sack of pistachios and a sack of hazelnuts, and I'll get the dish ready for you," the boy said. So day in and day out, night after night, the boy ate the nuts, sang and ate more nuts.

"Here, my time is almost up, and that fool is in there singing and eating nuts," the smith said to himself, sure that the dumb-looking boy could never accomplish this most difficult task. Finally, at the end of the week the boy opened the door and gave the unusual dish to his master.

When the girl saw the dish, she smiled because she knew that the youngest prince was alive and well. Now she said to the prince who wanted to marry her, "I want you to get me a pair of slippers which will fit into a walnut shell."

Meanwhile, the boy left the goldsmith and found work at the bootmaker. "If I clean and tidy your shop, will you give me a place to sleep?" he asked. The bootmaker agreed to this, feeling sorry for the ugly youth.

One day the bootmaker returned home very sad. "What is the matter? Why are you so sad?" the boy asked his master.

"If I am not sad, if I don't worry, who should worry?" the bootmaker said. The prince has ordered that I make a pair of slippers which will fit into a walnut shell. Is such a thing possible? And I have only forty days' time to do this, or I will lose my head."

When the master had told his *kal oglan* [bald-head] what the prince had demanded, the boy said, "Don't worry, just bring me a sack of pistachios and a sack of hazelnuts. I will have the walnut for you in a week."

The master supplied the youth with the pistachios and hazelnuts and the boy locked himself up and started to eat. He did this day in and day out, night in and night out. Meanwhile, the bootmaker was listening outside the door, anxious about his head. "Here it is almost the end of forty days, and that fool is in there singing and eating nuts."

Finally, the boy opened the door at the end of his promised time and handed the walnut containing the shoes to his master. The bootmaker was happy, grateful that his life had been spared. When the prince gave the walnut to the girl, she was happy. "Now, I want you get me a gown that will fit within a walnut," she said. So the prince called his tailor and gave his instructions and warned that unless the gown was ready within forty days, the man would lose his head.

Meanwhile, the boy left the bootmaker and went to the tailor shop, looking for work. He said to the royal tailor, "If I clean and tidy your shop, will you give me a place to sleep?" The tailor agreed to this, feeling sorry for the ugly youth.

One day the tailor returned to the shop, sad and worried. "What is the matter? Why are you so worried?" the boy asked his master.

"If I don't worry, who should worry?" the tailor said. "The prince has ordered that I make a gown that will fit into a walnut shell. Is such a thing possible? And if I don't succeed in this within forty days, I'll have my head cut off."

"Oh, is that all?" the boy asked. "Don't worry! Just get me a sack of hazelnuts and a sack of pistachios, and I'll get the gown ready for you within a week's time." So the tailor brought him the nuts, and the boy locked himself in a room, ate nuts and sang day after day, night after night. The tailor, who was listening outside the door, was very angry. "Here it is almost the end of my time, and that fool is in there singing and eating nuts."

Finally, at the end of the week the boy opened the door and gave the walnut to his master. The tailor was very happy because his life was spared.

When the prince gave the walnut containing the dress to the third girl, she said, "I want to see the person who made these unusual things."

So the prince called the goldsmith, the bootmaker and the tailor to the palace. "Who made the things which I required of you?"

Each said that a strange young man, wearing a sheepskin cap, had made the required articles.

The prince ordered, "Find the boy or you will lose your heads!" The three men looked and found the poor boy in the sheepskin cap and took him to the palace.

When the girl saw him, she immediately recognized him. "Do you know who this is?" she asked the king. "This is your youngest son, the third prince. He is my fiancé." Then she told the story of the treachery of the two older brothers.

The king was very unhappy to hear this story and was ready to punish his two older sons. But the third prince said, "We are brothers. Let us forget what has happened." And this is what they did.

The third prince and the beautiful girl were married and celebrated a wedding for forty days and forty nights. They reached their purpose, and may we reach ours. From the sky fell three apples: one to me, one to the storyteller and one to the person who has entertained you.

35. The Son of the Gray Horse

Welcome. From the sky fell three apples: one to the storyteller and two to the listeners. Here is my story:

At one time there was a king whose name was Kramat. He was a rich king and had forty herds of cattle and sheep. Every year he hired people to graze these herds and look after them for a whole year, and then bring them back to his palace.

Now this king had a very beautiful daughter. He said to her,

This story was told by Kasar Bogosian.

"Daughter, you are so beautiful, I cannot find a suitable husband for you. Go out into the world, and find someone you want to marry and return with him to my palace." So the maiden left the palace and traveled throughout the world. But not finding a man whom she wanted to marry, she returned home and told her father of her poor luck.

"Well, daughter, since you don't have a husband, I fear that you will become sad and moody. I am going to give you forty beautiful girls to keep you company and to make you happy," the king said. And this he did.

But the princess was discontented for she had no work to do. One day at the end of the year, she said to her father, "Father, it is a pity to waste all this money on servants when they don't do anything. Let me and my companions go to the mountains and take care of your sheep this year."

"But, daughter," the king protested, "remember that you are my daughter and a beautiful princess who is old enough to be married. It is not safe for you to do what you want to do, and it is a great disgrace for me to have my daughter do such work."

But as the princess insisted, the king decided that perhaps it was best to let her do as she wished. He proclaimed throughout his country that no man could go near the mountain where his daughter and her forty women lived. Then he said to his daughter, "Remember, no man must see your face while you and your women are serving as shepherds."

The princess and her companions took food and drink and, driving the forty herds ahead of them, climbed the mountain to remain there for a whole year. For some time the women were happy, but one day the princess became very ill and cried in misery. Days passed, yet she did not get better. She became pale and thin, yet there were no healers or wise men to help her. No one knew what was troubling her.

One of the servants, a crippled woman, said to the princess, "Your Highness, you are very sick, and if you remain like this, you will undoubtedly die. I am just an ignorant woman, but let me try what I have in mind. If you die, you die. But perhaps you will live."

The princess nodded her head, so the crippled woman went among the horses and said to some of the women who were with her, "Whichever horse urinates first, let me know quickly." The women watched, and when they saw a gray horse beginning to urinate, they quickly told her. She ran to the horse, collected the urine in a jug and made the princess drink it. And in a short time the princess became well again.

The women were happy once more, but several months later they saw that their princess was pregnant. They were all puzzled. The princess herself was puzzled. What were they to do? What could they say to the king?

Finally the women decided to go back to the palace and tell the king that his daughter was pregnant. When he heard the news, the ruler became very angry and wanted to know which man had dishonored his daughter. The women told him that they had not even seen a man's face during their stay in the mountains. "There was no man at all," the crippled servant said, "but our princess became very sick in the mountains, and I had her drink the urine of a gray horse. Perhaps this has caused her to conceive."

"Do you mean that my daughter has married a horse?" the king asked, astonished. The crippled woman nodded her head. "Very well, then," the king said, "we will wait until the child is born. If it has any characteristics of the horse, then we will believe what you have said. But if it is a normal child, then the princess, her women, and their families and friends will be slaughtered!"

So the people waited. When the little boy was born with ears slightly longer than human ears, the king said, "Yes, his father is a horse; see his ears—they are horse's ears!"

The women were safe, and so were their families and friends. The little boy was known as Son of the Gray Horse. Instead of growing from day to day, he grew from minute to minute. He was a very brave and strong boy. When he was old enough, his grandfather, the king, sent him to school to learn how to read and write. On his way home one day he became angry at another boy and grabbed him by his arm. And off fell the arm! He hit another boy, and the boy died.

The people began to hear of the great strength of Son of the Gray Horse and became frightened. "Someday he will kill all our children," they thought. As the years went by, the boy grew stronger and stronger. Finally the people went to the king's palace and said, "Our King, you must either get rid of your grandson, or we will all leave your country and live somewhere else. Our children are dying right and left because of him."

The king thought for a while, then answered, "You stay, my people; I will get rid of my grandson." So he called Son of the

Gray Horse and told him to leave the country and never return. The boy sat on Gray Horse, who was his father, and left the country.

Gray Horse took him to a high mountain where he saw a middle-sized man lifting huge rocks. The boy was amazed and asked, "How can you, a little man, lift such huge rocks?"

"Oh, this is nothing," the rock-lifter said, "I have heard of a youth whose name is Son of the Gray Horse, and his strength is truly amazing."

"I am Son of the Gray Horse."

"Wherever you are going, let me join you."

"Come along," the boy said, and the two started out. They climbed to the top of a mountain where they saw trees all around them. There they saw a middle-sized man cut down the thickest, heaviest, tallest tree with one stroke.

The boy was surprised at the man's power and said, "Man, your strength is amazing!"

"Oh, this is nothing," the tree-cutter said. "I have heard of a youth whose name is Son of the Gray Horse, and his strength is truly great."

"Man, this is he," the rock-lifter told the tree-cutter. And the tree-cutter, impressed with the youth, asked to go along with him.

"Come along," Son of the Gray Horse said, and the three climbed to the very highest peak of the mountain where they saw a beautiful palace. They entered it but found no one inside. The boy said, "The people who live here must have seen us coming and, being frightened of our looks, left their things and ran away. So this palace is ours now, and we will live here."

"Let one of us stay here one day while the other two go hunting. The next day the second one will stay, and the other two will go hunting. The third day the third one will stay, and the other two will go hunting. The one who stays home each day will cook, wash and clean the house," the tree-cutter said. And the others agreed to this plan.

The next day the tree-cutter and the boy went hunting, and the rock-lifter stayed home, cleaned the house, made the supper and waited for his friends to return. Suddenly there appeared before him a little man eighteen inches, or a span and a half, high. He had a long beard which touched the floor. He sat down at the table and said to the rock-lifter, "Friend, I am hungry; won't you give me something to eat?"

The rock-lifter looked at the little man and said to himself, "Why not? He probably can't even eat a spoonful." So he gave a spoonful of the food to the little man. The little man ate it quickly and said, "Is that all I get?"

The rock-lifter said, "Yes, the rest will hardly be enough for us."

The little man became angry and began to grow taller and taller until he finally reached the ceiling. Then he hit the rock-lifter squarely on the head, and the strong man fell to the floor. Thereupon the tall man became small again, ate all the food and left.

Soon the tree-cutter and the boy returned to see their friend on the floor and their supper missing. They helped the rock-lifter to his feet and asked him what had happened. He told them about the little man with the long beard. "Ho! Ho!" the friends laughed, "that is impossible!"

The next day the tree-cutter stayed at the palace while the rock-lifter and the youth went hunting. The tree-cutter cleaned the house, made the supper and sat down to wait for his friends. Soon the little man with the long beard appeared and asked for food. The tree-cutter gave him a spoonful. The little man quickly ate it and said, "I want more! I have not had enough!"

"But I can give you no more," the tree-cutter said. "This will hardly be enough for the three of us."

The little man became angry and grew taller and taller until he reached the ceiling. Then he hit the tree-cutter on the head, sat down at the table and ate the food.

When the rock-lifter and the boy returned to the palace, they saw their friend on the floor. They helped him to sit up and asked him what had happened. The tree-cutter told about the little man, and the rock-lifter nodded his head, "Just as I said! Just as I said!"

The next morning the tree-cutter and the rock-lifter went hunting while the boy stayed behind. He cleaned the house, made the supper and sat down to wait for his friends. Soon the little man with the long beard entered and said, "I am hungry. Will you give me a little of your supper?"

The boy gave him a spoonful of the food, but the man was not satisfied. "I am still hungry. Give me more!"

The boy said, "I can give you no more because the rest will hardly be enough for my friends and me." When he heard this, the little man became angry and grew taller and taller; but the boy did not become frightened. Instead, he took hold of the man's beard and shook him so hard that he crushed him and there remained only his bones. The boy put these into a handkerchief and placed the handkerchief on the windowsill. When his friends returned home, they were surprised to see the boy well and happy. They asked about the little man, and the boy said, "He came, and I killed him. Here are his bones!" showing the bundle of bones on the windowsill. His friends praised the boy's bravery and decided to bury the bones the following morning.

But the next morning the bones were missing. So the boy decided to stay home that day, too, to see if the little man would come again. After he cleaned the house and made supper, he sat waiting for his friends. Soon the little man appeared and asked for some of the food which the boy had cooked.

The boy gave him a spoonful, but the little man was not satisfied and asked for more. When the boy refused to give him more food, the little man grew taller and taller. Again the boy reached up to grab his beard, but instead of holding to it, he found himself with only two hairs in his hand. The little man ran out of the palace, and the boy ran right after him until he saw the little man enter a deep, rocky cavern in the mountains. The boy quickly blocked the entrance with rocks and sat on them so that the little man could not get out. When the boy saw his friends returning home, he called to them. The rock-lifter threw heavy rocks into the cavern, and the tree-cutter laid trees over it. Surely the man would not be able to get out again. "Tomorrow morning I will go down there and finish him," the boy said to his companions.

So the next morning the friends tied a rope around his waist and let the boy down into the cavern. When he saw a door, he opened it and found himself in a room where he saw the little man kissing first one, then another of three beautiful girls. The boy became angry and called to the man with the long beard to stop. When the little man saw the boy, he cried, "Who are you to enter my house! For this, you shall die!" The little man began to grow taller and taller, but the boy quickly grabbed his beard and holding to it, threw the little man about. He finally smashed him so fiercely that only his bones remained. Then he called up to his friends, "I am sending up a beautiful girl for my friend the rock-lifter." He tied the rope around the first girl, and they pulled her up.

In the same manner he sent up the second girl for the tree-cutter and the third girl for himself. The men saw that the third girl was the most beautiful of the three, and they wanted to cut the rope which they had tied around the boy's waist. But fearing the return of the little man with the long beard, they pulled the boy up. They all went to the palace, and the boy put the little man's bones, wrapped in a handkerchief, on the windowsill with the thought that the next morning he would bury them. The next morning, however, the bones had again disappeared.

Before the men went hunting, the little man with the long beard appeared and killed first the rock-lifter, then the tree-cutter. He so seriously injured the boy that he thought the boy would surely die. But since the boy was still alive, the little man ordered the girls to look after him. The girls were happy to do this and took good care of the youth.

When the boy was well, the little man said, "You cannot get rid of me—neither you, nor anyone else. And no one can escape my vengeance, either. But I do admire your courage, and I will free you on one condition: you must bring me Haji [pilgrim to Jerusalem] Zareh's daughter. If you do this, then I will let you go your way."

So early the next morning the boy started out to find the daughter of Haji Zareh. He was tired and hungry when at sunset he saw a lonely hut with smoke arising from the chimney. Thinking that he might find shelter there for the night, he knocked on the door. An old woman opened the door for him. She was so old that she might have been Time herself. "Mother, may I stay here tonight?" the youth asked.

"My son," she said, "I have been here at least two hundred years, and I have never seen a human face. You are the only human being ever to stop here. Come in, come in." The woman gave the boy food and drink and asked, "Tell me, what is your grief? What are you doing in these mountains?"

So the boy told her his story. The old woman listened carefully and finally said, "When you find Haji Zareh's daughter, bring her here before you take her to the little man. If you forget to do this, you will die when you return to his dwelling."

The next morning the boy started out again and went from town to town, from village to village, asking about Haji Zareh. Finally, he reached the town where the Haji lived, but he didn't know this. He went to a well-to-do merchant and asked for work. The merchant told him to dig a deep well in front of his store. So the boy got on his hands and knees and began to dig the ground with his fingernails until he finally found water. The merchant was greatly surprised to see such strength, so he called the boy in and said, "Son, you will work in my store and be my chief assistant. You will live in my house and eat at my table."

That night the merchant and his wife went to their bedroom, and the boy went to his. But about midnight he heard footsteps in the attic above. "Who can be up there? My master and his wife went to sleep in the room across from mine, and these are the only bedrooms in the house. I think I will go up and see." The boy quietly went up to the attic. There he saw that his master, who had been drugged, had a rope tied around his waist and was being carried out of the attic window. The wife and her lover were working together to do this. He went outside and waited for the rope which was slowly being lowered with his master attached on the end of it. When the merchant reached the ground, the boy shook the man to awaken him and told him about his wife and her sweetheart. The merchant asked the boy to kill the wife and throw her into the well which he had dug in front of the store that very day. The boy did so.

The merchant was indebted to the youth and wanted to give him much money, but the boy shook his head and said, "My sorrow is much too great to be settled with money."

"What is your sorrow, youth?" the merchant asked.

"I am looking for the daughter of Haji Zareh," the boy said. "I have looked everywhere for her, but I wonder if she really exists."

"Is that all you want?" the merchant asked. "Haji Zareh is our neighbor, and his daughter goes to the river with her two servants once a week to wash clothes. Next time she goes, I'll show her to you."

The merchant did as he had promised, and the boy went to the river to watch her and discovered that she was indeed beautiful. When she saw the boy, her three-hundred-and-sixty-sixth vein popped, which is to say that she fell in love with him. Possessed of magical powers, she immediately knew what the boy wanted. As her father was an evil spirit who flew through the air, she took out her magic handkerchief and gave it to the boy to cover his head so that her father could not harm him. In this way, they started for the old woman's hut.

The old woman was happy to see them and said to the youth, "Leave this girl here, and I promise to treat her as though she were my own daughter. You listen and do as I say. Go to the top of this mountain where you will find a brook. Every morning at sunrise a red bull goes to this brook to drink. Just as the sun begins to rise, the steam and foam rush forth from the bull's mouth. When he is foaming like this, hit him so that he will fall down. Then cut open his forehead, and you will find a little box. In this box there are three birds. Only when all three of these birds are dead will the little man with the long beard die, but not until then."

So the boy hid himself by the brook and waited for the bull. When the sun rose and the bull began to foam at the mouth, the boy quickly hit him on the head and knocked him down. Then he cut open his forehead and found the little box. First, he killed one bird, and the little man became pale and sick and quickly took to his bed. The three girls who were still with him became happy at this sign.

The boy took the two remaining birds home to the old woman's hut, and the daughter of Haji Zareh killed the second bird. The little man now became very sick. The boy thanked the old woman and with the girl, went to the palace of the little man where he killed the third bird. The little man with the long beard died, but the moment he died, he began to get taller and taller and finally became fourteen feet long. The girls and the boy buried him.

Haji Zareh's daughter loved Son of the Gray Horse, and so did the other three girls. But she knew that she could not marry him for it was not written on his forehead that it should be so. And the three other girls were not to marry him either. So she said to them, "Sisters, as we cannot marry the one who has our hearts, let us leave him." So they parted; the boy went one way, and they went another.

Son of the Gray Horse sat on his horse and started out. He rode for many days and many nights until finally he came to a small, peaceful country. As it happened, the son-in-law of the king was chasing a deer this very same day. When the deer passed the boy, he caught it and would not let it go further. The son-in-law who had been unable to catch the deer, became angry because this reflected on his ability as a hunter. But he soon realized that the boy was no common man, for such strength was rare. He told him, "In this country there are only three homes open for a man such as yourself. You can look for lodging at the

palace, at the home of our chief spy, or at the home of one of
our heroes."

The boy thanked the hunter and rode on. He began to think,
"As I am not a spy, I do not belong in the home of the spy; I am
not a king, therefore, I do not belong in the palace; I belong in
the home of the hero." By asking, he learned where the town's
greatest hero lived and went to that house to seek shelter.

As it happened, this town's greatest hero was the king's
son-in-law, and it was the king's oldest daughter who greeted
the traveler when he asked for shelter. She recognized a man
of quality when she saw one, and she knew that this stranger
was no ordinary man. So when she had made him comfortable,
she sent messengers to her husband to return home immediately. When the son-in-law returned home and saw the youth, he
smiled and asked, "Why did you come here? I am pleased to
have you as my guest and want you to know that you are very
welcome. But tell me what made you decide to come here."

The boy said, "As I am not a spy, I did not want to go to
the spy's house. As I am not a king, I did not want to go to the
king's palace. I am a warrior, a fighter, and so are you. You
are the greatest hero, they tell me. Therefore, I came to your
house."

The son-in-law was pleased and said, "My friend, it is
seldom that we meet men like you. Come, let us be brothers. You
will live here and consider this your home."

Since the boy liked the son-in-law and liked the way he
spoke, he accepted his proposal, and the two became brothers.
But the king's son-in-law, who was also the head of the government and advised the king on all matters, spent most of the day
at the palace. So during the day the youth stayed at home with
the princess and at night welcomed his brother home.

Soon the boy tired of doing nothing all day, and his brother
noticed this. He said one day, "Come brother, come with me to
the palace to see our king so that you can visit him during the
day and will not be lonely." The son-in-law took his brother to the
king who liked the boy and would spend long hours playing
chess with him. But the boy was so cunning that the king always
lost heavily.

Now this king was good, honest and sincere, but he had a
man who always followed him about and gave him evil advice.
This man was the spy of whom the son-in-law had spoken before. The king had a very good fortune-teller who said to the

ruler one day, "Your Majesty, it is wise for you to adopt this boy and make him your own son, for in times of need he will do the work of one million men."

The king was impressed with this and decided to speak to his son-in-law. "What kind of a man is this that you have brought to my palace?"

"My brother is strong and brave, honorable and sincere," the son-in-law said to the king. He told how they had first met, and the king was so impressed that he decided to adopt the boy.

One day as the king and the boy were playing chess in the courtyard, the spy looked up and saw Zabelle, the young princess, intently watching the boy. But since the boy's back was turned toward her, he could not see her. The next day the spy had them change places so that the boy, when he looked up, would see the princess. As it happened, the boy looked up and saw the princess Zabelle watching him. When she saw that he was looking at her, she quickly went inside the palace. He did not know who she was, but from that moment on he could not play a good game. He lost for the first time that afternoon. The king was greatly surprised, but later the spy told him why the boy had lost.

The king became angry and gave orders that the boy be hanged. The boy did not complain or cry. When the son-in-law heard of these plans, he ran to the king and threatened to burn down the palace if one hair of the boy's head was touched. So the king began to laugh. "Ho! Ho! I did not really want to kill him. I wanted to test his bravery. I wanted to see if he would beg for his life. Now I know that he is truly brave, and I am not sorry that I have made him my son."

The boy went to his brother's home that night and asked about the king and his wife and his daughters and friends. The oldest princess said, "We are two, my sister Zabelle and myself. Our mother is dead. I am married, and my sister is to be married." The boy knew then that his loved one was soon to be another's. The next morning he went to the palace and asked to see his sister Zabelle. They greeted each other as would a brother and sister and, hand in hand, walked through the garden. The boy became sleepy and asked if he could put his head in Zabelle's lap and rest. She sat down, and he laid his head in her lap and soon fell asleep.

The wicked spy saw them like this and quickly told Zabelle's fiancé, who came into the garden, sword in hand, to take revenge on Son of the Gray Horse. Zabelle looked up and said, "You cannot do him harm. He is my brother." He ordered her to leave the boy and follow him. So she slid her brother's head off her lap, put it on a rock and followed her fiancé.

Meanwhile, during all these years the grandfather of Son of the Gray Horse had been growing more and more powerful, and his country was becoming larger because of many war campaigns. He now wrote a letter to the king of this peaceful country, where Son of the Gray Horse was staying, and sent it by messenger. He said, "You have not paid me the money you owe me for the last ten years. If you do not pay forty thousand gold pieces in the next twenty-four hours, my armies will march on your country."

When the good king received this news, he became frightened. "We do not have that much money. Yet if we do not pay him, we will be slaughtered. What shall we do?" When Son of the Gray Horse heard this, he laughed. He tore the paper up and wrote, "Not only will I not give you money, but I will destroy your armies and your country, too. I am known as Son of the Gray Horse." The messenger returned with this message.

Meanwhile, Son of the Gray Horse and Zabelle went walking in the king's garden again. The youth being tired, sincerely asked if he could lay his head on Zabelle's lap. She consented, so he placed his head in her lap and fell fast asleep.

The spy saw them once again and ran to tell Zabelle's fiancé. The man became very angry this time and with his sword in hand, ran into the garden. He hit the boy so hard that he completely separated the boy's head from the rest of his body. Then he took Zabelle, and together they returned to the palace. No one at the palace knew where the boy was or what had happened to him.

In that land there was a band of robbers numbering forty who lived in the mountains. They slept by day and robbed by night. That night they decided to go near the king's palace to see what they could find. In the royal garden they found the hero beheaded, but he was not yet dead! They marveled at this and decided to help him. They carried him to the mountains, and the leader sent five of his men down to the village to get the best healer in the land.

The five men went down the mountain, found the healer and brought him back. The leader said to him, "If you cannot heal this man in five hours, we will kill you."

"Leave me alone, and I will cure him in one hour," the healer answered. And this he did. Then the five robbers took him home and had the healer's wife write on a piece of paper that her husband had been returned home safely. When she had done this, the robbers returned to their mountain.

The following day the forty robbers, taking their new captive with them, went down to the village to rob and plunder. But when Son of the Gray Horse saw that the armies of his grandfather were attacking his father's meager army, he killed so many soldiers left and right that only ten of the enemy soldiers were still alive to report the day's battle. The forty robbers, amazed at this show of strength, were greatly frightened.

The second day the boy fought against the new armies that his grandfather had assembled. But the king, who did not know who this great warrior was, commanded that he be captured. When the boy was ready to leave the field, he was caught and taken before the king who recognized him as his adopted son. "Oh, son, I was afraid that you had run away because you were afraid of the war," the king said. "Forgive me, forgive me!"

The boy spoke gently to the good king and told him about his intended death and about the robbers who had befriended him. The king became very angry and ordered that his daughter's fiancé and the spy be killed immediately. Then he commanded that a great feast be prepared for the victory they had just won.

Meanwhile, the boy was falling more deeply in love with Zabelle. He could neither eat nor sleep. All he wanted was to be with Zabelle. Finally, he revealed his passion for Zabelle to his brother who spoke of it to his wife, Zabelle's sister. She said to her brother, "If my sister loves you, she will give you a token of her love. When I see this, I will go and speak to my father and see if I can help you." So Son of the Gray Horse went to Zabelle while she was at the river washing clothes and asked for a token. "Wait until I return to the palace, and I will give you a token which is worthy of you." But no! he would not wait. What could she do? She had nothing with her that she could give him but a few golden coins. The boy took these to the older sister, but she smiled and said, "No, this is not a real token. Go back and ask her once again."

By this time the princess had returned to the palace and was waiting for him, for she knew that the coins would not be acceptable. When he arrived, she gave him a ring which King Solomon had worn. He took this to the older princess, and she smiled. "Yes, she loves you," she said and went to the palace to speak to her father.

The king was happy to have a marriage arranged and they had a wedding which lasted for seven days and seven nights. They lived happily together, and after a year Zabelle bore a child whom she called Joseph.

Several years later the grandfather of Son of the Gray Horse heard about the marriage of his grandson and the birth of Joseph and became very jealous. Since he knew that he could not harm the boy by force, he planned to harm him by trickery.

He wrote a letter to his grandson and said, "Come to my kingdom; let me be your son's godfather." The grandson did not think that any harm could come of this, so he replied, "Come here, and you will be my son's godfather." So the grandfather came to the peaceful land and acted as the child's godfather. He was so gentle that Son of the Gray Horse thought that perhaps he had been mistaken, that his grandfather really was a peaceful man. This is just what the grandfather wanted him to think. When he returned home, he sent an invitation to his grandson, his wife and the little boy to visit him.

Zabelle's father did not like the grandfather and would not permit Son of the Gray Horse to take Joseph along with him on the visit. So Zabelle and her husband went alone. The grandfather treated them very well, but when they were almost ready to leave, he had them chained and imprisoned. Now that his enemy's strongest warrior was in his prison, the grandfather declared war on Zabelle's father again and overran the country. The king and his young grandson, Joseph, escaped to another land and stayed there for ten years.

About this time Joseph was playing with a friend of his when this friend made him angry. So Joseph pulled all the hair from the boy's head. The boy ran home and told his mother, and she came with him to see Joseph. "If you are so strong," the mother said bitterly, "why don't you go and save your parents? They are to be hanged soon."

Now, Joseph had never heard anything about his parents. He knew only his grandfather. When he asked the old man about his parents, he learned about the wicked godfather who had imprisoned both Zabelle and Son of the Gray Horse. Joseph decided that he would go and save them. He set out and walked until he came to a town where all the stores were closed and there was no one working. He stopped and asked why this was so.

"Haven't you heard?" the people asked him. "Our princess has died, and the king has ordered that a young man guard her grave each night for one hundred nights. But the last two nights, two of our best youths have been killed."

The boy learned where the grave of the princess was and he dug a deep pit nearby and hid himself. That night when the young guard arrived, he got up from the pit and said, "Go home and sleep. I will guard this grave tonight." And the guard did as he was told.

The boy waited. Soon he saw an evil spirit fly through the air, come down to the grave of the princess, take a whip and lash the grave. Suddenly the ground opened, and the princess sat up and smiled, for she was not dead. The spirit kissed her.

When the boy saw this, he grabbed the spirit's wrist, which broke instantly, and took away the magic whip. The spirit, seeing that his end was near, cried out, "My boy! My boy! Leave me alone! Spare me! Someday when you are in great need, I will help you."

The boy thought about this and said to himself, "The princess is no longer dead. I can do no more here, anyway." So he spared the spirit, giving him back the magic whip and setting the broken wrist in place. The spirit instantly flew away and disappeared.

The rest of the night the boy stayed at the grave with the princess, and in the morning she led him to her father and king. The king insisted upon giving him a reward, but the boy refused and told him the story of his parents. The king then said, "Son, if you are to help your parents, you have to hurry for the cruel king who has captured them decided many years ago to imprison them for ten years and then to hang them. The time is almost up. May God help you!" He gave the boy a fast horse and hurried him on his way.

The boy went to the country where his father was imprisoned and saw that there was a great celebration: stores were closed, no one worked, tables were heavy with food, and there was singing and dancing everywhere. He joined the happy people and asked what they were celebrating. He learned that Son of the Gray Horse and his wife were to be hanged that very day. He decided that he would save his mother because she was a woman and defenseless, but he would not save his father if his father proved to be a coward. "It is better that he die if he is a coward," the boy said to himself.

Meanwhile, Son of the Gray Horse was tied to the tree

upon which he would soon be hanged. His hands were heavily chained and so were his feet. His dear Zabelle was tied to a tree nearby. Her husband cried to his grandfather, the cruel king, "*Ach!* [Alas!] if you were a man, you would free my wife or untie my hands that I might free her!" The grandfather only laughed and threw wine into his grandson's face.

The boy saw that no matter what was done to him, his father did not complain of his own condition and never begged for mercy. He only asked that his wife be freed. "I will help him, too," Joseph decided.

One of the soldiers who was drunk decided to go up to Zabelle and kiss her beautiful face. When Joseph saw this, he took out his sword and cut off the heavy chains from his father's hands and feet. Then together they killed all in their path and escaped with Zabelle. Son of the Gray Horse and Zabelle did not know, however, that their rescuer was Joseph. At the end of the first day of their journey Joseph pitched a tent for his parents and another for himself. Before going to bed, Son of the Gray Horse entered Joseph's tent to thank him for saving their lives. Joseph told him the truth: he had saved his own father and mother. Then Zabelle and Son of the Gray Horse embraced their brave son and wept tears of joy.

The three of them were very happy and started together through the mountains toward the home of Zabelle's father. One day as they were walking along, an evil spirit flying through the air grabbed Zabelle and flew off with her. Father and son followed the spirit which guided them like a star. On the eighth day they lost sight of the spirit in the mountains. During the time of their pursuit they had neither eaten, slept nor rested. On this eighth day they finally felt hungry and looked about for food.

They heard an old voice calling, "Apples for sale, apples for sale," and saw an old woman selling apples. They had enough money for one apple, but as they were very hungry, they took two apples. When they had finished eating, they found themselves in a deep, rocky pit far below the earth. At the mouth of this pit there was a tiny hole through which light streamed in. The father and son looked about and finally decided that there was no way out. What could they do? Were they to die here?

Just then the spirit which the boy had released at the princess' grave appeared and said, "My son, it seems that you are having trouble. Can I be of help to you now?" Eagerly the boy begged him to help them.

"That woman who was selling apples is none other than my mother," the spirit said. "Soon she will take the form of a bird and will come in here and begin to chirp. When she does so, you must take your sword and kill the bird with one stroke. If you can do this, you will be safe." Then the spirit disappeared.

Soon a big bird appeared in the pit and began to chirp. When it did so, the boy took his sword and with one stroke killed the bird. Suddenly he and his father found themselves in the open air, under the bright sun.

Father and son walked along until they came to a cave. The boy said to his father, "Father, this must be where my mother is hidden. You wait outside here for me for three days. If I do not return by then, come for me." He went inside and, after walking some distance, he heard his mother crying. "Mother, mother, don't cry. My father and I have come to rescue you," the boy said and embraced her.

She was happy to see him and told him about the cruel spirit which had captured her. The boy told her, "Mother, when he returns, laugh and sing with him, kiss him and learn his secret. I will hide in the long passageway outside and will come to you when he leaves."

The mother did this, and the spirit was greatly flattered by her attention. He boasted about all the things he could do that her husband could not do. "Why, he is nothing! Anyone can kill him by killing his body. They can never do that to me!"

"What can they do then?" she asked. "Are you immortal?"

"Ah!" he said, laughing, "do you see that huge sword on the wall there? My soul is in that! No one can hurt me!"

When the spirit left the cave that day, the boy came in, and his mother told him what the spirit had said about the sword. He quickly took down the large sword and began to pull it out of its scabbard. He worked all day and pulled it out only four inches.

That night the mother was again gentle with the spirit and asked about his soul. Again he gave her the same answer. When he left the next morning, the son came in and tried to pull the sword out of its scabbard but succeeded in pulling it out only eight inches.

The next night the mother again asked the spirit about his soul, and again he gave her the same answer. The third day the boy pulled with all his strength and finally the sword came out entirely. At that instant the spirit died, and the mother and her son made haste to leave.

Meanwhile, the father had waited one day, and his son had not returned. He waited another day, and still there was no news. When the boy did not return on the third day, the father was certain that the spirit had killed him, so he began to pull down the rocks of the mountain in rage.

However, at the same time the boy and his mother were trying to reach Son of the Gray Horse, but the rocks which were falling left and right made their escape impossible. The boy told his mother to return to the spirit's cave. Then, stumbling among the rocks, he finally reached his father and made him stop hurling rocks about. Together they went inside the cavern and led Zabelle out.

Their happiness was great, and after many embraces they resumed their journey to the country of Zabelle's father. Meanwhile, everyone in the world had heard of the bravery of Zabelle's son, and all the soldiers and rulers who occupied her father's country left in fear. Then Zabelle's father, who was now very old, returned to his beautiful and peaceful country and ruled his people. And Son of the Gray Horse, his wife Zabelle and their son Joseph lived with the old man.

36. The Helpful Spirit

Once upon a time there was a king who had two sons and a daughter. This king was most fortunate because he received the help of a kind spirit which lived in a marble slab in his garden. As the king was getting old, he wanted at least one of his sons to receive this magical help once he died.

So one day he told his eldest son that if he could pull out the sword in the marble slab in the garden, he would be a happy man for the rest of his life. The prince tried but did not succeed. When the second prince tried, however, he did pull out the sword. As he did so, a huge genie appeared before him and asked, "What do you wish, master?"

"Nothing at present," the surprised prince said, "but I will call you later." When he returned to the palace and told his father, the old king was very much pleased and congratulated

This story was told by Mrs. Katoon Mouradian.

his son. So the king told his wife and she summoned the prince to her and said, "Son, you are now ready to go out into the world. In your journey you will come upon three travelers. Do not form a friendship with any one of them until he has given you the largest piece of his bread and has kept the smallest one for himself. May you have a good journey, and may God's hands be upon you."

So the prince took his leave. He traveled far or near, I don't know which, and finally came to a clear brook beside which he found a fellow traveler. They exchanged greetings and sat down to rest and refresh themselves. The boy immediately noticed that the man gave him the small portion of his bread and kept the larger part for himself. "No, this is not my man," he decided and soon made an excuse to go on his way.

Again he walked for some time and came upon another brook where another traveler was resting. They exchanged greetings and sat down to refresh themselves. This man, like the first, gave the youth a small portion of his bread and kept the larger piece for himself. "This is not my man, either," the prince said, and he resumed his journey.

Finally, he came to a third brook and saw a third traveler. They exchanged greetings and sat down to refresh themselves. But the prince saw that the man offered the largest portion of his bread to him and kept the small piece. "Ah! I have found my man!" the prince said to himself.

The two men decided to seek their fortunes together and set out the next day. After walking for some time, they came upon a town where everyone was sick. The friend told the prince, "They will not let us into this town because there is much sickness. But if you tell them that I am a healer and can cure them, we can enter."

Just as the friend had said, the guards stopped them until the prince spoke of the great healing powers of his companion. Then the friend was allowed to walk through each street, and as he did so, all became well again. The king was so pleased that he gave the prince, whom he thought to be the master of the healer, his entire kingdom.

The prince and his friend continued their travels and soon came to another town. The friend said, "In this town whoever sleeps with the princess is found dead the following morning. The king has promised his kingdom and his daughter to the man who sleeps with the princess and is still alive in the morning. They will not let us enter this town unless you tell them that you want to sleep with the princess."

As the friend had said, the guards would not permit them to enter the place until the prince promised that he would sleep with the princess. That night while the prince and the princess were sleeping, the friend, who possessed magical powers, slipped into the room unseen. Toward midnight a huge snake came out of the princess' mouth and started creeping toward the prince. The friend, who was watching, cut the snake into tiny pieces, put the pieces into a bag and left the room. In the morning as the boy was still alive, he won both the princess and the kingdom. A few days later, the two friends started back on their journey, taking the princess along with them.

They traveled for some time until they came to a little town which was in flames. The friend said, "They will not allow us in this town unless we can promise to put out the fire." When the guards refused to let them in, the prince promised to put out the fire, and they were admitted. The friend walked through the flames, and as he did so, the flames died down. Soon the great fire was extinguished, and the town was saved. The king was so happy that he gave his kingdom to the prince as a reward.

Then the three started back home. When the friend reached the brook where he had first met the prince, he said, "Well, my friend, this is where we met, so this shall be where we must part. Come, let us divide our fortunes." So the prince and his friend divided all the money they had gathered. "Come, come, now we must divide the princess between us," the friend said.

"But the princess is much too beautiful to die. If you want her, take her. But whatever happens, let us not kill her," the prince said.

"No, you hold one hand, and I'll hold the other while with my sword I'll slice her in two," the friend said and prepared his sword. Upon seeing that she was to be killed, the princess became so frightened that she opened her mouth to scream and something fell out of it.

"Ah! That is all I wanted. You may have your princess now," the friend said, bending down to find a knot of baby snakes. "You see, if you had taken your wife home with this in her stomach, some night these snakes would have strangled you. Now, as it is, you are quite safe."

The prince and the princess were grateful to him. "Now, let me tell you a few more things. Before you reach your home, your wife will bear you a child. When you get there, I'll be there and ready to help you whenever you need me," the friend said. He took off his clothes and jumped into the brook nearby. The prince saw a pair of wings unfold on the body of the friend who was then suddenly transformed into a maiden. "Ah! So this must have been the spirit in the marble slab—not a genie but a lovely maid!"

The prince and his wife continued homeward. True enough, before they reached their country, the princess bore her husband a son. When the prince reached the palace, he immediately went to the garden to see the marble slab and found that it was unbroken. Then he knew that the fairy spirit had returned to it.

37. Ludwig and Iskander

Once there were two kings who each had a son. These boys, who were sent away for an education, met at school and immediately became close friends. They looked like twins, dressed alike and were inseparable. The one prince was known as Iskander and the other, Ludwig.

One day Iskander asked his friend to spend a month with him at his home. Ludwig was pleased but needed to ask his father's permission. As Iskander's father was a very powerful king, Ludwig's father was very pleased by his son's friendship and quickly gave his permission. After a very pleasant visit, during which he was introduced to all the people at the palace, Ludwig was ready to leave. But Iskander said, "Ludwig, I haven't introduced you to my fiancée yet. You must see her and tell me if you think that she will be a good wife for me."

Arm in arm they went to see the girl. Ludwig immediately fell in love with her, but he did not tell anyone. When he reached his country, he became very ill, and day by day he grew worse. The healers were called in, but they could find nothing wrong with him. "There is nothing wrong with him except that he is worrying too much, he is thinking too much," they said to the king.

"Son, what is on your mind, tell me," the king asked.

"Father, only Iskander can help me," the youth said.

So the king immediately sent a messenger to Iskander and

This story was told by Mrs. Mariam Serabian.

told him of his friend's condition, and Iskander came immediately to see his friend.

At first Ludwig did not tell him why his heart ached. Finally he said, "You must know my trouble, and you can help me. But I will not tell you how."

"I would do anything in the world for your sake," his friend replied.

"Since the first time I saw your fiancée, I have been sick with love."

"If that is so, that is nothing. I haven't married her yet, and to save your life I would give up forty such girls."

After asking the king if Ludwig could come along with him, Iskander returned home. The two princes looked so much alike that Iskander's fiancée could not tell them apart. Iskander said, "Ever since my friend first saw you, he has been sick with love for you. We are both princes, and we both look alike; will you marry him and make us both happy? I am happy when he is happy."

Since the girl accepted, the two were married, and Ludwig returned to his own country, saying to his friend, "If ever you need help, you must let me know."

Many years later a war broke out. The armies of Iskander's father were defeated, and both father and son became very poor. Iskander had forgotten Ludwig's parting words until, one day, he said to himself, "I wonder if he will help us." He sat down and wrote a letter to Ludwig and told him about his condition. As soon as Ludwig received the letter, he sent his friend one thousand pieces of gold and told him to come to his country. But actually Ludwig had prepared an unusual plan to help his friend. He told his guards not to let Iskander enter the palace but to follow him and learn where he would go.

Iskander tried to see the prince, but he was not admitted. Finally, convinced that his friend would not see him, he set out to find lodging. Ludwig's guards followed him and reported back to the king. An aged woman came to the inn where Iskander was staying and asked if she could have a room next to his. After having settled herself there, she knocked on Iskander's door and asked him who he was. "I am Iskander, former prince of a great land. My good friend, Prince Ludwig, invited me here, and when I arrived, he would not see me. That is why I am passing the night in this inn," he explained.

The old woman said, "I have a business proposition to make

to you. I will open a large store for you and also give you two million pieces of gold. In three years you can either marry my daughter and we shall keep the money in the family or, if you choose, we will divide in half whatever profit or loss these years have brought." The boy was much pleased with this plan.

The old woman did as she promised. She opened a large store for him and gave him two million pieces of gold besides. Iskander became very rich, and after three years this aged woman and her daughter came into the store one day to fulfill the rest of the bargain. The girl was very beautiful, and the boy was most eager to marry her.

In those days if a girl had more than one suitor, the suitors were expected to fight a duel, and the winner would marry the girl. Now, this girl had another suitor, and Iskander did not know how to duel.

There was a ball one night to which Iskander and his fiancée were invited. All these years Iskander had not seen Ludwig. Suddenly he saw that Ludwig was dancing with his fiancée. He went into a room and locked the door behind him. "I am not going to watch him take away my second fiancée," Iskander said to himself. Ludwig left his dancing partner and followed his friend. He knocked on the door and asked, "Why did you leave the room and lock yourself in here?"

"Because after having taken my first fiancée, you are now trying to take my second," Iskander answered.

"Since when is it wrong for a brother and sister to dance?" Ludwig asked. "She is my sister. I was the one who did not permit you to enter the palace. I was the one who sent that old woman to you; she is my mother. Now you take my place, and I will take yours until this duel is fought. You cannot duel, I know, but I will do so in your place without anyone's knowledge."

Ludwig won the duel, and the two friends returned to their former conditions. Iskander and the beautiful princess were married, and the wedding lasted for forty days and forty nights. Taking his wife and many riches, Iskander returned to his former land where, after many years, he had two sons.

Meanwhile, Ludwig became very ill and looked poor and miserable. Since everyone felt sorry for him, he decided to go to the mountains and spare them their pity. "Before I do this, let me go to see my brother once again," he said. So he found his way to Iskander's land. When Iskander's wife, Ludwig's sister, opened the door to him, she did not recognize her brother.

"For the sake of your brother, for the love of your husband, give me a place under your roof," he said. So she took him in and fed him. When Iskander returned that night, he saw the sick man but did not recognize his best friend.

That evening Ludwig dreamt that if Iskander's sons were killed and if their blood were rubbed on his body, he would get well. The next day while he was asking for water, he said to Iskander's wife, "If your brother were in my condition and if you could restore his health by killing your two sons and anointing him with their blood, would you do it?"

"Yes," she replied, "not only my two sons, but ten sons if I had that many."

"I am your brother, Ludwig."

"Brother, brother, what a condition you are in!" she said, throwing herself upon him. She quickly killed her two sons and rubbed their blood on her brother, and he immediately became well. When it was time for Iskander's return, she hid Ludwig.

"If my brother had been in the condition that sick old man was in yesterday and if you were able to restore his health by killing your sons, would you do it?" she asked him.

"Not only two sons, but I would kill ten if I had them," he answered.

"Well, I have killed your two sons, and Ludwig is well again," she said, pulling her brother out of his hiding place. Iskander and Ludwig embraced.

"Let us bury the bodies of the boys," Iskander said. They went to the spot where they had left the boys, and to their great surprise, they found them well and happily playing with each other.

So Ludwig was cured, and the little boys did not die after all.

38. Buzz-Buzz Aunty

Once upon a time there was an old woman who had only one daughter, who was lazy just like me. She slept all night and didn't wake up until the afternoon of the following day. When she did get up, she would eat and run out to play instead of helping her mother as a girl should.

"My daughter who spins eighteen pounds of wool, come

This story was told by Mrs. Mariam Serabian.

home, come home," the mother would cry. The mother said this purposely so that people hearing her would have a high opinion of her daughter.

Once a rich caravan merchant was passing by and happened to hear the mother's customary cry. The merchant was in a great hurry to marry the girl because she was such a good worker. "The sooner I marry her, the richer I will become," he said. He went into the mother's house and, after a few polite greetings, asked to marry the girl. Needless to say, the mother was delighted.

"I will not marry her here, but I'll take her to my own town and get married there," the merchant said, expecting objections from the mother. But the mother was so happy to get rid of her lazy daughter that she did not care where the merchant married her. So the merchant took his future wife to his town and, directly after the wedding, bought wool for her to spin. "Wife, I am going away with my caravans. Take the wool which I have bought for you and spin eighteen pounds of it daily so that when I return, I can sell it," he said.

"All right," the girl answered. "When you return, it will be ready."

The husband went on his way and was happy to have married such an industrious wife. But the wife was worried. What was she to do? She took the wool in her hands and tried to spin it, but she didn't even know how to start. After some time she made a lumpy supper of mush and spread it over her two shoulders. Now she could try to work and eat at the same time! She started to play with the wool, but nothing happened. So she began to lick first one shoulder, and then the other, then back to the first, then to the other. And still nothing happened to the wool! "Oh, *mairig, mairig* [little mother], how am I going to do this?" she asked, licking first one shoulder then the other. She hit her hands on her knees and continued licking her shoulders.

There were fairies in the room who, seeing and hearing the girl, began to laugh at her. At times she would see them, then they would disappear. They laughed at her and mocked her. They would lick first one of their shoulders, then the other in imitation.

"Who are you?" the girl angrily asked.

The fairies didn't answer but kept right on laughing.

"*Vhy, vhy, vhy, vhy* [alas], I didn't want a husband. Why did my mother marry me to this man? I'm hungry," she said, licking one shoulder, then the other. Again the fairies laughed at her and mocked her. Suddenly she saw all of the fairies in one group and became very frightened.

"Don't be frightened," they said. "We won't do you any harm. We can spin all that wool for you."

She began licking her shoulders and crying. "My husband will be home soon, and I haven't spun any of the wool yet."

The fairies, meanwhile, set about spinning the wool, unseen by the girl. Presently she glanced by her side and saw that all the baskets were empty and that all the spinning was done. "My, who did this?" she asked, licking one shoulder, then the other. The fairies imitated her. One of them was wearing bells, and each time he moved, the bells chimed loudly and frightened the lazy girl. "My, what a good worker I am," she said proudly to herself, first licking one shoulder, then the other. "I did all this by myself."

Just then her husband walked in and looked at her. Was this his wife? She had lumps running down her back and arms, and her hair was strewn all over. She was dirty and wearing old rags. Was this his wife? But then he looked at her side and saw the empty baskets. Oh, his wife was a good, industrious woman! "My, how well you work, wife dear!" her husband said. "But what is that running down your arms and back?"

"Oh, this is my supper," the girl said, unashamed.

Just then, a buzz-buzz* flew in through the window and made a fearful racket in the room. "Buzz-buzz aunty, come here," said the girl. When the husband objected, she turned to him and asked him to be quiet. Then to the bee she said, "Buzz-buzz aunty, come here."

"What are you saying, wife?" her husband asked. "How can a buzz-buzz be your aunt?"

"That buzz-buzz was a girl just like me, but she did so much spinning that she turned into a buzz-buzz," the girl answered.

"If that is so, wife, do not spin any more," he said. "I don't want a buzz-buzz for a wife."† Smiling to himself as he walked along, he said, "What a woman!" He went to his store and took care of his trade. When he returned home that evening, he found many people at his house. There were musicians about, and

* Informant called this creature a "buzz-buzz" rather than a bumble bee.

† The story should logically end here, but this informant continued with the "nonsense" to the last possible detail. This story, which I heard many times, always ended in this manner.

everyone was dancing and having a wonderful time. "What is happening?" he asked his wife when he finally pushed through the crowd.

"My buzz-buzz aunty wants a husband. Won't you marry her?" she asked and climbed on her husband's shoulders and began jumping up and down. The husband was very much embarrassed until, by chance, she fell down. Finding himself free, he ran away and left her.

39. The *Halva*-Maker

Once upon a time there was a young man who was a *halva*-maker [candy-maker]. His business was very poor, and he could hardly provide for himself. One day a dervish was passing the dingy little store and decided to go in.

"Son, will you give me a piece of *halva?*" the dervish asked. "But let me tell you first that I have no money to pay for it."

"Father, take as many pieces as you want," the boy said. The dervish had several pieces, then sat down to rest. That evening the boy made up his little bed in the back of the store, and the dervish asked if he, too, might sleep in the store. "Father, I have very little, but whatever I have, you are welcome to it," the young man said, and the dervish slept on a nearby rug.

The next morning the boy got up and to his amazement, saw his counters full of *halva,* and *halva* very different from his own. How was this? He had not made any *halva* the preceding night. How was it possible that the counters were full in the morning? "Father, I made no *halva* last night, and look how my counters are full this morning. Is it possible that an enemy of mine has stolen these from someone else and placed them in my store?"

"You are a good-hearted person. God gave you this *halva*. If anyone should question you, I will protect you and tell them the truth," the dervish said.

But the boy continued, "Perhaps the *halva* is poisoned and has been placed here so that when someone eats it, he will die and I will be hanged for it. Let me try a piece and see for myself," the boy said. To his surprise it was the best *halva* he had ever tasted. How fortunate he was to have his whole store full of such delicious *halva!*

This story was told by Hovhannes Kaprelian.

Soon his few customers discovered the great improvement in the *halva* he sold and told their friends; their friends tried the sweetmeat, and they, in turn, told their friends. Finally, the whole town was talking about the delicious *halva* the young man was selling.

One day the princess and her servants were passing the store when someone mentioned the fame of the *halva* sold there. "Is this the *halva* that all the town is talking about?" the princess asked. When she was assured that it was, she entered the little shop. The princess was veiled, but to taste the *halva* she had to throw her veil back.

In that brief moment or so the *halva*-maker saw her beautiful face and fell in love with her. The princess was delighted with the *halva* and having purchased some, left the store.

Meanwhile, the dervish noticed that the young man had fallen in love with the princess. However, to be sure, he asked the boy, "Son, why are you so sad today?"

"Father, why do you ask? My sorrow is so great that you can do nothing to help."

"Tell me, son, I may be able to help you," the dervish said.

"Father, if you must know, I am in love with the princess."

"Don't worry, my son," the dervish said. "I will go to the king and ask for the princess to be your wife."

"But father, who am I, and who is the princess? Even if the king were to give her to me, what would I do with her? Will a princess live in my shabby store?"

"Son, don't worry about this; just leave everything to me," the dervish said. So the old man went to the palace and said to the king, "My King, I have come to ask for the princess for a promising young man of our town."

"Who is this young man?"

"He is the *halva*-maker whose reputation has spread throughout the country," the dervish said.

"What? A *halva*-maker for a son-in-law? Aren't you ashamed to come here with such a proposition?"

"Your Majesty, you are rich, you need not work; the young *halva*-maker is poor, and he must work. But both of you have been born of man. Perhaps some day you will be poor, and he will be rich," the dervish said.

When the king refused again, the dervish said angrily, "I will have your daughter for the *halva*-maker. Understand this well: it shall be so!"

Meanwhile, the dervish made plans for a large wedding and told all the townsfolk that the princess was to become the bride of the *halva*-maker. When the king heard this, he was furious. "Have that old man and the *halva*-maker brought here so that I can hang them!" he ordered his vizier.

The guards went to the store of the *halva*-maker and said, "*Halva*-maker, the king has ordered that you be hanged," and they took him away. They tried to put a rope around the boy's neck, but as they pulled on one arm to control him, the arm fell off. The men were surprised and still more so when they pulled on the other arm and it, too, fell off.

"Come, come, what is happening here?" the vizier said, pulling the boy's head down and pulling his ears to make him behave. But just as he did so, the ears fell off. The men were amazed but continued trying to get the rope around the boy's throat. But the rope would not stay in one place. When the men thought that the rope was in place, they would look up, and it would be around the boy's chest, or stomach, but never around his throat. Finally, in despair, they decided to bathe the *halva*-maker that day and hang him the next. When they freed him, his arms and ears were magically replaced.

The vizier went to the store again, this time to arrest the dervish. The dervish turned the vizier into a donkey, but the poor man did not realize that he had been transformed. Only his head was his own; all the rest of his body was that of a donkey, except that he had two feet. The coat which he was wearing previously now became a saddle on his back.

The vizier's men who had come to arrest the dervish forgot everything and began laughing. They laughed and laughed and the vizier became very angry, for he did not know what they were laughing at. He decided to go before the king and tell him of the misconduct of his troops.

When the king saw that his vizier had been transformed into a donkey, he was most angry. He sent another man to arrest the dervish, and this one became a dog. When the man returned, the king became still angrier. Then the king sent a third man, and the dervish turned him into a cat. By this time the king was so discouraged that he decided to end the whole matter.

Meanwhile, preparations for the wedding had been going on even though there seemed to be no bride. The king called the dervish before him and said, "Friend, I will give my daughter to your boy if you will promise me that he will never be a *halva*-maker again." The dervish agreed to this.

So the proposed wedding became real, with a bride and a bridegroom, and the guests all sang and danced and ate for forty days and forty nights. After the wedding was over, the king had a beautiful palace built for his son-in-law, and the former *halva*-maker and his bride lived in it contentedly to the end of their days, without a worry in the world.

As the *halva*-maker reached his goal, so shall we reach ours. From the sky fell three apples: one for me, one for the story-teller and one for the person who has entertained you.

40. *Tushcoon* Eigna

There was once a rich merchant who had an only son. When he died, he left his fortune to his son, but the youth fell in with bad companions and lost all of his inheritance. So he and his mother became poor and hungry, yet the boy was too proud to ask for work.

One day his poor mother said, "Son, they are building a church in honor of St. Sarkis down in the center of the town, and they need workmen. Why don't you go and ask for work so that we can have a few *para* [Turkish coin] and can eat again?"

The son gave many excuses, but his mother was persistent. Finally, seeing that there was no other way open to him, he set out for the church. When it came time for him to ask for work, he sulked and sat down in a dark corner and soon fell asleep.

While he was peacefully sleeping, St. Sarkis came to him in a dream. "Go to the king and ask to marry the princess," the saint commanded, and he disappeared. When the boy awoke, he laughed at himself for even dreaming so foolishly and did not tell his mother of his dream. The next morning he left to go to the church, saying that he was going to work. But once again he fell asleep and had the same dream. In this way he pretended for a whole week that he was working. Every day, however, he had the same strange dream as he slept in a dark corner of the church. One day his mother said, "Son, you have been working for a week now. How much money have you?" When he confessed to his mother that he had not been working, she became very sad. But what could she do to change matters?

This story was told by Mrs. Mariam Serabian.

Thinking that his mother might forgive him, the boy told her about his dream. "A strange thing happened to me last week. Every day while I was sleeping, St. Sarkis came to me in a dream and told me to go to the palace and ask to marry the princess. Imagine my marrying a princess—I, who don't know what it is to have a full stomach!" He started to laugh, and his mother joined him.

The next night St. Sarkis came again to the boy and said, "It has been a week now since I gave you an order, and you still haven't fulfilled it. Do as I ask, or you and your family will be punished."

The next morning the son told his mother of St. Sarkis' threat, but she explained that probably he was having such dreams because he went to bed hungry. The following day, however, he had the same dream; and on the third day, when St. Sarkis repeated his warning, he told the boy that this was his last opportunity to help himself.

"Mother, St. Sarkis told me that this was my last chance to help myself and if I did not do what he has commanded, we will be punished. There is no other way, Mother. You must go to the king and ask for his daughter."

"What, my son, are you out of your head? We can't even take care of ourselves. How can we hope to provide for the princess?"

"Mother, I know that it doesn't sound sensible. But why does St. Sarkis repeatedly tell me to do this very thing? There is something here that doesn't meet the eye."

"No, my son, I will not go to the king's palace to ask for his daughter."

"Would you want St. Sarkis to punish both of us? You must go."

So finally the poor mother set out for the palace. When she saw the king, she said, "My King, we all know of your kindness and mercy. You have a grown daughter, and I have a grown son. I have come humbly to ask for the princess, *Tushcoon* [sad] Eigna to become my son's wife."

"You beggar, how can you come here with such a proposition? Who are you to mention my daughter's name with that of your ragged son? My daughter is most wise and beautiful! Guards, take this woman and throw her all the way down the stairs. And when you have done that, give her a sound whipping and send her home!" the king ordered. When the old woman returned home, the boy saw her misery and wondered if St. Sarkis had made a mistake.

That night, however, St. Sarkis came to him in his dream with the same demand. "But, St. Sarkis, my mother went to the king today, and he insulted her and beat her and sent her home."

"Very well, have her go back again tomorrow. If she does not, I shall punish both of you," St. Sarkis said and disappeared.

The next morning when the boy noticed the bruises on his mother, all his courage of the night before disappeared. But remembering St. Sarkis' threat, he turned and faced her. "Mother, St. Sarkis came again last night," he said slowly.

"He did, did he? And what did he say this time?"

"St. Sarkis made the same demand and said that if you did not go to the king again, he would punish both of us."

"If I go, I will be punished; if I don't go, I will be punished. What am I to do? If I go to the king, I alone will be punished. If I don't go to the king, St. Sarkis will punish both my son and me. I will go to the king," the old woman sighed.

When she asked for the princess a second time, the king became very angry and ordered that she be thrown down the stairs and beaten twice as hard. So she was rolled down the stairs and whipped twice as hard as the day before. Her son felt shamefaced when he saw her. That evening St. Sarkis came and asked for an account of the day's happenings, and the boy told him. "Have her go again tomorrow," St. Sarkis said.

"Again? St. Sarkis, the poor woman has suffered enough."

"Never mind what has happened. She must go again tomorrow, and if she should not do so, both of you shall be punished," St. Sarkis replied, and he disappeared.

The next morning the boy faced his mother and told her that she must ask for the princess a third time. Alas! mother's love is great, and the poor woman did not want to see her son punished. So she went to the king with the same request.

The king was surprised to see her again but said to himself that this nonsense must stop. "If I have her beaten, she will come again tomorrow. She is poor, that much is evident. I must ask for such an enormous amount of gold that she will give up the idea of marriage between her son and my daughter." Then, turning to the woman, he said, "I will give you my daughter if you will bring me seven *deegs* [measures] of gold and seven *deegs* of pearl rings!"

The woman left without another word. When she returned

home, she told her son of the king's request, and he was as discouraged as his mother was.

That night when St. Sarkis appeared before him in his dream, the boy told him what the king had said. "Come with me," St. Sarkis commanded, and he led the boy to a faraway mountain. At the foot of the mountain there was a trap door. At first, this door was invisible to the boy, but by the power of St. Sarkis, he saw it.

"Open that door and you will find a stairway leading down to the ground. When you reach the bottom, you will see many barrels of gold and other valuables. Take seven *deegs* of gold and seven *deegs* of pearl rings and come back to me," St. Sarkis instructed.

The boy did as he was told. He found the valuables and returned with them to the saint. "Now take these to the king, and he will keep his promise. However, there is one thing which I will ask from you. Every evening before you go to sleep, you must call my name. Do not forget to do this or misfortune will come upon you."

The next morning the boy showed the *deegs* of gold and pearl rings to his mother and told her of what had happened the preceding night. So mother and son carried the valuables to the palace. The mother said to the king, "My King, you told me that if I could bring you seven *deegs* of gold and seven *deegs* of pearl rings, you would give the princess to my son in marriage. I trust that you will keep your word."

The amazed king had the valuables counted by his guards. They opened the lids of all fourteen *deegs* and saw that they were full to the brim. The court jeweler was called to test the stones and found them to be of the finest quality. The king was caught: he could not break his promise. Looking at the woman, he could not help thinking that she was very poor and yet she had brought the treasure which he had demanded. So the king kept his word, and it was arranged for *Tushcoon* Eigna to marry the boy.

A wedding of forty days and forty nights was to take place at the palace. On the first night all the guests were assembled, and there was plenty to eat and drink. The bride wore a dress of pure gold and sparkled like the sun. Everyone was having a happy time and was looking forward to the other thirty-nine days and nights.

The boy was so happy that first night and very excited!

Tushcoon Eigna took off her wedding dress, folded it, and, putting it beneath her pillow, she prepared for bed. The boy completely forgot St. Sarkis' command and that night—of all nights!—forgot to say "St. Sarkis."

At midnight St. Sarkis came to the bridal chamber and took away the princess. Across high mountains, fields and rivers they went until they finally reached a beautiful palace in the lonely town of Adana.* St. Sarkis told *Tushcoon* Eigna, "This is to be your home now. You will live here alone." There was nothing the new bride could do about her situation: she did not know whom it was who had carried her to this town or why she was there, but she had many servants and lived very comfortably.

Months later a son was born to *Tushcoon* Eigna. The baby, from the first moment of its birth, cried constantly. Day in and day out, night in and night out, sleeping, eating, playing, the little boy always cried. "There is something wrong with this son of mine, for why should he be continually crying," *Tushcoon* Eigna said to herself. So she had many healers look at the boy, but none of them could find anything wrong. *Tushcoon* Eigna became discouraged and did not know what to do. She decided to ask the dervishes to discover through their magic what was causing her son to cry. So the dervishes were called, and they began in their strange way to sing and pray. One of them finally said, "This child of yours will continue to cry until his father holds him in his arms."

Tushcoon Eigna could not locate her husband and did not know whether she ever would be able to do so, but she thought, "If I should do something so startling that word about it spread far enough, perhaps he will come to me." *Tushcoon* Eigna knew that the cross of Jesus was buried near Adana. Since she had much gold, she took handfuls of it and threw it over the ground where she thought the crucifix was buried. The poor people, seeing that a great lady was throwing gold on the ground, scrambled to pick it up. Word started to spread that there was a great lady in Adana who had so much money that she was throwing it away. Everyone from far and near hurried to get a few pieces of gold. But while people were picking up gold pieces, they were loosening the earth which covered the cross of Jesus. After a time they found the crucifix which, thanks to *Tushcoon* Eigna's foresight, is still preserved today.

Anyone could pick up the gold pieces which *Tushcoon*

* Town selected at random by informant.

Eigna had thrown over the ground if he consented to hold the crying baby in his arms for a little while. By this method she had hoped to find her husband, but he was not among the men who came.

In those days bridges were rare, so *Tushcoon* Eigna announced that she planned to build forty bridges over the Adana river. No one knew enough about the building of bridges to be willing to attempt the task. "Very well," *Tushcoon* Eigna told her workers, "if you are unwilling to build it, I shall drop *deegs* and *deegs* of gold into the water until a solid structure arises." But the men convinced her to save her wealth and agreed that they would build her the bridges. Word went from village to village and from town to town that a great lady in Adana was building forty bridges across the Adana river and that there was work for everyone.

Now to come back to *Tushcoon* Eigna's husband. The morning after his wedding he woke up and saw that his wife was missing. He asked for her, but no one had seen her; he couldn't imagine what had happened to her. When he lifted her pillow, he saw her wedding dress, neatly folded, so he took it and hid it among his belongings, telling no one about it. When the king discovered that his daughter had disappeared, he blamed his son-in-law and exiled both the boy and his mother.

Once again the boy and his mother were as poor as ever. The boy had *Tushcoon* Eigna's dress, but it was so valuable that he was afraid people would think he had stolen it; so he kept it carefully hidden under his shirt.

One day the mother said, "Son, I hear that a great lady in Adana is building forty bridges over the Adana water. There is work for everybody. Let us go and see what our luck will bring." And so they went to Adana.

Meanwhile, *Tushcoon* Eigna and her attendants insisted that each one of the bridge workers hold the crying infant son. When it was her husband's turn to take the boy in his arms, the child stopped crying. The attendants ran and told *Tushcoon* Eigna. Thereupon she hurried to see who the man was, but since he did not recognize her, she said nothing to him of what was in her mind. Instead she told him, "You need not work with the rest of the laborers any more. Merely play with this child."

The child, who was now two years old, had not stopped crying for a minute since he had been born until his father held

307

him in his arms. So needless to say, everyone was relieved when the crying stopped.

Tushcoon Eigna treated her husband so well that he wanted to do something for her. "Mother, I still have *Tushcoon* Eigna's wedding dress. Why shouldn't I give it to this great lady in appreciation for all she has done for me?" he asked his mother. The mother agreed that this was a good thought, so the next day he took the beautiful dress to the mother of the child. "My Lady, here is something that I wish to give you," he said, handing her the dress.

When *Tushcoon* Eigna saw the dress, she began to cry and asked, "Where did you get this dress?"

"I did not steal it. It was left to me," the boy said, and he told her about St. Sarkis, *Tushcoon* Eigna, the wedding dress and all that had brought him to Adana. *Tushcoon* Eigna was convinced now that he was her husband.

"Do you still love this person, *Tushcoon* Eigna, after all that has happened to you?" she asked him.

"I have always loved her."

The girl told him to bring his mother to her, and when she saw the old woman, she kissed her hand.

"My Lady, what are you doing?" mother and son cried.

"You call me by a fancy title now, but both of you have called me by another name at one time," she told them. "Do you remember *Tushcoon* Eigna?"

"How could I forget my wife?"

"How could I forget my daughter-in-law?"

"Well, then, I am *Tushcoon* Eigna, and this is our child," she said, presenting the two-year-old boy to her husband. Then *Tushcoon* Eigna, who had changed so greatly that they could not believe that they were seeing her once more, told them her story. She told how St. Sarkis had brought her to Adana, of the birth of her son and of her attempts to bring her husband to her and to their son.

They were all joyous over the reunion and lived happily together for many many years.*

---

* St. Sarkis, held in high esteem by Armenians, is believed to be the personification of the winds and a substitute for the old wind god. Although no fasting days are assigned by the Armenian church for St. Sarkis, the five-day fast in February usually honors him. Young girls keep this fast religiously in hope that St. Sarkis will reward them with good weather for their wedding day instead of snow or rain. (Abeghian, *op. cit.*, p. 95.)

MORALISTIC TALES

41. The Rich Boy and the Poor Boy

AT ONE TIME there was and there was not, there was a widow
who had an only son. They were poor, and the mother worked
very hard in the homes of others to support her only child. As
the boy grew older, he saw his mother's hard life and decided
to earn enough money to bring her comfort in her old age.

The poor boy had a good friend who came from a rich
family. When the poor boy decided to leave home to seek his
fortune, he told his friend about his plans.

"If you go, I am going, too," the rich boy said.

"Why should you want to leave your home and family? You
are already rich."

"No, I don't want you to start on such a dangerous journey
alone," the rich boy said. When the rich boy told his parents
of his plans, they tried to convince him to stay home. But the
youth was determined, and the two friends started on their adventure together.

They decided that they would each work for three years
and divide their fortunes equally before their return home. They
walked and walked until they came to a town in which they decided to live. The rich boy found work quickly, but the poor boy
had no luck. So finally the poor boy decided to go somewhere
else to find work, and the two friends parted, making an agreement to meet three years later.

In the new town the poor boy's luck was open,* and he
made much money. At the end of three years he loaded his
wealth on donkeys and started out to find his friend. But the
townsfolk said to him, "Yes, he lives in this town, but it is better
that he die than live like this."

"Why? Is he sick?" the boy asked, alarmed.

This story was told by Nishan Krikorian.
See Comparative Studies for another version.
* Armenians refer to bad luck as "luck being closed" and to good luck
as "luck being open."

"He is well enough, but he has left his old ways and is leading a bad life," they said.

"Where can I find him?"

"Where else? Search the taverns," they told him.

So the boy looked and found his friend in a pitiful condition, just as the people had told him. When the friend was rested and better, the poor boy suggested that they return home because three years had passed.

"But how can I return home? Look at my condition! I haven't even a *para* [Turkish coin]," the rich boy objected.

"We are partners, don't you remember? Our agreement was to divide equally whatever we had," the poor boy said. The rich boy protested again and again. But his friend said, "Come, let's go; I'm anxious to see my mother again. We have enough money here for both of us."

Finally the two friends started on their way back. When they had almost reached their village, they decided to send their caravan before them and follow it the next morning. So that night the two friends slept together in the woods. During the night the rich boy began to think: "If I go home with him, he'll tell everyone that I was poor and that all the wealth is his. This will not do. What am I to do?" Finally the rich boy decided to kill his companion, so he took out his sword. He was about to press it against his friend's neck when the boy suddenly awoke.

"Friend, what are you doing?" he asked in surprise.

"I am going to kill you," the rich boy said.

"Why would you kill me?"

"Because when we get back home, you will tell everyone how it was that you found me."

"Don't you remember our agreement? I would be in your position if you had earned more money than I did, but I wouldn't have killed you for that. We are going to share alike whatever we have. There is no reason for jealousy," the poor boy said.

"No, I don't trust you; I'm going to kill you now."

"Then tell me if you will spare my life if I give you all my money and go away promising never to return," the poor boy asked. The rich boy agreed to this, very happy that he was getting the best of the deal.

So the poor boy escaped with his life and went his way while the rich boy returned home. The poor boy walked and walked until he came to a road which branched into seven paths. He didn't know which of these seven paths to follow but finally decided to take the road that lay farthest to the left. He walked along for some time until he saw that the road led to a high mountain. He climbed the mountain, and as he looked down from the summit, he saw a beautiful field of green grass below and a beautiful palace.

The poor boy was hungry and decided to go to the palace and ask for food. He descended the mountain, went to the palace and knocked on the door. When no one answered, he opened the door and went inside. He found a lamb slowly roasting on a spit and a huge bowl of pilaff steaming on the table. So he sat down and ate the lamb and pilaff to his heart's content. Suddenly he heard a great thundering noise outside. Terribly frightened, he searched for a hiding place and found a little hole into which he squeezed himself.

The door opened, and three giants entered. Each giant had seven heads with one lip of each head reaching to the heavens while the other reached to the earth. When the giants breathed, it seemed that they could swallow a human being with each breath. "There must be a human being here, for I smell human flesh," one giant said, sniffing around.

The others agreed, so they searched everywhere. But they could not find the boy and finally sat down to eat their food.

"Well, brother, what have you learned today?" the eldest giant asked his youngest brother.

"In Marash there is a little boy who will climb a tree to steal a bird's egg from the nest.* Unless someone stops him from climbing, this boy will fall from the tree and die."

"Well, what have you learned today?" the first giant asked his second brother.

"In Moush there are two farmers who will soon be dividing their crop of wheat. There will be no trouble until they come to dividing their last bushel. They will fight with each other on how to do this, and unless someone interferes, they will kill each other," the second brother said.

"And what have you learned today?" the younger brothers asked.

"The king's daughter in the town of Van is sick, and none of the healers in the world can cure her. A demon has crawled into her stomach, and no one can get him out. And what's more, all her body is full of ugly sores. But if someone were to climb

* Towns and names mentioned in the story were associated with the listeners in this particular storytelling situation.

Mt. Massis and from the summit of it, look to the south, he would see a tiny stream on each side of which stands a rosebush. If someone were to cut a rose from each of these rosebushes and boil them in some of the water from that stream, then give the rosewater to the princess to drink, she would be cured immediately," the first giant said.

After they had eaten, the giants slept, and early in the morning they left the palace. The boy crawled out of his hiding place, ate some food and started on his way. After walking for some time, he saw a little boy running away from the village and toward the woods. The boy interested him, so he followed to see what the youngster would do. The little boy raced to a tree and looking quickly all about him, began to climb. The poor boy suddenly remembered the prediction of the third giant, so he quickly ran to the tree, took the boy down, gave him a little spanking and set him on his way home.

He continued walking until he came to two farmers who were quarreling. Again the poor boy remembered the giant's prediction and asked the farmers why they were quarreling.

"We are partners, and we have divided all of our wheat except this one bushel," one of the farmers said. "He says that it is his, and I say that it is mine. And that is why we are quarreling."

"Well, if that is all, then don't worry. Get me a small coffee cup and I will divide this last bushel equally between you," the boy offered. With the coffee cup he divided the bushel equally between the two farmers. They were so happy about this division that they stopped quarreling. They took the poor boy home with them and treated him as an honored guest and insisted that he spend the night with them. The next morning the boy started on his way, intending to find the mountain that the first giant had spoken about.

The boy found Mt. Massis and climbed to the very summit. He looked down to the south and saw a stream with a rosebush on each side of it. He descended, picked two roses and collected some water from the nearby stream. He boiled the roses in the water, and with the rosewater in a jug he started for the palace.

Meanwhile, the princess remained very sick, and healer after healer turned away in despair. The king became impatient and ruled that anyone who attempted to cure his daughter and proved to be unsuccessful would be killed.

The poor boy went to the king and said that he was a healer and could cure the princess in six hours. He had the princess drink some of the rosewater; the pain stopped immediately because the liquid caused the demon to run away. All the ugly sores disappeared, too, and the princess became more beautiful than ever.

When the six hours were up, the poor boy invited the king and the queen to see the cured princess. "Daughter, daughter, where are you? Come to us if you can," the king called.

And the princess ran to her father. What happiness! The beautiful girl was cured! "Youth, my daughter was dead, and you made her live again. You are my son. She will be your wife, and when I die, you will rule my kingdom. She is my only daughter. She is yours!" the king said. So the poor boy and the princess were married with great happiness, and the wedding lasted for forty days and forty nights.

Meanwhile, the rich boy had returned home and told the villagers of his good fortune. Everyone was proud of him, and the villagers gave big feasts to honor him. When the poor boy's mother heard that her son's friend had returned, she ran to him to ask about her son.

"Where is my son? How is it that he did not return with you?" she asked.

"Oh, your son! When I last saw him, he was a bad man, leading an evil life. By this time he is most probably dead," the rich boy answered.

The mother cried and returned home.

One day the prince remembered his old mother whom he had left behind. "I wonder what has happened to her; I wonder if she is alive or dead," the prince thought to himself. He said to the king, "My King, I am indebted to you for many favors, but I must ask one thing of you."

"Yes, my son, ask."

"You know, I have an old mother in Akor, and I haven't seen her for a very long time. Give me your permission to visit her."

So the king agreed to this and had his messengers ride ahead and notify all the towns and villages of the royal journey. When the prince passed through a town or a village with his large troop of soldiers, he was treated with honor, and finally, he reached the village of his destination.

"Guard, I want all the horses of my men to be fed and kept at Serabian's stable," the prince ordered.

The messenger notified the rich boy that the prince had ordered food and shelter for all the horses of his troop. The rich boy became angry because he did not want to waste his grain and he did not want his stables used. He volunteered to distribute the horses throughout the village, but the messenger insisted that the rich boy alone was to be responsible for the horses.

The next morning the prince went to his old mother's hut and found her washing clothes. Of course, she did not recognize him because she did not know of his great good fortune. He went to her and said, "Don't you recognize me? I'm your son."

"Don't make a fool of me in my old age, sir. My son has been dead now for many years."

"Mother, I am your son; believe me," he said, throwing himself on her neck, weeping. Then upon holding him off and looking at him more closely, she recognized him, and the two wept and wept until they were parted. The prince ordered his servants to bathe and clothe his mother.

Meanwhile, the rich boy heard of this. "Well, well, so my good friend is back again. What shall I do? After treating him as I did, he will most certainly kill me," he said to himself, going to the prince's quarters.

When he came before the prince, he said, "Your Majesty, how well you look! You do remember me, don't you? We were such good friends when we were younger! Come, let bygones be bygones and let us be friends again." As the prince was a bighearted man, he could not hold a grudge. So he forgave and began speaking pleasantly to his former friend.

"Tell me, how did you become a prince?" the rich boy asked.

So the poor boy told of his adventures. "I did as the giants predicted: I saved the boy, I saved the two farmers, and I saved the princess. Then the king married me to his daughter, and here I am," the boy said.

The rich boy returned to his home, ordered his servants to prepare his fastest horse and rode off in a hurry. He found the road which had seven paths leading from it. He took the one to the extreme left, climbed the mountain and looked down to see the palace. He descended, he knocked on the door, and when he received no answer, he opened the door and went in. He ate some food and suddenly heard a great noise. He looked for a hiding place and succeeded in finding the hole where his friend had hidden.

The three giants entered the palace and began sniffing around. "I smell human flesh!" one said after the other.

"Brothers, let's search very carefully today," the first giant said. "Someone must be here because the last time we smelled human flesh, nothing which we predicted happened. There is only one explanation for this: someone is hiding here and listening to what we are saying."

So the three giants looked through the palace very carefully and finally found the rich boy hiding in the hole where he had taken refuge. There was a huge kettle of boiling water on the fire, and the giants took the boy and threw him in it. When he was bright red, the giants sat down to eat a delicious supper.

The prince returned to his kingdom, taking along his aged mother. They all lived together very happily. The prince decided that there was not to be poverty in his country, so he did not collect taxes and helped everyone so generously that no one suffered from want. In the course of time, the king died, and the prince became a ruler who took good care of all his subjects. I believe that he is still reigning, still not collecting taxes and living happily with his subjects as though he were one of them.

42. The Devoted Son

There were once a mother and a son. The boy was a merchant and supported his mother. One day his mother asked, "Son, why don't you get married?"

"Why should I get married? My wife would not treat you well," the boy answered. But the mother, who did not think that this was possible, kept insisting. So finally, one day the boy got married.

"Wife, I am going away with my caravans, and I want you to take good care of my mother. Do not mistreat her, or I will settle with you upon my return," the husband instructed his wife.

Now, the wife always had her eye outside.* When her husband left, she wanted to get rid of her mother-in-law so that she could be free to do as she wanted. "I'll send her to school. Then she'll be gone all day," the wife said to herself. So she went to the schoolteacher and asked, "If I send my mother-in-law to you and give you this much money, will you keep her with you all day? You won't have to teach her anything, only keep her away from my house."

This story was told by Mrs. Mariam Serabian.
* A popular Armenian expression which means that a person is looking for more amorous experiences.

The teacher thought it over. "Well, why not?" he asked himself. So it was decided that the mother-in-law should go to school. Morning after morning the wife packed a lunch, tied a school bag around her mother-in-law's neck and sent her to school. The teacher kept her there all day and sent her home late at night. This went on day after day for almost a whole year. One day the son returned home unexpectedly. "Where's my mother?" he asked when he found her absent from the house. He sat down to wait. In the evening the mother returned with her books under her arm.

"Mother, where have you been?" her son asked.

"I am going to school, my son," the mother answered.

"School? What are you saying? School, at your age?"

"I have been going to school for nearly a year," the mother replied.

"Ah, this is how my wife takes care of my mother! I have no need for this kind of wife!" So saying, the boy divorced his first wife.

After some time the mother again began to ask her son why he did not marry. "Mother, you saw what happened to my first marriage. What will a second be like?" he answered.

But his mother was not to be quieted, and finally, the boy entered into a second marriage. "I want you to treat my mother well. If you do not, what happened to my first wife will happen to you," the boy threatened his wife when he was about to start with another caravan.

"Never fear, I will not disobey you," she assured him. But when her husband was gone, she, too, wanted her mother-in-law out of the way. She went to a dressmaker and asked, "If I give you so much money, will you keep my mother-in-law with you all day and send her home at night?"

The dressmaker thought it over and said, "Why not?" So the mother-in-law was apprenticed to a dressmaker. She would be driven out of the house early in the morning and was not allowed to return until late at night.

One day the husband unexpectedly returned to find that his mother was not at home. "Wife, where is my mother?" he asked.

"She is visiting," the wife answered. So he sat down to wait for her return. When she finally came home, he asked, "Mother, where have you been?"

"I am apprenticed to a dressmaker, my son," the mother answered.

"What? At your age? Haven't you worked hard enough all your life without this?" he shouted. So he divorced his second wife, too.

But the mother still had not learned her lesson. "Son, you should marry and have a family," she remarked continually.

"Mother, I have already had two unsuccessful marriages."

But his mother was a persistent woman, and he was forced into a third marriage. "Wife, remember you must treat my mother with kindness. Think of what happened to my other two wives," he said, leaving again with another caravan.

"Ah! his other two wives were foolish! I won't make the mistake they made. I have a better plan," she said to herself. She went to the priest and asked, "If I give you so much money, will you bury my mother-in-law, even though she is not dead?"

"How could I do that?"

"We can dig a grave and make a burial sack to put into it. I will have a gravestone made and set up on the grave. No one will know but you and me, and I will make it well worth your while," she said.

As the priest was in need of money, he consented to take part in this plan. Accordingly, it was announced that the mother-in-law had died and that the burial was to be private. The grave was prepared, the burial sack was put into it and the grave was closed. A beautiful gravestone was placed over it. "Now, that is done; but what shall I do with this mother-in-law of mine?" the wife asked herself. As if to answer her question, a group of gypsies passed by the house. "Oh, gypsies, gypsies, come here!" she called after them. One of the gypsies came to her. "If I give you so much money, will you take this woman away with you?" she asked. The gypsy was happy at the thought of getting both money and woman and quickly accepted.

So now the third wife finally was rid of her mother-in-law, and she began to enjoy herself. One day, suddenly, her husband returned. "Where is my mother?" he asked when he entered the house.

"Our worthy mother is dead," the third wife said, hanging her head and crying. She took him by the hand and led him to the garden where she and the priest had pretended to bury the mother. The son saw a beautiful gravestone, a well-tended grave and sadness on his wife's face.

"At last, with my mother's death, I have found a real wife!" he said. "What sadness she has on her face."

"Ah!" said the wife to herself. "My plan is working very well. He thinks that I am a good woman, and he has no doubts that his mother is dead!" The husband did not say any more about his mother's death but silently prayed for the peace of her soul.

Now the gypsies to whom the man's mother had been given wanted to earn money through the talents of the old woman. They made her dance and sing for groups of people while they collected coins. She would dance a few steps, snap her fingers and begin singing: *

"We were a mother and a son,
Wealthy and very happy;
I insisted that my son marry,
But he said, 'No, my wife will not treat you well!'

"But I insisted and he married;
Soon he had to leave with his caravans,
And he left his wife and me alone.
My daughter-in-law sent me to school
    to stay all day, to be out of her way.

"So I went to school, day in and day out,
Until one day, many months later,
My son came home to find me gone.
When I returned that night, he asked me,
    'Where have you been, mother?'

" 'Son, I am going to school,' I told him.
'School, mother? At your age?' he asked me.
When he discovered that his wife forced me to go,
He divorced her.

"After some time, I insisted on a second marriage,
So my son married a second time.
Soon, he had to leave with his caravans
Leaving his second wife and me alone.

"Now, my second daughter-in-law apprenticed me to a dressmaker.
I went out early in the morning and returned late at night.
This continued for some time, until one day,
My son returned home.

" 'Where is my mother?' he asked his wife.
'She is visiting,' she answered.
When I returned home, he asked me where I had been,
'I am apprenticed to a dressmaker, my son,' I told him.

* Informant did the same.

318

"He was very angry and divorced his second wife.
After some time, I forced him into a third marriage.
Soon, my son had to leave with his caravans;
My daughter-in-law and I were left alone.

"For a time, we were happy and content to be together.
One day, she saw gypsies passing our house.
She called them in and gave them some money;
They took me with them. Now I dance and sing, dance and sing."

As she danced and sang, the people were greatly amused, and the gypsies were happy. One day the gypsies saw that she was getting tired and could not get around as she once did.

"I think that she is going to die. I don't want blood on our hands. Let us take her back where we got her. If we leave her anywhere in her old neighborhood, she will find her way back home," one of the gypsies said. The other gypsies looked at her and felt so sorry for her that they agreed to take her near her home and leave her there.

Now the woman's son, who was a rich merchant, owned a large market. One day he was standing in his market and looking down the road when he saw a group of gypsies stop near his store. A crowd gathered, and the gypsies made an old woman perform.

"What is this? Why do those gypsies treat such an old woman so? If I have to, I will buy her from them and free her from this slavery," he said, not knowing who she was. The son was standing in his store watching the old woman when suddenly he began to reflect upon her song. "Why, that is my mother!" he said, running out. But as the mother did not recognize him, he did not say anything to her but went to the gypsies. "What are you doing with this old woman? Aren't you ashamed of yourselves?" he asked.

"Do you want her?" the gypsies asked, glad to find someone to take care of her.

"Yes," the boy answered.

"Well then, you take her," they said and went along.

The son ordered his servants to take his mother home without letting his wife see her. He ordered them to wash, clothe and feed the old woman. Then he went to his wife. "Isn't it a shame that my mother had to die so soon?" he asked.

"Yes, poor mother," she said, her face all innocence and sadness.

"Oh, what a fool I have been!" the husband said to himself. But aloud he said, "Wife, I am going to call all the townsfolk to my mother's grave." And all the townsfolk were called, including the priest. "Friends, how many of you witnessed my mother's burial?" he asked them. As the burial had been a private one, no one had been permitted to attend it, so none of them could speak out.

"Father, did you bury her?" he asked the priest.

"Yes, my son, I did."

"Wife, were you present?"

"Yes, I was."

"Then tell me, how could you bury someone who is not dead?" he asked them.

"Absurd! How could that be?"

"Well, I will open her grave and prove it to you."

"But you can't open a grave until you have a permit," the priest said.

"All right, then I will get one." The son went to the town official, and because he was a wealthy man, he received a permit. And the grave-diggers began their work. Soon they uncovered the burial sack, but when they opened it, there was nothing in it.

"Do you understand now?" the son asked the people.

"What is the meaning of this?"

"Well, here is my story. We were two: mother and son. My mother forced me into a marriage. But when I was away with my caravans, my wife sent my aged mother to school. When I learned about this, I divorced her. Then my mother forced me into a second marriage, and after some time, when I went away again, my second wife apprenticed my aged mother to a dressmaker. When I learned of this, I divorced my second wife. But that was not enough. My mother forced me into a third marriage. And when I went away with my caravans, my third wife sold my mother to gypsies. Then she gave the priest some money and had a grave dug, leading people to believe that my mother was dead. She even had a beautiful headstone set. When I came home, I was told of my mother's death, and I believed it. Today a group of gypsies was dancing and singing, and among them was my old mother, dancing and singing the story of her misfortune. Now tell me, friends, what shall I do with such a wife?" he asked them.

"Put her in that burial sack and close the ground over her," the bystanders shouted.

So the third wife was placed in the burial sack and was

buried. Then the boy went into the house and brought his mother out for the people to see. The kind mother, when she learned of her daughter-in-law's death, began crying. "She was young; you shouldn't have punished her so."

The son paid no attention to her words, and the two of them lived very happily together for many years.

43. The Ditch-Digger Falls into His Own Ditch

There was once a beggar who went from village to village on certain days of the week to ask for alms. One village which he visited regularly was very generous to him. When anyone gave him food or a few *para* [Turkish coin], he did not thank them but instead would say, "May you receive what you have given." Because of this phrase, everyone liked him and gave him all the more.

In this village which was especially kind to him there lived two brothers-in-law who were both rich merchants. But as they were merchants, they seldom stayed at home, and their wives were lonely. Soon they began receiving the men of the village in their homes. Whenever the two women helped the beggar, he would say, "May you receive what you have given." The women, not knowing that he said this to everyone who helped him, took the statement personally.

"Sister, we must get rid of that beggar. He knows of our affairs and will tell our husbands some day. Every time we give him anything, he says the same thing. Certainly he knows something which will bring us no good," one of the sisters said to the other.

"Yes, it will not do for him to tell our husbands. We must get rid of him," the other sister agreed.

One day the two sisters got together and made some *gatah* [coffee rolls] and put some poison in them. They put nice decorations on them and made them as pretty and as tempting as possible. Each took one to the beggar. The poor man thanked them in his usual way. The women were angry but said softly, "We shall see what you will receive."

That day the husbands of the two sisters were riding past the beggar. "Brother, I am so hungry that I cannot possibly ride home without food," one brother-in-law said to the other.

"Yes, I am hungry, too. Perhaps if we ask this beggar, he

This story was told by Hovhannes Kaprelian.

will sell us some of his bread," the other replied. So they asked the beggar for some of his food. The beggar, seeing that the two men were rich merchants, looked through his provision sack, pulled out the two pretty *gatah* and gave them to the men. The merchants threw him some money, ate the *gatah* and rode on.

But before long one brother-in-law said to the other, "Brother, I feel sick. There is something wrong with my stomach. I can hardly stay on my horse. Let us ride faster."

"Yes, I feel sick, too; I can't draw my breath."

When they finally did reach home, they fell down and fainted. The wives called the healers and learned that their husbands had been poisoned. "What did you have to eat? When did you last eat?" the healers asked the men.

One of the merchants told of the beggar on the road. The healers questioned the beggar and discovered that the two *gatah* that he gave the merchants had been given him by the merchants' wives. "Why did you give poisoned *gatah* to this poor beggar?" they asked.

The women were forced to admit their unfaithfulness and told why they wanted to get rid of the beggar.

So, you see, the ditch-digger falls into his own ditch; don't do wrong to others so that you won't find wrong done unto you.

44. Foretelling the Future

The wife of a farmer was taking care of the sheep in the fields when she gave birth to a child. A shepherd nearby saw an angel descend from heaven and write something on the baby's forehead. But since the shepherd could not see what was written, he asked the angel, "What did you do to that child?"

"I wrote his future on his forehead," the angel said.

"Why? Is he such an unusual child?"

"All human beings have their future written on their foreheads when they are born," the angel said, preparing to leave. "This child will fall from a tree and die at the age of seven."

The shepherd was very much interested: "I'll ask that woman's name, and after seven years, I will return to see if the angel's prediction comes true." And this he did.

After seven years he decided to find the woman and see how the child was. He found her house but saw that there was a

This story was told by Antrias Amboian.

large crowd gathered around it. "What has happened?" he asked a neighbor.

"The little boy who lives here fell from a tree and died, and the parents want to kill the other boy who was playing with him. They say that because their son died, his playmate must die, too. Of course, the playmate's parents won't permit this, and so the two families are quarreling."

"Oh, oh! the angel was right," the man said to himself, "but one death is enough. I must try to stop the second." He pushed through the crowd, went inside the house and asked the family about the trouble.

The first woman said, "My son was playing in the tree with this woman's son, and my boy fell off the tree and died. This woman's son should die, too."

"If your son fell off, why should my son die?" the second woman asked.

"Listen to me for a minute," the shepherd said. "Do you remember me?" he asked the first woman. "I am the shepherd you saw on the day your son was born in the fields. That same day, at the same time your son was born, an angel came down from heaven and wrote on his forehead. I asked the angel what he had written, and I was told that the little boy would fall from a tree at the age of seven and die. Now it has happened, and no one is to blame. Come, spare this little boy's life."

The first woman, seeing the truth of the argument, stopped asking for the life of the little boy. "What God has determined, we cannot prevent," she said.*

45. The Soul-Taking Angel

There was once a poor man who had so many children that no one wanted to be godfather for his family because it would

This story was told by Nishan Krikorian.

* Armenians even today believe that the writing on a man's forehead is predetermined. The Writer, or Grog, is believed by many to be the good angel who sits on the right shoulder of each of us, urging us to do good things and keeping accurate records of such doings. The bad angel, on the other hand, sits on the left shoulder and encourages us to do wrong. (Abeghian, *op. cit.*, pp. 16, 50–56.)

This writer, Tiur (Tir), was the scribe of the supreme god, Aramazd. He kept a record of good and evil deeds of men, and probably the events which were to come. These records were kept on heavenly tablets as well as on the forehead of each child born. (Ananikian, *op. cit.*, p. 30.)

be too costly.* After asking one person after another without any success, the father decided to find a godfather somewhere else than in his own village. He walked and walked until he came across a man who was the angel Gabriel in disguise. But, of course, the father did not know this. The angel knew the man's problem and wanted to help him. "Friend, where are you going?" he asked.

"I am going to find a godfather for my children," the father said.

"Will no one be godfather for you in your own village?"

"No, I am too poor, and I have too many children. My townsfolk say that it would be too costly."

"Well then, don't worry about it. I will be your godfather," the angel said.

So the father and the angel went back to the village. When the christenings were completed, the angel made ready to leave. "Friend, I feel sorry for you because you have so many children and so little money; let me help you. I will give you a few herbs and a suitcase. This will enable you to work as a healer. But there is one thing you must remember: when you are called to a sick person's home, I will be there, too, though no one but you will be able to see me. If I am standing at the head of the sick person, that person will die, and you must not do anything to save him. But if I am standing at his feet, give him a little of any of these herbs, and he will get well immediately. But remember—if I am at the head of the person, do not attempt to cure him," the angel said, and he left.

The father did as the angel directed and soon became known all over as a great and wise healer. Of course, with each success, he received money. Soon his family was in better circumstances than it had ever been before. One day the princess of the country became very sick, and a great reward was offered to anyone who could cure her. The father wanted to claim the reward so he decided to try. But as he looked at the princess, he saw that the angel Gabriel was standing at her head instead of at her feet.

"Ach! [Alas!] Of all times for the angel to stand at the head

* According to the informant, in Armenia the title of godfather also carries with it certain financial responsibilities. In the case of a girl, the godfather pays such expenses connected with the christening and gift for the child, food and sometimes music for the guests. If the child to be christened is a boy, the godfather pays all the above expenses and frequently the wedding expenses when the godson is married.

of the sick one!" he said to himself. He thought about it a bit and couldn't see why he should lose the reward just because the angel was in the wrong position. Again he thought: "How unfortunate that the angel should be standing where he is!" He had an idea: how would it be if he changed the position of the princess so quickly that the angel could not change his place as quickly? Then the angel would be standing at her feet, as was necessary for the cure of her sickness. "Your Majesty," he told the king, "I can cure your daughter if you will give me four alert men."

The king called his swiftest men before him and said, "Do anything this man tells you to do."

"Now listen very carefully to what I have to say," the man began. "When I give you the signal, you quickly change the princess' position. Place her feet where her head now is, but do it so fast that no one can see what is being done. If you will do this, I can promise you that the princess will be cured."

So they all went into the princess' room, and still the angel was standing at her head. The doctor gave the signal, and the men quickly changed the position of the princess, placing her feet where her head had been. And it was done so fast that the angel, who now stood at her feet, did not realize what had happened. Then the doctor immediately took out one of the herbs and gave it to the princess. Very soon she was well again.

Now the angel was very angry at the healer for disobeying him. He had ordered the man not to touch the person at whose head he was standing, but this man had done just that very thing. The angel was intent on punishing him. One day the angel came and stood at the doctor's head.

"Welcome, godfather, how are you today?" the man said, trying to convince himself that the angel was not calling for him.

"I am happy to see you, father of the children that I have christened. I have come to take your soul, as you well know."

"Now, godfather, you don't intend to do that?" the man said, trying to take a jesting tone.

"Yes, I do. Because you disobeyed me by changing the position of the princess, you will be punished," the angel said.

"But I have a large family, and you are godfather to my children. What will happen to my wife and children?"

"Leave them to me. I will see that they are taken care of."

"Very well then, if you are intent on killing me, kill me. Only grant me one last request," the man asked. The angel consented to this. "Do not let me die without saying the Lord's Prayer."

"All right, I will not take your soul without your having said the Lord's Prayer," the angel agreed, and he waited. As the prayer wasn't being said, he asked after some time, "Well, what are you waiting for? Say the Lord's Prayer."

"I don't intend to say it," the man replied.

"But you must!"

"I won't say it," the man answered, knowing that the angel could not kill him until he had said the prayer. And this he had no intention of doing!

Finally, seeing that there was no way out, the angel left. He was intent, however, on having the man say the Lord's Prayer at the earliest possible time.

One day the angel disguised himself as a little boy. He took a copy of the Lord's Prayer underneath his arm and, crying, began to walk in the direction of the man. The man, seeing a poor little boy in tears, asked him what had happened to make him cry. "What should happen? My teacher has given me this book to read, and I can't read it. He told me that if I couldn't read it in the next class, he would whip me," the boy said, weeping some more.

Now the healer was a soft-hearted man, and he could not endure seeing a small boy crying over such a small matter. "Don't cry, my son, I will help you. Come, let us see what the book says." So the man began reading the Lord's Prayer, and the little boy read after him. As soon as the prayer was finished, the little boy changed to his original form—that of the angel Gabriel.

"Now that you have finished saying the Lord's Prayer, I will take your soul," the angel said, and he swiftly did this. Then the angel went to the man's family and asked for the oldest son. He told the son of his father's death and of the cause of it. "Now, I want you to start where your father left off," he told the boy. "I will give you the same herbs I gave to your father. And I will give you the same warning. Do not touch a sick person if I am standing at his head. If I am standing at his feet, then give him any of these herbs, and he will immediately get well. But remember do not touch anyone at whose head I am standing. Don't do as your father did."

As far as we know, the son did not repeat his father's mistake, but worked according to the angel's wishes and became very famous and rich.

Their goal was realized, and so will ours be. The story is ended. From the sky fell three apples: one to me, one to the storyteller and one to the person who has entertained you.*

46. The Gold Piece

There was once a boy who wanted to get married so he told his parents of his intentions.

"Very well, son, you can get married if you will bring me a gold piece which you have earned by your labor," the father said.

The boy smiled, thinking that this was indeed an easy test. The next day he gave his father the necessary gold piece. The father took the money and threw it into the river. "Well, father, now may I get married?" the boy asked.

"No, my son. I told you that you must earn the gold piece. You have not earned this money."

The boy was surprised that his father knew the truth; but the next day, he borrowed a gold piece from his mother and took it to his father.

Again the father took the gold piece and threw it into the river. The boy was surprised but asked again, "Why do you do this? I have brought you a gold piece. May I get married now?"

Again the father refused permission, saying, "You did not earn this gold piece."

The boy started to think that this could go on for a long time and that he might never get married, so he decided to find work and earn the gold piece. After many days the boy took the

This story was told by Mrs. Hripsima Hoogasian.

* Armenians believed that the angel Gabriel, frequently referred to as *Grog*, was the Soul-Taker [*Hok-eh-ar*] who supposedly pulled the soul first to the knees, then to the heart, throat, then through the mouth. If the man had not led a good life, his death was painful because he fought fiercely with *Grog*, otherwise, he died with a smile on his face. (Abeghian, *op. cit.*, pp. 16–17.)

In older times, Armenians believed that the departed soul not only stayed near the body as long as it was not buried, but also stayed near the grave. On the day after the funeral, the soul went to the place of judgment, a trip which took seven days. Meanwhile the good and bad angels prepared their records for the Judge. If the good deeds were heavier, the soul went to heaven; otherwise, it went to hell. The bridge to heaven, called the *Mazer* [hair] Bridge, was believed to be so fragile that it would break if the sins of the soul were heavy and weighed it down. (Tcheraz, *op. cit.*, p. 257; Abeghian, *op. cit.*, p. 20.)

gold piece he had earned to his father. When the father started to throw the money into the river, the boy threw his arms around him and cried, "No, father, don't throw it away. I have spent many back-breaking days earning it."

"Now, my son, you can get married," the father said. "At last you know the value of money, and you will spend it with wisdom."

So the boy got married and never spent his money foolishly.

47. The Emperor's Lesson

Once there was a great emperor who would change his clothes every night and walk among his people to learn more about their condition. One night he walked for miles into the country and saw a light through the woods. As he approached it, he saw that it came from a tiny cottage. Being tired and hungry, he knocked on the door, and a farmer opened it and invited him in.

"Do you want a visitor?" the emperor asked.

"Yes, we welcome a visitor, but we are hungry and poor and cannot treat you as a guest should be treated," the farmer said. He did not realize, however, that he was speaking to an emperor.

"What do you do here?" the emperor asked.

"What are we to do? We are poor and hungry," the farmer said.

"How many children do you have?"

"I have two daughters and one son, a wife and myself to feed."

"Well, how do you live then?"

"How are we to live? We gather the grain and eat it, and if there is no grain or grass, we do not eat. Toward the spring it is a little easier," the farmer said.

"Why don't you plant seeds? You have much empty land around you," the emperor asked.

"We don't have oxen, we don't have seeds, how shall we plant?" the farmer asked. "You have come and reminded us of our troubles again."

"Well, I am not rich," the emperor said, "but I can do you this much of a favor. I will give you five pieces of gold; go get what you need for planting."

This story was told by Mrs. Mariam Serabian.
Three unpublished versions are located in the Comparative Studies.

"Ha, you see my poverty and want to give me five gold pieces, but if you should come and want them back, what would I do?" the farmer asked.

"Go! Plant, reap, and I will give you five years to repay me," the emperor said, giving him the five gold pieces, and he returned to his palace the next day.

The farmer and his family bought a pair of oxen and some seeds and started planting. They married their two girls, and three years later they married their son.

Five years later the emperor remembered his debtors. "Let me go and see what has happened to them," he said, putting on his old clothes again. When he reached his destination, he saw a very pretty little boy playing outside the cottage door. The emperor was happy to see the child. "This child seems to be a very smart boy; if those people don't repay me, I'm going to take him home with me," the emperor said to himself. (The emperor's great misfortune was that he had no children of his own and was raising his niece as a daughter.) He went into the cottage and found the people much happier and their living conditions much better.

While the emperor was talking with the farmer, they saw a dervish passing the house and called him to read the little boy's fortune. "You have a beautiful child, and because of him, you are going to receive many riches. This boy will someday be the son-in-law of the emperor," the dervish said.

"Oh, so this child is going to be my son-in-law; he's going to get my kingdom, is he? I must get rid of him," the emperor said to himself. "Have you the money to repay me now?" he asked the farmer when the dervish left.

"No, I don't have it all saved yet," the farmer said.

"I'll give you another year to pay me. If you don't, I will take this child in payment for the debt!" the emperor said. The farmer had nothing to say. The emperor stayed at the cottage for eight days. At the end of this time he asked himself, "Why wait a year to get that boy? Why not take him now?" So he said to the farmer, "Either you must give me back my five pieces of gold or you must give me this child. I will stay here until you do."

The grandparents begged him not to take the boy away from them.

"I'll give you anything you want for the child. And you can have another baby next year," the emperor said.

Finally, the emperor took the boy and gave the farmer and

his son much money. He carried the child quite a distance from the farmer's cottage, tied his feet and hands together, put a big rock on his stomach and left him on the ground in the woods. Then he returned to the palace, thinking that the child would surely die.

Several days later, the baby's parents and grandparents went looking for grape leaves which they need to make *sarma* [a mixture of ground meat, rice, seasonings wrapped in grape leaves]. As they went deep into the woods, they came across the baby. But he had changed so much that they did not recognize him as their own. "That man took our child away. Let's take this one home with us and raise him as our own," they said. So they took the little boy home and found deep gashes in his arms and legs. They applied several remedies but still the scars remained. In time the boy grew to be sixteen years of age.

"Let me go and see what those people are doing now," the emperor said one day. He changed his clothes and went to the farmer's cottage again. He saw a husky youth of sixteen working hard in the fields. He went inside and was welcomed. The farmer did not remember that this was his former visitor.

"When did you have this child?" the emperor asked during the visit.

"You know, many years ago a man came and took our child away. A few days later we went to gather grape leaves and found a little boy with his feet and hands tied together, so we brought him home with us and made him our child," the farmer's daughter-in-law said.

The emperor, who had a little beard, stuck the tip of it in his mouth when he heard this. "Oh, so this is the same boy after all!" When he looked at the boy's arm, he saw a scar and asked about it. The farmer told him that they had tried different kinds of medicines on the boy's wounds after they brought him home but that the scars had remained.

"I like you, my son," the emperor said to the youth. "I am going to send you to the emperor's palace with a letter telling them to give you anything you want." So he wrote, "*Aman, aman* [for goodness' sake], if this boy reaches you in the morning, kill him in the morning; if he reaches you at night, kill him at night." He gave the letter to this boy to carry to the emperor's palace.

The boy took the letter and went to the palace and was taken into a beautiful room to wait for the vizier. The emperor's niece happened to be passing by and when she saw the youth, was struck by his great beauty.

"What are you doing here?" she asked, taking his hand.

"I have a letter for the emperor's vizier," he answered.

"Let me see it," she said, taking and opening her uncle's letter. She was very much surprised at the contents of the letter and wrote on another sheet of royal paper, "I am sending this boy to the palace; as soon as he arrives, marry him to my niece. If you fail to do this, all of you will have your heads cut off upon my return."

She gave the boy the letter she had written, took his hand and led him to the vizier. When the vizier read the letter, there was not much he could do but carry out the emperor's orders.

"Will you marry this girl?" he asked the boy. The boy quickly agreed to this, and a wedding was arranged which lasted for forty days and forty nights. And so the boy and the emperor's niece were married.

When the emperor returned to his palace from his trip, he saw a wedding taking place. "What is this?" he asked his vizier.

"Your Majesty, we have acted according to your letter," he said, showing him the girl's letter.

The emperor stroked his beard and thought for a while. "God's order shall be fulfilled," he said. "I tried to get rid of this boy twice, but both times I was unsuccessful. I will accept him as my son-in-law and give him my kingdom." The emperor carried out his promise and accepted the boy as his son-in-law.

One day the boy came before him and asked if he might bring his parents and grandparents to the palace. "My son," the emperor replied, "God's will shall be fulfilled. Go, bring your family here."

The emperor came down from his throne and seated the boy upon it. "Now you are the ruler of my kingdom," he said. Then he ordered that the news of the change of rulers be spread throughout the kingdom. And so it was done, and everyone lived happily ever after.

Understand that God has written our destiny on our foreheads. No one can change his own destiny or that of anyone else.

48. Honor

There was once a very rich man who had a wife and a very beautiful daughter. In those days it was proper for rich folk to

This story was told by Mrs. Akabi Mooradian.

make a pilgrimage to Jerusalem. This rich man was planning such a journey with his wife. However, he did not want to take his daughter along because he feared that her rare beauty might bring her harm. So he went to the highest priest of their town and said, "Father priest, I leave my daughter in your care. Although she has all the necessary protection she needs, she will be much safer if you look after her. Here are the keys to my house."

The priest who was to guard the daughter was a rather young man and had always admired the girl. He was extremely happy at this turn of events and could hardly wait for the departure of the girl's parents. After they had gone, he saw the beautiful girl daily and revealed his feelings.

"No, never, never! I would rather die than to yield to you," she said, shuddering.

The priest was not discouraged but kept repeating his requests. "You are unworthy of the title of 'priest,'" the girl said one day. "Everyone respects you and thinks that you are a sinless man. When my parents return, I shall tell them about you."

This caused the priest to think: what if this girl should tell her parents of his behavior? What would become of him? "I must do something and must do it soon to protect myself," the priest said to himself. "I cannot wait until her parents' return, or she will tell them all." So he wrote a letter to the girl's father and told him that his daughter entertained a different man every day and that he could no longer be responsible for her.

The father was very angry and bitter. "Just as soon as we are out of the way, this is what she does!" he said. He wrote the priest a letter saying, "Before our return, you must get rid of our daughter and show us her bloody shirt." The priest was overjoyed for this solved the problem! He found a big husky man and said to him, "You must take the girl for a three-days' walk. When you have gone that distance, kill her, dip her undershirt in her own blood and bring it to me."

The priest went to the girl and said, "Your parents are returning, and I am sending you to meet them. I am also providing a protector for you so that no harm befalls you."

The girl and the strong man started out, and they walked for three days. Then the man took out his knife to cut her head off, but he knew of her innocence and could not move his hand to do it. "If I let you go free, will you promise me not to turn back but to go straight ahead?" he asked.

"Why are you doing this? Why did you bring me here? What have I done?" the innocent girl asked.

"I cannot tell you more. I was told to bring you here and kill you, to dip your undershirt in your own blood and take it back with me. Give me your shirt so that I may dip it in the blood of some animal," the man said. She thanked him for sparing her, took off her shirt and gave it to him. He wished her luck and left, taking the blood-stained shirt to the priest.

"I have been deceived," the girl said to herself, crying. "What have I done to deserve this?" She tried to find shelter, but it was impossible because she was in the woods, surrounded on one side by hills, and on the other, by high mountains.

Meanwhile, the priest kept the shirt until the girl's parents returned from their journey. Then he went to meet them and presented the shirt with great ceremony. "Sir, here is your honor. I have preserved it," he said. The father was very happy that no one would know of his daughter's disgrace and bestowed huge gifts upon the priest.

The girl in the forest looked around and, finding a shady tree, cried herself to sleep under it. That day a prince was hunting through the woods with his dog. The dog ran toward the girl and then back to the prince. He repeated this three times until the prince said to himself, "I wonder why my dog is behaving in such a strange way?" He went in the direction his dog had taken —and what did he see but a beautiful girl sleeping under the tree! She was so beautiful that she could say to the sun, "Sun, sun, go away, I will shine on the earth today." He didn't want to awaken her, but he was unable to control his dog when it began barking. The girl jumped up and saw them by her side.

"What are you doing under this tree?" the prince asked.

"I have always lived in this forest. I don't know who I am," the girl said, not wishing to tell him the truth because she was sure that he would not have a very high opinion of a girl who had been ordered killed.

"How do you live in these woods?" the prince asked her. "Come home with me."

"I live as I can," she answered.

"I am taking you with me and will make you my bride."

"If luck will have it, so it shall be," she answered.

"Why don't you ask me who I am?"

"Whoever you are makes no difference to me."

"My father is the king of a tribe of white Indians. Come home with me," he said.

When they reached India, the boy told his father that he intended to marry the girl. "But, son, you must remember your position. Who is she? Who are her parents? What sort of a woman would live in the mountains? Is she fit to bear your sons?" the king asked.

"I don't care who she may have been. She is mine now," the prince answered.

"If that is so, if your love is so great, you have my permission to marry her," his father said. They had a wedding for forty days and forty nights, but the bride secretly cried to herself: "The only daughter of a rich family and neither my parents nor my friends are present at my wedding!" She tried to keep her grief hidden from her new husband.

Four years later she was the mother of two sons, one three years old and the other yet in the cradle. One night when her youngest son had fallen ill and she was singing him a lullaby, she began to cry. The prince, who was sleeping, was awakened by her crying and immediately went to her. "What is wrong? Why are you crying? I have noticed that you have been very sad in recent months."

"Nothing is wrong," she answered.

"If you don't tell me, I will leave you."

"You have never given much thought to this, but how can a person ever be born in the mountains and live without human help? Yet this is what I told you I did, and you believed me. Of course, I have parents, too." When the prince asked how far away her parents were, she said, "It would take us seven days and seven nights to reach their home."

"You are just homesick," her husband said. "I will send you home to visit your family for a few months. I will give you a strong guard, and you take our children with you. Your parents will be happy to see them."

In those days when an important person traveled, he had a large caravan with a troop of guards to protect him. So tents, soldiers and a full caravan were prepared for the princess.

The princess, with her children and the guards provided for them, started on their journey. They walked and walked until it was dark, then they pitched their tents. The princess was in her own tent with her two children. As it happened, the commander of the guards was infatuated with her. Now that her husband, the

334

prince, was not there, he felt that he could go ahead with his plans. He walked into her tent and announced that he was going to spend the night with her.

"I will never let you," she cried in horror.

"If you don't, I will kill your older son."

"I cannot help what you do, but I will never permit you to dishonor me," she said. So the commander killed the older son and buried him beneath the tent.

The second day they walked until it was dark, and the princess went into her tent with her younger son. The commander renewed his proposition of the night before. When the princess refused him again, he threatened to kill her younger son.

"I cannot help what you do. You have already killed one of my sons, and you may kill this one, too, but I will never submit to what you ask. Even if you kill me, I will not be your tool," she said.

So the commander killed her younger son and buried him beneath her tent.

The third day they walked until it was dark. The princess was all alone in her tent when the commander again walked in to say that he was going to spend the night with her. "If you don't consent, I will kill you."

"Very well, then I consent. But you must permit me to go outside for a moment," she said. The commander hesitated because he did not trust her. "Tie one end of a rope around my waist, and you hold the other end," she said. "Then you can be sure that I will not escape."

So the commander did just that. She walked out of the tent and went into the woods. There she untied the rope from her waist and tied it around a tree. She started running toward her father's country, and when she was too tired to run further, she hid in a cave.

The commander pulled and pulled the rope but nothing happened. He followed the rope and saw that it was tied around a tree. He was so angry at being tricked by a woman that he blew on his horn and gathered all his soldiers. "Get ready, we are turning back," he ordered. When they arrived at the palace, the commander told the prince a story very different from the truth.

"Your Highness, the princess has run away," he said.

"Didn't I tell you, my son, that a person found in the mountains would not make a good wife?" the king asked his son.

"What the commander says is not true," the prince said. "You

335

must give me soldiers, father. I must learn what has happened to my wife."

Taking a troop of soldiers and that same commander, the prince started to search for his wife. They walked all day, and when it was dark, they set up their tent on the very spot where the older boy had been killed.

"Do you see this spot, Your Highness?" the commander asked. "It is the grave of your first son. Your wife killed him."

"Guards, dig the ground," the prince ordered, and when they did, they found the body of the first son. The prince wept, but what could he do?

The next day they walked and walked until it was dark and set up their tent on the spot where the second son was killed. "Do you see this spot, Your Highness?" the commander asked. "It is the grave of your second son. Your wife killed him here."

The prince ordered his soldiers to dig the ground and found the body of his second son. Again he wept bitterly.

The third day they walked until it was dark, and then they pitched their tent. "Do you see this spot, Your Highness?" the commander asked. "This is the spot where your wife ran away."

After they had walked four more days, they came to the country of the princess' father.

Meanwhile, the princess had walked through woods and mountains, trying to reach her father's country. When she arrived there, she was tired; her feet were bruised and bleeding. But she walked to the place where her father's many shepherds were tending his vast herds of sheep. All the suffering that she had endured had changed her so much that the shepherds did not recognize their former mistress. She went to one of them. "Whose shepherd are you?" she asked.

"I am ———'s shepherd," he answered.

"How much does he pay you?"

"So much."

"If I give you three times as much as that, will you give me your clothes and let me do your work?" she asked.

The shepherd was very happy to accept this trade. And as the princess had much gold with her, she gave him a few pieces. The shepherd gave her his clothes and went home. The princess wore the shepherd's clothes over her own and cut her hair short so that no one could tell that she was a girl. She wore a sheepskin cap and looked very ugly.

Meanwhile, the prince was still searching for his wife. "God will open a door," the prince said as he sat beneath a shady tree to rest. "If we ask that shepherd over there for information, perhaps he will be able to help us." The guards called to the shepherd (who was the princess in disguise).

"Whoever wants to talk to me must come here," was the reply of the shepherd. "If you need me, come here. When I need you, I will come to you." The prince was very angry upon hearing these words but finally went to the shepherd.

"Who are you?" the prince asked.

"I'm one of God's images," the shepherd replied.

"Whose land is this? Whose are these animals and these shepherds?"

"They are _____'s."

"I am the prince of India, and these are my men. Can you take us to your master as his guests tonight?"

"I can take you to my master, but whether he will accept you as his guests is his own affair," the shepherd said.

They went to the master's house, and the rich man welcomed them and had a big feast quickly prepared for the royal guests. After the feast the prince asked everyone present to tell a story to discover who was the best storyteller. The high priest and the commander were present in the room, and the princess (who had on her shepherd's disguise) had a difficult time controlling herself as she sat in the corner trying to look dumb.

All the others told stories before her time came.

"Well, baldy (they thought that she was bald because she kept on her sheepskin cap), what story will you tell?"

"I have a story to tell, and all must listen to what I have to say."

"What do you have to say?" they asked, mockingly.

"But once I start my story, no one can leave this room," she continued. "If you must go out for any reason, go now. For no matter what happens later, I will not let you leave."

They agreed, and all who wanted to go out did so, and soon everyone was ready to listen to her story. "Put all the windows down and lock the doors," she said. After that was done, everyone waited to hear what the shepherd had to say.

So the princess told her own story in such a way that it seemed as though she were speaking of a stranger. When she came to the part where the parents entrusted their daughter to a priest, the high priest started complaining about his stomach and rushed for the door. But since she had given orders beforehand, the man could not get out. So the princess went on with her story. When she came to the part where the prince sent his wife and children to her family for a visit, it was the commander who suddenly tried to escape. But he had no more success than the priest, and the princess went on with her story. The prince, of course, had listened to the very end, and when she revealed who she was, he rushed to her and embraced her.

The high priest and the commander were found guilty and were tied to the tails of wild jackasses. When these jackasses were whipped, they ran in all directions, over all sorts of roads, until the two men's bodies were torn to pieces.

From the sky fell three apples: one for me, one for the storyteller and one for the person who has kept you entertained.

49. Nature's Ways

There was once a king who had only one daughter. He wanted her never to marry so that he could take care of her and have her under his watchful eye. He wanted her to know nothing of the world, nothing of life, and never to love anyone but himself.

After much thought he called in his adviser and discussed this problem. Together they planned a beautiful palace on a lonely island in the middle of a lake. The girl, only seven at this time, was to live there with women servants only and a female teacher.

The king carried out his plan. He had a beautiful palace built for his daughter, and several female servants and a woman teacher were hired. There were no windows in the palace so that the girl could not see out. She had no visitors except her father who saw her for three or four hours on Sunday. All the doors of the building were locked, and only the king had a key to the outside door.

Years went by until this daughter became eighteen years old. She learned a great many things, but it seemed to her that the books she read were dull and said nothing. She began to think for herself. "What kind of a life is this? All my servants are women; my teacher is a woman. If all the world is peopled only by girls, what is my father?" If she had had more courage, she

This story was told by Mrs. Akabi Mooradian.

would have asked her father about this, but as it was she only asked her teacher.

"I am going to ask you a question, but you must tell me the truth. I have no mother, no sister, no friend. You are everything to me. Answer me as a mother. Why am I on this island alone? All the people around me are women, but my father is different. How is this?"

The teacher had been told not even to whisper of such matters to her pupil. So she said, "I am not to speak or think of such things, and neither are you. Never let your father hear you saying such things or our lives won't be worth even one *para* [Turkish coin]."

But the girl persisted in asking questions and wanted books which would explain life and the world. The teacher finally brought her such a book but asked the girl not to tell anyone about her reading.

The girl began thinking of her future. "Am I going to spend all my days in this prison?" she asked herself over and over again. Now this girl had learned a good deal about magic. One day she asked her teacher to get her flour, eggs, butter and milk with which she was going to make some dough. After she had kneaded the dough, she modeled the form of a man with it. She drew the features and made the figure of human size.

She used all her magic in making the image and then began praying to God to give this image the soul of a human being. "I made him with my hands, I drew him with my mind, and with my tears I pray that this image may become a human being," she said. She repeated this prayer over and over again, always asking God to give this image a soul.

Finally, God heard her voice and granted her wish: the image was given a soul. The teacher managed to bring clothes for the man. The two young people fell in love, and the girl was careful to hide the boy so that no one saw him except the teacher who, of course, had helped them.

The girl knew the time of her father's weekly visits and was careful that he should not discover her secret. But one Sunday she overslept, and so did the man and so did the teacher. The father entered the palace, and what did he see but a man by his daughter's side! He was enraged! He had gone through much trouble and expense to stop this very thing! The king took all of them—daughter, man, teacher and servants—to prison and ordered that the boy and the girl be killed immediately.

339

"Give us an opportunity to defend ourselves," the girl pleaded with her father. Finally, because he loved his daughter dearly, the king consented to listen. A court was assembled and the guilty ones brought before the judge. The princess, as the chief wrong-doer, spoke first, telling the truth about the matter, from the very beginning to the very end.

"My father did not want me ever to get married, and so he built a prison and put me in it. All my servants and my teacher were women. Yet I could see that my father, who visited me each Sunday, was different. I wanted to live and to know what love was! With my knowledge of magic, I made the image of a man with flour, butter, eggs and milk. I made this image with my hands, drew it with my mind and, with my tears, prayed God to give it a human soul. God, through His kindness, heard my voice and granted my wish. This man standing beside me, I have made myself. He has no family, no ties. If you kill us, you will commit the greatest crime imaginable. I have had my wish: I have lived, I have loved and been loved. If you kill me, I have no regrets."

"Is such a thing possible?" all were saying to one another.

"I will have an investigation made of this," the king said. However, the investigation revealed that the princess was telling the truth, that the man had no family and there was no evidence that he had ever been born.

"My children, I have committed a great crime. I shall try to undo the harm and suffering that I have caused you. I am having a beautiful palace built and furnished for you. May you live in peace forever," the king told his daughter and her mate.

The king fulfilled his promise. A beautiful palace was built for the young people, and they lived in happiness forever after.

From the sky fell three apples: one to me, one to the story-teller and one to her who has entertained you.

And so you see: Nature helps man understand God's laws, the way of life. No one can or should change these natural laws.

50. The Shepherd's Dream

Once upon a time there was a shepherd who had a very beautiful wife and two small sons who were six and seven years old. The family was very poor, and they looked to the shepherd for their meager livelihood. One night the shepherd had a dream.

This story was told by Antrias Amboian.

A man came to him and said, "Both something good and something bad are to befall you. Tell me, which do you prefer first?"

The next morning he told his wife of his dream. "Which one shall we have first?" the wife asked.

"Wife, let us have the bad first. We are still young and can endure hardships. Then when we are old, we shall enjoy the good when we most need it. On the other hand, if we were to have good luck now and bad luck in our later life, we might not take it as well."

"All right, husband, if that man comes again tonight, tell him that we will have our bad luck now and our good luck in our later life," the wife said.

That night the man in the dream came to the husband again. "What have you decided?" he asked.

"We would rather have our bad luck in our youth and enjoy our old age," the shepherd said.

"If you want your bad luck now, you must leave this town and go eastward," the man in the dream said, and he disappeared.

So the next morning the husband and wife packed what little they had and with their two small sons, set out toward the east. They walked for a time until they came to a deep river. There was a ferry waiting to take them across. The wife stepped onto the boat, and the rest of the family was making ready to get aboard when the boat started to move. No one knows why it left the dock, but it did—with the wife aboard. On this boat there was a captain who, as soon as he saw the shepherd's wife, fell in love with her and made her his own.

The shepherd could not join his wife as the water was deep and the boat was traveling rapidly. "Well, since I cannot do anything for my wife," the shepherd said to himself, "let me try to take care of my sons. I will swim across with one of them, then return and cross with the other."

He took one of the boys across the river, left him on the opposite bank and returned for the second boy. When he was only half-way across with his second son, he saw that a wolf was running off with his first-born. He cried and tried to swim faster to overtake the wolf. But he became so excited that, somehow, his second son slipped away from him and was carried down the stream by a swift current. So it was that the shepherd could save neither son.

The wolf grabbed the first son with his teeth and started

running, but a shepherd saw the wolf and killed him. He rescued the child and raised him as his own son.

The second little boy floated in the water until he was caught in a mill, and the mill immediately stopped working. When the miller went to see what was wrong, he found a beautiful little boy whom he took home and reared as his own.

Meanwhile, the father of the boys walked until he came to a town. The ruler of this town had just died, and the people were about to choose another. When the whole population was gathered together, the officials freed a pigeon, and the person on whose head the bird alighted was to be the next ruler.

Thousands of people had gathered, each man hoping that he would be selected. The shepherd, however, sat on the steps of a house nearby, sadly thinking about the events of his life. The pigeon flew around and around and finally alighted on the shepherd's head. But when the people saw how poorly the shepherd was dressed, they decided that he would not do as their ruler. So the pigeon was freed again, but for the second time he alighted on the shepherd's head. Still, the people would not accept him. For the third time the pigeon was released; and for the third time it alighted on the shepherd's head. The people, seeing such an unusual thing, decided to accept their fate, and the shepherd became their ruler.

Meanwhile, one day the shepherd's foster son and the miller's foster son, who, of course, didn't know that they were brothers, met and grew to be good friends. They lived close to each other and met daily. One day when they were about eighteen and nineteen years old, they decided to go together to another land and find work. As luck would have it, they went to the land where their real father was the ruler.

"Let us go to the ruler of this town and ask for work," one said to the other. So they went to the ruler, who, seeing that the young men were very handsome and strong, gave them work.

One day the ruler invited the town's great sea captain to a royal feast, saying to him, "Such a hero as yourself should be honored. You have brought fame and distinction to our land."

Although the sea captain was greatly pleased, he would accept the invitation only if his beautiful wife, whom he dared not leave alone, be allowed to come to the palace. Once there, he insisted that she be placed in a guarded room, so great was his concern for the beautiful woman.

Now this sea captain was the same one who many years before had married the shepherd's wife. And as the ruler trusted the two boy guards, he assigned them the task of standing outside the locked door of the beautiful woman and protecting her from all harm.

As the festivities continued, the two young guards on duty became sleepy. The captain's wife inside the room heard one boy say to the other, "It is a long time that we have known each other, yet we have never told each other anything about ourselves. Suppose you tell me about the life you had before we met, then I will tell you about mine. Let's try to keep awake." They agreed to do this, and the older one started.

"I cannot remember much, but I do remember that my father was a shepherd. I don't know how it happened, but one day he left his work and took my mother, my younger brother and me away. On our path we came upon a river to cross; my mother got into the ferry boat first, and it mysteriously started off with her. My father crossed with me to the other bank of the river and left me there while he went back to get my younger brother. But while my father was gone, a wolf came and carried me away. A shepherd, seeing the wolf carrying something in his mouth, killed the wolf. It was this shepherd who found me and brought me up as his son and told me part of this story. I remember the rest."

"Now, let me tell you what happened after that," the younger boy said. "While my father was carrying me across the river, I lost hold of him. I was carried downsteam by the current and finally got caught in a mill. A miller found me and brought me up as his son."

"We are brothers!" the two exclaimed, embracing each other.

The captain's wife, who had been listening to this conversation, at this point threw open the door and cried, "And I am your mother!" The three began crying and embracing each other.

The captain and the ruler, hearing the confusion, hurried to see what had happened. They found the two young men embracing the captain's wife.

"Why did you do this? Why did you disgrace me?" the ruler asked the guards.

"We are brothers, and this woman came running out and said that she was our mother."

"Why did you run out of your room and say that you were the mother of these boys?" the captain asked his wife.

"Because those two unfortunate boys are my sons," she said. "My husband and I and our two sons were traveling eastward.

We had to cross a deep river. I got on the ferry boat, but it started moving, and I was separated from my family. You, the captain of that boat, carried me away and married me. These boys, whose story I have just heard, are the sons from whom I was parted."

The ruler, realizing that the woman was his wife and that the two boys were his sons, ran to them, embracing all three and saying, "My sons! My wife!"

Of course, they were very happy at being reunited, and the man ruled his land wisely and well as long as he lived.

51. The Soul-Taker

At one time there were three sisters who lived in the hills and worshipped God. One day they came upon a large kettle full of gold. The kettle was so huge that it had seven handles and it required seven men to lift it. "Oh, the soul-taker! Run, sisters, run!" one said to the others, and all three began running as they had never run before.

Six robbers happened to see these sisters running. "Why are they running so fast? Something very unusual must have happened," they said. So they stopped the sisters. "Tell us, why are you running like this? What are you running away from?"

"We are running away from the soul-taker," they said, trying to escape from the robbers.

"What is a soul-taker?" the robbers asked. "You must show us what this is."

So the sisters took the robbers and showed them the gold. "This is the soul-taker," they said and ran away.

The robbers laughed at them. "Just imagine! Calling gold a soul-taker!" Since these robbers had not stolen for some time, they were very poor. What's more, the government had been pursuing them so closely that they had not eaten in a long time. "Brothers, let three of us stay and guard the gold and three of us go to town and bring some food," one of them suggested. They thought that this was a good idea and divided the work amongst themselves in this way.

The three robbers who were left to guard the gold began to plot: "If we divide this gold among six of us, each of us will have

This story was told by Mrs. Akabi Mooradian.

only a small share. If, on the other hand, we divide it among three of us, each will have more gold."

"What are we to do then?" one asked the others.

"Let us gather large stones and hide them behind this big rock. We can hide there, too. When our comrades return with the food, we'll stone them to death. Then we can eat the food and run off with the gold." They agreed to this plan, and all three of them started gathering stones.

Meanwhile, the three robbers who had gone to town to buy food were also plotting: "If we divide this gold among six of us, each one of us will have a small share. But if we divide it among three, each of us will have much more gold."

"But what are we to do?"

"We can poison the food, and when the others eat it, they will die. Then all the gold will be ours. We won't eat any of the food, and if they ask, we can say that we have already eaten in town." They agreed to this plan and bought both food and poison when they reached town. They poisoned the food and carried it up the mountain. The three robbers who were guarding the gold saw them and started stoning them.

"Stop! Stop!" the others cried.

But the men wouldn't stop until all three of the robbers who had gone for the food were killed. When this was done, they said, "Now we will eat some food and then divide this gold." They sat down and ate to their hearts' content, not knowing that this was their last meal. Half an hour later they swelled up like balloons and died. The gold remained undivided.

After several weeks the sisters returned to the spot where they had found the gold. They saw three of the robbers stoned to death on the path going up the mountain and the other three poisoned to death, still guarding the gold.

"When we told them that it was the soul-taker, they didn't believe us. Now see what has happened to them!" they said as once again they ran away from the gold.

52. There Is Righteousness

Two friends decided to leave their wives and children and travel to Constantinople to make their fortunes and then return. One of the wives said to her husband, "Husband, you are going

This story was told by Hovhannes Kaprelian.

345

and leaving me here alone. You will be gone for many years, and I have no way of knowing that you will ever return. Promise me one thing."

"Whatever you want, I will promise," he answered.

"When you get there, do not let a day go by without working. No matter how little you receive, no matter how hard you must work, don't refuse the job. Promise me that, and I will be content."

The husband promised.

The wife of the other man, however, had another plan for her husband. "Husband, you are going away and are leaving me here alone. I ask only one thing of you. Will you promise to do it?"

"What do you want, wife?" he asked.

"Promise me that you will not waste yourself doing menial jobs. Don't work unless the job pays at least one *lira* [Turkish money]. Then you will make a great deal of money and will return very soon."

The husband promised to do as she asked.

So both friends left for the big city. Every morning the two went to the marketplace and waited for prospective employers to come. The employers would tell the men what sort of work they wanted done and what price they would pay for it. Of course, the price would not be much, and the second man hardly ever did any work. The first man, however, worked day in and day out, at any price that was offered him.

At the end of three years the first man had enough money to return home. He went to his friend and suggested that they return home together.

"But I do not have enough money to go back," the friend replied.

"Well, if I return, your family will feel unhappy because you have not returned to them. Come, we have been good friends. We will divide the money I have earned equally between us. Then we will both go back," the first man said.

"If you do that, when we go back to the village, you'll tell everyone how you befriended me and gave me all this money. No, I will not accept."

"But I promise you that I will never say a word about it. Only God above and we two below will know."

Finally, the second man agreed to share the first man's earnings. They went to the marketplace, and the first man bought gifts for his family and for the other man's family, too. They shared everything like brothers.

Soon they started on their journey home. When they were almost there, the second man turned to the first one and said, "Friend, I have changed my mind: I am going to kill you."

"Why, this is no time for joking! We are almost home!" the first man said.

"I am not joking. I am going to kill you," the other man replied.

"Why should you kill me?"

"When we get to the village, you will tell everyone how you gave me all this money."

"Friend, my promise is a promise; my word is true. I will not tell anyone. Only you and I will ever know about it."

But no, the second man was intent on killing his companion. Finally, seeing that nothing could be done, the first man asked his friend if he would fulfill a promise. "Promise me that you will have my wife change my son's name from 'Thomas' to 'There-is-law-but-no-righteousness.'"

"I promise to do so," the second man said, and he killed his companion. He buried him, and with all the money in his pocket, he returned to the village. Everyone was happy to see him, especially now that he was so rich.

The first man's wife, hearing of his return, ran to him and asked, "Tell me, where is my husband?"

"When we reached Constantinople, he became sick and, after suffering for a while, he died. I buried him with my own money. But before he died, he told me to have you change your son's name from 'Thomas' to 'There-is-law-but-no-righteousness,'" the man said.

The poor woman went home and changed her son's name. Because she had no money, she continued to clean other people's houses, do their washing and cook their meals to support herself and her son.

One day a group of boys were playing at the edge of the village as a group of soldiers were passing by. The first man's son was not in sight, so his friends called him repeatedly to come and see the soldiers.

The captain of the soldiers heard the unusual name and wanted to know to whom it belonged. He asked for the leading citizen of the village and was directed to the second man. "Why do you have a boy in this village with such a name?" he asked.

The rich man explained that just before he died, the boy's father had asked that his son's name be changed to the present one. The wife was called in and told the same story.

"Soldiers, arrest this man!" the captain said, pointing to the second man. He sent people to Constantinople and succeeded in proving that the leading citizen was lying. So he forced him to tell the truth.

"Now you must change your son's name to 'There-is-law-and-there-is-righteousness,'" the captain said. He also instructed that a large stone with these words inscribed on it be placed in the center of the village.

53. The Test

There was once a beggar who sat at the foot of a bridge and asked for alms from the passersby. Every day a rich young merchant stopped to throw him a few *para* [Turkish coin]. One day the merchant had a larger shipment than usual and did not have enough money to pay the caravan owners. As he went to borrow the necessary funds from some friend or other, he was preoccupied. He passed the bridge, forgetting to give a few cents to the beggar.

The beggar, seeing that the young man passed him, was surprised. "Why didn't he give me money? Is something wrong?" the beggar said to himself. "Young man, come back, come back!" he stood up and shouted. The merchant turned around and came back. "Why did you forget to give my money today?" the beggar asked.

"I was in a hurry and forgot," the merchant said, throwing a few *para* to the beggar.

"I don't want your money," the beggar said. "I just want to know why you forgot. What is the matter?" he asked.

"Well, if you must know, I have to get some money from my friends to pay a caravan owner," the young man said.

"How much do you want?"

"I want ———," the young merchant replied.

"Come to my house tonight after dark, and I will give you the money," the beggar said. When the young man protested that the beggar had no funds, the beggar said, "Never mind; you come

This story was told by Hovhannes Kaprelian.

to my house tonight and you'll have your money." And he gave the merchant directions to get to his house.

That night the merchant went to the beggar's house and, to his amazement, found that it was even more beautiful than the homes of his rich friends. A charming girl invited him in and made him comfortable. After she had served him Turkish coffee, the beggar came in. "Ah, you have come," he said to the merchant. "Daughter, bring me the money bag," he ordered. The daughter brought the money bag, and they counted out the amount of money that the merchant needed. "You can return this loan whenever you have the money. There is no need to hurry," the beggar said.

The merchant thanked them and went home. But at home he began thinking of the loveliness and grace of the beggar's daughter and realized that he had fallen in love with her. Several days later when he returned the money to the beggar, he asked to marry the girl. "Do you have a trade?" the beggar asked.

"You know that I am a merchant," the young man replied.

"Do you have a trade other than this?"

"No, that is the only kind of work I know," the young man replied.

"Then you cannot marry my daughter except on one condition." When the young man asked what this condition was, the beggar replied, "I want you to wear my clothes and sit at the foot of the bridge and beg for a day. If you do that, I will let you marry my daughter." As the merchant refused to do so, the beggar shrugged his shoulders, ending the discussion. But the merchant's love for the girl was so great that he went to her father again and this time agreed to beg for a day at the foot of the bridge.

The next morning, in old, worn-out clothes, the merchant sat at the foot of the bridge and begged alms of the passersby. Looking at him, they recognized him and knew that once he had been a rich man. Everyone felt pity for him and threw money into his lap. The merchant was bitterly embarrassed, but what could he do?

That night he went to the beggar's house and put the alms money on the table. "Well, son, you have done it, have you?" the beggar said, pushing the money toward the merchant. "I don't want the money; I just wanted to test you to see how much you loved my daughter. Now, I know that even if your business should fail, you would beg to support her," he said.

The young merchant and the beggar's daughter were married, and the beggar was pleased to see them happy.

54. The Ball of Gold

At one time a rich couple and a poor couple lived next door to each other. The poor people, who had a small child, laughed and had great happiness every day. The rich people had much money but were never happy; no sounds of laughter were heard in their house.

One day the rich woman said to her neighbor, "You are poor; you are hungry. Why is it that you are so happy all the time? Every night laughter fills your house and spills outside. It even touches us next door."

The poor woman merely said, "We have a ball of gold. I toss it to my husband, and he tosses it to me. This it what brings us so much happiness."

"A golden ball?" the rich neighbor asked.

"Yes."

So the rich woman went home and told her husband that their neighbors tossed each other a ball of gold each evening. This was the cause of their happiness.

"If that is all, that's nothing," the husband said. "I'll have a beautiful golden ball made. Then we'll toss it to each other, and we'll be happy, just like our neighbors." So the man had a beautiful golden ball made. But when the husband tried to throw it to his wife, it was too heavy to lift. When the wife tried to catch it, it bruised her fingers. Instead of happiness that night, they shed tears of pain.

The next morning the rich woman visited her neighbor again. "Tell me, what kind of a golden ball is it that you have? My husband had a golden ball made for us, but it is too heavy to throw and crushes our hands as we catch it. What kind of a ball is it that doesn't hurt you but brings happiness instead?"

"Our golden ball is this beautiful child," the poor woman said. "We toss him to each other, and his joy brings great happiness to us. He is the ball of gold which fills our home with laughter and love."

So you see: the rich try to find happiness in their wealth, but

This story was told by Mrs. Hripsima Hoogasian.

frequently it is without joy. Real happiness is found in family and children. And in this way, the poor can be richer than the rich.

ANECDOTES

55. A Treasure Hunt

ONCE UPON A TIME, many generations back, there were two brothers who were married and lived in one section of Armenia. They were very rich—so rich, in fact, that their wives wore enough gold in their hair to fill a bushel basket.

As it happened, one of the brothers had a serious quarrel with another man—we don't know about what—and the brother was so angry that he killed the man.

Now, as we have said, the brothers were very rich and, like all rich and intelligent men, had many enemies. They knew that if either one of them should be taken to court, he would most likely lose his head. As they valued life more than gold, they decided to leave that part of the country. Accordingly, they gathered all the gold they could carry—the women hiding much of it in their hair and clothes—and ran away from the law of the town. They settled in Kharput, right next to St. Hagop's Church.

At the present time it is the general belief that the brothers did not take even one-fourth of their wealth. Yet even with the small amount they carried with them, they were considered very wealthy. Again, people were jealous of them. To kill the jealousy and ill-will which were directed toward them, the brothers decided that it would be safer to bury whatever gold they did not absolutely need. So the gold was buried in the basement of their house.

Generations after generations lived in that house, without knowing where the gold was buried. One day, however, my grandmother's grandmother had a dream. In this dream she was told the exact location of the gold. She was told, also, that she must cut her little finger and let blood flow before she could find the treasure. After she had dreamt this for three nights in suc-

This story was told by Mrs. Mariam Serabian.

cession, she was convinced that there truly was something in the basement.

"Husband, let us go down and dig where I was told the treasure is buried," she told her husband on the fourth day.

"If there was gold, do you think that they would give it to you?" he asked.

"Well, why do you think they would tell me about it if there were no treasure?"

So the husband, with great reluctance, helped her dig. As they worked, they could hear hollow noises from under the ground. Grandmother's grandmother was encouraged by the sounds. And her husband, hearing the noises, was convinced that his wife was right—that there was a treasure. But, not wanting her to know that he thought so, too, he said, "Ha, ha, where is your gold?" To show his disbelief, he passed wind several times.

Now his wife, who was digging, became flustered because of her husband's behavior and forgot to cut her finger. "Husband, keep quiet. Don't mock me—pray, instead!" But the man did not listen to her. Finally they struck something solid. When the wife, with the help of her husband, pulled it out, they found a tall vase which contained something heavy. On top of the vase they found a most extraordinary little Turkish coffee cup. It was made of gold, with beautiful designs, but it was cracked in half.

They lifted the cup and stuck their fingers in the base. Unfortunately, they did not find the gold that they had expected. In its place they found red sand—beautiful red sand.

The belief is this: Because my grandmother's grandfather did not believe that the gold was buried there and because he passed wind (showing disrespect), confusing his wife so that she forgot to cut her finger, the gold turned to red sand and the beautiful coffee cup cracked in two. The family was convinced that this was so because there was no red sand of this type anywhere in that part of the country.

56. The Curse

Once upon a time my grandmother's grandfather's father was walking through the town, deep in thought, when suddenly he looked up and saw a female *elk** running with the liver of a hu-

This story was told by Mrs. Mariam Serabian.
* See discussion of *als* and *elks* on pp. 64–65.

man being in her hands and a bunch of little *elk* children racing after her, yelling for food.

"Mama, food!" they cried one after another.

"All right, all right, wait until I get to the river where I can dip this liver into water. You know that you can't eat it yet," the mother said, running in the direction of the river.

Now this ancestor of mine was a good man, and when he saw this sight, he shuddered. He knew that the liver was that of a human being and that, according to tradition, when it was dipped into water, the person to whom it belonged would die immediately. He had to stop the female *elk*—yet what was he to do? Suddenly he remembered stories of *elks* and recalled that they could be stopped from doing evil if a needle were pinned to their clothes.

In Armenia men wore turbans in the fashion of the Turks. Quick as thought, this ancestor removed the pin which held his turban together and stuck it on the *elk* mother's clothes. The woman stopped in her tracks. When the *elk* children saw their mother caught, they left her and ran swiftly away.

"Remove the pin and I will do anything you ask," the *elk* begged the man.

"Whose liver is this?" the man asked.

The dwarf did not answer. When he asked her again, she told him that it was the liver of one of the young brides of the town who had just borne a child.

"Oh, you take the liver of an innocent young bride when you know well enough that just as soon as you dip it into water, she will die. And yet, when you are caught, you expect pity. Why should I pity you? Take that liver and put it back into the body from which you wrenched it. Hurry, and when you have done that, return to me," he commanded. The young bride, from whose body the liver had been torn, was in great agony and near death; but when the *elk* replaced her liver, she began to breathe easily and soon recovered.

The *elk* returned to her captor and begged him to release her. "Let me go. I have children to feed; I must take care of them," she said.

"You ask me to give you your freedom so that you can take care of your children, yet you would leave that young, newborn child an orphan to satisfy the appetites of your children."

The *elk* was put to work in the home of her captor. She did all the cooking, baking, cleaning and serving. As she was an excellent worker, she never lagged in her duties although she always asked people to remove the pin from her clothes. But as everyone knew of her evil deed, no one would free her. So she worked year after year, always begging for her release. Finally, after seven years, she approached her master once more: "Remove the pin and set me free. I will not bother you or harm you or seven generations of your family," she promised.

"But if I let you go, I know that you will harm us in one way or another."

"If you set me free, I will not harm seven generations of your family. I will only cause all of your wooden spoons to break easily." Soon the mother *elk* was liberated and kept her promise. She has not yet harmed the people in our family, but true to her curse, in Armenia our spoons did break easily.*

57. A Great Catch

One winter it was so cold that the Yeprad River was frozen. We could easily walk on the ice without fearing that we would fall in. A group of men from our village decided to go fishing up the river. So I went with them.

We walked along, and when we came to the place where another river joined ours, we saw that the ice had thawed and that the fish were abundant. We cast our nets and pulled up an enormous load. We took our net and laid it on the shore so that we could rest. The town's officials tried to take our catch away from us, but we would not give it to them.

When we weighed it, it weighed four hundred liters. We had to load fourteen camels to take it all back to our village.

This story was told to the author by her father, Kazar Hoogasian.

58. One Way to Catch a Fish

One summer my father was fishing with his friends on a raft which was supported by several *deegs*.† He knew that he should

This yarn was told by Kazar Hoogasian.
* Author's note: I am the eighth generation and still possess a liver, as of this writing.
† According to the storyteller, many sheep, known as *mackee*, were very large, weighing about two hundred pounds. When a *mackee* was killed, a small slash, made on its broad tail, into which the men blew very

have inflated them before starting out that day for the raft looked thin, but, as he told us, he was so eager to fish that he did not take the time.

When they had paddled quite a way into the river, the men cast their nets. As luck would have it, they caught a huge fish. They quickly pulled the net in. But the fish was so heavy that the raft almost collapsed. My father hesitated only a second. "Men, throw the net back!" he called.

The men did as he asked. My good father jumped into the river and chased the fish until he caught it. Then he threw his arm around the neck of the fish and would not let go. The fish and he swam side by side until finally they reached the shore.

When this fish was weighed, it weighed seven Armenian liters.

59. What a Fish!

One day my father, bless his good soul, told me to climb our big tree and cut off a branch which was getting too heavy. I climbed the tree and had just started cutting the branch when I heard a cry from some women who were washing clothes in the river below. I wondered what had happened. Just a little distance from us there was a deep whirlpool. Had one of the village children fallen into the river? Was he being carried toward the whirlpool? I jumped off the tree and into the water. I swiftly swam near the women and cried out, "What has happened? Did a child fall in the river?"

The women had left their clothes in the river and were huddled under the trees. "A great white thing appeared in the water in front of us, but we don't know whether it is man or

---

hard, caused the skin to stand away from the rest of the body. This skin was peeled off the carcass, and the head and feet of the animal were cut off.

When the fleece was dry, the men removed the wool from it and let the skin dry for weeks. They ground the rind of a pomegranate into a fine meal. They rubbed this on the skin from time to time together with salt, until the skin was so tough that not even a bullet could tear it.

Then they tied the skin around the openings of the neck and the four legs securely. When the skin was inflated, it became very light and buoyant. This was then called a *deeg* or *caïque*. Several of these together made an effective raft.

This yarn was told by Kazar Hoogasian.

beast. It's going that way!" they said, pointing in the direction toward which I was swimming.

I started in pursuit of the big creature which was so clumsy that it could not cut through the water as fast as I could. When I caught up with it, I sprang on its back and tried to control it for I saw that it was a huge fish. Trying to escape, it turned over, and I fell off its back.

Again I chased it. I caught it and jumped on its back. This time I held on tight, determined not to let it escape. But it swept down low and, getting some sand on its tail, threw it into my eyes. Then suddenly its great body turned, and I fell into the water, momentarily blinded. Again it swam away.

Quickly rinsing my eyes, I looked about and saw that the fish was heading away from me. I knew that it must be pretty tired, and I was determined that it would not escape from me a third time. Swimming as hard as I could, I overtook it and again jumped on its back. Somehow I managed to stick my hands into its gills, push them into its mouth and keep them there. The fish struggled and struggled, but could not breathe. Finally it quieted down. With my hands still in its mouth, I dragged it ashore. When its heavy tail flapped against my thighs, I thought the force of the blows would surely kill me.

The people of the village had all gathered to see the fish and were shouting their congratulations to me. When I was sure the fish was dead, I took off my long sash and tied the ends together. Then I put it through the gills and the mouth of the fish. I threw the remaining part of the sash over my shoulder, and, with the fish swinging on my back, I went home.

What a fish! It felt like soap, it was so slippery! It weighed four Armenian liters.

60. Saint Snakes

In a village in Armenia there were two big, black saint snakes which were about twelve feet long. One was male and the other, female. Every spring they bleated like sheep; when winter came, their cries stopped. These snakes were able to jump from place to place, about seventy-five feet at a time.

At one time a shepherd was grazing his sheep in the hills when he saw a huge snake coming toward him. The man became

This story was told by Mrs. Katoon Mouradian.

frightened and lost his voice. He saw only the one snake, which he knew was one of the saint snakes, and did not want to kill it. But he knew that it was a question of survival: either he or the snake had to be killed. He picked up his rifle and shot twice at the snake, but the snake did not stop. He shot twice again, and the snake began rolling down the hill. Meanwhile, the villagers, hearing these shots, ran to the hill to see what was happening. They saw a snake rolling down, and when it reached the bottom of the hill, they saw that it was very black and as thick as a log. They dug up a plot of land and buried it in there.

After this, the mate of the snake who had died never cried again.

61. The Rising Snake

One day I was grinding wheat when I heard cries behind me and turned around to see what was the matter. My mother-in-law was pointing to the mountain near our house and said, "Look at the snake!"

I dropped my work and stood up to look. It was a huge thick red snake. It was very long and seemed to be suspended in mid-air. It slowly climbed upward, upward, upward, and soon we were unable to see it any more.

I believed that God called it to heaven to send it somewhere else.

This story was told by Mrs. Katoon Mouradian.

HUMOROUS TALES

62. Fool's Luck

ONCE THERE WAS an old woman who had two sons. The elder son was a bright boy who worked and supported his mother and brother. But the younger boy was slow-thinking and rather

For reasons which will be apparent the informant wished to remain anonymous.

foolish. Their mother, who was old and feeble, was bedridden and had to be cared for by her sons.

"Brother, bathe Mother today and put her to bed," the older brother said one morning as he left for work.

The younger brother did as he was told. And when the older brother returned from work, he found that the aged mother had been well cared for.

The next morning as the older brother was about to leave for his day's work, he again instructed his younger brother to bathe their mother and put her to bed. That day the stupid younger brother heated the water until it was boiling. Then he took his sick mother from her bed, unclothed her, scrubbed her hard and poured the hot water over her head. Of course, the old woman was scalded and died immediately. But the younger son was so foolish that he did not realize his mother was dead. So he clothed her again and laid her in bed. As he did so, he noticed that her face was very red, but thought that this was because he had scrubbed her so well.

That evening the older brother returned and asked, "Brother, did you do as I asked?"

"Yes, I washed her so well that her face is bright red. She hasn't bothered me all day; she's been fast asleep."

"Let me see," the older brother said, taking a look at his mother. "You fool, you have killed her!" The younger brother was surprised at this, but merely shrugged his shoulders. "Come, let us move away from here," the older one said since he feared for the welfare of his brother. So the two of them ate and started out.

"Don't forget to lock the door," the older brother said, moving on ahead. When he turned around, he saw his brother dragging along the front door of their house. "Brother, why do you take the door along?"

"Well, since we must not let anyone enter our house, what surer way of doing this is there than taking the door with us? Now they can't open it," the younger brother said.

The two of them walked and walked until it was dark and they were very tired. They climbed a tree to escape the wild animals in the woods. But the younger brother insisted on carrying the door up the tree with him.

As luck would have it, a group of merchants passing by decided to camp right beneath that very tree that night. They ate their food and sang songs and were content.

The younger brother poked his brother and said, "Brother, I have to make water."

"You can't do that! There are people right below us," the older brother said. But the younger brother could not wait and urinated on the group below. The merchants looked up and, seeing no one in the dark, thought that it was sprinkling.

A little later the young brother poked his older brother and said that he had to finish his toilet.

"But, brother, you can't do that here," the older brother protested.

"But, I must!"

The merchants looked up and were a little surprised, but thought that it was the work of a lonely bird.

Soon the younger one said to his older brother, "Brother, I'm going to let this door fall. I can't hold it any longer."

"But brother, you cannot do that. There are people below us: they'll get hurt."

"I can't help it. I must let go!" the younger brother said. The door fell on the merchants below who were so amazed and frightened that they left everything behind and ran away as fast as they could. Then the two brothers climbed down and looked at the things the merchants had left. They found gold, jewelry, rugs, silks and other valuables. The older brother, being the wise one, took all the gold and jewelry, while the younger brother took the rugs and the silks. Both of them were delighted with their unexpected luck.

As the hours passed, the night grew colder and colder. The younger brother wrapped himself in one of his thick rugs and went to sleep. The older brother, however, was freezing.

"Brother, brother, give me a rug so that I might keep warm," the older brother begged.

"No, you took the gold and left me the rugs. I will not give you any of my rugs," the younger brother said. So, not long after, the older brother froze to death, and the younger one took not only his rugs, but his brother's gold and jewelry as well.

63. Ingratitude

The king and his vizier were walking through the country in disguise one day when they saw a shepherd sitting on a hillside,

This story was told by Hovhannes Kaprelian.

playing his flute. Upon hearing the music, all the sheep which were scattered far and near, gathered about him. The king, who had never seen anything like this, was much surprised. He noticed that some of the sheep were scattered quite a distance.

"My friend, how is it possible for you to gather your sheep like this?" he asked the shepherd.

"Oh, this is nothing," the shepherd said, "not only can I bring them together when I want them, but I can feed them salt, take them to the river and bring them back thirsty."*

"That is impossible," the king said. "Feeding animals salt and taking them to the river and denying them drink is impossible!"

"I will show you then," the shepherd said. So the shepherd fed his sheep salt and played his flute. As he did so, the animals wandered toward the river to drink. But just as they were about to drink, the shepherd played his flute again, and the animals turned away from the water, obeying their master's command.

One black ram, however, was very thirsty and did not turn away from the water but lingered behind. However, every time that he thought of drinking, the music called him back until finally he, too, joined the rest of the sheep.

The king, very much surprised at what he had just seen, said to the shepherd, "How happy you must be to possess such a talent. I wish that I could do my work as successfully as you do yours."

"Happy? How can I be happy when I cannot marry the girl that I love? I am so poor that her father will not give me his daughter."

"Who is this beautiful girl?" the king asked.

"She is the daughter of Levon Beg."

"Wait a minute, I know this person," the king said. "Here, I'll write a line, and you will take it to him. He surely will give you his daughter." The king really did not know the rich man, but because he was king, he had great power over all the people of his land.

So the shepherd took the letter to the rich man who, seeing that it was a royal command, gave his daughter in marriage to the shepherd.

After several years the shepherd decided that he would go to Constantinople where his friend (the king in disguise) was

---

* A popular Armenian expression to imply an individual's wit and cunning.

living and thank him for promoting his marriage. So, fixing a basket of eggs, butter and cream, he started for the city. When he reached there, he asked where he could find a man by such-and-such a name. But as the shepherd knew only the king's first name, he was told that there were many in the city with that name. Finally the shepherd asked a government official and was directed to the palace.

The guards told the king of a poor shepherd who was saying that he wanted to see the man who had helped him get a wife. The king, immediately remembering the shepherd, told his guards to admit him.

The shepherd entered the beautiful room and put his basket down, saying to the king, "Friend, I have brought you some good things to eat from the country. I came to thank you for your letter because your friend let me marry his daughter."

"That is well," the king said. "How are you now? Are you happy?"

"Yes, I am, friend," the shepherd said. As he looked about the palace, he said, "This is very beautiful. Did you build this place or did your father?"

The king answered, "My father did."

"I knew you didn't build it for you could not even build a hen's nest," the shepherd said.

The king, fearing what else this shepherd might say, decided to get rid of him. He gave the ungrateful man some gold and told him to forget the man who helped him marry a wife.

64. Outwitting Giants

Once upon a time there was a man who was afraid of everything. Although he was big and strong, he was afraid even of going out of the house without his wife. His wife was ashamed of him, but still he refused to go out without her. One night he dreamt that he had robbed someone, and the experience seemed so real to him that he could not forget it. So he told his wife about it in the morning.

"Who, you? Why, you are afraid of going out of the house without me! How could you go into someone else's house and rob them?" she asked. But he insisted that he had robbed someone. Finally, his wife became so tired of these arguments that she

This story was told by Nishan Krikorian.

put him out of the house, telling him not to return until he had conquered his fear. So the man walked and walked, thinking bitterly of his wife. Finally he became very tired and decided to get some sleep. He wrote a large sign which stated that he was the strongest and bravest man in the world. He set this beside him and went to sleep.

Three giant brothers were passing when they saw him. "Now, we have our supper," one of them said. But when they went closer, they read the sign. "Oh, we'd better be careful. He is the strongest and bravest man in the world. It would not do to have him as an enemy," they said to one another. While the giants were hovering about him, the man awoke. He saw the huge creatures and became very frightened. But he was smart enough to see that the giants were afraid of him, too.

"Who are you? Where are you going?" they asked him.

"I am going wherever my journey leads me," he said.

"Why don't you join us? We are three brothers alone in the world."

"I will," the man answered. So they lived together and worked together for many months. But in time the giants became more and more frightened. "What if this strong man should turn around and eat us someday?" they wondered. So they planned to get rid of him.

The man, on the other hand, was afraid of the giants. "What if these three brothers turn around and eat me someday? What can I do?" he thought. So he planned to get away from them.

One day when the three brothers thought their friend was asleep, they whispered to one another, "We must get rid of him."

"Yes, we must do that and do it quickly," the second agreed.

"But, how?"

"We'll pour boiling water over him when he is sleeping tonight and burn him to death," one suggested, and the others agreed to do this. But the man, who had been listening and heard their plan, was prepared for them. He arranged his bed so that it seemed as though he were asleep. Then he really hid behind the door and waited. Soon the three giants opened his door and threw a big kettle full of hot water on the man's bed. Then they quickly closed the door and disappeared.

When the water had drained off, the man got back into bed. It was not long after when the giants opened his door to see if he were dead. But to their great surprise, there he was, snoring away. "Brother, how did you sleep?" they asked him when he awoke the next morning.

"I slept very well, but the night was so hot that I sweated," the man answered. "My bed is wringing wet."

The giants looked at one another in disbelief. Was such a thing possible? Here they had poured a whole kettle full of boiling water on this man, and he said that the night was so warm that he sweated! Now the giants were more determined than before to get rid of him. They began to plan something else. "Let's shoot him tonight," one suggested. However, the man heard this plan, too, and prepared for it. He arranged his bed as before and hid behind the door.

Soon the giants pushed the door open and began shooting at what they thought was his body, feeling sure that they were rid of the man this time. But he, unharmed, went back to bed. Soon the giants opened the door to remove his carcass, but to their surprise, they found him snoring away. When he awoke in the morning, they asked him how he had slept.

"I slept very well, but there was a great deal of noise; I can't understand what it could have been," he said.

The giants were amazed that he was alive and well. They didn't know what to do. Here they had showered all those bullets on him, and he only complained about the noise! They were more afraid of him than ever. Still determined to get rid of him, they tried a different plan.

"Brother, you are human, why do you want to live with giants like us? Surely, you have friends and loved ones of your own?" they asked him.

"Yes, I do, but I don't mind living with you."

"Well, if you will go back to your own kind, we will give you a share of our fortune to take back with you," they said. So the giants took their treasures and divided them into four equal parts, one for each of them and one for the man.

"But," he said, "I can't carry all this back home. I guess I'll just keep my share and stay with you."

"No, no! Don't worry about that! We'll carry you and your share back where we found you," they said.

So the man agreed to this, but the giants, who were all afraid of being left alone with him, did not want to undertake this task. They decided to draw lots, and it fell to the youngest giant to carry the money and the man on his shoulders back to his home. When they finally reached their destination, the giant opened the door and took the man inside. "Friend, will you straighten up so that I can reach the ceiling?" the man asked.

"Why do you want to reach the ceiling?"

"Because my father's great sword is hidden there," the man said.

Hearing the word "sword," the giant dropped the man on the floor and fled.

The man chuckled to himself, happy that he had everything he could wish for. His fame and courage, the result of his outwitting the giants, grew and spread throughout the land. With his share of the giants' treasure, he lived happily with his wife to the end of his days.

65. Vhy, Vhy, Vhy

In a village in Armenia there once lived a happy family of three who were tenants of a rich man. Unfortunately, as luck would have it, the father was killed by an horse-drawn carriage.

While the widow was making *sarma* [ground meat, rice, seasonings wrapped in grape leaves] one day, she began thinking of her future. "How long am I going to remain a widow? My landlord is a rich widower. I think I will marry him," she said as she worked.

Her son, however, was hiding behind the door and heard what she was saying. "That is what you think! So you are going to marry the landlord! You are not going to marry the landlord because *I'm* going to marry the landlord's beautiful daughter," the boy muttered to himself.

The mother placed the *sarma* on the stove and put a *gush-goor** on top of it. She continued talking to herself: "I must marry that landlord. I must marry that landlord. Well, what am I going to do, eh? *Vhy, vhy, vhy,* [alas], and my *sarma* is on the stove!"†

She sat down a while and thought, then started again: "Eh, what am I going to do? What am I going to do? I will marry my

This story was told by Mrs. Mariam Serabian.

* A mixture similar to peat except that it was made with a combination of manure and straw dried and formed into cakes. It was used to heat homes and as fuel for cooking. The mother put it on top of, instead of under, the pan.

† Throughout the story, the informant frequently chanted this phrase, rocking her body, clasping her hands together or hitting her hands on her knees for emphasis.

landlord, but what is my son going to do? What shall I do about my son?"

Her son, who was hidden and listening to her, came into the room just then. "What are you doing, mother?" he asked.

"*Vhy, vhy, vhy,* and my *sarma* is on the stove, *vhy, vhy, vhy,*" the widow said, not answering her son.

"Mother, get that idea out of your mind. You can't marry our landlord because I am going to marry his daughter," the boy announced.

"*Aman* [my goodness], and my *sarma* is on the stove! *Aman,* and my *sarma* is on the stove! Nice boy, good boy, come let me marry you to the girl from Constantinople. *Vhy, vhy, vhy,* and my *sarma* is on the stove, *vhy, vhy, vhy!*"

"I'm not going to marry any girl from Constantinople. I'm going to marry our landlord's daughter."

"My son, good boy, you can't marry our landlord's daughter because I'm going to marry our landlord! *Vhy, vhy, vhy,* and my *sarma* is on the stove!"

"I'm not going to marry the girl from Constantinople. She paints her face and fixes her eyebrows," the boy said. "I'm going to marry our landlord's daughter."

"*Vhy, vhy, vhy,* and my *sarma* is on the stove, *vhy, vhy, vhy!* Well, son, you know that I want you to marry the girl from Constantinople and not the landlord's daughter."

"Oh, I know why you don't want me to marry the landlord's daughter! You don't want me to marry the landlord's daughter so that you can marry the landlord!" the boy said.

"*Vhy, vhy, vhy,* and my *sarma* is on the stove, *vhy, vhy, vhy!* And the *gushgoor* has most probably softened and has fallen in the *sarma!* I should look after it! *Vhy, vhy, vhy,* and my *sarma* is on the stove," the widow said, crying and pulling her hair.

"What are you crying for?" her son asked. "Do you think that you are going to marry the landlord? No! I am not going to let you! I'm going to marry the landlord's daughter."

"*Vhy, vhy, vhy,* and my *sarma* is on the stove, and it's probably soft now, *vhy, vhy, vhy!* Son, let me go and call the priest," she said.

She ran without shoes, without stockings, with her hair flying wildly and her dress torn, to call the priest. "Oh, father priest, father priest, come with me!"

"What has happened?" the priest said, running after her, thinking that he was called to perform rites at a deathbed.

When they reached her house, she pushed the priest onto a stool. "Father priest, *vhy, vhy, vhy,* and my *sarma* is on the stove, *vhy, vhy, vhy!* Let me go and see what has happened," she said, leaving the priest sitting there amazed.

She came back and started crying. "Oh, my *sarma* has softened," she said, without taking it off the stove. "It's boiling hard," she added. "*Vhy, vhy, vhy,* and my *sarma* is on the stove, *vhy, vhy, vhy!*"

"What do you want, my people?" the priest asked.

"Father priest, could a mother marry the father and the son marry the daughter?" the widow asked.

"What is this?" the priest asked.

"I'm going to marry my landlord, and my son wants to marry his daughter. Can we do this?" the widow asked. "*Vhy, vhy, vhy,* and my *sarma* is on the stove."

"Father priest, I'm going to marry the landlord's daughter, and she wants me to marry the girl from Constantinople. She wants to marry the landlord herself," the son said.

"My people, this will not do. If your son marries the landlord's daughter, you cannot marry the landlord. If you marry the landlord, your son will have to marry another girl," the priest told them.

Soon mother and son were fighting each other and pulling each other's hair. Every once in a while, the mother would continue her "*Vhy, vhy, vhy,* and my *sarma* is on the stove, *vhy, vhy, vhy!*"

"What is this? Let me get out of here before they turn on me!" the priest said, amazed at the sight, and ran out. He went to the landlord and told him of the scene he had just witnessed. "And the mother says that she is going to marry you, and the son says that he is going to marry your daughter. Right before my very eyes, they began fighting."

"Well, I'll have to take a look into this," the landlord said, stroking his beard and laughing as he had never laughed before.

That very afternoon, the landlord went to see the widow. He found her crying. "What are you doing, my good woman?"

"Oh, did you come, *effendi* [Turkish: lord]?" the widow asked. She jumped to her feet and flung herself on his neck. The landlord moved away from her. She began with her "*Vhy vhy, vhy,* and my *sarma* is on the stove, *vhy, vhy, vhy!*"

During the visit, the son was hidden behind the kitchen door and heard and saw everything that went on.

"Why were you fighting?" the landlord asked.

"*Effendi,* you know, *vhy, vhy, vhy,* and my *sarma* is on the stove, *vhy, vhy, vhy,* I want to marry you, and my son wants to marry your daughter," she said.

"Is your son here?" the landlord asked.

"I don't know," the widow said. She went around the house calling her son. Finally, the boy came out from behind the kitchen door.

"*Effendi,* could a mother marry the father, and the boy marry the daughter?" the son asked. "I'm going to marry your daughter, and my mother wants to marry you."

"*Vhy, vhy, vhy,* and my *sarma* is on the stove, and the *gushgoor* has fallen into my *sarma!*" the widow said, hitting her hands on her knees and crying.

"My boy, you can't marry my daughter because she is already engaged to a schoolteacher. You can go and test his knowledge, and he can test yours. If you can answer everything that he asks you, then you can marry my daughter," the landlord said.

"I'll go right away," the boy said, running quickly to the schoolteacher's house.

We were not told of the happenings in this cottage, but, of course, we know that the widow's son could answer very few of the questions he was asked.

Meanwhile, the widow and the landlord were left alone. "*Vhy, vhy, vhy,* and my *sarma* has been on the stove for three days now, and I don't know what has happened to it, *vhy, vhy, vhy,*" the widow said, hitting her hands on her knees and crying. She jumped up and tried to kiss the landlord.

"Don't worry. Sit down. I'm going to marry you," the landlord said.

"*Vhy, vhy, vhy,* and my *sarma* is on the stove, *vhy, vhy, vhy.*"

The landlord escaped, muttering under his breath. He went to the schoolteacher's cottage and found the boy still there. "Go home now, go home since you have lost," the landlord said to the boy.

"I have beaten him, I have beaten him," the widow's son said.

"Go home. We'll have a wedding very soon," the landlord said, pushing the widow's son out of the house. The boy went home very happy. "Yah! You are going to marry the landlord, eh? I am going to marry the landlord's daughter! I've beaten the teacher," he said.

"Go ahead, go ahead, get married! *Vhy, vhy, vhy,* and my *sarma* is on the stove, *vhy, vhy, vhy!*" the widow said. She was not worried any more because the landlord had told her that he would marry her.

Several mornings later a messenger came to inform them of the weddings, so the widow and her son hurried to get ready. The widow fixed her eyebrows, painted her face, and they were ready to go to the large house of their landlord.

Let me say that the landlord had hired a male cook for his household. Furthermore, the schoolteacher's sister was an old maid. The landlord called his male cook and the schoolteacher's sister to him. "You are going to get married today," he told them. They were both very happy and dressed for the joyous occasion, even though they didn't know whom they were going to marry.

Meanwhile, all this time, the *sarma* had been cooking on the stove.

When everyone had arrived, the weddings began. There were three couples to be married. The first couple was the widow and the cook, but the widow didn't know that she was marrying the cook. The second couple was the widow's son and the school-teacher's sister, but neither one of them knew who the other was. The boy thought that he was marrying the landlord's daughter. The third couple was the schoolteacher and the landlord's daughter. But they knew exactly what was happening.

Everyone was quiet, and the priest started the ceremony.

"Oh, my *sarma* is on the stove, *vhy, vhy, vhy*, and it is most probably all softened now, *vhy, vhy, vhy!*" the widow broke out. Everyone began to laugh at her. The cook, who was standing next to her, poked her and told her to keep quiet. Finally, the weddings were over, and the landlord told each of the bridegrooms to take his wife home.

The widow pulled off her veil, and what do you think she saw! An old, fat cook! Of course, she couldn't do anything about it now that they were already married. "Well, any sort of husband is better than no husband at all," she said, taking the cook's arm and walking home.

The widow's son didn't know that he had been tricked. He took his wife and ran away, laughing at his mother and reminding her of his prediction that the landlord would not marry her.

"*Vhy, vhy, vhy*, and my *sarma* has been on the stove now for five or six days!" the widow said, pulling her husband along.

The cook was amazed at what he heard! Could it be that someone would leave *sarma* on the stove for five or six days?

"My dear, sit down while I go get the *sarma* and we can eat it for our wedding feast," the new bride said.

And what do you think she found? The *gushgoor* was mixed with the *sarma*, and the whole thing looked like black dirt! "Well, it doesn't matter what it looks like. We must have it for our wedding feast after I have taken so long to cook it," the new bride said as she poured the lumpy mess in the dishes and set it on the table.

"Is this *sarma?*" the husband asked, amazed.

"Yes, and what's more, it took me five days to cook it!"

The cook was furious. "Cook me something else or I'll leave you right here and now!"

"*Vhy, vhy, vhy,* after I spent five days to make the *sarma*, you call it dirt and refuse to eat it," the wife said crying. Just then the landlord was passing by to see if everything was all right. He heard crying and went in.

"What is this, a lovers' quarrel already?" he asked.

"She poured this lumpy thing in front of me and called it *sarma*. I refuse to eat it, and I told her that if she didn't prepare something else for me, I would leave her right now," the cook said.

"All right, my good man, don't get upset. I'll send you something from the house," the landlord said, leaving hurriedly.

The landlord did as he said he would. They had a nice wedding feast after all, and they took the precious *sarma* and threw it out the window.

TRICKERY AND WIT

66. The Ashman's Money

Once there were two very good friends who were both married and had families. "We'll never get anywhere in this town; let us go to Constantinople to seek our fortunes," one said to the other. And leaving their wives behind, they started for the big city.

When they reached Constantinople, one found work in a factory and the other as an ashman, one who emptied ashes from

This story was told by Antrias Amboian.

different houses. The factory worker put his money into the bank for safekeeping, but the ashman put his into the hands of their honest mayor. "Whenever you want your money, come to me, and you will have it," the mayor said.

Two years passed, five years, ten years, and these two friends saw each other from time to time. One day the factory worker told his friend, "I am going home soon. You come with me, too."

"Wait for me," the ashman said. "I'll go to the mayor and get my money. Then we can start out next week." So he asked the mayor for the money in his safekeeping.

"What is this? Who are you to have dealings with me? Look at your clothes! Aren't you ashamed to say that you have given me money? You are an ashman; how did you get money? Don't you ever say that I have money of yours again or I will have you thrown in prison!" the mayor said. The ashman went out of the room much bewildered. Now what was he to do? The week after, the factory worker went home, but the ashman could not go with him.

Now, this ashman was a cheerful person and did his work with zest. But after this adventure with the mayor, a great sadness came over him. One day while taking ashes out, he gave a big sigh. "*Ahk! Ahk!* [Alas!] To think that I must see such days," he said.

The mistress of the house, who was a rich woman, heard his moan. "What is wrong? What makes him moan? He is usually so happy," she said, going to investigate. "Why did you say '*Ahk!*'? What is your grief?"

"You can't help me; attend to your work," he replied.

"I can help anyone. Tell me, what is troubling you?" she asked and finally persuaded the ashman to tell her his story.

"I came to Constantinople ten years ago with my good friend. He worked in a factory and put his money in a bank, while I worked as an ashman and gave my money to the mayor so he would keep it for me. Several days ago we decided to go back home. My friend took his money from the bank, but when I asked the mayor for my money, he refused to give it to me," he said.

"If you listen to me, I can help you, but you must do exactly what I tell you to do," she said. She called in her maid, and the three of them started planning. "I will pack my jewelry into a bundle and take it to the mayor," the rich woman said. "I'll tell the mayor that while I go visit my husband who is in Van, I am giving my jewels to him for safekeeping. While I am still talking with him, you walk in and ask for your money. The mayor, trying to make a good impression on me, will give you your money back. When you leave, my maid, pretending to be my daughter, will enter and tell me that her father has just arrived from Van, making it unnecessary for me to give the mayor my jewels after all."

The next day the woman took her jewelry to the mayor. "My husband is in Van," she said to the mayor, "and I wish to join him. I have been looking around for an honest person, and I find that there is no one more honest than yourself. So I want to leave my jewelry with you."

"You have come to the right person, my Lady. I am an honest and sincere person." And the mayor began to tell of his great honesty. Just then the ashman walked in and asked for his money. The mayor, trying to make a good impression on the rich woman, gave the ashman every cent of his money. "Go, my man, and always remember that you met an honest man once," the mayor said kindly.

When the ashman left, the rich woman and the mayor began to talk again. Just then the maid, disguised as the rich woman's daughter, came into the room. "Oh, mother, mother, come home, quick! Father has just returned from Van!"

"Oh, I will not need to give you these jewels after all," the rich woman said, withdrawing them quickly. The rich woman was so happy at the success of her plan that she began dancing around the room.* The maid was so happy that her part in the plan had gone off smoothly that she began dancing, too. The ashman was so happy to receive his money that he began dancing vigorously. All three of them were dancing because their plan had worked so well. And just then the mayor joined them in dancing so that now there were four people dancing.

"This man is dancing because he received his money which he thought he would never see again," the rich woman said, referring to the ashman. "I am dancing because my husband has returned from Van; my daughter is dancing because her father has come home. What are you dancing for?" she asked the mayor.

"In my forty years in office, I have never seen such a trick. That is why I am dancing," the mayor replied.

So the ashman received his money and returned home.

* Informant danced just as each character did.

371

67. The Clever Boy

There was once a rich man whose wife died and left behind a beautiful daughter. When the girl was sixteen years old, she developed a very bad headache that no one could cure. The rich man was unhappy and one day set out to find a good healer in other lands.

On the way he met a dervish who said to him, "Your daughter has a very bad headache, and you can do nothing to stop it. Go to the mountain in your town, and there, among others, you will see a big black rock. Chip off a piece of this black rock and grind it to a powder. Put this powder in water and have your daughter drink it, and she will be cured."

The rich man did not believe that so simple a cure could help his daughter, but he decided to try it. He went to the mountain, found the black rock, chipped some of it and ground it to a fine powder. He put the powder in water and had his daughter drink the mixture, and, indeed, she became well.

Soon after, however, the daughter became pregnant. The rich man could not understand this turn of nature. "I am certain that my daughter has done nothing wrong. How could she be pregnant?" he asked himself again and again. He decided to wait until the child was born, and this he did. When a son was born to his daughter, he sold all of his possessions and with his daughter and grandson, went to live in another town, telling everyone that his daughter was a widow.

In those days the game of polo was very popular. Huge crowds attended these events. One day when the boy was about six years old, the grandfather took him to ride on a horse and play this game. The boy sat on the horse, his grandfather sat on his horse, and a government official, who was the rich grandfather's friend, sat on a third horse. The boy pressed his thighs into the sides of his horse and knew that she was with foal. "I cannot ride this horse," the boy said, "because my horse is with foal. In less than three weeks she will bear a colt which will be blind in the right eye."

The official was greatly puzzled by this and together with the grandfather, helped the boy get off his horse. "I will wait and see if this boy is right," the man decided. And in less than three weeks the horse bore a colt which was blind in the right eye. The official was surprised that the boy's prediction had come true

This story was told by Hovhannes Kaprelian.

and developed a great respect for him. Shortly afterwards the official was sent to another town where the king often stayed and there took up his work.

One day a fisherman in this town caught a very beautiful fish and decided to take it to the king. The king, upon seeing the grace and coloring of the fish, asked that it be taken to the queen. So the fish was placed on a golden platter and taken to her. The servants knocked on the queen's door and said, "We have a fish which the king has asked us to bring to you."

"Is it a male or a female?" she asked, covering her face.

At this, the fish jumped up and down on the platter and rolled with laughter. The servants were surprised and quickly called the king to witness the strange sight. The king could not understand why a fish should behave in such a way, so he called in all the wise men of his kingdom and asked their advice. "Tell me why that fish is jumping up and down and rolling with laughter," he demanded, but no one could answer him.

The official who had newly come to the town heard of the matter and went to the king and said, "Your Majesty, I don't think that your wise men will ever solve this problem. Let me tell you of a young boy whom I know." So he told about the little boy who was able to tell that a horse was with foal and would bear a colt which was blind in the right eye. The king was so impressed with this that he ordered the boy and his grandfather brought to the palace. When the boy was taken before the king, he said, "Your Majesty, I can solve your problem if you promise that you will not get angry at anything that I do or say." When the king agreed to this, the boy asked that two guards go to the queen's room and bring forth the queen's forty maids.

"Unclothe them," the boy ordered the two guards. At first the guards hesitated, but when the king commanded them to do so, they began to unclothe the forty maids. They discovered, to their great surprise, that these were not maids at all but handsome young men. The king became very angry.

"Your Majesty," the boy said to the king, "the fish laughed and rolled from side to side because he was only a fish and it does not make much difference which sex it is. But the queen already had forty males in her room, and in comparison, her question was indeed very foolish."

The king saw the truth of the boy's judgment and ordered that his wife and her forty men be killed. Then he married the boy's mother, and the boy, his mother and his grandfather lived at the palace.

68. The Dead Snake and the Young Wife

There was once a very rich family with seven sons, all of whom were married and living with their parents. But despite their wealth they were never content or happy; the house was always in disorder. Finally, the youngest of the wives persuaded her mother-in-law to let her take charge of the household for a time. Soon, to the amazement of all, the young woman brought order and cheerfulness to the house of the seven couples.

But two of the older brothers were jealous of the ability of their youngest brother's wife. Now, the young wife had made it a rule that no one was to come home from work empty-handed. They were each to bring in firewood and pile it in the meadow. The two jealous brothers one day found a dead snake and decided to throw it on the wood pile to scare the youngest wife so that she would resign her leadership. After they had thrown the dead snake on the pile and departed, a stork happened to pass by with the most precious and most beautiful crown ever beheld by the human eye. Seeing the dead snake, the stork swooped down, dropped the crown, picked up the snake and flew away.

When the young wife went to inspect the pile of wood, she saw the crown and hid it. During supper the two jealous brothers were surprised and disappointed because their sister-in-law apparently had not been frightened by the snake. Of course, they didn't know what had actually happened.

The next day the young wife gave the crown to her father-in-law, telling him to take it to the king but to refuse any reward that the king might give him. The bewildered man took the crown to the king and refused all the riches which were offered him.

After a few days the king ordered seven mules to be loaded with gold and taken to the home of him who had brought the crown. When the mules arrived, the young wife refused to accept the gift, but the messengers insisted that they had brought the treasure at the king's command. Then they proceeded to pile up

Collected from Ohannes Tarpinian and translated by Mardiros Tarpinian, a student at Wayne State University.

the gold at the door of the house. When the brothers saw the treasure, they praised the young wife for her cleverness. She never told them the truth, and from then on she was the ruler of that home—and a happy home it was for the seven couples.

69. The Dilemma

Once upon a time not long ago the people in Akor,* Armenia, were having great difficulty because their priest had died and no one was prepared to take his place. Who was to become the new priest?

In that little village there was a coarse farmer, unlettered, yet very jolly and witty. The people liked him and decided to make him their priest. The man protested, but to no avail. So when he was chosen priest of the village, he resolved to do his best.

One day the bishop visited the village church to observe the new preacher. However, the preacher, who could not read, was unable to conduct the ceremony correctly. He knew that it was necessary to win the approval of the bishop so he said, "Father, if you permit me to stay on, if you don't embarrass me, I'll give you two horses, three cows and two sheep. Tell them how good I am, and I'll give you two horses, three cows and two sheep."

The bishop began to think: what did he have to lose? All he needed to say was that the man was good, and all these animals would be his. So he agreed to do as the preacher asked. After the ceremony all the churchgoers surrounded him to have a glimpse of the holy man. "My people, take good care of your preacher, he is as good a man as can be. He is a holy man; respect and always listen to him; pay attention to what he says," the bishop said.

Everything went along very well for a time, but the people were not entirely satisfied. Their good preacher had one great fault. He would not conduct a funeral in public but insisted upon being left alone with the corpse. One day several men got together and began to comment on this. "I wonder what he does or says that he will not have a witness," one said.

"No one has ever been able to watch or hear him," the second man said.

"I know what I'll do," the third man said. "I'll sew myself in a

This story was told by Kazar Hoogasian.
* Informant's own village near Kharput.

shroud and pretend that I'm dead. You take me to the priest and tell him to read the funeral service for my soul. Then I will listen to what he says, and I will tell you later." Accordingly, the man had a shroud made and sewed himself up in it. He was taken to the priest who asked for absolute privacy to read the funeral services. When the two were left alone, the priest began, "You son of a dog, why did you die and give me all this extra work. Get up, ———," he said, kicking the body.

Upon hearing these exclamations, the man inside the shroud, who was not dead at all, could not help laughing. When the priest heard laughter, he grew angry. "What kind of a corpse is this that is not entirely dead? I'll have to help God get rid of him." Saying this, he sat on the body, found the neck and pressed it until the man beneath him was really dead.

Then the preacher walked out and said, "Friends, what kind of a corpse was that? He surely took a long time to go to the other world. You can bury him now." The two friends were greatly surprised. Just a short time ago their friend had gone into the church safe and sound, and now he was really dead. But upon thinking the matter over, they became convinced that the priest was not so simple after all!

70. It Happened in a Bath

An Armenian was waiting in Marseilles for the arrival of money from friends in America so that he could migrate to that country. He waited and waited, but the money did not arrive.

"I'll write and ask someone else," he said, writing a letter to another friend. But letter after letter brought no reply, and he became discouraged. He was in Marseilles, in a foreign land, with no friends and no money. The innkeepers, learning that he was to go to America, were sure that he was rich. When, after six months, they discovered that he was penniless, they were quite angry and said, "What shall we do? The longer he stays here, the more expense he is to us. It would be much cheaper for us to buy him a boat ticket and return him to Armenia."

So it was not long before the Armenian found himself on a cheap boat, bound for his own country. He would have been very happy if it had not been for the lice which infested his body and his quarters on the boat. But finally he reached his destination.

This story was told by Hovhannes Kaprelian.

With his feet firmly on his native soil, he stuck his hands in his pockets and pulled out the money he had. When he counted it, he found only four *para* [Turkish coin]. He began to think, scratching himself meanwhile, "What can I buy with four *para?* I cannot get a meal, I cannot get a suit of clothes, I cannot get a pair of shoes. What can I do with four *para?*" He stood lost in thought. "Well, poverty is from God, we cannot help that; but cleanliness is the work of man for we can bathe once in a while. I think that I'll take a bath with these four *para.*"

He entered the bath house, undressed, put a towel around his body and was ready to bathe. He saw several passages but did not know which of them lead to the bath. Then he saw two tall attendants standing at one of the entrances, and he went up to them.

"Which of these passages leads to the bath?" he asked them.

But the attendants did not take the trouble to answer him. They saw that he was no one of consequence, so they ignored him. However, without their notice, he managed to get past them and through the entrance they were guarding. Inside he saw a man sitting draped in beautiful, colorful silks. He went up and touched the gown, then touched the man. But the man did not move, and suddenly the poor man drew back! That man looked exactly like himself! He gazed in the mirror, then again at the seated man, and again noted the great resemblance. Once more he touched the man and discovered that he was dead.

"What will I lose?" he asked himself as an idea came to him. "This man is already dead. Certainly I can try it!" He removed his towel, then unclothed the rich man, put the towel around him and wrapped himself in the silks of the dead man.

As he started out of the entrance, the two attendants fell before him and with the words, "Pasha, Pasha," they led him to a private chamber where they undressed him and bathed him. As they were drying him, the bath-owner came in to announce that the pasha's servant was waiting with the horse.

"Ah! I understand that I am a Turk, I have a servant and he has a horse ready for me; that means that he will lead me to my house," the shrewd Armenian said to himself. When he was ready to leave, he stuck his hand in his pockets and found them full of gold pieces. He gave five of these to the bath-keeper, and five to each attendant. "My friend," he said to the bath-keeper, "in that bath there is a dead man with a towel tied around his stomach. Here are sixty gold pieces. Give him a decent burial with a priest to read over him and place a stone on his grave."

Outside the bath the servant was having a hard time keeping a fiery red horse under control. The two attendants and the servant helped the man mount the horse, and they started out. The servant walked alongside the horse, his hand on the animal's mane, leading him to the pasha's house.

"Ah! Now I will know where I live, but how will I know which part of the house is the men's division?"* he said to himself. But as he was climbing the steps leading to the house, he stumbled—purposely, of course—and began to moan, "Oh, my foot, my foot!" The servants, hearing their master's cry, ran out to help him. "Master, master, which division would you like to go to, the men's or the women's?"

"Take me to the women's division," he said softly. "Now, I wonder if I am supposed to have a family?" he said to himself.

They took him into a lovely room, and soon a very beautiful woman came to him. "My Pasha, are you hurt?" she asked, making a loving gesture. But suddenly she drew back, stared at him and said, "If you are my husband, you will go to the king's palace tomorrow; if you aren't, you won't be able to," and she left.

"Ah! that means that I'm in the service of the king," the man said to himself. "Well, I must go to the palace tomorrow then." In the morning he started limping again, and his servant helped him mount his horse and led the horse to the king's palace. "My good man, I am unable to go to the king by myself today. Help me, then return home," the pasha told his servant. The servant, thinking that the pasha made this request because he was limping, helped his master to the king's room. "Ah! the servant has shown me which room is the king's," the man said to himself. As he entered the room, he gave a ground-sweeping bow to the king. "Ah! again you have made me happy," the king said, with a self-satisfied smile.

"Um-m! that means that I am supposed to be the king's official jester, making him laugh and keeping him contented. Well, let me see what I can do to entertain him," he said to himself. "Your Majesty," he said to the king, "how would you like to hear a story today?"

"If it's a good story, why not?" the king asked.

So the man told his own story, how he entered the bath, how he stumbled on the stairs of his house, and so on.

* Turkish houses were divided into separate sections for men and women.

"But is such a story possible? Are you making it up, or is it true?" the king asked the pasha.

"Your Majesty, it is true! I am that person."

When the king was certain that the man before him was not the real pasha, he had him locked in a room. "Call the bath-keeper here," he ordered.

When the man arrived, the king asked him, "Did a richly dressed man give you sixty gold pieces to bury a man who was found dead in your bath?"

"Yes, Your Majesty, he gave me sixty gold pieces to call a priest and have a gravestone made for the dead man. The man is buried in ———— cemetery," the bath-keeper said.

The king had the grave opened and had the real pasha's body examined to see if he had been purposely killed. It was determined that the death was a natural one.

The king called the false pasha before him. "My man, I have found your story to be true. Luck will have you eat bread, and you help it do so. Why should I stop you? House, wife, position, money—they are all yours!"

So the man went back to his house, his wife, his money, and continued pleasing the king until the end of his days.

71. Quick-Witted

At one time there were three little boys who were brothers. As their parents were dead, the first brother, who was ten years old, decided to leave the others and find work somewhere as a servant.

He walked until he came to a brook which he decided to cross. But as he started to do so, an old man who was sitting nearby called out, "Boy, I am very old and cannot cross by myself. Won't you help me?" The boy, sorry for the old man, did what he was asked and with great difficulty helped him to the other side of the brook.

"Where are you going?" the old man then asked.

"I am looking for work," the boy answered.

"Well then," the old man said, "come work for me." The boy, thinking that the old man looked kind, agreed to do this. So they went on together and finally reached the old man's house. Now,

This story was told by Mrs. Katoon Mouradian.

although this man looked gentle, he was really a dervish—and a bad one at that.

The next morning he said to the boy, "Here are my oxen; you must take them to the fields. And this is my dog; wherever my dog stops, you must put the oxen to work. At night when you are ready to return home, you must chop wood and load it on the dog's back before you start for home. Here is a jug of buttermilk. You must bring this same bottle, with the same amount of buttermilk which is now in it, back to me tonight. If you fail to do any of the things that I have mentioned, I will take the skin off your back, and you will die."

So the boy took the oxen, the dog and the buttermilk to the fields. But the dog ran up the mountain, so the boy could not work. Soon he became hungry and drank the buttermilk, and before he knew it, darkness came, and he didn't have enough time to cut any wood. So he returned home without the buttermilk and without the wood. When the dervish saw what had happened, he took the skin off the boy's back and hung his body in the cellar.

Several months later the second brother, seeing that his eldest brother had not returned, decided to look for some work and, if possible, find his lost brother. When he came to the brook his brother had crossed, he met the dervish, helped him across the stream and accepted the offer to work for him. The old man gave him the same orders that he had given the first brother, and the boy, like the first one, failed to carry them out. He drank the buttermilk, did not chop the wood, did not plow the fields and was consequently skinned and killed, and his body was hung in the cellar.

Several months later the youngest of the three brothers decided to find work and look for his two older brothers. He walked along and came to the brook. He was about to cross it when the dervish said, "Boy, I am old, won't you help me cross that stream?"

"I am just a little boy; I cannot help you cross it. Cross by yourself; you are old enough," the little boy said. The dervish was surprised to hear such a sharp answer from such a small boy.

The dervish managed to cross the brook very well, and then asked the boy, "Where are you going?"

"I am looking for work," the boy said.

"Then come and work for me," the dervish said, and the boy

knew immediately that this dervish had something to do with
the death or disappearance of his two brothers.

The boy agreed to work for the dervish and went home with
him. The next morning the dervish said to the boy, "Take my
oxen and my dog with you to the fields. Wherever my dog stops,
you must plow the fields. At night, when you are ready to return, you must chop and load wood and bring it back home.
Here is a jug of buttermilk. You must bring the same amount
of buttermilk home with you tonight as I give you now. If you
fail in any of these things, I will take the skin off your back."

So the boy took the oxen, the dog and the jug of buttermilk
with him to the fields. The dog tried to run up the mountain,
but the little boy, being angry, took his whip and struck the dog
until it died. Then he sat down and drank the buttermilk. When
he had finished it, he urinated into the jug. He chopped some
wood and loaded it on the oxen. When it became dark, he started
back for the dervish's home.

"Have you chopped and loaded my wood?" the dervish
asked.

"Yes, I have," the boy said. The dervish looked and saw
that the boy was telling the truth.

"Did you bring back my jug of buttermilk?" the dervish
asked.

"Yes, here it is," the little boy said, giving the jug to the
dervish.

"Where is my dog?"

"He is coming along slowly," the boy said.

"All right, then," the dervish said, "tomorrow you will go to
the fields again."

When the dervish and his wife had gone to bed, the little
boy slipped out and decided to explore the dervish's house. When
he entered the cellar, he saw the bodies of his brothers and became very, very angry. He decided to kill the dervish and went to
bed to make plans.

The dervish, meanwhile, was telling his wife, "We must run
away from here, for I know that this boy will cause my death.
If he killed my dog, if he urinated in the jug and brought it
back to me as buttermilk, then I am sure that he will try to kill
me. And if he has gone downstairs and has seen the bodies of
his brothers, then I am even more certain that he will kill me.
During the night, get up and make some *bagharch* [cake or rich

bread with melted butter poured over it], and we'll leave this place."

But the little boy heard this and was ready to leave with the couple. The dervish's wife put the *bagharch* in a big sack, and when she was not looking, the little boy hid himself in the sack, too. The dervish threw the sack on his shoulder, and with his wife, he started out. After some time, the boy urinated, and the urine ran down the dervish's back. The dervish thought that it was melted butter of the *bagharch*. "Wife," he said, "you have used a great deal of butter in this *bagharch*. Just look how it is oozing out."

As they went on, the dervish said, "Oh, I am glad that we left the boy behind." But no sooner did he say this than the boy cried from within the sack, "I am here; let me out."

The dervish was so surprised and frightened that he dropped the sack to the ground. The boy climbed out and stood before the old man. "You tried to get rid of me, but I was too smart for you. I am going with you, and wherever you go, I'll go, too."

So the dervish, his wife and the little boy walked along until it was dark. The dervish said to his wife when he thought the boy couldn't hear: "Let's sleep on that bridge tonight. I'll sleep in the middle; you sleep on one side of me, and the boy will sleep on the other side. When you say 'hum,' I'll say 'gum,' and we'll push him into the river below."

So they slept on the bridge that night, but the little boy had heard the conversation between the dervish and his wife and was prepared. During the night he traded places with the dervish, and when the dervish's wife said "hum," the little boy said "gum," and together they shoved the dervish into the river below.

The next morning the dervish's wife and the little boy took the dervish out of the water, seated him on his donkey, tied him securely, then they started out again. Soon they came to a town where the royal gardens were very beautiful. The donkey went into the garden and trampled the fruits and flowers. The king, notified of this, ordered that both the donkey and the man be killed. When the guards had done this, the dervish's wife and the little boy fell upon the dead man. "My husband!" the woman shrieked. "My father!" the little boy yelled. And the king, hearing of the sorrow he had caused, gave his garden and all the fruits and trees in it to the widow and the little boy. They sold everything that was in the garden and made a great deal of money.

They put the twice-killed dervish on his donkey and started

out again. They came to a town where the royal wheat fields were very high, and the donkey went in and began to eat the wheat. The king was notified and ordered that both the donkey and the rider be killed. When the guards obeyed the order, the dervish's wife and the little boy again fell upon the dead man's body. "My husband!" the woman shrieked. "My father!" the little boy yelled. The king, seeing the sorrow he had caused, gave the royal wheat fields to the widow and the little boy who sold them and again made a good deal of money. But the boy was becoming a youth and wanted to settle down, so he said to the king, "You must also give me your daughter in marriage." The king agreed, and so the boy married the princess.

A few days after, the boy said to the dervish's wife, "Now what must I do to you? I am going to take the skin off your back just as your husband did to my brothers."

"Oh, no!" the woman cried, "I am an old woman. Consider me your mother. I promise to stay with you and your wife and look after your children in years to come."

So the boy did not kill the old woman, but let her stay with him and his wife.

72. Matching Wits

There were once two robbers. One stole during the day, and the other stole during the night. Both were married to the same woman, but neither of them knew this.

One day, the day robber decided that he wanted to go to another town to try his luck. That very same day, the night robber decided to go to another town to try his luck, too. The day robber said to his wife, "Wife, wrap up some food for me for I am going to leave this town for a while and see what I can do somewhere else." That same night, the night robber said to this same woman, "Wife, wrap up some food for me for I am going to leave this town for a while and see what I can do somewhere else."

So the woman cut a chicken exactly down the middle and cooked each part separately. She put one half in one man's lunch and the other half in the other man's lunch. Then she put the very same kind of bread and fruits in the two lunches and gave her night husband one bundle and her day husband the other.

This story was told by Hovhannes Kaprelian.

The night robber started out of town, and so did the day robber. Finding themselves on the same road, they walked along together as friends. Soon they became hungry and stopped beside a brook to eat.

The day robber opened his bundle and thought to himself, "Ah! my good wife has given me a nice lunch. I wonder what this fellow has to eat?" When he looked over, he saw that his companion's lunch was identical. "Let us see if these two halves will make a whole chicken," he said, putting the two pieces of chicken together. They were amazed to find that both halves fitted together perfectly.

"Ah! this is strange!" the night robber said. "They seem to be from the very same chicken." So the two men told each other about their lives.

"I am a robber," the night robber said.

"I am a robber, too."

"I am a night robber, and I rob the whole city," the first one said.

"Well, I am a day robber, and I, too, rob the whole city."

"Where do you live?" the night robber asked. "It is strange that I have not met you before."

"I live in the Mezzereh with my wife Mariam."

"Why, I live there, too," the night robber said.

"But my wife's name is Mariam, and we live in the Mezzereh," the day robber insisted. The two men argued back and forth with great excitement. They gave each other a description of the house, of their woman.

"Well, this means that both you and I live in the same house and have the same wife," the night robber said. "No use arguing about it."

"Well," the day robber said, "I don't mind your living in my house, but I don't want you to have my wife. Therefore, let us see who is the cleverer thief, and the better one of us will also win our wife." And so it was agreed.

Together they entered the town, and as it was daylight, the day robber decided to do his work right then and there. He saw a man who had his wife's jewels tied up in a handkerchief and was on his way to the jeweler. "Now, you watch and see how clever I am," the day robber said. Without the man's knowing it, he took away the handkerchief, removed the jewels, set rotten onions in their place and put the handkerchief back again. "Let us go along and see what will happen," he said as they followed the man.

The man, handkerchief in hand, went to the jeweler and said, "I have brought my wife's jewels to be cleaned." But when the handkerchief was opened, all they could find was the rotten onions. The husband was much embarrassed, and his face turned red. "Please forgive me," he stammered, "I must have taken the wrong bundle."

The jeweler was puzzled but let the man go without a word. The husband was very angry as he walked homeward. The day robber again snatched away the bundle, removed the onions and replaced the jewels. When the man reached his home, he called to his wife and said, "What is this? What are you planning? You gave me this bundle to take to the jeweler, and when I got there and opened it, it was full of rotten onions. Are you laughing at me?"

The wife was puzzled at what she heard. "But I gave you my jewels," she insisted. Her husband insulted her and threw the bundle to the floor. She picked it up and opened it to find her jewels. Now she became angry at her husband. There was only one thing for him to do: he gathered the jewels in the handkerchief and again went to the jeweler. The two robbers, who were outside the house, saw this scene and were laughing so hard that they almost died.

The day robber decided to have some more fun. So again he snatched the handkerchief away, removed the jewels and substituted the rotten onions. When the husband reached the shop, he put the handkerchief on the counter and said, "It was my mistake; here is the correct bundle." When he opened it, again he found the rotten onions. "What does this mean?" the angry jeweler asked.

The man could not understand. Surely there was no mistake for he himself had put the jewels into the handkerchief. His face reddened, he stammered an excuse, put the onions back into the handkerchief and quickly left the shop. As he walked homeward, the day robber again snatched the handkerchief and substituted the jewels for the rotten onions. The robbers followed the man home to see what would happen.

"Wife, what does this mean?" he said, throwing the bundle down.

"Husband, husband, what has happened to you? These are my jewels, don't treat them so roughly!"

"Jewels, are they?" the husband said. "I have taken them twice to the jeweler, and when I opened the handkerchief, I have found onions. What kind of jewels are they?"

The wife hastily bent down, picked up the bundle and opened it to find her jewels. "Here, husband, what has happened to you? Don't you see them?" she asked.

The husband was very much surprised and quietly picked up the bundle and started out for the jewelry shop a third time. The day robber snatched away the handkerchief, and took the jewels out and substituted the onions. When the man got to the jewelry shop, he said to the jeweler, "Friend, I don't know what there is in here, but we'll see!"

But when they opened the handkerchief and found the onions, the jeweler could only laugh at the man for he thought him a fool. The man became very angry, took the bundle and started out for home. But this time the day robber did not change the onions to jewels, but kept them for himself. The night robber could hardly stand up because he had laughed so hard. He said, "Now let me show you what I can do tonight."

That night, the night robber took along with him forty steel spikes and with his friend went to the palace. He told the day robber to sit on his shoulders, and together, they started to climb the high palace wall. The day robber had a wooden hammer and pounded the spikes into the wall as they climbed up.

Inside the wall they saw the royal henhouse. There they found a nice big turkey, and the night robber lighted a fire and roasted the turkey over it. The day robber was afraid that someone would see the fire and catch them. However, they ate in peace, and when the turkey was finished, they left the bones right there.

They entered the palace and went to the king's bedroom. There they saw an enormous slave fanning the king, who was fast asleep. But the slave was also sleepy and was chewing gum to keep awake. The night robber threw a snare to pull out the gum that the slave was chewing, and the big man soon went fast asleep. The night robber then shook the bed, and the king was aroused. He sat up in surprise and asked what had happened.

"Your Majesty, just lie back and hear the story that I am going to tell you," the night robber said. "There were once two robbers who were married to the same woman, but neither of them knew it. One day, the day robber decided to go to another city and told his wife to pack him a good lunch. That very day, the night robber decided to go to another city, and he, too, told his wife to pack him a lunch. As it happened, these men met on the road and learned that they were married to the same woman. They decided that each would do his best in stealing or cleverness and the best one would win the woman—for, as you know, two men cannot be married to the same woman.

"The day robber saw a man with a bundle in his hand. The man was taking his wife's jewels to the jeweler. The day robber opened the handkerchief, took out the jewels and put in rotten onions instead. The man, when he opened the handkerchief at the shop, was greatly embarrassed. When he was on his way home, the day robber opened the handkerchief, put the jewels in and took the onions out. The man went home and scolded his wife, and when she opened the bundle, she saw her jewels. The robber did this three times, and the third time, he no longer returned the jewels, but he kept them for himself. That was indeed clever, wasn't it?"

The king nodded his head and laughed. "Now," the night robber continued, "here is what the night robber did. With his companion, the day robber, he went to the palace. He carried the day robber on his shoulders, forty steel spikes and a wooden hammer in his hand. The day robber pounded the steel spikes into the wall of the palace, and they both climbed up.

"Inside the palace grounds the night robber went to the royal henhouse and stole a turkey. After he had killed and cleaned it, he made a fire and roasted the turkey, and the two robbers sat down to eat. When they were finished, the two robbers entered the palace and went to the king's bedroom. The night robber saw that the royal slave, who was fanning the king, was chewing gum so that he could stay awake. The robber threw a snare and pulled the gum out, and the slave soon fell asleep. Then the night robber sat down and told a story to the king. Now, what do you think of that?"

"Oh, that is impossible!" the king said. "The night robber would have been caught when he roasted the turkey, or if he had not been caught then, the guards in the palace would surely have caught him later."

"No," the night robber answered, "I am that night robber, and no one has caught me yet. Tell me honestly, which of these two robbers was more clever?"

"Oh, the night robber, of course," the king said. So the night robber won the contest, and the wife was his alone. The king fell asleep again, and on his way out the night robber put the gum back into the slave's mouth. With his companion, he fled from the palace.

The next morning the king remembered something about the contest, but it sounded so strange that he thought it was all a dream. He was ready to forget it when he received news that a turkey had been stolen from the royal henhouse during the night and had been killed and eaten right on the spot, for the bones were left behind. Only then did he realize that this was not a dream: such a contest had really happened!

73. The Story of the Robbers

At one time there was a man who was a master thief. He was so clever that no one could catch him. As the years went by, he grew old and decided that he wanted his young nephew to know all the secrets he had learned. So he taught the young boy all the tricks of his trade. One day when he thought his nephew was sufficiently prepared, the uncle took him along to rob the king's treasury.

So uncle and nephew drilled a hole in one wall and entered the treasury, took as much gold as they wanted and left again. When this had occurred several times and the thieves could not be caught, the king ordered that a pit be dug by the wall and that it be filled with tar.

The next time the uncle and his nephew drilled a hole in the wall to enter the room, the uncle stepped right into the pit. He called out, "Son, son, wait a minute. Put your foot here, and here, and here." By directing him so, he got his nephew safely across the room to where the gold was hidden. With similar directions the nephew safely reached the other wall. "Now, son, take your sword and cut off my head," the uncle said.

"But you are my uncle, how can I cut off your head?"

"You heard what I said, didn't you?" the uncle asked. "I have been caught, and there is no way of escaping. If they recognize me, they will also catch you. How is a man recognized? By his head, of course. Therefore, cut off my head so that I will not be recognized."

So the nephew cut off his uncle's head and buried it. The next morning the king went to his treasury and found his money

This story was told by Hovhannes Kaprelian.

missing and a dead man with his head cut off. He began to think of another way to catch the thief. He ordered that gold pieces be strewn all about the palace grounds. Then he hid himself and waited to see who would bend down to pick up the coins. He believed that whoever did so would be the thief.

When the nephew heard that there was much gold sprinkled around the palace, he put tar under his shoes and walked about the building. Whenever he stepped on a gold piece, it stuck fast to his shoe so that when he returned home, he had a great many gold pieces and he had not once bent down. The king saw that this plan had failed.

Next, the king asked an old woman to march up and down the streets wearing beautiful jewels and ornaments. Guards were watching her from all sides so that whoever touched her would immediately be caught. The king thought that he would thus catch the thief. But the nephew was carefully watching the old woman, and when she turned a corner, he grabbed her and ran away so fast that the guards lost sight of the old woman altogether. So they returned to the king and told him that someone had not only stolen the jewels on the old woman, but the old woman herself.

The king became very angry and this time ordered a camel to be heaped with jewels. The camel walked slowly up and down the streets with guards watching its progress from all sides. The king thought that whoever touched the camel would be the clever thief. But again the nephew stole both jewels and camel before the guards could act. So they went back to the palace and told the king what had happened.

This time the king was indeed very angry. What else could he do? He thought about it day in and day out. To make matters worse, the king of Russia heard of this clever thief who lived in Armenia and and sent word to the Armenian king, saying, "What kind of a king is this king of Armenia? He can't even catch a thief!"

The Armenian king announced that the robber would not be hurt if he came forth and presented himself. So the nephew went to the king and said, "Your Majesty, I am the robber."

"Oh, so you are that clever person who has outwitted all my guards! Tell me how you did it," the king said.

So the nephew told about cutting off his uncle's head and putting tar under his shoes. The king was pleased with the cleverness of the lad and said, "My son, nothing in the world would

please me as much as your going to Russia and stealing something valuable from the king's palace."

The nephew said, "Not only will I do that, Your Majesty,
but I will bring back the Russian king himself."

"Well, son, if you can do that, what else could I want?" the
king said.

"All I need to carry out my plan is a box which I can make
bigger or smaller as I wish and a big bearskin coat with bells
tied to each hair," the nephew said. So the king gave him the
box and the bearskin coat, and the youth set out for Russia.

He reached the royal palace at night, climbed the wall and
found the king's bedroom. He wore his bearskin coat with the
many bells, and danced about and made a great noise. The king
jumped up and saw this frightful creature before him.

"I am the angel Gabriel, and I have come to take your soul.
But because you are a king, I am going to take not only your
soul but your body, too. Quick, get into this box!" the nephew
said.

The king, never having died before, didn't know that this
was not an angel, so he quickly got into the box. "Now listen to
what I have to say," the nephew said. "As we go along, we will
pass through many kingdoms of animals. When we pass the kingdom of cats, I will ask you to meow, and they will let us through.
When we pass through the kingdom of dogs, I will ask you to
bark, and when you do, they will let us through. If you want
to go to heaven, you must do all that I ask you to do. Is it
understood?"

The king called from within, "Yes, yes, I will do that!"

So the nephew took the box to Armenia. When the king and
all the nobles had gathered, he said, "Your Majesty, we are passing through the kingdom of cats: meow!"

The king began to meow with such earnestness that the bystanders could hardly control their laughter. "Now, Your Majesty,
we are passing through the kingdom of dogs: bark!" And the
king began to bark fiercely. "Now, Your Majesty, we are passing
through the kingdom of donkeys: bray!" The king cried out in a
loud voice, "Hee-haw, hee-haw!"

Then the nephew opened the box and helped the king out.
But this wasn't heaven. It was the palace of the king of Armenia!

"Your Majesty, king of Russia," the Armenian king said, "this
angel Gabriel is my thief. Now do you see why I couldn't catch
him?"

74. The Test of the Chicken

At one time there was a poor old couple who had only one chicken. The husband said to his wife one day, "Wife, kill this chicken and cook it. I am going to take it to the king." She could not guess what his plan was but did as he told her to. When the chicken was cooked, he took it to the palace and said, "Your Majesty, I have brought you this chicken."

The king was amused. "I have many chickens; but most probably this is the only one you have. Since you have brought it here, distribute it to the members of my court."

The poor man cut the chicken and gave the head to the king, the wings and legs to the members of the court and kept the hind end for himself. The king was much surprised and asked him to explain why he had done this.

"Well, Your Majesty," the man said, "you are the head of the government, and, therefore, you must get the head because you control everything. These men are your helpers, and they do as you order. Therefore, they get the wings and legs. I am only a poor peasant, and, therefore, I trail far behind: I get the hind end."

The king was highly pleased and ordered that a chicken the same size as the one the man had brought be put on a scale and weighed. "Give this man as much gold as that chicken weighs," the king ordered. And this was done. The poor peasant returned home a rich man.

A Jewish neighbor noticed the sudden wealth of the old couple and knew that something unusual had happened. So he instructed his wife to become a good friend of the peasant's wife to learn their secret.

So the Jew's wife did this. One day she asked the neighbor how she could buy the things she wanted without ever worrying about money. "I don't need to worry about money," the peasant's wife answered. "My husband has much gold!"

"But how did he get it?" she asked.

"He took a chicken to the king and was rewarded."

The Jewish woman quickly returned home and told her husband about the chicken. "Quick, then, cook a chicken so that I can take it to the king and he will give us gold, too." The woman quickly cooked a chicken and gave it to her husband to take to the king. He went to the palace and said, "Your Majesty, I have

This story was told by Hovhannes Kaprelian.

brought you a chicken."

The king said to him, "Very well. Distribute it among the members of my court."

So the Jew disjointed the chicken and gave the best part, the white meat, to the king, and the rest to the men present. "Tell me why you did this, why did you give me this part?" the king asked. The Jew was unable to answer, of course, and the king became very angry and had him hanged.

75. The Devil's Yallehr

There was once a man who wanted to seek his fortune. So he packed a good lunch and started out. On the way he met the devil. He knew who it was because the devil has a tail. The devil, upon seeing the man, decided to play a trick on him. "Friend, where are you going?" he asked.

"I'm going to seek my fortune," said the traveler who was a man from Argun.

"Do you mind if we go together?" the devil asked.

"No, come along."

After they had gone a little way, the devil began to get tired. "Friend, how would you like to carry me for a while, and then I will carry you," the devil said.

"That is fine, but on one condition. I will carry you as long as you can entertain me with a song or a story. As soon as your song or your story is finished, you must get down and carry me," the man said.

"That is a good plan. Let me climb on your back first," the devil said. So the devil got on the man's back, and they continued their journey. The devil began telling the man a story and tried to stretch it as far as possible; but soon his story came to an end, and he had to get down from the man's back. Then the man got upon the devil's back. "Friend, I cannot tell a story, so I am going to sing a song," the man said. He cupped his hand to his ear and began singing in his loudest voice, "Yallehr, yallehr, yallehr . . . yallehr, yallehr, yallehr . . ."* When one group of "yallehrs" was finished, he started on another group.

This story was told by Mrs. Hripsima Hoogasian.

* According to informant, Turkish: unending tale. Even today, long-winded conversations are referred to as the devil's yallehr.

In another version of this story, the trick words are "Yar, hey!" [Turkish: "Sweetheart, hey!"]

The devil became a bit tired and asked his passenger, "Friend, what comes after '*yallehr, yallehr*'?"

"That is all there is: '*yallehr, yallehr*,'" the man said.

"Well, then, how long is the song? When will it end?" the devil asked.

"Friend, this song can continue until the end of time," the man said.

When they reached their destination, the man got off the devil's back and said, "Go, friend, but remember that a devil can never fool a man from Argun."

76. Rooster-Brother

There was once a poor widow who had only one son. She wanted this son to have a trade so she placed him as an apprentice with a tailor. Although the boy was young and short of stature, he was very shrewd.

One day the tailor was expecting company and was making many preparations. "Boy," he instructed, "take this rooster to the bakery and have them put it in the oven to roast. Tell them that you will call for it later." So the boy took the rooster to the bakery, had it put in the oven and returned to his master.

When the tailor was ready for the roast, he told the boy to bring it to him. So the boy went to the bakery shop where he found the bird well roasted and very tempting. The baker covered the pan with a piece of paper, and when everything was ready, the little boy started back with it to the tailor's shop. But he was not to go far, for a group of thieves, who had seen him, went up to him and snatched the pan from his hands. As the boy was alone against many, he did not fight but took a good look at the thieves and vowed to take revenge. "Someday," he said, "I'll do the same thing to you, or I am not worthy of my name!"

From that time on he made it his business to trace the thieves continually and to watch what they were doing. One day he saw them take a big lamb to the bakery. "Ah! now we shall see!" he said when he heard them telling the baker that they would call for it in the afternoon.

A half-hour before the time set, he went to the baker's shop and said, "Mr. Baker, my masters have sent me here to carry home the lamb."

This story was told by Mrs. Akabi Mooradian.

"All right," the baker said, putting a paper over the lamb and giving it to him.

The little boy went outside and attached a note on the door of the bakery saying, "Rooster-Brother took your lamb, and you wait to see what else he'll do."

Shortly thereafter the thieves asked for their roast from the baker, who was very much surprised. "Your apprentice called for it just half an hour ago," he said.

"Apprentice!" the thieves exclaimed. There was nothing they could do, however, and they did not know who had played the trick on them until they saw the sign on the door. "Oh, that must have been the boy whose rooster we took," they said, and they were greatly angered to have been fooled by such a small boy.

One day one of the thieves went to the tailor to buy a suit. Again the little boy was watching. The tailor measured the thief for the suit and was paid in advance, promising the man to deliver the suit on Saturday, let us say, at three o'clock.

"Ah! now we will see what this thief will do!" the little boy said to himself. A few hours before the suit was due to be delivered, the boy went to the tailor's shop. "Mr. Tailor, my master sent me for his suit. He will need it before three o'clock."

"All right," the tailor said, and he gave the suit to the boy.

The thief waited and waited for the suit which he was to receive at three o'clock. Finally, very angry, he went to the tailor's shop. "You promised me that my suit would be delivered to me at three today. Look at the time now! Where is my suit?" he asked.

"Your apprentice called for it before three," the amazed tailor said.

"He did, did he?" the thief exclaimed, going to the door where he found Rooster-Brother's message posted on the door. It read: "Rooster-Brother took your suit, you wait and see what else he'll do." The thief was very much surprised and angered to have been tricked by a mere boy, but there was nothing he could do about it.

Sometime after this one of the other thieves went one day to a jeweler. He ordered a beautiful watch made and asked that it be delivered at two o'clock on a given day. Rooster-Brother overheard the conversation, and just an hour before the watch was to be delivered, he presented himself at the jewelry shop. "Mr. Jeweler, my master needs the watch before two o'clock and sent me to get it."

"Very well," the jeweler said, giving him the watch.

The thief waited and waited for the delivery of the watch, but no watch came. Finally, he lost patience and went to the jewelry shop.

"You promised to deliver my watch at two o'clock today. Look what time it is now!" he said, very angry.

"But your apprentice called for it an hour ago!" the jeweler replied.

"Apprentice!" the thief echoed. When the man went out the door, he saw the message: "Rooster-Brother took your watch, you wait and see what else he'll do."

Now the thieves were really afraid of the boy. "We'd better move away from here, or one day that boy will give us away to the police," they said. That evening they put all their stolen goods on mules to move away from little Rooster-Brother. But the boy knew of this move and followed them to their new hideout.

One evening while the thieves were robbing, Rooster-Brother went into the cave. A huge dog pounced on him, but he quickly pulled out some food from his pockets and gave it to him. The dog took the food and let the boy enter. Inside the cave Rooster-Brother saw an old woman who looked like a witch. "Mother, please take me in," he begged. "I am a homeless orphan; I am hungry and tired. Give me a place to sleep."

The old woman looked at the slight boy and felt sorry for him. "This is not my house; I am not master here. The masters must not know that you are here, or they will kill us both."

"I'll stay only tonight," the boy said.

"Very well then, but you must not cough or sneeze, or the men who live here will find you," she cautioned.

Rooster-Brother looked around and saw a thick rope hanging from the ceiling. It was the thieves' custom to bring their victims into the cave, rob them of all their valuables, and then hang them, and later, bury these bodies. But the boy didn't know about this, so he asked, "Mother, what is that rope for?"

"The men who live here tie that rope around people's necks," she answered.

"Like this, mother?" he said, mounting the stool under the rope and loosely throwing the rope around his neck.

"Oh, you bad boy! Why must you understand everything? Come down from the stool, and I'll show you how," she said.

Rooster-Brother slipped his head out of the noose and stepped off the stool. The old woman mounted the stool and put her neck in the noose.

"Is the rope that loose?" the boy asked innocently.

"No, it must be tight, like this," she said, pulling the rope tighter.

Rooster-Brother kicked the stool from beneath her, and she hung dangling in mid-air. In a few minutes she was stone dead.

The food that Rooster-Brother had given to the dog was full of needles so that when the dog swallowed it, he died almost instantly. The boy took a few valuables, left his usual message on the door and went back home to his mother.

Late that evening the thieves came home and wondered why the dog was not barking to welcome them. They went in and saw that the dog was dead and that the corpse of the old woman who had cooked and washed for them was hanging in mid-air. They looked around and found Rooster-Brother's message. "Rooster-Brother killed your servant and your dog, you wait and see what else he'll do," it said.

"Let's run away before that boy kills us," the three thieves said, running out of the cave, without taking a single valuable with them.

The next morning when Rooster-Brother went to the cave to see what had happened the previous evening, he found that the thieves had fled, leaving everything behind. "Ah! I never expected such luck as this!" he said. He took all the valuable articles to his mother's house, and he and his mother became very rich and lived peacefully ever after.

ANTI-FEMININE TALES

77. The Honorable Wife

THERE WAS ONCE a man who wanted to get married but was very particular about his future wife. He wanted her to be very honorable. After much searching, he eventually found a woman whom he thought as honorable as he wished her to be. "No man ever sees my face," she told him. "I never go out to the stores."

"This is the woman I am looking for," he said. "No man sees

This story was told by Mrs. Akabi Mooradian.

her face, she never goes out. She is truly very honorable." So he married her. And she never did anything that her husband considered dishonorable. One day he went to a tailor to order a dress for his wife.

"I must measure her if I am to make a dress for her," the tailor said.

"How dare you suggest laying a hand on my wife? She is an honorable woman. Here, I have her measurements; use them," the husband said.

"But I cannot make a dress unless I measure and fit in my own way," the poor tailor said.

"Aren't you ashamed of yourself? I tell you that my wife is an honorable woman. No man ever sees her face; she never goes to the stores!"

"She is fooling you; she is a dishonorable woman to say such things."

The husband became so angry that he almost killed the tailor. "How dare you say that? What proof have you?"

"Only a person who wants to remove suspicion from herself will say such things," the tailor said. "Watch her and see."

"How shall I do that?" the husband asked when he saw the soundness of the tailor's argument.

"Tell her that you are going away for a while; then hide and see what she does."

So the husband went home where he found his wife in seclusion. "Wife, I am going on a trip which will probably keep me away for at least a week. When I return, your dress will be ready so that you and I can go visiting," he said.

When the wife was sure that her husband had left, she called in her maid. The husband, however, was hidden and saw and heard everything that happened.

"Go tell the candle-maker that your mistress is at liberty and will see him tonight," she said.

The maid went to the candle-maker. "My mistress is at liberty and will see you tonight," she said.

"Oh, I am so sorry," the candle-maker replied, "but the prince is getting married at the end of this week, and I have to prepare many candles. Here, take this set of beautiful candles that I have just made and give them to your mistress. Present my apologies and tell her that I will come another night."

The maid went home with the candles and told her mistress, "The candle-maker said that he was very busy making candles for the prince's wedding at the end of this week. But he sent you these beautiful candles and asked me to present his apologies. He said he would come another night." The wife took the candles and hid them behind the door, but her husband saw the hiding-place.

"Very well, then, go the *halva*-maker [candy-maker] and ask him to come to see me tonight," the wife said.

The maid went to the *halva*-maker. "My mistress is at liberty and would like to see you tonight," she said.

"Oh, I am so sorry! I cannot possibly come. I have to make so many pounds of *halva* for the prince's wedding! Here, take this tin of *halva* to her and present my apologies. I will come another night," he said.

The maid took the *halva* home. "Mistress, he is busy. He has so many pounds of *halva* to make for the prince's wedding at the end of the week that he cannot come tonight. He sent this *halva* with his apologies and said that he would come another time," the maid reported. The wife took the *halva* and hid it beneath the stove. "Very well, go call the goldsmith. He won't be busy," the wife said.

So the maid went to the goldsmith. "My mistress is at liberty and would like to see you tonight," the maid said.

"I'm sorry, so very sorry," he said, "but the king has given me so many orders, and unless I fill them, I will have my head cut off. Here, take this gold piece and give it to your mistress. Present my apologies and tell her that I will come another evening."

So the maid took the gold piece and returned to her mistress. "The king has given the goldsmith many orders, and unless he fills them, his head will be cut off. He cannot come to see you tonight, but he sent you this gold piece. He told me to present his apologies and to tell you that he will come another evening," the maid reported.

"Ah! well!" the wife said, putting the gold piece under the sofa.

"What a wise man that tailor was!" the husband said to himself. "I'd better stop her before she invites someone else." Quietly he slipped out of his hiding place and went to the stable. He mounted his horse and made much noise outside the house as if he were arriving from a great distance.

The wife and her maid ran out to meet him. "Oh, the worst thing happened to me!" he said. "I was riding along the road when the biggest snake, as thick as all those candles put together that you have behind that door, came across my path. It had the biggest head, as big as that tin of *halva* beneath the stove, and its eyes were as large as the gold piece under the sofa."

"What an unusual circumstance! If he knew how I got those things, it wouldn't be very good for me," the wife said to herself, very much afraid. "Why do you think such things, husband?" she asked him softly.

"How dare you tell me such lies? You don't go the tailor, you don't do this, you don't do that! You tried to make a fool of me, but I know everything. Tell me, what am I to do about it?" he asked.

"Oh, husband, it is all a mistake on your part," she said.

"No, wife, it is no mistake at all! You have been lying to me from the start, all these years," he said. "I must settle this tonight —now!"

Saying that, he proceeded to kill his wife right then and there. After that he went to the tailor and said, "I was in great error; you were right about my wife. But, now, after having learned a very valuable lesson, I have killed her. I am leaving this town because I cannot live in disgrace."

He walked and walked for many months and came to another land. All his money was gone, and he had nowhere to go except to the churchyard. The very night he reached this new country, there was a big robbery. The guards searched all over but were unable to find a trace of the robber. For fifteen years robberies had been committed, and not even one little stolen article had ever been found. Upon discovering a strange man in the churchyard, the guards thought that he must be the robber and arrested the traveler.

"I'm not a thief, I haven't stolen your goods," the arrested man shouted. But they did not listen to him, and he was beaten unmercifully. "Free me and I promise that I can find you the guilty one," the man cried. "If I don't, you can kill me then."

The guards, thinking that he would tell on his partners, let him go, but he was always under their eye, he was always in their sight. One day he saw a great crowd coming down the street. A group of people wearing bells and making much noise walked before the sheik, and a great many people walked behind him.

"Who are those people? Why are they wearing those bells?" the man asked his neighbor.

"That is our holy sheik. He is so God-fearing that those men preceding him wear bells to make the insects get out of his way. He never commits a sin, never even kills an insect," his neighbor proudly said.

"Aha! I have discovered our robber," the husband said to himself. He went to the guards and told them of his discovery. "How dare you insult our holy sheik?" they asked him, giving him another beating. The more he insisted that the sheik was the thief, the more they hit him.

"Please don't hit me any more," he begged. "Just give me three guards, and I'll prove that I am right."

So they gave him three guards and together they went to the cave where the sheik lived. Now, this sheik, who would not indulge in the comforts of a house, was considered so holy that no one could go within a certain distance of his barren cave.

The traveler, however, slipped inside the cave to watch the holy man. The sheik undressed and approached his altar, pulling the day's robberies from under his robe as he did so. At the altar he fell on his knees, opened a secret door and disappeared through a secret passageway. The man ran outside the cave and signaled the guards. They followed him and saw the sheik in the very act of disposing of his day's thefts. Thereupon, they took him to their headquarters.

Meanwhile, special officers inspected the secret passageway and found that all the stolen articles for fifteen years back were hidden there! The people were told of the discovery, and anybody who had lost a coat, a ring or any other valuable came to claim it. Not one thing had been sold. The people took their goods and spit into the sheik's face. "But how did you know that the robber was this sheik?" they asked the husband.

"I knew because of something I experienced earlier in my life," he said. "You see, I had a wife who, I thought, was very honorable. She told me that no man ever saw her face, and she refused to go to the tailor shop to be measured. Then, when I finally learned that she had three sweethearts, I killed her. It was the same with our sheik. He was so innocent that he wore bells and made others wear bells so that no insects would die under his feet. It was only natural for me to suspect that there was something unusual about him."

"True, we had never thought of that," they replied. "You are a wise man; you must have a high position in our government."

So the husband became a high official and remarried, but this time he had better luck and remembered his lesson well.

78. The Rooster's Advice

One day a passerby saw a big snake swallowing a small snake. He quickly killed the big one, thereby saving the life of the little one. In gratitude the small snake said, "With the power of my breath, I will make it possible for you to understand the language of animals."

The breath of a snake is so fiery that a man must stand quite a distance away to avoid getting burned. So the man found a long hollow tube and put one end of it to the snake's mouth and the other end to his own. When the snake breathed deeply into the hole at the end of the pole, the man received his breath. Thereafter he was able to understand the language of all animals. The snake warned him, however, that the moment he revealed the secret to anyone else, he would lose his magical ability.

One day the man and his wife were riding together. His wife's horse said to his horse, "You can go faster than I can, but don't think that it is because you are fast. I am pregnant, and my rider is pregnant. It is a shame that my load is so heavy that I cannot keep up with you."

The man bit his tongue and said to his wife, "Wife, let us change horses."

She wanted to know why he suggested such a thing, but he would not tell her. "Tell me!" she insisted again and again. But every time he denied her request. This went on so long that finally the man was ready to tell his wife what she wanted to know. Just then he heard a dog bark at a rooster. The rooster said, "I am happy that I can control twenty wives, whereas this master of ours can't control even one wife. You see all these hens? I control all of them for I am the only rooster among them. As for that wife of his, I would use a good whip on her, and you would see how I would make her hold her tongue and behave herself as a wife should."

The man said to himself, "Alas! I am not even as good as a rooster!" But he took the rooster's advice, and when his wife repeated her demand, he took his whip and beat her so that she never asked him another question.

This story was told by Hovhannes Kaprelian.

79. The Talkative Wife

In an old hut in the forest lived a man and his wife. The wife was the most talkative woman on the face of the earth. Day and night, night and day, she nagged, she scolded, she chattered. The only time she was silent was when she fell asleep, which was not often enough.

One day the husband lost his patience and devised a scheme to get rid of his wife. He invented a story about a well filled with gold and jewels and told his wife that she could go along and help him haul the treasure out. When the couple arrived at the well, the wife, who did not trust her husband, said that she was the one who should be lowered into it. The husband answered that, as usual, she could have her way. After he had let her down for some distance, he cut the rope, covered the well and left her, as he supposed, to her destruction. But the woman was not alone for in the well was the evil spirit.

Six months later the husband returned to the well and uncovered it. From the depths he heard someone, whose voice was not that of his wife, begging to be released. After he had secured a rope and lowered it, he drew up the owner of the voice who turned out to be the evil spirit. The spirit told the man that he was going to reward him for saving him from the constant six-month-long chatter of that woman in the well.

The evil spirit told the man that he should go to the kingdom to the south and see the daughter of the king. While the man was on his way, the evil spirit entered the head of the princess and drove her mad. When the man arrived in this new land, the spirit told him to go to the castle and offer to cure the princess for the king had offered the richest rewards to anyone who could restore her mind. The man succeeded and won the reward—enough to last him a lifetime.

A few months later the evil spirit again saw the man and told him that he was going to the northern kingdom to drive the princess of that country mad. But the spirit warned the man not to go to that kingdom for if he did, he, too, would go mad.

In a few days word came that the daughter of the northern king had lost her reason and that there was a rich reward for anyone who cured her. The man who had cured the princess of the southern kingdom was unhappy. He pitied the princess and

Collected from Rouben Karagousian and translated by Mardiros Tarpinian, a student at Wayne State University.

longed for the reward, but he remembered the warning of the evil spirit. Finally he thought of a way to trick him.

As he had expected, when he arrived at the northern kingdom, the evil spirit met him and recalled his warning. The man, however, told the spirit that he had left word behind that if he should go mad, a certain woman was to be freed from the well and told the whereabouts of the evil spirit. Upon hearing this, the evil spirit shuddered and begged the man not to set that talkative woman on his ears. So the man proceeded on his way, cured the princess and received the reward. As for the wife, she is still chattering away in the well, more talkative than ever.

80. Today's Laughter, Tomorrow's Sadness

There was once a lazy woman who never wanted to work. One day she decided that she would become a *khanum* [Turkish: lady] and not do any work all that day. "Husband, I am going to be a *khanum* today, and I am not going to do anything," she informed her husband as he started for work. He did not answer her and left the house. After he had gone, she cleaned the chicken and put it on the stove to cook over a low flame.

After she had done this, she sat down, folded her hands in her lap and said over and over again, "I am a *khanum* today, I am a *khanum* today."

Soon a beggar came asking for food. "Can you give me some bread?" he asked her.

"My friend, I would gladly go to the kitchen, but I am a *khanum* today so you can go back there and help yourself to bread," she said.

The beggar went into the kitchen and began looking around for the bread, but he saw that a chicken was cooking on the stove. "Ah! such luck!" he said, taking the bird out of the pot and putting it into his knapsack. He took off one of his heavy, dirty shoes and put it in the pan in place of the chicken. Then he looked around, and when he found the bread, he stuck it into his little bag, too. He noticed that the woman had been washing the day before and had not yet taken the things off the line. So he quickly put the clean clothes into his bag. Then he looked out the back door and saw that there was a mule standing in the yard. "Aha! a mule even! This is my lucky day!" he said, and he

This story was told by Mrs. Mariam Serabian.

went to bid the lady of the house farewell. "Thank you, *khanum*, you have been very kind to me," he said.

"I believe in helping others less fortunate than myself," she answered. "Come, sing a song, dance, amuse me!"

The beggar snapped his fingers, danced around a bit and then began singing this song:

> "Legend, legend, my father,
> The clothes on the line are in my bag.
> The mule in the yard will be beneath me,
> The bread in the basket is also mine,
> The chicken in the pan is in my bag,
> Today's laughter, tomorrow's sadness."

He sang the verse, danced around a bit then repeated the same verse. The woman was greatly amused. "What a beautiful song! Sing it again!" So he repeated the song again and again. The *khanum* enjoyed it without realizing that it applied to her. Finally the beggar left the house and quietly went to the yard, sat on the mule and rode away.

Late that evening when her husband returned, she said, "Husband, I was a *khanum* today: I haven't done a thing. Come, let's have supper. Go inside. The chicken is on the stove. Arrange the table and I will come and eat with you." The man was angry, but what could he do with a crazy wife? He went inside, took the lid off the pan, and there he saw a black thing in the water. What could this be? "Wife, what is this in the pan?" he called.

"Chicken, husband, chicken," she answered.

He pulled the black thing out and saw, much to his surprise, an old, worn-out shoe! "Wife, who has been here today?" he asked, showing her the shoe.

"There was a beggar who came and asked for some bread. I told him to go into the kitchen and help himself. He did, and as he was going out, he sang this song:

> "Legend, legend, my father,
> The clothes on the line are in my bag,
> The mule in the yard will be beneath me,
> The bread in the basket is also mine,
> The chicken in the pan is in my bag,
> Today's laughter, tomorrow's sadness."

The husband ran again and looked for the bread—there was none left. He looked for the clothes on the line and was unable to find them. He looked outside for their mule, but alas! that, too, was gone.

"Wife, you remember the last line of that song, 'Today's laughter, tomorrow's sadness?' Well, come here now," he said, and he beat her until she could feel no more pain.

SAGAS AND LEGENDS

81. Gohc *Amu* and the Tax Officials

ONE DAY the Turkish agents were due at the home of Gohc *Amu* [uncle] to collect his tax* But as Gohc *Amu* knew that they were coming, he hid in the chimney and waited. The agents, along with the Turkish police, entered the house and asked for Gohc *Amu*.

"He isn't here," Aryohn, his elder son, said.

"Where is he?"

"He is grazing the sheep."

The agents looked all around the house, searching for the man, but he was not to be found.

"Well, since your father is not here, we'll take you to jail instead," the tax collectors said to the son. But the boy begged the officials to wait until his father returned.

After waiting for some time, Gohc *Amu* came down the chimney and entered from the front door. "What is this? What are you doing in my house?" he asked the officers, pretending surprise.

"Man, you either pay your tax or go to jail," they informed him.

"Well, I haven't any money. Here, take my elder daughter instead," Gohc *Amu* said.

"What are we going to do with your daughter? We want your money," they insisted.

"I haven't any money. Here, take my daughter with you," he

The Gohc *Amu* stories were told by Mrs. Mariam Serabian.

* Gohc *Amu*, who had a wife, two daughters and two sons, lived near informant. He was a tricky man, and many stories were told about him. These are just a few of them.

said, shoving his daughter upon them. The officers ran out of the house, calling back that they would return the next day.

The next day Gohc *Amu* sat down on the floor with a glass of water before him. He looked into it and said, "They come, they go; they come, they go," pretending all the while that he was seeing objects in the glass. And just at that moment, the tax collectors entered the house and asked Gohc *Amu* what he was doing.

"I'm looking into the future," he said.

"Are you ready to pay your tax?"

"Here, take my wife," Gohc *Amu* said, shoving his wife toward them.

The collectors didn't want his wife, so they began hitting Gohc *Amu*, who began to scratch his sheepskin cap. He made such a racket that finally the tax collectors went to the local official to tell him of the trouble they were having with Gohc *Amu*.

"How many children does this Gohc *Amu* have?" the official asked.

"He has four—two sons and two daughters," they replied.

"Well, if he has that many, he has enough problems; let him stay on his land," the official said, releasing Gohc *Amu* from the debt.

82. Aryohn, *Gullah*

One day Gohc *Amu* [uncle] took his cane in his hand and went into his garden. There he saw a stray sheep which belonged to a neighboring Turk. "Ah! how lucky I am today," he said. "Now we'll have a little more to eat." He hid the sheep and went inside the house.

Later in the day the Turk and his friends went from house to house, from yard to yard, searching for the lost sheep. They searched Gohc *Amu's* yard but could not find the animal they were seeking. When the Turks left, Gohc *Amu* and his elder son, Aryohn, went into the yard with a large pan. They killed the sheep, put some of the meat in the pan and started a small fire to roast it. The rest of the sheep they buried in the ground until another time when they would be ready to eat it.

"Aryohn, *gullah* [gulp], Aryohn *gullah*," Gohc *Amu* said to his son.

Aryohn was eating so fast that the meat stuck in his throat. He could get it neither up nor down. Gohc *Amu*, seeing his difficulty, took a hammer and hit Aryohn on the back with it. Everything was all right after that.

83. Gohc *Amu* and the *Toot*

One summer Gohc *Amu* [uncle] sold watermelons and saved his money. "Wife, keep this money so that we can buy *toot* [mulberries] later in the season," he said, giving her the money.

The wife, on the other hand, seeing that her daughters were going without shoes, took the money and bought each daughter and herself a pair of shoes. She did not tell her husband what she had done, however. One day Gohc *Amu* went to the market and saw some beautiful *toot*. He bought two sacks full and had two hamals carry them to his home.

When they reached Gohc *Amu's* home, he shouted, "Mako, Kano, Mooreh [his womenfolk's nicknames], where are you? Where are you, women?" he yelled when he found that his wife was not there. "Hurry and find her," he ordered the girls.

The hamals, eager to return, asked for their money. "Brothers, there is no wife, so there is no money. You must wait," Gohc *Amu* told them. The girls found their mother and brought her back home. "Marto-churto, where's my money for the *toot*?" he asked her.

"*Archevud sahdgeem* [let me die in front of you], I spent the money for shoes for the girls and myself," she said, shrinking away from him. Gohc *Amu* was terribly upset and cried, "Here, hamals, here's my one daughter and here's another one. They are your money. Leave the *toot* here and go!"

"*Vodkud bahkneem* [let me kiss your feet], what are we going to do with your daughters? Give us the money and let us go back," they begged.

Gohc *Amu* didn't answer but started pushing the girls on the hamals' shoulders. The girls began crying and screaming, but their father did not pay any attention to them.

"Brother, don't act like this. Give us the money and let us go," the hamals begged.

"No money, only girls," Gohc *Amu* said.

"We don't want girls."

"Well, I guess you'll have to take the *toot* back then," Gohc *Amu* said, his mouth watering for the delicious fruit.

84. Gohc *Amu* and the Running Water

In the section of Armenia in which we lived there was a dam which supplied water for all the people of the community. Each family had certain hours when it could use the dam to irrigate fields and farmlands.

On this day it was Gohc *Amu's* [uncle's] turn to use the dam. So he took his son Aryohn with him to help. "Aryohn, be careful, don't waste any of the water, be sure it runs down into our fields," he said over and over again. As it happened, the dam broke and the water was flowing in the wrong field. But Gohc *Amu* was determined to make use of every drop of water coming to him so he pushed Aryohn into the hole, and directed the flow of water where he wanted it. When his hour of use was finished, he went to his son and shook him. "Everything is just fine, Aryohn, let's go home now," he said.

But Aryohn was almost frozen and could not get up; he couldn't even move. "Aryohn," Gohc *Amu* said, continuing to shake him.

No answer came from Aryohn.

People had gathered around to witness what was happening. "Folks, *vodkerneed bahkneed* [I'll kiss your feet], shake him so that he'll wake up," Gohc *Amu* begged.

The people began shaking Aryohn, and he opened his eyes a little. Father and son went home together.

85. Gohc *Amu* and the *Matzoon*

Gohc *Amu* [uncle], who always tried to get something for nothing, was especially fond of *matzoon* [yogurt]. However, as he disliked working, his family never had the money to buy milk to prepare the *matzoon*. So he always sent his wife to the neighbors to ask for some.

One day he sent his wife to a certain neighbor whose *matzoon* was thick and sweet. However, she was tired of continually supplying Gohc *Amu* with *matzoon* and refused to give him any more. "I'm going to sell this *matzoon* at the market today. I can't give any of it to Gohc *Amu*," she told the poor woman.

The wife went home and told her husband what the neighbor had said. "Why, who is she to say such a thing to me? I'll get that *matzoon* right away, you wait and see," he said.

He began groaning and making terrible sounds. "Oh, I'm dy-

ing, I'm dying," he cried. All the neighbors ran to his house to see
him. The neighbor who had refused to give the *matzoon* earlier in
the day also ran to Gohc *Amu's* house. All of them saw that the
unusual man was in a very bad condition and near death.

"*Vahk! Vahk!* [alas!] if I had known that he was dying, I
would have given him some *matzoon*. Here, I gave it to him every
other time; why didn't I give it to him today, too? Now my conscience will bother me all the rest of my life. Maybe if I had not
refused him, he would not be in this condition. I'll run home and
bring some, and we'll force it into his mouth. As long as I know
that he tastes it before he dies, my conscience will be quiet," the
neighbor said.

She ran home and brought a bowl of *matzoon*. They opened
Gohc *Amu's* mouth and forced a little spoonful of *matzoon* in.
Then the neighbors sighed, made the sign of the cross and left the
room. The woman who had brought the *matzoon* and I were the
last ones to leave.

Just as soon as the door closed behind us, Gohc *Amu* jumped
out of bed and cried, "*Hehreef!* [my goodness!] I thought that
they would never get out of here. Wife, did you see how quickly
she brought the *matzoon?*"

The neighbor who had brought the *matzoon* was right outside the door, and when she heard this, she became very angry.
She opened the door and said, "Not only do I bring you *matzoon*,
but you laugh at me and belittle my family!"

Gohc *Amu* didn't pay the least bit of attention to her when
she spoke but kept right on eating his *matzoon*. I just stood near
the door and saw and listened to everything which was said.

About six months later, when Gohc *Amu* really died, nobody
would believe it. "If he pretended he was dead for bowl of *matzoon*, who knows what he is hungry for now?" they said.

His corpse lay in the house for three days before the people
finally believed that he was dead. And when they buried him,
they didn't give him a church burial because they thought that he
had no chance of going to heaven.

86. The Bear Husband

Once upon a time there lived in a little Armenian village a
young girl named Mariam. One day Mariam, with several of her
friends, went to the woods to gather greens. The girls were talk-

This story was told by Mrs. Mariam Serabian.

ing and having a carefree time when suddenly they saw a huge bear appear, grab Mariam and make off with her. They were so frightened that they all ran home as fast as they could and told Mariam's mother and the villagers what had happened.

The village men organized a party and looked for Mariam through every part of the woods and the mountains. But since she was nowhere to be found, they came to the conclusion that she had been eaten by the bear.

The bear took Mariam to his den in the mountains and put a huge stone at the mouth of the cave where he lived so that no one could come in or go out, except himself. He made Mariam his wife, and she bore him a little child who was also a bear. During the five years they lived together, Mariam lost all her beauty and became black in color. Her clothing was reduced to rags, and heavy dark hair covered her entire body.

Every day, the bear pushed away the rock, went out, re- placed the rock and found food for the evening meal. He never forgot to put the rock in place for he feared that Mariam would run away from him. One day the bear wanted fresh bread, so he decided to go to the miller and get some. He left the cave, put the rock at the mouth of it as usual then walked toward the mill. He entered quietly and stood before the miller. When the miller looked up and saw the bear, he was terrified, but instead of run- ning away, he waited to see what the bear would do.

The bear began mumbling his request as best as he could, but the miller could not understand. Then the bear gave him a sack and motioned to him to fill it with flour. After the miller had done so, the bear left the mill quietly. He went home and told his wife to knead the dough to make bread the next morning. She did as he asked.

When morning came, the bear decided to go out and find some wood for a fire to bake the bread. In his haste he forgot to place the rock at the entrance of the cave. When Mariam saw the opening and realized that her husband was gone, she placed the baby bear by the rising dough and ran to the village. She went to her mother's house and knocked on the door.

"Who is it?" her mother asked from within.

"It is your daughter," Mariam replied.

"Who is it?" the mother asked again, thinking that she had not heard aright, because she supposed that the bear had eaten her daughter.

"It is Mariam, your daughter."

The mother opened the door and saw standing before her a wild animal. She shuddered! Yet she took her daughter in and scrubbed her. After having used two squares of soap, she was still unable to remove the grime and dirt which her daughter had collected in five years. But finally the mother fed her daughter, then put her to bed.

The bear, meanwhile, returned to the cave with the wood and found Mariam missing. He began crying, "*Manna, Manna, khumoruh tutuu-tutuu, chagan laleh-laleh*" [poor Armenian usage: "Mariam, Mariam, the dough is sour, sour, the baby is crying, crying"], yet his wife did not answer. He repeated his cry several times, but, hearing no answer, he decided that he would hurl rocks at the villagers for he thought that they were hiding Mariam. So he started rolling large rocks down the mountain into the village, thereby killing several people.

Finally Mariam's mother called the village folk together and told them why the bear was rolling rocks down the mountain. "He is angry because Mariam ran away from him. But I cannot give her back to him. What are we to do?" she asked.

One of the village youths said, "Don't worry, I'll see what can be done." One day as the bear was again rolling rocks down into the village, the youth shot at him. The first bullet missed, but the second one hit him and the bear tumbled head over heels all the way down the mountain and lay there dead.

Several young men skinned the bear and threw the meat into a hole which they dug. As for Mariam, she never lost her black skin or her hair but remained disfigured for the rest of her life.

87. The Town of Stone

There was once an Armenian king, a ruler of a little town, who did not believe in God. "Who is God?" he would say to anyone who tried to change his mind.

No one was able to persuade the king, and because of his disbelief, the people of the town suffered. For ten years not one drop of rain fell, and vegetation of all kinds ceased to grow. The sheep could not find grass to graze and were dying. The people became hungry, and yet there was nothing they could do. They killed such animals as they had and ate them, but soon these, too, were all gone.

This story was told by Mrs. Mariam Serabian.

One day the people saw a strange thing happening among them. Many of them were slowly turning to stone, starting from their feet and moving upward. Soon all the people had become completely petrified. Then the king grew frightened that he, too, would turn to stone. "Guards," he ordered, "arrange everything so that the queen, myself and all my guards can climb that tall mountain and run away from this disease."

Very soon the king, the queen and all the king's guards, laden with food and tents, climbed the mountain in an attempt to get away from the disease. But do you think that they could run away from God? No, they could not because God is everywhere.

Very soon the king began to turn to stone, starting from his feet. The queen was afflicted next and then the soldiers. But the queen, who had expected this, had provided herself with writing materials and began writing this verse:

My town is sitting crying, crying,
There is no one to say "Don't cry, don't cry!"
With my sorrows I am consumed
Yet there is no one I can trust.

Ahk! Vahk! [Alas!] I have spent my life,
My eyes have been blinded with tears.
To live as an orphan has been my lot,
Luck has forgotten me entirely.

And now this!
Whoever touches my clothes will become like me;
Whoever takes away anything from my person will find that it will
crumble into dust.

By the time she had finished writing this verse, she had entirely turned to stone.

One day a traveler passing through the town saw that all the people had turned to stone. Surprised, he climbed the mountain near the town, and there he saw the king, the queen and all their guards standing as stones. He saw the beautiful crown which the queen had worn and decided to take it back home with him. But, as he lifted it off her head, it crumbled into dust. The man, seeing the danger that could come to him, left it there and ran as fast as he could down the mountain.

As far as we know, that town is still in existence, and the people in it are still petrified. And if a person should climb the mountain near the town, he would find the king, and the queen and all their guards, standing quietly as stones.

88. Retribution

At one time a bridal party was moving toward our village from a far-off town. The people were very thirsty, and the groom said, "If God would grant us a nice cool drink, I would offer Him a *madagh* [sacrifice]." Suddenly, a clear, cool spring appeared at the entrance of the village, and the people drank abundantly of the good water. They looked about and, across the river which gushed from the spring, saw an old shepherd with his many sheep and greeted him.

When they were refreshed, they sat on their horses and crossed to the other side of the river. The groom completely forgot his promise, and had no intention of making a sacrifice. God read his mind and decided to punish him so he turned the whole company into stone. The bride on her horse, the groom on his horse, the parents, the visitors, the gifts and the shepherd with his sheep—all were transformed into stone.

A beautiful cross made of stone appeared at the spring. These stone figures have remained to this day and remind us of the ingratitude of man.

This story was told by Mrs. Katoon Mouradian.

89. The Old Fort

There was a big underground fort which was a very old place near our house. Poor people who could not put together enough money to pay rent found refuge in the fort. There was a large stream of water which gushed from under the fort and ran through it. On one side there was a circle of very old, but beautiful, furniture. This furniture was so old, in fact, that if one touched it, the fabric would crumble to ashes.

One day a Turk who had heard that there was gold in the fort decided to find it. He came upon a room, pushed open the door and found a statue of a big slave with an enormous sword in his hand. The Turk knew that if he stepped on the threshold of the door, the sword would fall on his head, so he jumped across instead. Seeing a big kettle made of gold, he lifted the huge gold lid and saw many gold pieces. He took as many of these as he was able to hide in his clothing and went to the door to open it, but it wouldn't open.

This story was told by Mrs. Mariam Serabian.

When he removed the gold from his person to become lighter, the door suddenly opened. Again he jammed the gold into his pockets, but the door stayed closed. Thereupon, he left the gold behind, and again the door opened. Finally, he managed to slip through the door with one gold piece hidden on his person. When he reached home, he could not talk. He wrote this story down on a piece of paper and showed the gold piece for proof. Three days later, he died.

90. Under Suspicion

One day King Dikran of Armenia went walking in disguise. "I want to see what my people are like and how they really live," he said. He walked and walked until he became very hungry. As he had no money and was in rags, what was he to do? He came upon a shepherd boy who was sitting under a shady tree watching his sheep. "Perhaps if I ask this boy, he will help me," the king said to himself. "Son, I am hungry and tired, can you give me some bread?"

"Here, I am not hungry. Eat my bread," the shepherd said, giving the king his coarse bread.

The king took the bread. He looked at the shepherd and saw that he was a very young boy. "Son, do you always take care of the sheep?"

"Yes, this is my work. You see, I am an orphan, and I take care of the sheep of a man in the village. In return, he lets me stay with him and gives me a few *para* [Turkish coin] now and then."

"Son, I am a rich man. How would you like to come along with me? I'll put you in school so that you will learn many things and someday you'll become a person of importance."

"Sir, if you will take me, I will most certainly go with you," the shepherd said.

"All right, we will go to the village and tell your master that you will no longer work for him," the king said, taking the boy's hand.

When they arrived at the master's house, the boy said, "Master, this man says that he is rich and wants to take me and put me in school so that someday I will be somebody of importance. Will you give me your permission to leave?"

This story was told by Hovhannes Kaprelian.

The rich man looked at the stranger and recognized him as the king. "Of course, son, if this man wants to take you, you must go away with him."

The king took the boy's hand and tried to lead him away, but the boy would not leave. "I have been working for this man for four years, and I want him to give me the money that I have earned," the boy said.

"Why do you want the money?" the king asked.

"So that you can pay for the cost of my schooling," the boy said.

"Come, son, I have much money. Don't look to this man for any," the king said. So the boy was sent to school and given many advantages while he lived at the palace.

The boy was not a disappointment to the king. He was as smart, as sharp a lad as ever was born. When he became older, the king made him treasurer of all his funds. In due time, with the permission of the king, the boy married, had a home and a family. Both the boy and the king were very happy.

Unfortunately, the king died, and his son became ruler. The officials of the government were old men and jealous of the young treasurer's success. "We have been serving the government all these years, and what are we? But this young man, in just a few years, has become treasurer of the land. We will have to fix it so that he will get into trouble with our new king." So they told the new ruler, "Your Majesty, the treasurer is cheating. He is taking money behind your back."

"Ah! I cannot imagine that he would do a thing like that," the king said. "However, we shall see." He had the treasurer called before him. "My friend, I want you to present an account which will show all the money received and the money paid out by you from the time you took office during my father's reign until now. I will give you three days to prepare this."

"Your Majesty, I can account at this very moment for all of the money entrusted to me."

"No, I will not hear you now, but I will wait for three days and then listen to you," the king said, dismissing him.

That day, as the king was walking through town, he saw a fountain of which only the foundation was left. "Where is the rest of this fountain?" the king asked the officials who were with him. As they were unable to answer him, when he returned to the palace, he demanded that the treasurer be brought before him. "My friend, there is a certain fountain in town which has only its foundation left. What has happened to the rest of it?"

"Your Majesty, that fountain was in that condition when I came to this land. I don't know how or why it is the way it is."

But when the officials were alone with the king, they said, "There used to be diamonds set in that fountain, but he has removed them."

The king, angry, demanded that the treasurer be brought before him. "I have been told that there were diamonds set in that fountain."

"Your Majesty, you have not been told the truth. But let us say that there were diamonds. Certainly, I couldn't have taken them for I couldn't have cut away the metal. I must have gone to an expert smith. Who is more expert than your smith? Call him before you and question him," the treasurer said.

The royal smith was called before the king and questioned. "That fountain was torn down years ago. The jewels on it were removed with the consent of the king, your father, and were placed on another piece of work," the smith said.

"Let us search the treasurer's house. I would not be surprised to find the jewels hidden there somewhere," one of the officials said. So the king and all his officials went to the treasurer's house to search for the jewels. They looked through every room in the house without finding the jewels. But as they entered the cellar, they found one room which was locked. "Open this door so that we may search the room," the king ordered the treasurer.

"Your Majesty, you have looked all through my house, and I have not made any protest. But please leave this room alone," the treasurer asked.

"Why do you want to stop us from entering that room?" the king asked.

"I have something in there which is my own, and I don't want to have anyone else see it."

"What else—the jewels!" the officials said, pushing the door open. Inside, they found only a worn-out shepherd's suit. They were stunned! Why should this rich man keep such worthless clothes locked up?

"I asked you to leave this room alone, but you would not listen to me. This suit is the one I wore when I first came to this palace. I never want to forget those happy, carefree days," the treasurer said.

"My man, I am sorry, please come back to your former position," the king said.

"Your Majesty, if you want me to come back, you must get rid of all these officials," the treasurer said.

"As you say," the king answered, doing as the man requested. And so the treasurer and his family lived happily with the king ever after.

91. The Woman in Blue

There was once a young bride who had just borne a child and was still in a weak condition. But her husband, an uneducated and selfish man, did not think it necessary for her to rest. "Up with you, woman, and get me some wine from the cellar," he ordered.

So the wife got out of her bed and went down into the cellar to get some wine for her husband. There she saw a woman who was sitting quietly, mending clothes. She was wearing a blue dress and a blue veil. The wife passed the woman and went inside to the wine cellar, but as she bent over to pour out some wine, she heard screams and strange noises in the wine jug. Greatly frightened, she left everything where it was and fled. When she reached the place where the woman in blue was sitting, she became faint and fell down, senseless.

Her husband waited awhile for his wife's return. "That lazy woman, why does she take so long?" he asked himself. He waited for a while longer, and when she still did not return, he angrily went down to the cellar. There he saw his wife lying on the floor, unconscious. He carried her upstairs, and when she regained consciousness, he asked her, "Wife, what happened? Why were you lying on the floor?"

"Oh, husband, husband, there were many people chasing me. They wanted to catch me and were saying, 'We're coming, we're coming!' They were chasing me so I ran and fell down at the feet of the woman in blue," she said.

"Woman in blue? Where is she?"

"I fell down at her feet," the woman repeated.

"But when I saw you, there was no one near you," he said.

She could not make her husband believe that she was telling the truth, but every so often she would faint and when she awoke, she would tell of *elks** and the woman in blue. One day the *elks* decided to remove her liver. They came to her and said, "Open your mouth so that we can pull out your liver!"

This story was told by Mrs. Mariam Serabian.
* For discussion of *als* and *elks,* see pp. 64–65.

But she would not obey them; instead, she closed her mouth all the tighter. After that, every time the *elks* visited her, they ordered her to open her mouth so that they could pull out her liver, but she would resist.

One day, while in one of her fainting spells, she saw the woman in blue again. "Come, come to my church, and I will cure you," she said.

"Which is your church?"

"My church is *Mairig Asdvadzadzeen* [Notre Dame]," the woman in blue said as she disappeared.

When the woman came out of her faint, she told her husband about the woman in blue (who in reality was the Mother of Christ). "All right, wife, we will take you to *Asdvadzadzeen* and see what happens," he said.

So with a *madagh* [sacrifice] and a mattress for the wife, they went to the church. After much suffering, the wife was cured by the Sainted Lady. After that, she did have fainting spells, but they were much fewer and less severe.

92. The Prize Bull

It was a bright morning; the village was in a festive mood because a wedding was to take place. As was the custom in Armenia, the bride was chosen queen for that day, and all the village girls were her attendants. Everyone was happy and gay except one, the bride, who, having been forbidden to marry the young prince whom she loved, was to marry one whom she did not love.

The handsome young prince of her choice, unwilling to stand by and see his love taken away from him, followed tradition and planned a way to win her for himself.

He had a beautiful, strong and intelligent bull which was the envy of the whole village and of the surrounding country. The bull was told by the prince to go to the village and wander among the maids, making friends with them. But when the queen of the day sat on his back, he was to gallop away swiftly to his stable.

The bull obeyed and went to the village. All the maids admired the wonderful creature and took turns riding him. Soon they begged the queen to mount the bull and take a ride. She

Collected from Ohannes Tarpinian and translated by Mardiros Tarpinian, a student at Wayne State University.

consented. But as soon as she had mounted the bull, he took to his heels and vanished from sight. Straight to the stable he ran, where the prince was waiting for his love. They were soon married and lived to a ripe old age, always revering the bull for the help he had given them.

93. The Sacred Sheet

A very poor man was harvesting a field of wheat when he saw a rich man pass by. "Hello, friend, where are you going?" he asked.

"I am going to Jerusalem," the rich man answered.

"Well, then, wait for me for I am going there, too," the poor man said. But the rich man did not want to walk along with such a poor man, so he pretended not to hear and went on. When the poor man finished his work, he quickly set out after the rich man. As he passed the prison, he saw a man standing in the yard. The man asked, "Why are you in such a hurry?"

"I have to catch up with the man ahead of me for we are going to Jerusalem together," the poor man said.

"When you reach Jerusalem, go to the church and get a sacred sheet. Bring it back to me, and when I am killed, make sure that I am standing on the sacred sheet so that my blood flows on it. If you do this, I will make it worth your while," the prisoner said.

The poor man promised to do as he was asked. "Now close your eyes," the prisoner said. The poor man did this, and when he opened them, he saw that he was almost in Jerusalem. How quickly he had arrived! The rich man arrived far behind him and wondered how that poor devil ever got there so fast.

The poor man went to the church and bought a sacred sheet and again quickly, as if by magic, returned to the prison. He asked for the prisoner and was told that he was to be killed the following morning. So the next morning the poor man took the sacred sheet and went to the prison. He begged the authorities to let the man be killed on the sheet, and finally they agreed to this.

After the prisoner had been killed, the poor man wrapped the body in the sheet and buried him. He guarded the grave for three nights. The first night the poor man heard a voice from the grave say, "I have died twice. At my first death my Master

This story was told by Mrs. Katoon Mouradian.

said, 'You are not dead since you have died without permission. Therefore, you cannot go to Paradise. You must die a second time, but this time it must be by the hands of the government.' So I was killed a second time."

The second night again the poor man heard the very same voice repeat these same words. But the third night after the voice had spoken, it added, "Whoever does as you ask, whoever goes to Jerusalem and brings you the sacred sheet, is worthy of Paradise as you will be. You will marry and have three children. You will be very rich, and when you die, you will go to Paradise. But, you cannot die and rest in peace until someone brings you the sacred sheet as you brought one for me."

And so it happened.

94. The Servant in the Monastery

There was once a poor man who served in a monastery. It was his job to go to the forest and cut down trees so that they could be used as firewood. But as it happened, the son of the nearby Turkish *beg* [lord] continually annoyed the poor worker.

The worker asked the rich boy, "Why do you bother me? I have much work to do; I am a poor man." But still the rich boy would not leave him in peace. So one day when the worker became very angry, he picked up some sand from the ground and threw it into the rich boy's face and said, "Become a donkey, and your clothing, a harness." And immediately this happened. The worker, who previously had three donkeys to carry his wood, now had a fourth one. After he had finished cutting the wood for the day, he placed it on all four donkeys and returned to the monastery.

The head of the monastery happened to be passing by and saw four donkeys. He knew very well that they had only three donkeys at the monastery. "My man, where did you get that donkey?" he asked.

"Oh, father, I found it straying about," the worker answered. But the rich boy, although he was now a donkey, could understand and feel like a human being. Often he would follow the chief monk and brush himself against the man's legs. The monk knew that this was most unusual and asked more questions of

This story was told by Hovhannes Kaprelian.

the poor worker. But although he continued his questioning for three months, he could learn nothing further.

Finally, one day when the monk asked so many questions from the worker, the latter said, "If you promise not to tell anyone, I will tell you about that donkey." When the monk had promised, the worker said, "This donkey is the son of Sarkis *Beg*. He was always annoying me and would not let me finish my work. One day he made me so angry that I picked up some sand from the ground and threw it into his face and said, 'Become a donkey, and your clothes, a harness.' And it did happen, so now I have an extra donkey."

But the monk, being foolish as all monks are, said to the worker, "Let him return to his human form and go back to his house."

"Now why should we do that?" the worker asked. "If he stays here, he will do as we say, and we will have an extra donkey. If we let him become the rich man's son again, he will tell his father what we did to him, and we will be in much trouble."

But the monk begged him day and night to let the donkey return to his human form. Finally the worker, against his better judgment, threw some sand into the donkey's face, and the donkey immediately became a man. The monk then told him that he could return home.

The rich boy quickly went home and told his father about the treatment which he had received. The father became very angry and with three or four hundred men started to make war on the monastery.

The head monk, seeing the *beg* and his men approaching the monastery, did not know what to do. He quickly found the worker and said, "Quick, tell me what to do! The *beg* and his men are marching on us!"

"I don't know what to do. I told you again and again that we should not have let that boy return home!" the worker said. But the priest pleaded so much with him that finally the worker said, "When I die, I will be transformed into a dog. You must promise that when this happens, you will bury me under the altar and pray for me forty days and forty nights. After that length of time I will become a man again, and you must bury me in the churchyard. If you promise to do this, I will save the monastery and the lives of the monks."

The head monk quickly agreed to do as the poor man asked.

The worker took a handful of black sesame seeds and threw them on both sides of the church while he said a prayer. Immediately the seeds became great fierce soldiers with guns in their hands. Then the worker threw some of these seeds on top of the roof, and soldiers appeared there, too. Soon the angry *beg* with his men arrived at the monastery, but when he saw the many soldiers with guns loaded, he became frightened and stopped his men from opening fire. Instead, he went to the head monk and asked forgiveness for what he had planned to do. He wanted to make a treaty with the monk so that neither would war against the other. Finally they agreed upon such a treaty.

When the rich *beg* was ready to leave, the worker said to him, "Every year of your life, you must agree to give ten gold pieces and ten head of cattle to the monastery." After the rich man had agreed to this, he returned home with his men. When the *beg*'s army reached his home, the many soldiers at the monastery disappeared, too.

Several years passed, and, as happens to all of us at one time or another, the worker died. When the head monk was notified of his death, he went to say a prayer over the good worker's body. But when he got there, he didn't find the man— all he could see was a dog. He remembered his promise, and he buried the dog under the altar. He prayed for forty days and forty nights, and on the fortieth day he saw that the dog had disappeared. In his place, there, sleeping peacefully, was his good worker. He had the man buried in the churchyard as he had promised to do.

CUMULATIVE STORIES

95. From Bad to Worse

THERE WAS ONCE a man who never spoke good of anyone. He was therefore called the "evil spirit" or the "evil heart." Once he met a traveler on the road and asked where he was going.

"I am going to Jerusalem," the traveler replied. "Say some-

This story was told by Hovhannes Kaprelian.

thing good of me, and I will bring you something when I come back."

But the evil spirit said, "If you are going to give me anything, you had better give it now for you may not return."

On his return from Jerusalem the traveler asked the man, "How is our black dog?"

The evil spirit said, "From eating the meat of your camel, he died."

"Then is my camel dead?"

"Yes, while hauling stones for your father's grave, the camel fell and died."

"Then is my father dead?"

"Yes, three days before your mother."

"Then, is my mother dead?"

"Yes, she thought so much about her dead children that the house fell down and she died."

"Are my brothers dead? Has our house fallen?"

"Yes, your brothers died, and the house fell, and the man to whom your father owed money came and took away the door."

96. It Started with a Thorn

Once there was a little rooster whose foot was pierced by a thorn. He went to his mother and cried with pain. The good woman removed the thorn and used it as firewood for baking her bread. Not long after, the rooster went to his mother and said, "Mother, I want my thorn back."

"I used your thorn to bake the bread," she said.

"Return my thorn."

"I don't have your thorn."

"Then you must give me a loaf of bread," the rooster said.

So his mother gave him a loaf of bread. He walked on and on and came upon a farmer. "Farmer, if I bring the bread, do you have milk so that we can eat bread and milk?" he asked.

When the farmer agreed to bring the milk, the two of them sat down and ate bread and drank milk. Soon the rooster said, "Farmer, I want my bread back."

"We just ate your bread."

"I don't care about that. Return my bread."

"But you know we ate your bread."

This story was told by Mrs. Mariam Serabian.

"All right then, give me one of your little lambs," the rooster said.

So the farmer gave him a little lamb, and the rooster went on his way. He walked and walked until he came to a house where a wedding was taking place. "I have a little lamb I can bring to your party. Let me come to the wedding, too."

So the people invited him in, took his lamb and roasted it. After they had eaten and the dancing had started, the rooster said, "I want my lamb back."

"You saw that we ate your lamb," the people said.

"Return my lamb."

"But we ate your lamb."

"Well then, I want the bride," the rooster said.

So the people gave him the bride. The rooster and the bride walked on and on until they came upon three musicians. "Dance," the rooster said to the bride, and the bride began dancing. "I'll give you this bride if you give me your *davool, zourna* [drum, horn]," the rooster said to the musicians.

So the rooster traded the bride for the instruments. He played the *davool,* singing as he did so,

> "I traded my thorn for a loaf of bread;
> I traded my bread for a little lamb;
> I traded my lamb for a bride;
> I traded my bride for this *davool, zourna.*"

He walked and walked and found himself in the mountains. He saw a light in the distance and walked toward it to see where it was coming from. He approached a cave, and when he entered, he found a very beautiful girl inside. "Oh, how did you get here?" she asked. "When my seven *dev* [giant] brothers return, they will eat you up."

But the rooster did not pay any attention to her words. Instead, he began to play and sing for her. When the brothers returned, they saw someone in the cave with their sister and were greatly angered. "We brought our sister to this cave so that she would not see anyone and would not get married; now see what is happening!" But the rooster, sensing their disapproval, began to sing and dance for them. They were so pleased with him that they adopted him as an eighth brother.

These giants were thieves by trade, and it was their custom to set forth each day to steal whatever they could. One day the rooster heard them talking about what their plans were next.

He quickly informed the authorities, and so the first brother was caught. The rooster plotted to catch the rest of the *devs*, too. The next day the thieves wanted to take the rooster along with them to take the place of their lost brother. But the rooster said to them, "Brothers, instead of all of us working together, let each of us go separate ways. We will gain much more."

"Yes, that is a good plan," the six giants agreed. When the rooster saw that each was going to the place which he had selected, he went again and reported the plan to the authorities. And this time all six of the giants were caught.

The rooster, now very happy, returned to the cave. "Your brothers are all in prison, and you are going to be my bride," he said to the girl. The beautiful sister was pleased and helped him carry all the gold and valuables from the cave. They returned with this fortune to the house of the rooster's mother and lived there with her happily ever after.

97. Munuck

Once there was a man who wanted to go to Constantinople to seek his fortune. He had a father, mother, brother and a little puppy named Munuck. "I'm going to seek my fortune," he told them one day and started off.

We don't know whether he had been in Constantinople for a long time or a short time when he heard that a man from his village had just arrived. "Let me go and see what he knows about my family," the fortune-seeker said. Now all the time that he had been away, the man had not missed his family as much as he had missed his little Munuck. "Haji Ovan," the fortune-seeker said to the visitor, "have you come from Van?"

"Yes," Haji Ovan said.

"What news is there?"

"What news do you want?"

"How is our dear Munuck, our Munuck, our Munuck?" the fortune-seeker asked.

"Munuck died," Haji Ovan said, very sadly.

"Does that mean that Munuck is dead?" the man asked in surprise.

"Yes, he ate the meat of your mule and died."

"Does that mean that the mule is dead?"

This story was told by Antrias Amboian.

"Yes, he died while hauling your father's gravestone."

"Oh, does that mean that my father is dead?"

"Yes, he lived two weeks after your mother's death."

"Does that mean that my mother is dead?"

"Your mother died of a broken heart when she heard of your brother's death."

"Does that mean that my brother is dead? Why don't you say that my family is lost, that my home is ruined?" the fortune-seeker asked.

"I don't know whether your home has been ruined or not, but when I came to Constantinople, they were planting grain where your house once stood."*

MYTHS

98. Lochman Hehkeem, the Great Healer

There was once an only son about twelve or fourteen years old who was taking a walk in the woods one day when he saw a small snake slide out of a hole. When the boy went over to look at it, he found that it was very pretty with green, blue, red and yellow spots along its back. However, he saw that there was a mark on the little snake which made it part human and part snake. Because of these unusual markings, the boy decided to take the snake home with him.

He put the snake in a large bowl full of sand where it grew daily. And day by day it became more apparent that the snake was half-man and half-snake.

The boy kept the snake with him for two or three years. One day he said, "The snake is growing so fast—it is not right to keep him here. I'll take him back where I found him so that he will be able to join his friends."

The boy went into the woods, but he could not remember exactly where it was that he had found the snake. He looked all

This story was told by Mrs. Mariam Serabian.

* Absolutely nothing had happened to the fortune-seeker's family, but because the fortune-seeker asked about Munuck before the rest of his family, Haji Ovan punished him in this way.

around and saw a little hill. "I will leave him on this hill, and he can crawl anywhere he wants," the boy said, and he turned to leave.

"Do not go," the snake cried out.

The boy turned around much surprised as this was the first time the snake had spoken.

"Don't go, wait until my father comes. He will give you a reward," the snake said.

So the boy decided to stay and see what would happen.

"No matter what my father offers you, do not take it. He will offer even half of his kingdom, but don't accept it. Ask him to touch his tongue to yours. Refuse anything else," the snake advised.

The snake left the boy and went to call his father. Soon the father snake came out of the ground. "You have taken care of my son, my child whom I thought I had lost. Ask for your reward. I am Shah Merer, king of snakes," the father snake—who was also half-man and half-snake—said.

"I don't look for a reward," the boy said.

"I will give you anything: food, money, clothing."

The boy did not answer.

"I will give you half of my kingdom," the king continued.

"If you really want to give me something, touch your tongue to mine," the boy asked.

"But I cannot do that," the king said.

"That is the only thing I want."

"Ask for something else," the king urged. "My son, you have been listening to others. Forget them and ask for your heart's desire."

"No, that is all I want," the boy insisted. So finally the king of snakes touched his tongue to the boy's, and at the moment the boy was leaving the cave, Shah Merer died. The boy knew of this death because now he could feel it. With the touching of tongues, the boy's soul had become a new soul, and he possessed great knowledge. Almost immediately the weeds all around him began talking, and the boy could understand them. One said, "If you have a stomachache, use me." Another said, "Use me to heal burns." Another said, "Use me for sore eyes." The boy sat down and wrote out all these different things so that he would not forget. One weed said, "If a person is dead, I can make him live." Another weed said, "If all a person's joints have been cut, sprinkle me on the joints, and I will bring them together and make them whole again."*

Presently he tried some of the weeds and saw that they did what they said they would do. He hired an assistant and started making medicines. All the people who were sick went to him to be cured, and all were satisfied. Of course, the boy became richer and richer. His fame spread all over the country, and he became known as "Lochman Hehkeem" [Turkish name].

One day Lochman Hehkeem said, "I have tried everything but to make a dead man live. I want to see if I can do this, too. If I succeed, the man will never die but will be immortal. If I fail, I fail."

He called his assistant and had him lie down. He first cut the young man's throat, then pulled all the joints apart, carefully placing the right-side joints on the right-hand side of the man and the left-side joints on the left-hand side of the man.

Then he sprinkled a weed over the joints and put them back in the right order. He started from the feet and worked toward the throat. When all the joints were in place, he closed the wounded throat, took some liquid which he had prepared and poured it into the assistant's mouth. Soon the man opened his eyes and sat up.

Lochman Hehkeem knew that he had succeeded. During the trial Lochman Hehkeem had written down exactly each step he had taken. "Well, I have succeeded," he said to himself. "This man will never die. Now I must have him do the same for me so that I, too, will live forever." To see if his assistant would remember what had happened to him, he asked, "My son, where were you?"

"Here, where else would I be?" the youth asked.

"No, you were not here at all. You were dead," Lochman Hehkeem said and told him what had happened. "I have written down exactly how I did this. Do you think you could follow my plan just as I have written it? I have given you eternal life; now you help me in the same way."

The assistant agreed to this, and Lochman Hehkeem told him exactly how things were to be done. When everything was

* Armenians believed that the waters rested for a moment during the magical night of the Ascension and that all flowers, mountains, earth and trees moved, greeted and embraced each other. All plants and soul-less things spoke and told each other what each could do in curing man's illnesses. If a man knew this very moment and could be nearby to listen, he could learn the cures for all mankind's illnesses. (Abeghian, *op. cit.*, p. 61.)

ready, the assistant laid his master down, cut his throat, and pulled all the joints apart. Then he put them back together very carefully and closed the wound on the throat. Finally, he was ready to pour the precious liquid into his master's mouth. At this point, however, God, who was witnessing this from above, became angry. "Only I have the right to give life," He said.

He sent an angel down to hit the jar containing the precious liquid with his wing so that it would fall and break, then throw Lochman Hehkeem's writings into the sea.

The angel hit the jar containing the life-giving liquid, and it fell and broke. Lochman Hehkeem begged his assistant to pour some liquid into his throat, but there was none left: nothing could be done. And soon Lochman Hehkeem died. Then the angel took all the wise man's books and his writings and threw them into the sea. The assistant carried on his master's work as best he could, but, in reality, he knew very little.

Lochman Hehkeem is supposed to have been the first doctor in the world. It is the general belief that if the angel had not thrown Lochman Hehkeem's books away, we would have been able to make men immortal now, just as he had done.

99. The Seven Stars

There were once six brothers, the youngest of whom was a very handsome youth. One day he went hunting and fell asleep by a brook. A beautiful girl had been sent by her mother to the brook for water. There she saw the handsome boy and fell in love with him. The boy woke up and, seeing her, fell in love with her. "Let's go away together and get married and set up our own house," the boy said.

"Fine," said the girl, "but let me take this water back to my family first."

So the girl took the water home and told her family that she was going to marry the boy at the brook and that, together, they were going away. The family, seeing that the girl was in love, knew that she could not be discouraged from following her plans. So they carried her away with them to a far-off land. The boy, meanwhile, fell into a deep sleep from the moment his beloved left home.

The family traveled for several years before returning to their

This story was told by Mrs. Katoon Mouradian.

old home. The girl was again sent to the brook one day, and there she saw the handsome young boy still asleep. She called his name, and he awoke. But he became an angel and started to fly away. No sooner had he left the ground, however, than he fell down and died immediately. Seeing that her lover had died, the girl also killed herself, and the two young people were buried together. They both became stars.

When they learned that their youngest brother had died so tragically, the five brothers also killed themselves, and all five of them became stars. They joined their young brother and the beautiful girl in heaven. Now there are seven stars grouped together in heaven. Some day look for the seven stars and you will see them.

100. The Sunset Lad

There were once a father, a mother and a son, who was a young man at the time of our tale. One day the boy became angry at the sun. "What is this? Now you come out and now you don't. Sometimes it is dark, and then it is light," he said. And the boy started cursing the sun.

The sun's mother, hearing the boy's words, became very angry. "I will punish that boy for saying such things to my child," she said. After some time, when the young man married and his wife was with child, the sun's mother punished him: he was destined never to see the sun again. He would die at sunrise, and only at sunset would he come alive. Because of this he came to be known as Sunset Lad.

Seeing that his wife and his mother could not bear to see his great affliction, he left his family and lived in the mountains. One evening when he came near his home, he heard his wife singing a lullaby. When she ended her song, he repeated the lullaby so that it sounded like an echo. This he did also on the following evening. His wife, who did not understand this, told her mother-in-law. The third evening when the lullaby was repeated, the mother-in-law opened the door and pulled the echo in.

To her amazement, she saw that it was her own son! She was very happy, and so was the boy's wife. He saw his child, and the

This story was told by Mrs. Mariam Serabian.
Another version appears in the Comparative Studies.

family had a happy reunion. But as soon as the sun was ready to rise, he ran away again into the mountains.

One day during his death-sleep period, he had a dream. An old man came to him and said, "If you would see the sun again, you must find the sun's mother and ask for her forgiveness. Go to a far-away well and descend by climbing down carefully. You will see a cave, and at the entrance of it, there sits a huge giantess with her right breast thrown over the left shoulder and her left breast thrown over the right shoulder. You must quietly and quickly kiss her right breast. When you have done this, she will tell you that you are her child and to ask of her what you will. She will see to the rest." And he disappeared.

Dead during the day, alive at night, Sunset Lad walked for many, many months. Finally he reached the well. Climbing down carefully, he reached the bottom and saw the giantess sleeping. He quietly bent over and kissed her right breast which, as the old man had said, was thrown over her left shoulder. The giantess awakened with a start! "What are you doing here? I would have killed you immediately, but you have kissed my breast: you are my child. Tell me, why have you come here?" she asked.

"I want to see the sun's mother," Sunset Lad answered.

"Why?"

"At one time I cursed the sun, and the sun's mother heard me and punished me. Now I can never see the sun. I die as soon as daylight comes and live only during the hours of darkness. I must see the sun's mother to ask for her forgiveness."

The giantess gave him two small red pitchers. She filled one of the pitchers with water from the bottom of the cave. The other pitcher she left empty. "Take these," the giantess said, "but do you know how to find the sun's mother?" The boy did not answer. "Then I will tell you. Go under this water and walk until you reach the other side. I will send someone with you so that you won't lose your way. When you get there, you will see a bright light: that is the sun's mother. Take the empty pitcher and fill it with water from the other side. You will hear the sun's mother say, 'Why do you take my water?' Then you must dump the water which I have given you and say, 'As I took your water, so now I replace it.'"

The giantess sent a guide with Sunset Lad so that he wouldn't lose his way. When they had reached their destination, the guide turned back, and the boy went alone toward the shore. As the giantess had said, he saw a bright light and a beautiful woman. Thereupon he took the empty pitcher and filled it with water.*

"Why do you take my water?" the sun's mother asked.

"As I took your water, so now I replace it," Sunset Lad said, dumping out the water which the giantess had given him.

"Tell me, how did you get by the giantess' guard?" she asked.

"It is enough that I was successful in doing this," he said, not wishing to explain further.

"What do you want?"

"Forgiveness, Mother of the Sun, forgiveness," he said, falling to his knees before her.

"No forgiveness shall be yours," she angrily replied. "You said hateful things about my child." But the boy begged and continued to do so until the woman said, "I forgive you, but remember: you are never to say such things again about my son. Now take my water and return to the person who permitted you to come here."

Sunset Lad took the pitcher full of water, went to the bottom of the lake and finally came out on the side near the giantess. This time he kissed the left breast of the giantess, and she smiled at him.

"You have returned, my child?" she asked. "Tell me what happened."

"I reached the other side and filled my pitcher with water. The mother of the sun asked me why I was taking her water. I dumped out the water you had given me and told her that I had replaced what I had taken. I asked for her forgiveness three times before she granted it to me. She asked me how I passed the guardian of the cave, but I did not give her a direct answer," Sunset Lad said.

"You have done well," the giantess said. "Where is the water that you brought with you?" Sunset Lad gave her the pitcher full of water, and she bathed him with it. "Now, my son, go back to earth again. But don't show disrespect for the sun in the future."

Sunset Lad ascended the well. He finally reached the earth,

* Armenians believed that the sun palace was in the East at the end of the world. As part of the palace, there were twelve dwellings, in the middle of which stood a lovely golden palace. It was here that the mother of the sun sat on a bed of pearls and awaited her son. When he returned from his day's journey, he was tired; the sun mother bathed her child in fresh water, nursed him (he was eternally young), and put him to sleep on her lap. (See Abeghian, *op. cit.*, pp. 29–49.)

which he was very happy to see again. The sun was shining, but the youth did not die! The next morning when the sun arose, again he did not die! When he knew for certain that he was cured, he started for home.

When he passed by a window of his house, he saw his wife lying next to another man. "Sunset Lad has returned, cured of his affliction, only to find his wife sleeping with a Sunrise Man," he said sorrowfully three times.

His wife heard this and went to see who it was who had spoken these words. She opened the door and saw her husband! But it was dark, and she never dreamt that he was cured: she feared that he would die again in the morning. Sunset Lad entered the house and embraced his seven-year-old son who had been only in the cradle when he last saw him. As Sunset Lad did not die the following morning, his wife was convinced that he was cured. Remember, too, that Sunset Lad was very handsome, much more handsome, in fact, than the Sunrise Man who was now his son's stepfather.

"My friend," Sunset Lad said to the other man, "I left my parents and my wife years ago because I had been terribly cursed and I didn't want my family to see my suffering. Now I am forgiven, the curse is lifted, and I want to have my wife back again."

"But your wife has already married me," the Sunrise Man said.

"It is not for either of us to say who shall be her husband," Sunset Lad replied. "Why don't we go on a picnic tomorrow and let her choose between us?"

The other man agreed to this, and the next day the wife, the boy, Sunset Lad and the Sunrise Man all went on a picnic together.

"Well, wife, what is your decision?" the two men asked.

"My first husband was Sunset Lad. I married a second time only because I thought he was dead. Now that he has returned, I will go back to him," she said. So Sunset Lad, his wife and their son returned to their home, and the other man went his way.

"Father, mother, come! I have a surprise for you," the wife said to her father- and mother-in-law. They rushed into the house and found their own Sunset Lad. They embraced and were very happy. Needless to say, they gave many, many thanks to God for this reunion.

IV

Comparative Studies

THE COMPARATIVE STUDIES identify both the Aarne-Thompson and Eberhard-Boratav type classifications. Bolte-Polívka references, when they apply, are also indicated. Similarities of the Detroit stories to Armenian tales in other collections and to folktales from countries which were geographically or historically linked with Armenia or were centers of Armenian migrations are briefly noted. Because of the considerable difficulties involved in locating and using the Armenian variants, references to such materials are frequently more complete, in hopes of making this material available to the reader.

Occasionally it was necessary to determine which of several versions collected in Detroit was to be published in its entirety. The remaining versions are briefly outlined in the study of the story under consideration. In most instances, the versions as well as published tales are treated as a whole in these studies.

Complete titles for the works cited in this section will be found in the Bibliography of Comparative Sources, Appendix C. Entries are listed by geographical grouping and by author's name alone, i.e., HUNGARIAN, **Ortutay,** except where more than one book by the author has been used in the study. When several ethnic groups or geographical areas are discussed in a single volume, the entry is made under the general geographical area and the specific group appears in brackets, i.e., CAUCASIAN, **Dirr,** [Georgian].

Abbreviated forms used are listed below:

AT	Aarne-Thompson
EB	Eberhard-Boratav
BP	Bolte-Polívka
Campbell, *Tribes*	*Tales from the Arab Tribes*
Market	*Told in the Market Place*
Dawkins, *MG*	*Modern Greek Folk Tales*
MGAM	*Modern Greek in Asia Minor*
45	*Forty-Five Stories from the Dodekanese*
Macler, *Ca*	*Contes armeniens*
Cl	*Contes et légendes de l'Armenie*

Cle	*Contes, légendes et épopées populaires d'Armenie*
Kúnos, Stam	*Türkische Volksmärchen aus Stambul*
44	*Forty-Four Turkish Fairy Tales*

1. The Ogre's Soul

AT 302A* & 302 & 304 & 552A; EB 213; BP II, 19 ff., 503 ff., III, 111 #3, 424 ff. **Clouston,** I, 318, 347–51: discussion of external soul motif in Russian, Hungarian, Scotch, Indian, Arabian as well as Egyptian romance of Anapu and Satu. II, 407–12: resuscitation of hero. **MacCulloch,** pp. 20 ff., 118–45, 313, 271, 367–68. W. R. Halliday in **Dawkins,** *MGAM,* p. 273 says: "The story ["The Ogre's Soul" in the Detroit collection] seems to be characteristic of the Balkan states and the Near East." Story 1 is the complete version as Halliday reconstructs what the original must once have been.

ARABIAN, **Campbell,** *Market,* p. 125: girl learns location of external soul.

ARMENIAN, **Khatchatrianz,** p. 99: heroine learns hiding place of external soul. **Macler,** *Cl,* p. 96: hero aids Without-Soul, even at great danger to himself. **Macler,** *Cle,* p. 69: very similar. Unusual suitors are fox, bear, wolf. Youngest brother finds portrait in river, loves girl, is advised by unusual brother-in-law how to find her, gets help from magical horse, on return throws magic object to ground to delay pursuit. Drop of water falls in front of hero, envelops him in sea. Beardless one catches hero, cuts him in pieces, puts pieces in sack on horse. Horse returns to brothers-in-law who make hero whole again. Boy returns for girl, has her learn hiding place of external soul: chest in which is red stone in which is sparrow. Similarly, hero must find black stone and sparrow: soul of black mule, villain's helper. **Seklemian,** p. 15: motifs of grateful eagle only. P. 127: youngest prince, Bedik, promises great giant to bring him princess from East, takes work as dumb gardener, tricks girl, takes her along. She learns location of giant's external soul. Bedik gets animal (bull on mountain) drunk, cuts stomach, removes fox, cuts stomach of fox (rabbit in Servantstian's version), removes pearl box, releases warm blood on lid of box causing it to open and finds seven sparrows: giant's soul. P. 169: only scattered motifs appear. See Seklemian notes for 4. "Clever Daniel." P. 85: "Mirza" has motifs of personification of time. Hero joins group of forty giants, cuts off heads by tricking them. See Seklemian notes for 5. "The Giant Slayer." Servantstian, p. 122 and Macler, *Ca*, p. 11: very similar to Katchatrianz' version above. Wlislocki, p. 160: only motif is soul can be separated from body, causing state of no feeling.

BASQUE, Webster, p. 77: only external soul motif. See Webster notes for 34. "The World Below."

CAUCASIAN, Dirr, [Georgian] p. 36: hero sets out to find cock and hen nightingale to complete church. Beautiful girl snatched away by beardless one whose external soul is in form of three birds in cage behind nine locks. See Dirr notes for 34. "The World Below." [Tatian] p. 138: only beginning motifs are similar.

GEORGIAN, Wardrop, [Mingrelian] p. 112: very similar. Hero dies; dog gathers bones in sack; unusual brothers resuscitate hero.

GREEK, Dawkins, 45, p. 157: only motifs are hero permits sisters to marry unusual suitors; quest for World's Most Fair; external soul motif absent. P. 169: very similar. *MG*, p. 123: basically same story with minor variations. *MGAM*, pp. 355, 379: very similar. P. 357: "To change the candlesticks and to drink up the drink by the princess' side is the regular mode of procedure and one of the tokens of their presence that heroes, under these circumstances, left behind." Author refers to Stokes's Indian story, p. 186, where moving sticks from head to feet or from feet to head of princess brings her back to life or sends her into death-like trance.

GYPSY, Yates, [Bulgarian] p. 78: very similar except external soul is absent. Hero's bones placed in sack. Unusual brothers-in-law resuscitate hero. Groome, [Moravian] p. 144: only motifs are hero tricks and kills twenty-four robbers as they climb palace wall, lays beside beautiful princess. When child is born, father is unknown. Princess builds tower. People tell her their stories. Finds husband. [Polish] p. 161: sisters sold to unusual suitors. Hero gains cloak of invisibility, saddle of magic flight through trickery. Dragon runs off with hero's wife. She learns secret: dragon can be killed only when putting on his boots. Hero finds key which opens oak tree, frees wife.

HUNGARIAN, Jones, p. 39: very similar except story ends with hero's marriage; external soul and eagle motifs absent. Ortutay, p. 199: hero is torn to pieces. Girl puts bones in sack, ties it around neck of horse who returns to source of magical aid. Hero is resuscitated.

IRAQI, Stevens, [Kurdish informant] p. 275: similar except external soul motif absent.

ITALIAN, Crane, p. 61: Sisters marry unusual suitors. Youngest brother succeeds in finding fair Florita with help from unusual brothers-in-law. External soul motifs absent.

PERSIAN, Lorimer, p. 169: only similar motifs are joining thieves to rob treasury and killing them as they descend wall.

RUSSIAN, Afanas'ev, p. 439: day, sun, night represented as white, red, black horsemen. P. 485: villain possesses external soul. See Afanas'ev notes for 37. "Ludwig and Iskander."

TURKISH, Kent, p. 19: mother wishes for child, makes one from wood, throws it out window. It becomes cypress tree. Heroine of this unusual birth changes position of candles at bedside of handsome prince. Bain, p. 112, Kúnos, Stam, p. 124 and 44, p. 102: similar except hero is killed by wind demon and his bones placed on horse. Unusual brothers-in-law resuscitate him. External soul: on surface of seventh layer of sea is island; on island ox is grazing; in belly of ox, golden cage with white dove. Kúnos, Stam, p. 114: dying king commands daughter be given to first suitor. When this is not done, misfortune follows. See Kúnos, Stam, notes on 34. "The World Below" and 35. "The Son of the Gray Horse." Tezel, p. 62: similar to Kent version above.

A Strong Will Wins, Version Two (Unpublished Version)

A dying king tells sons: give three daughters to whoever asks for them; keep his body for three years, then put it on camel, letting it travel where it will. Wherever camel finally stops, that spot will be grave. Each son is to take turns watching father's grave, having in his hand a lighted candle. Whoever has lighted candle in hand the next morning will be new king.

Although there are unusual suitors (bear, lion, eagle), youngest prince insists upon approval of marriage proposals. Brothers follow father's request for burial. Two older ones lose light before morning; same happens to third brother, but seeing a light far off, he sets out to find it.

Hero finds palace with three beautiful girls, kills seven-headed giant whom he hits only once, takes girls to his brothers. On road, hears call for help, sees man tied with forty chains. Girl implores hero not to set chained man free, but when hero does so, man hits hero, runs off with wife.

Hero, in search for wife, receives supernatural help from brothers-in-law. Eagle tells hero: in sea is small island; in sea is water buffalo who, every Friday, goes to island to drink water. In horn of buffalo is soul of strong man: bird. With help of brother-in-law, death of bird is accomplished. (Informant: Mrs. Katoon Mouradian)

Variants of the above are:

ALBANIAN, **Dozon,** p. 121 and TURKISH, **Garnett,** II, 327: unusual marriages for sisters; hero kills giants, liberates prisoner who, half-man, half-iron, disappears with princess. Hero starts search, receives help from unusual brothers-in-law. Flight on unusual bird and external soul motifs appear. Hero is killed, cut into pieces, resuscitated.

ARMENIAN, **Macler,** *Cl,* p. 130: dragon snatches hero's wife, releases her only when hero brings him princess of Tchin-e-machin. In his search, hero fills suitor tasks with magical help, marries girl. Fierce *dev,* captive of king, has ear nailed to palace door, begs youth to ask for his release, promising to be his servant forever. When boy releases him, *dev* runs off with wife. Boy follows, receives help from sea horse which appears when hero throws special nail into water. Girl learns location of *dev's* external soul: in country of Devastan, in stomach of lion Ghachghan: three sparrows. In search, boy learns lion is stopping all water; he fills water holes with vinegar. Lion drinks, dies. Hero kills sparrows.

HUNGARIAN, **Ortutay,** p. 199: tabu is broken: do not help tied-up man. Misfortune follows.

RUSSIAN, **Afanas'ev,** p. 553: unusual brothers-in-law marry sisters. Boy marries beautiful princess, helps chained man who runs off with girl. Brothers-in-law help hero, even to resuscitation. Hero searches for fiery horse to escape villain. External soul motif absent.

SERBIAN, **Mijatovics,** p. 43: only motif is villain begs youth for water, breaks his bonds, runs off with beautiful girl. Hero serves old man to gain speedy horse. P. 146 and **Petrovitch,** 247: hero befriends Bash Tchelik, strong man, who then runs off with girl. External soul motif appears.

The Ogre's Soul, Version Three (Unpublished Version)

Similar to original version except that villain is a cripple who, on his magic horse, overtakes hero and heroine. Magic horse puts hoof on hero's shoulder; boy burns to death. Heroine puts bones into bag, ties it around horse's neck.

Horse returns to hero's brother-in-law who, by putting bones in correct position, brings youth back to life. Hero is instructed to capture newborn colt. Mare lives in the water but will come to shore when bridle which brother-in-law gives to youth is present. With newborn magic colt, hero rescues heroine. Villain dies. (Informant: Kazar Hoogasian)

2. Nourie Hadig

AT 709 & 437, cf AT 894, 425G; EB 185; BP I, 450 ff. Mac-Culloch, pp. 30–34: magic sleep.

Another version (Detroit collection) of question asked of new moon is: "New moon, tell me, who is the more beautiful, I or you?" New moon replies, "You are the most beautiful down there, I am the most beautiful up here."

ALBANIAN, **Dozon,** p. 1: similar; jealous sisters harm girl. Motifs of sleeping youth and Stone of Patience do not appear.

ARMENIAN, **Servantstian,** p. 129: only motif is like token of hero: magic sword of lightning.

ASIA MINOR, **Carnoy-Nicolaïdes,** [Greek] p. 91: see Carnoy notes for 32. "The Story of Mariam."

GREEK, **Dawkins,** *MG,* p. 177: almost identical except old woman takes credit; heroine asks for Knife of Slaughter, Rope of Hanging, Stone of Patience. P. 181: only motif is lamenting of heroine to stone. *MGAM,* p. 441: queen wants beautiful child, becomes jealous, orders it killed. Girl put into temporary sleep by wearing magic ring. P. 285: girl will marry ash-seller and nothing can change prediction. P. 347: twelve brothers leave home. Sister later is born, finds them, cooks and cleans for them. Old woman mistreats girl. She steps on bone, faints. Brothers think she is dead. When bone is removed, awakens.

HUNGARIAN, **Jones,** p. 163: beautiful mother wants to destroy more beautiful daughter, uses magic ring, gold and diamond pin on shawl, hairpin. Finally, believing girl dead, benefactors place her in golden coffin on elk antlers. Persian prince sees her, marries her. Motifs from 31. "The Golden-Haired Twins" appear at this point. Letter to prince is switched by witch. When evil-doer is caught, learn she is sister of beautiful queen mother whose soul was in hands of devil. **Ortutay, p.** 533 [quoting Laszlo Benko]: story of the "dead bridegroom . . . and the Lenore-type are related and interfere with each other in Hungarian folklore. He believes that the original core of the type arose among the Slavic people in the sixth and seventh centuries from ghost stories linked to the return of the dead."

IRAQI, **Stevens, p.** 114: mother jealous of daughter's beauty, orders child killed. Instead, she is befriended by seven super-natural creatures. Poisoned gum causes death-like sleep. P. 157 [Armenian informant]: heroine asks for Saber Dashee, pours out her story which is overheard by hero.

ISRAELI, **Noy,** [Yemen] p. 117: girl dreams that for seven years she will be hungry; for seven years she will be thirsty, no matter how much she drinks; for seven years she will tend dead man in locked house. It so happens. One day girl sends down rope, brings up pretty girl to help her. Second girl takes credit for vigil, will marry youth. Patient girl asks for Stone of Suffering (when someone reveals all his sufferings to the stone, it comes to life, swallows storyteller). Boy overhears, rights wrong.

ITALIAN, **Crane, p.** 326: teacher insists widower marry her. When he does, she mistreats his daughter. Eagle flies with girl to the fairies. Door closes. She remains within. Stepmother sends witch with poisoned sweetmeats, poisoned dress. Girl falls into death-like sleep which is broken when dress is removed.

PERSIAN, **Lorimer, p.** 19: princess criticized too much, with slave girl leaves home, comes to place where door opens for her, locks behind her. Slave girl left outside. Passing caravan owner paid to hoist slave through window. Girls come upon boy in magic sleep brought about by needles which, when removed from his body for forty days, cause him to awaken. Slave is to marry hero. Girl asks for Marten-Stone, tells story, is overheard.

SCOTCH, **Campbell,** I, 220: only motif is heroine destined to watch over dead man.

TURKISH, **Garnett,** [Albanian] II, 314: long-awaited daughter promised to sun at age twelve, returns home to visit mother. Motifs from 33. "Yeghnig Aghpar" of stag and girl in tree appear. Once home, girl visits a palace, door closes, cannot be opened; must not sleep three days, three nights, three weeks to turn king's statue to life. Almost through task, girl buys slave to help her. Slave exchanges clothing. King marries her. Girl laments fate to Stone of Patience, is overheard. **Bain, p.** 188 and **Kúnos, Stam, p.**

215 and *44,* p. 182: bird prophesies girl will find herself behind large well unable to get away. Boy's care requires forty days; otherwise, same. **Kúnos,** *Stam,* p. 204 and *44,* p. 174: treacherous mother asks moon who is most beautiful, harms beautiful girl. Magic hairpin causes sleep. **Tezel,** p. 51: girl escapes stepmother, is befriended by seven *devs.* Poisoned ring causes sleep. See Tezel notes for 30. "Cinderella." P. 57: girl sees teacher as man-eater, keeps secret, marries. Her two sons are destroyed by man-eater. Husband remarries. Girl asks for Saber Dashee, pours out grief. Children restored. P. 101: heroine in magic sleep. See Tezel notes for 7. "The Seven Giant Brothers." P. 164: similar; poisoned objects are ring, belt, apple. **Ekrem,** p. 103: similar prediction; Stone of Patience.

Saber Dashee (Unpublished Version)

Wife, husband, daughter are on pilgrimage to Jerusalem. Daughter is thirsty, asks for water at isolated house. Once inside, door won't open so she stays and cares for hero who is in magic sleep.

After three years girl buys passing gypsy girl to help her. Seven years pass, hero awakens and, thinking gypsy has looked after him, decides to marry her. Heroine asks for *Saber Dashee,* pours out her story to it; hero overhears. (Informant: Mrs. Hripsima Hoogasian)

The Dead Bridegroom (Unpublished Version)

Prediction occurs in dream that young girl will marry a dead man. Family moves away to avoid this. They rest under a dead tree; the next morning it is bearing blossoms. Tree calls after them, "Your daughter will marry a dead man."

The family comes to a river and crosses a bridge, but girl walks through river. River predicts marriage, too. They come upon a palace. Both parents try to open door but cannot. Girl succeeds, but door closes behind her, and since she can't get out, family leaves her behind. Inside, girl finds youth in death-like sleep. From this point on, refer to outline of the variant "*Saber Dashee*" above. (Informant: Mrs. Katoon Mouradian)

RUSSIAN, **Afanas'ev,** p. 200: only motif is fatal dream: girl will marry goat; nothing can change prediction. See Afanas'ev notes for 26. "The King of Snakes."

3. The Fairy Child

AT 923B & 533 & 412 I; BP II, 79 ff., 229 ff., 273 ff.

ARAB, Campbell, *Market,* p. 29: introductory motifs absent; similar otherwise.

ARMENIAN, **Tcheraz**, p. 67: only unusual characteristics of beauty appear. See Tcheraz notes for 31. "The Golden-Haired Twins." **Wlislocki**, p. 72: only motifs are characteristics given newborn child. No talisman. When mother does not follow instructions of magic woman, girl is cursed, becomes raven except for one hour a day. Magic holy water destroys curse and transformation. BP II, p. 282: similar.

ASIA MINOR, **Carnoy-Nicolaïdes**, [Armenian] p. 107 and TURKISH, **Garnett**, [Armenian] I, 278: youngest princess marries poor boy. King is angry. When child is to be born, king forbids anyone to help in its birth. Three nymphs aid princess, grant baby: talisman to protect her from all maladies; if she smiles, imperishable rose will come to her cheeks; as she walks, grass will become flowers; her tears will become precious pearls; when her head is washed, water will become golden. Rest of story follows "The Fairy Child."

GREEK, **Dawkins**, *MG,* p. 49: motifs from 33. "Yeghnig Aghpar" start story. Identical except life token does not appear. Prince discovers heroine when he asks each girl in town to tell her story.

GYPSY, **Yates**, [Bulgarian] p. 62: poor girl, in delousing a god, becomes golden and beautiful; stepsister becomes uglier. Stepmother blinds beautiful girl for a drink of water. Later girl trades pearls for eyes. Girl is transformed to pear tree, then poplar tree which is finally cut down. Life token is piece of poplar wood nailed to door.

IRAQI, **Stevens**, p. 14: introductory motifs quite similar; life token is missing. Heroine wears wooden dress while working as servant in king's palace.

RUSSIAN, **Afanas'ev**, p. 327: wicked maid puts out eyes of mistress, takes her place as king's wife. Blind girl befriended by old man, makes beautiful embroidered crowns, retrieves eyes. King finds girl, but queen kills her, keeps girl's heart which is in shape of egg. Old man buries all pieces of girl except heart. Little boy is taken to palace, cries hard. Queen gives him heart to play with. He runs away with it to old man. Girl restored to life.

TURKISH, **Bain,** p. 30 and **Kúnos,** *Stam,* p. 29 and *44,* p. 31: identical except for life token: little deer on hilltop has little coral eye in its heart. **Tezel,** p. 17: child of unusual beauty blessed by three magical women; magic bracelet is life token. Rest of story is similar. **P.** 44: only motif is that heroine is blinded, sells beautiful embroidery for return of eyes. **P.** 101: see notes for 7. "The Seven Giant Brothers." **Ekrem,** p. 21: very similar.

4. Clever Daniel

AT 315 & 304; EB 149 & 213; BP I, 528 ff., II, 140 ff., 503 ff. **MacCulloch,** pp. 202–4: spirit controls magic sword.

ARMENIAN, **Chalatianz,** p. 63: similar to Wingate's version discussed below. **Seklemian,** p. 169: stepmother plots with giant lover to get rid of hero. Hero tasks set for mother's health: melon of life, milk of fairy lioness, water of life. Hero steals two lion cubs who, with kind old woman, save his life. When mother sees hero return from impossible quests, she plucks three red hairs from his head, causes his death. Body is cut into small pieces. Lion cubs take pieces to old woman who puts them together, anoints connections with lion's milk, places melon of life beneath hero's nostrils to make him sneeze, pours water of life down his throat to resuscitate him. **Tcheraz,** p. 115: woman who has adoring son becomes ill, asks for certain apples from garden in special place. Boy sets out, meets, addresses ogress as mother, goes to second and third ogresses, enters garden, exchanges grass in front of lion for meat in front of lamb, takes apples, returns. Mother recovers, but becomes ill again. Boy repeats mission. Mother recovers, but needs difficult-to-find apples a third time. Ogress tells boy that mother feigns illness. Boy returns secretly, observes mother frolicking with lover, kills both. **Wingate,** *Folk-Lore,* XXIII, 95: hunter dies, warns son of tabu hunting grounds. Son breaks tabu, kills goblin, lives with forty wives, remembers mother, brings her to him. She plots with goblin for hero's destruction; impossible feats required. Grateful animals help. Unusual escape motif. Hero is killed but with magical help from animals and old woman, lives again. **Surmelian,** p. 201: motif of striking villain only one blow.

GEORGIAN, **Wardrop, p.** 25: king wants to keep daughter "pure." She eats large apple, becomes pregnant, bears strong son. Mother sleeps with *dev*, plots against hero, who is sent on impossible tasks, befriends grateful animals who later rescue him from certain death.

GREEK, **Dawkins, *MG*, p.** 145: daughter born into family of boys is *strigla* [female monster born of human parents who sucks blood and devours first horses, then men]. Brothers run off; youngest boy takes mother, finds safety. Mother falls in love with ogre, tries to get rid of son. Faithful animals help hero.

GYPSY, **Groome,** [Bukowina] **p.** 29: similar to Romanian-Gypsy story discussed next. [Romanian] p. 24: hero kills eleven dragons, keeps twelfth captive in room tabu to his mother. She breaks tabu, finds giant, loves him. They plot hero's destruction. Impossible tasks set to regain mother's health: porker of sow in other world; apple from golden apple tree in other world; water from great mountains. Heroine keeps genuine objects, substitutes others for boy to take. Mother finally defeats boy in card game. Dragon kills hero, places pieces in saddle bag, sends horse off. Heroine restores hero with magic objects in her possession.

ITALIAN, **Crane, p.** 52: youngest son falls in love with stepmother. Giant conspires with woman to harm boy. Difficult tasks imposed for hero. When boy's golden hair is cut, he loses strength. Princess cures him.

POLISH, **Zajdler, p.** 61: boy with magic sword seeks fortune with sister, kills twelve giants who are brought back to life with magic water. Sister loves giant, plots against hero; befriended animals help him.

RUSSIAN, **Afanas'ev, p.** 304: brother and sister befriended by bullock who, when killed, becomes Little Fist. Sister loves robber, plans to kill brother. Impossible tasks set by sister; young wolf, bear, lion help boy. Hero marries very strong woman.

SIBERIAN, **Coxwell,** [Ostyak] **p.** 537: only motif is sister in league with giant to kill brother. [Russian] p. 701: general theme of sister who, with lover (snake), plans harm for brother; animals help him. P. 703: similar to outline above with different tasks, different animals; lover is robber. [Yukaghirs] p. 101: father, to save self, promises Fabulous Old Man his son and daughter. With animals' help children escape their fate. Sister plans to betray brother and bring about his death. His bear and wolf companions kill her instead.

TURKISH, **Tezel,** p. 82: see Tezel notes for 14. "The Magic Horse."

5. The Giant-Slayer

AT 304, cf AT 306; EB 213; BP II, 503 ff., III, 78 ff.

ARMENIAN, Seklemian, p. 85: very similar to following version. Servantstian, p. 143: very similar. When brothers are careless about occupying throne, uncle gains power. Brothers break tabus; the first night youngest, Mirza, kills seven-headed snake wearing jeweled crown, hides on second night and sees enormous female *dev* place earrings causing sleep on each of his brothers. He follows her to cave, kills her and her nine sons. The third night, when it is Mirza's turn to watch, he sleeps momentarily; fire is almost extinguished. In search for a light, he meets Time, begs for a longer night, enters giants' cave, takes light, leaves. Next day, Mirza joins these forty giants to rob king's palace, cuts off their heads as they climb wall, changes position of candlesticks at head of three princesses, drinks their sherbet, puts golden apple at head of each girl, kills snake about to attack king. At great wedding, girls are married to three brothers. Soon they tell their husbands they have a lover, Gorgatchanee, who has spearmint and roses growing on his chest. Mirza kills giant in white palace, liberates beautiful girl, kills black *dev* in black palace, freeing second girl. Red *dev,* about to be killed, turns into sandstone; his head becomes that of huge fish and smoke pours from his head. Mirza jumps on the mountain, pushes his sword in the fish, wrecks inside of stone, kills *dev,* frees princess, reaches Gorgatchanee's palace, begs place as servant, kills him with his own sword, removes small piece of the feather dresses of his wife and sisters-in-law, returns home. Unfaithful girls are punished; brothers marry rescued princesses. **Surmelian,** p. 260: only vague similarity of uncle ruling Sassoun.

HUNGARIAN, **Jones,** p. 39: similar. Mountain is tabu; during watch, fire goes out; youngest son meets Dawn and Midnight, comes upon twenty-four robbers, cuts off tips of noses and ears, changes candle positions of princesses. See Jones notes for 1. "The Ogre's Soul."

ROMANIAN, **Creangă,** p. 1: similar tabu motifs.

TURKISH, **Bain,** p. 143 and **Kúnos,** *Stam,* p. 164 and *44,* p. 133: king leaves tabu for forty sons: avoid large spring, caravanserai, desert. Youngest son kills seven-headed dragon whose last head rolls into well, finds forty girls, treasures. External soul motif occurs. **Bain,** p. 102: only motif of hero's discovering infidelity of princesses occurs. He brings back proof of their conduct. See Bain notes on 12. "The Magic Bird-Heart."

6. Wisely Spent

AT 923B & 910B, cf AT 910G; EB 308; BP IV, 149. **Clouston,** II, 317–21.

ARMENIAN, **Seklemian,** p. 141: very similar. Three sayings: she whom one loves best is most beautiful; patience leads to safety; always is good in patient waiting. **Servantstian,** Part B, p. 20 and **Macler,** *Ca,* p. 139: similar except hero enters deep well where Arab asks him to select most beautiful; correct answer brings reward. **Tcheraz,** p. 93: king permits three daughters to select husbands; youngest selects Baron Dzouil [Mister Lazy-One], giant in nearby mountain. King disowns daughter. Girl encourages husband to work as hamal at docks because of his great strength. At one place, Dzouil descends well to see what is stopping water, finds gigantic Arab gazing fondly at frog. Arab asks hero, "Who is most beautiful of all beautifuls?" Giant answers, "For a man, that whom the heart loves is most beautiful." Arab gives giant three pomegranates full of jewels which man sends to wife. She builds great palace. After many years, man returns to wife and beautiful son.

AZERBAIJAN, **Hermann,** p. 97: very similar except only one saying: "Only that which heart loves is most precious and beautiful."

CAUCASIAN, **Dirr,** [Avarian] p. 75: only similarity is suitor task: hero must learn why woman and dog are placed on same chain. **Haxthausen,** [Persian-Armenian] p. 363: see Haxthausen notes for 19. "The Riddles." **Dirr,** [Imertian] p. 268: servant takes wise sayings instead of wages.

GEORGIAN, **Wardrop,** [Mingrelian] p. 109: man learns wise words, does not heed them, suffers consequences.

GREEK, **Dawkins,** *MG,* p. 420: only motifs concern hero's answer to "Which is most beautiful?" He is given three apples full of precious stones; wife builds beautiful palace. P. 444: tinsmith, setting out to seek fortune, buys wisdom: never mix yourself in other's affairs; you have seen nothing, you know nothing; never leave the king's highway; first think, act afterwards. On return hero finds wife and young man sitting by the fire; doesn't shoot. *MGAM*, p. 293: although wise sayings differ, theme is identical. *45*, p. 237: similar to Crane version below.

ITALIAN, **Crane**, p. 157: hero takes advice instead of wages. Similar.

PERSIAN, **Lorimer**, [Bakhitari] p. 269: hero told to buy wisdom; statements which he buys are different. Story combines with 20. "The Magic Ring" as hero receives supernatural help from cat and mouse.

RUSSIAN, **Afanas'ev**, p. 289: close parallel although only two wise sayings. Woman sleeping with man on either side: her sons.

SIBERIAN, **Coxwell**, [Ostyak] p. 518: only motif is hero, Aspen-Leaf, returns after long adventures to find wife in bed with man on either side: her sons.

TURKISH, **Kent**, p. 74: although only one wise saying, plot is similar. P. 48: similar except sayings differ: waste no breath and fear no death; in the eyes of the lover, the beloved is beautiful; that which you understand not, judge not. P. 162: only motif is saying: do not betray hand that feeds you. P. 119: very similar: sayings are: do not leave road you have chosen; do not meddle with things which do not concern you, leave problems of today to be settled tomorrow. **Tezel**, p. 2: sayings are: don't betray hand that feeds you; don't go where you're not wanted; don't keep away from where you are wanted; whoever the heart loves best is most beautiful. Faithful servant, observing admonitions, becomes rich. P. 75: sayings are: you can't die before your time; whomever you love is the most beautiful; don't arrive at conclusion until you have all the facts. P. 81: similar to Kent, p. 119, above. P. 199: only motif is wise answer and reward of pomegranates.

The Helpful Genie (Unpublished Version)

Two friends seek their fortune together. One steals three gold pieces and returns. Other earns three gold pieces which he spends to learn wise sayings from dervish: you know; don't comment on quality of food; if someone is drowning, let him drown.

On travels hero is asked direction, answers, "You know." Finds shelter in home, doesn't comment on hostess and dog chained together. Hero receives reward and learns story of wife's unfaithfulness and faithfulness of dog.

On road, sees man drowning, doesn't help and claims horse with much gold left behind. Hero meets dervish on road, learns cure for sick princess: blood of black dog. Hero cures, marries princess; opens box. Genie appears, gives hero two hairs from beard which serve as source of magic. Hero tells wife of this power. When hero is imprisoned, wife uses magical source to help him. (Informant: Mrs. Katoon Mouradian)

(Cf EB 204 for episode of woman and dog.)

7. The Seven Giant Brothers

AT 451 & 709A, I, cf AT 451A, 451*, 897; EB 166, especially III, 5. BP I, 70 ff., 427 ff.

BASQUE, **Webster**, p. 49: three brothers in service to Basa-Jauna [wild man]; sister finds them. Man is vampire, sucks her blood. Brothers transformed to oxen; girl causes their return to human form. P. 187: sister sets out to find seven brothers, cooks, cleans for them. One day breaks tabu, goes to neighbor for fire, is given herbs for foot bath. When brothers use this, they become cows. King marries girl; she takes cows along. Witch pushes her off precipice. Baby is born to her; witch substitutes herself for girl, asks for death of cows. King investigates, finds wife.

GREEK, **Dawkins**, *MGAM*, p. 301: only motif is appearance of snake in girl's stomach as result of stepmother's treachery. P. 347: girl seeks twelve brothers, cooks, cleans for them, borrows fire, is frightened by woman, faints, bone enters foot. Brothers believe girl dead, but when bone is removed, she lives again. See Dawkins' notes for 2. "Nourie Hadig."

IRAQI, **Stevens**, p. 142: only motif is sister cures brother. P. 114: only motif is girl cleans house for seven men who then make her their sister.

ISRAELI, **Noy**, [Yemen] p. 157: boy saves serpent who enters his mouth, then makes him weak. Boy marries princess being punished by father. She cuts, sells wood; they live. Snake leaves boy's stomach; he regains health. The two dig, find snake's treasure, become wealthy.

ITALIAN, **Crane**, p. 54: king curses; six sons disappear. Seventh child, a girl, sets out to find brothers. Tabu: must not speak for seven years. Prince marries girl, goes off to war. Mother-in-law plots against girl. When child is born, truth is out.

SCOTCH, Campbell, II, 383: only motif is snake leaves girl's mouth; (supposedly true story: girl had been reaping, fell asleep on sheaf of corn in field, slept with mouth open; serpent ran down her throat. Doctors put milk in saucer, put her in dark room on her side; serpent emerged).

TURKISH, Tezel, p. 101: young princess disappears in hole, enters cave of forty robbers, hides. Her brother is there, aids her. Pet cat scratches her, is killed. Garlic plant grows at this spot; brother eats it, becomes monkey. Nail enters girl's foot, causing magic sleep. Prince awakens girl, marries her, in jealousy boils monkey who becomes human again.

8. Abo Beckeer

Cf AT 313, IIIb; BP I, 442–43, II, 517 ff. Clouston, I, 442, discusses story in *Katha Sarit Sagara*, Ch. 39, in which daughter of Rakshasa helps lover perform difficult tasks which her father has set. Demon father sends boy to bring fierce brother. With magic objects: earth (causes creation of mountain), water (causes creation of river), thorns (cause creation of thorny wood), chase is hampered. MacCulloch, pp. 167–69, 171–72, 174: transformation and obstacle flights.

ARMENIAN, Seklemian, p. 169: only pursuit motifs. P. 33: only obstacles, transformations, thankfulness of animals and objects which have received help. See Wingate's discussion of 14. "The Magic Horse."

CAUCASIAN, Dirr, [Imertian] p. 29: similar escape motifs. See Dirr notes for 100. "The Sunset Lad."

GREEK, Dawkins, *MG*, p. 61: girl in hands of Moskambari [son of ogress] escapes ogress by enchanting all guardians by flattery. Impossible tasks fulfilled with boy's help. Ogress sends girl to sister to eat; on road girl changes position of things so they are more comfortable. Pursuit unsuccessful. 45, p. 213: girl marries crab husband, returns to his home. Jealous mother sets difficult tasks for her; reconciliation without disaster. P. 484: only similar pursuit motifs in discussion of these variants from Lesbos and Samos. P. 171: flattery to unpleasant objects.

GYPSY, Groome, [Bukowina] p. 124: only common motifs

are pursuit and transformations. [Romanian] p. 62: similar pursuit and flight motifs.

HUNGARIAN, **Jones**, p. 25: hiding, transformation motifs. Mother's curse: "May you never remember each other!" Dream finally breaks curse; otherwise story quite different. P. 157: similar pursuit motifs. **Ortutay**, p. 84: only motif is curse which delays childbirth. P. 332: pursuit, transformation motifs occur and curse which makes hero forget girl.

ITALIAN, **Crane**, p. 1: girl marries man who becomes bird because of her curiosity; she follows him. Pursuit details, mother-in-law tasks occur. Curse is uttered complicating childbirth. P. 72: only pursuit motifs.

PERSIAN, **Lorimer**, p. 25: only pursuit motifs. See Lorimer notes for 18. "The Country of the Beautiful Gardens."

RUSSIAN, **Afanas'ev**, p. 351: only escape motifs. P. 366: escape motifs. P. 427: transformation motifs. **Ransome**, p. 75: pursuit motifs.

SCOTCH, **Campbell**, I, 53: impossible tasks set by giant; daughter helps youth.

SIBERIAN, **Coxwell**, [Ostyak] p. 518: only motif of hero changed in form to escape being eaten. [Polish] p. 953: only transformation motifs.

TURKISH, **Kent**, p. 38: only motif is compliment given unpleasant objects who help in escape. P. 79: pursuit motifs. **Bain**, p. 74: princess marries horse who is youth at night. When she reveals secret, he disappears; she sets out to find him. Hero hides wife, transforms her, helps her accomplish tasks set by mother. Pursuit by aunt causes further transformations to bath house and attendant, spring and pitcher, tree and serpent. Curse does not occur. **Kúnos**, *Stam*, p. 76 and *44*, p. 58: only similar transformation motifs. *Stam*, p. 88 and *44*, p. 70: very similar tasks, transformations, pursuits. **Tezel**, p. 121: girl marries horse, breaks tabu, sets out in search of him. Drops ring he gave her into his wash water as recognition. Boy's mother, *dev,* gives girl impossible tasks. Girl succeeds with husband's help. Pursuit, transformation motifs. Boy becomes human, kills mother.

Mark in Her Palm (Unpublished Version)

Princess and vizier's son love each other, but marriage is forbidden. Boy seeks advice of young fortune-teller who also loves him. When she transforms lovely princess into giantess, boy marries fortune-teller.

Giantess must have a girl to eat each month. A wise girl knows a pool of water is guarded by four giants. She steals some of this water, throws it into giantess' face, causes reversal of transformation. However, drop of water splashes on her palm, leaving mark.

Giants discover some water has been stolen. Youngest and most handsome of four giants, Abo Beckeer, sets out to find thief. He sees, recognizes mark in girl's palm. He marries her; they have two children. After several years they decide to travel to husband's country. He constantly asks about mark in her palm, but she never tells him the truth. Because of her refusal, he kills their sons. When they arrive at her husband's home, mother-in-law wants to eat girl, sets difficult tasks.

Rest of story is similar to "Abo Beckeer" as presented in text. (Informant: Kazar Hoogasian)

9. The Giantess Leader

Cf AT 519; EB 215, IIIb.

ARMENIAN, Seklemian, p. 59: almost identical with Servantstian, p. 129 version. Servantstian, p. 129 and Macler, Ca, p. 23: Detroit story is a fragment of this Zoulvisia story. Zoulvisia, beautiful woman, leads men to their death with her loud yelling. Hero sets out to find destroyer of brother and friends, meets friendly devs, leaves razor, mirror, scissors with them. When blood appears on scissors and razor and perspiration on mirror, they will know he is in danger. Hero avoids hearing Zoulvisia. She marries him, gives him lock of her hair which falls into stream. King sees it, demands owner be brought to him. Old woman gains confidence of Zoulvisia and her husband, learns boy's strength is in sword, tricks Zoulvisia, takes her to king. Three devs, seeing magic objects show hero in danger, come to his rescue. Boy escapes with Zoulvisia. Servantstian, p. 193: only motif of hero's cousin having such great voice that he can be heard from morning to night. Servantstian, Part B, p. 31 and Macler, Ca, p. 156: youngest son of king befriends old man, St. Sarkis, who later helps him break talisman of beautiful warrior girl, Unseen and Unbelievable. Hero marries her. King hears of her beauty, sends old woman to bring beauty; boy kills old woman. Another is sent who drugs hero, cuts his right arm off, removes talisman, takes girl away. St. Sarkis makes boy well again, gives him oil to heal sores of king. Hero cures king, is asked to cure Unseen and Unbelievable who is wasting away from sadness. The two fly away together; boy defeats king in war. **Macler,** *Cl,* p. 152: boy, Djan Polad, tramples field; old woman curses him with love of Oski-Dzan [the golden one]. He meets prince of Occident, prince of Orient; kills two demons, liberates girls, leaves princes behind with talisman which will indicate his danger. Boy strikes middle head of third demon, killing him; marries Oski-Dzan. One day lock of her hair falls into river; king finds it, sends old woman to bring beauty. Old woman learns boy's secret: soul is knife kept under his arm. She cuts arm off, throws knife into river, takes girl away. Hero's friends come to his aid, retrieve life symbol, give him health. Boy cures king, runs off with girl.

10. The Miller and the Fox

AT 545B; EB 34; BP III, 487.

ARMENIAN, **Macler,** *Cl,* p. 85: similar. **Toumanian,** p. 86: identical. **Wingate,** *Folk-Lore,* XXIII (1912), 220: hunter shares food with fox; other animals join group, help hunter marry princess.

CAUCASIAN, **Dirr,** [Avarian] p. 70: identical.

GREEK, **Dawkins,** *MGAM,* p. 455: almost identical.

HUNGARIAN, **Jones,** p. 1: almost identical.

ITALIAN, **Crane,** p. 127: grateful fox makes it possible for youngest brother who has pear tree to marry princess. Hero, ungrateful, kills fox. P. 348: youngest brother is left a cat by dying mother. Cat helps him gain fortune, wife, become king.

ROMANIAN, **Ispirescu,** p. 87: boastful man marries princess. Beggar, whom hero has befriended, gives help as fox does in Detroit version. Task: know questions which nine dwarfs will ask. With help of friend, hero succeeds. **Kremnitz,** p. 113: befriended old man has role of fox.

RUSSIAN, **Afanas'ev,** p. 168: close parallel.

TURKISH, **Garnett,** [Kurdish] II, p. 163: similar except miller dies before fox's plans can be realized. **Kent,** p. 87: man has pear tree which has two pears daily. Fox eats fruit, befriends owner. Rest is similar except fox, discovering poor character of friend, causes him to lose wealth. **Tezel,** p. 66: similar to Kent above.

11. The Work of the Genii

Cf AT 884A for concluding episode. Clouston, II, 212 ff. discusses motif of falling in love through dream.

ARMENIAN, Seklemian, p. 9: prince and princess, far apart, dream of each other, are given each other's ring. Hero sets out to find her for his own. On return, evil ship captain runs off with her. She escapes, is captured by king, escapes again, taking thirty-nine girls with her. Disguised as man, she is selected as king. Her statue on central fountain in center of town serves to catch captain, king, hero.

12. The Magic Bird-Heart

AT 567 & 567A, cf AT 518; EB 174; BP I, 528 ff., III, 3 ff. Clouston, I, 72–85: invisible cap, shoes of swiftness, inexhaustible purse. 445–47: transformation by eating fruits or grass. 462–63: eating head and heart. 93–102: magical powers of eating bird parts. W. R. Halliday in Dawkins, *MGAM*, p. 263, says: "Two details are characteristic of the Eastern story: paying of various sums for seeing the wanton's face and figure; selecting a king by means of a royal hawk." "The Magic Bird-Heart" in the Detroit collection contains both details.

ARMENIAN, Macler, *Cle*, p. 30: father finds both eggs and bird; gaining of magic objects does not occur. Girl tricks second brother, makes him vomit heart which she then eats. Boy eats fig, becomes donkey, eats grape, is transformed back to man, takes some figs and grapes, returns, changes girl and her servants to donkeys. Older brother who has eaten head is chosen king through flight of bird, in fulfilling task set by dream, meets brother. When princess vomits heart, younger brother reverses her transformation.

AZERBAIJAN, Hermann, p. 66: Refer to Hermann notes for 13. "The Magic Figs."

GEORGIAN, Wardrop, p. 11: only motif is hero gets wishing stone by tricking *devs* who were his hosts. With this, he trades for various objects, always keeping both old and new.

GREEK, Dawkins, *MG*, p. 117: Jew convinces woman to kill unusual bird and save heart, head, liver. Her sons, by mistake, eat these pieces. Boy who eats liver gets many gold pieces from his mouth. Beautiful girl learns secret, makes him vomit liver, throws him out. Boy wanders, finds tree with black figs which produce horns, white figs which make eater normal; returns, transforms people at palace. *MGAM*, p. 479: father finds eggs and bird; daughter eats liver; son, heart; boy produces much gold. Wanton motifs appear. Apple transforms girl to donkey; hero makes her vomit and eats heart again. P. 411: three sons eat heart, head, liver of unusual bird. Jew wants to kill boys and eat bird parts; boys escape. First son becomes king; second, his vizier; third, a rich merchant who daily has bag of gold on his pillow. Boy becomes friend of dervish from whom he receives magic objects: cap of invisibility, magic pipe. Fountain water causes transformations to asses. Hero finds fig tree whose fruit causes horns to grow and to disappear. Beautiful princess tricks boy with *raki*, makes him spew out liver of bird, in time also gets cap and pipe. Boy sells figs. Princess and her forty maidens grow horns. Hero retrieves magic objects, changes girls to asses. Brother begs him to reverse transformations; he does. *45*, p. 427: hero is forsaken on mountain top, befriended by old man and woman, receives magic objects, is tricked, loses all; eats figs, horns grow on forehead; other figs cause reversal. Hero returns to palace, causes princess to be transformed, marries her as price of cure.

GYPSY, **Groome**, [Bukowina] p. 95: very similar except person eating unusual bird's: head, becomes emperor; heart, has much money; claws, becomes seer. Evil princess makes hero vomit bird's heart which she takes. Apple changes princess to ass, crabapple reverses transformation.

ITALIAN, **Crane**, p. 136: only motif is tricking robbers by promising to arbitrate, thus getting magic objects.

PERSIAN, **Lorimer**, [Bakhitari] p. 197: boys don't eat head and liver but carry as amulets. One brother tricks and gains bag, carpet, vial of antimony which, applied to eyelids, causes invisibility. Princess drugs old wine, learns boy's secret, gets objects, has boy cast away. On island boy overhears birds, learns that: by wrapping bark around feet he will be able to walk on sea; twig from tree and word *"Haush"* will turn person into donkey; swish with same twig and word "Adam" will transform back to man. He learns, too, that leaves cure blindness.

RUSSIAN, **Afanas'ev**, p. 292: hero is mistreated by princess, kills dragon, marries princess. She plots to get rid of him. In woods hero tricks men, gains magic walking boots, flying carpet, magic tablecloth. Princess tricks him, takes objects. Hero eats apples, horns grow; another apple removes horns. Justice done to princess. P. 541: incomplete version: one brother becomes king when his candle lights; another spits gold; princess motifs absent.

SIBERIAN, Coxwell, [Darvash] p. 1028: only motif is existence of magic objects: cap, ass, bullet of wood and rock. [Finn] p. 644: similar; first son chosen tzar by having his candles light in church. Second boy spits gold, fulfills suitor task to feed town for three years, tricks devils, keeps stick which produces army and anything desired, changes princess into horse. Tzar (brother), imprisons him to learn why he won't sell horse; reunion. [Kalmuck] p. 183: two dragon-frogs stop water; human sacrifice required. Khan's son understands their language, with friend, kills and eats heads; vomit jewels, gold. Meet woman and daughter who treat them badly. Youths meet tests to become rulers of land: ceremonial cake falls on their heads, they vomit great jewels. Boy marries princess; friend learns of her infidelity. They turn first two women into asses. [Lapp] p. 626: suitor task: snatch star from sky. Hero succeeds, on return home tricks and gains invisible cap, boots which carry one anywhere, staff which causes pestilence. [Russian] p. 674: hero breaks evil charm, marries princess. Life token: beautiful trees. Evil spirits put hero into long sleep. Hero tricks devils, gains magic carpet, boots, invisible cap, returns to wife, answers her riddle: recognition as husband. [Votyak] p. 589: two brothers eat heart, head of golden eagle. One brother becomes tzar because fire comes from palm; another spits gold. Three daughters of general trick him. Youngest girl becomes snake, swallows hero, throws him on island. There, he eats apple, becomes horse; second apple causes reversal to man, third, to raven. Hero rights wrong.

TURKISH, Kent, p. 102: only motif is tricking demons, gaining their inheritance. Bain, p. 102: hero tricks brothers, gets magic turban, magic whip, magic carpet. Kúnos, Stam, p. 107 and 44, p. 87: only possession of magic objects through trickery. Stam, p. 11 and 44, p. 12: only method for selecting ruler. Tezel, p. 154: three boys eat kidney, head, drumstick of chicken; story deals only with boy who eats kidney and produces bag of gold daily. Rest is similar. Magical fruits: apple produces horns; grapes cause horns to disappear; figs cause transformation to donkey.

13. The Magic Figs

AT 566; EB 175; BP I, 470 ff., III, 3 ff. Clouston, I, 445–47: transformation by eating fruits or vegetables. In an Indian story, hero is abandoned on island by girl after taking four magical objects from him; eating of mangoes causes transformation. P. 461: inexhaustible purse stories. **MacCulloch,** pp. 158–60: transformation by eating or drinking.

ARABIAN, **Campbell,** *Tribes,* p. 43: only motif is paying money to see beauty of girl.

ARMENIAN, **Seklemian,** p. 197: particularly close parallel to Servantstian discussed next. **Servantstian,** Part B, p. 12 and **Macler,** *Ca,* p. 127: rich merchant begs son never to visit Tiflis. When father dies, son breaks tabu, spends fortune gazing at Duenia Gezeley, returns home penniless. Mother gives him magic purse which, for a time, changes *para* to *lira.* Boy returns to Tiflis, is tricked by beauty who takes purse, returns to mother, receives *kula* [wool hat] which makes wearer invisible. Returns to Tiflis, tricked by girl again, returns to mother who gives him her last magic object: horn which, blown from one end causes soldiers to appear, from other end, soldiers disappear. Boy returns to Tiflis, again tricked, since mother cannot help him, decides to board ship for America. Ship is wrecked; boy flings self on log, reaches island. One day eats apple as large as man's head, becomes donkey; eats small apple on ground, transformed back to man. Picks several apples of each kind, sees passing ship, signals, returns to Tiflis, sells large apples for ten *lira.* Princess buys two apples, divides them with guests, all forty become donkeys. Boy, dressed as doctor, announces in streets he is famous Dr. Carabobo from America, can cure anyone. Since no one has been able to change donkeys to humans, boy is eagerly sought, retrieves magic objects from princess, gains promise of marriage, reverses transformations. **Surmelian,** p. 227: "hair long, brains short."

AZERBAIJAN, **Hermann,** p. 66: Ahmed saves girl pursued by large snake. She advises him to ask her father for pouch, hat, flute as reward. Pouch turns anything placed in it to gold. Boy becomes rich, wants to marry princess. Suitor task: win at cards. Boy loses much money; girl learns secret, takes pouch, throws him out. Boy returns with magic cap which makes him invisible. Girl tricks him. Flute brings forth soldiers. Girl tricks boy again, has him taken far away. He finds red pear, red apple, retrieves magic objects, causes transformations, marries princess.

GREEK, **Dawkins,** *MGAM,* p. 415: close parallel. 45, p. 411: only motif is transformation of hero to ass, reversal by drinking water. See Dawkins notes for 27. "The Nine-Seeded Apple." P. 427: only motif is transformation caused by eating fruit. See Dawkins notes for 12. "The Magic Bird-Heart."

HUNGARIAN, **Ortutay,** p. 424: only motif is trading magic objects.

ITALIAN, **Crane,** p. 119: suitor task: make princess laugh. Boy finds ring which makes everyone sneeze; although girl laughs, youth is punished. In tree overhears robbers speak of magic tablecloth, magic purse, magic horn which makes everyone dance. King takes magic objects from hero, jails him. He digs way out; in forest eats black fig, develops two long horns; eats white fig, becomes normal. Returns to palace, transforms entire royal family.

SCOTCH, **Campbell,** I, 181: princess tricks hero, gains magic objects. Hero taken to lonely island; apples cause horns to grow, other apples reverse transformation. Hero returns, punishes princess. P. 195: similar except red apples transform to animal, and gray, back to man.

TURKISH, **Kent,** p. 170: similar; only princess is transformed to ass; magical fruit is apple. **Tezel,** p. 157: only trickery motifs to gain magical objects. P. 183: magical objects are gun belt (produces gold), flute (calls forth soldiers), shirt (magical transportation), drain (brings forth magical garden: apple produces horns, pear produces donkey, green grass returns to normal).

14. The Magic Horse

AT 551 & 531; EB 81; BP I, 503 ff., II, 394 ff., III, 18 ff. **Mac-Culloch,** pp. 225–52: animism in folktales.

ARABIAN, **Campbell,** *Market,* p. 48: similar except great bird, Bashak, is helper instead of horse. P. 197: similar.

ARMENIAN, **Chalatianz,** p. 10: similar to Wingate's version discussed below. BP III, p. 30: hero catches bird with glowing stone in head. Tasks: build tower. Three *devs* give him three magic objects; grateful animals help fulfill five hero tasks. **Khatchatrianz,** p. 32: motifs describing battle between hero and adversary differ, but story is basically same. **Seklemian,** p. 159: only introductory motifs of father's blindness. P. 33: very similar to Wingate's story discussed below. **Servantstian,** p. 163 and **Macler,** *Ca,* p. 50: hero shoots beautiful bird, presents it to king. Further tasks: room of ivory, *aslan* skins, princess of India. Boy throws self at breast of giantess, gets help from forty sons in fulfilling tasks. King rewards hero for faithfulness by giving princess to him as wife. **Wingate,** *Folk-Lore,* XXI, 507: king builds church for many years, is not satisfied with it, tears it down; repeats this three times. Sets sons to return with Hazaran Bulbul. After many trials, youngest succeeds with advice of hermit. Brothers drop hero in lower world, village women help boy out of well. Same story appears in translation in *Armenian Review,* II, No. 8 (1949), 152. **Wlislocki,** p. 27: similar to Wingate's version above. **Surmelian,** p. 176: father's magic horse is hidden, awaiting hero son's claim.

ASIA MINOR, **Carnoy-Nicolaïdes,** [Greek] p. 57: combines 14. "The Magic Horse" and 20. "The Magic Ring." Hero, gardener's son, befriends old woman, receives her help; learns method for rejuvenation: kill, burn, take ashes of black, white, red dogs; throw sultan into boiling cauldron until bones separate from skin, puts bones together, sprinkle with ashes. When king asks hero to name his reward, boy asks for bronze ring; with bronze ring, hero wishes for beautiful ship; befriends rich rival who has fallen from fortune, brands him on buttock. Hero returns with rich ship, exposes rival as his slave. Marries princess. Rest of story follows "The Magic Ring."

AZERBAIJAN, **Hermann,** [Armenian] p. 120: goatherder tells sheepherder unusual dream; sheepherder buys it for three sheep, sleeps that night in cemetery. After midnight, someone arouses him, they ride hard, travel great distance. Herder discovers riding companion is woman, marries her; dangles feet in well, finds two precious stones, gives one to king as tribute. Task: find more. Boy returns to well, finds girl who produces jewels magically, returns with jewels and girl. Further tasks: from garden of 1000 nightingales, draw from well which gives eternal life, bring bouquets of flowers growing there. First wife advises hero to ask for forty measures of wheat, forty measures of cake, forty containers of wine. Boy comes to kingdom of birds who peck at him, leaves wheat for them, leaves cake with army of ants. At end of road, he sees large body of water; fish surround him; provides them with wine. They open path through water for boy and caravan, give boy wishing pearl. Inside magical garden, boy picks flowers, takes flask of water, is attacked by huge heavenly bird, fights violently, defeats bird who discards feathers and becomes beautiful maiden. Boy returns with her to home, marries all three maidens, becomes king of land. P. 26: hero Samed buys dream, marries princess, throws bottle against rocks, killing external soul of giant, releases girl of whom king is jealous. Boy must fetch letter from Paradise. Girl advises him to build great fire, enter it and be transformed to bird, enabling him to fulfill impossible task. When king tries same procedure, burns to death.

BASQUE, **Webster,** p. 16: jealous suitor sends hero on impossible tasks: bring Tartaro's horse and diamond, Tartaro himself. Through cleverness, hero succeeds with magical help. P. 182: blind king has three sons. Task: find white blackbird. Two brothers play cards with three women, lose all their money, are thrown in prison. Youngest avoids this, pays their debt as well as that of another; brothers return home. Fox joins hero. To get bird, he must find princess; to get princess, must find horse. Boy tricks and keeps all three. Brothers trick him, take bird. Fox saves hero and girl. When right is restored, king is cured; bird sings.

CAUCASIAN, **Dirr,** [Avarian] p. 86: king's blindness can be cured only by fruit from virgin queen's garden; youngest son succeeds in task. [Georgian] p. 50: only motif is help of magic horse. See Dirr notes for 27. "The Nine-Seeded Apple." [Kabardian] p. 117: disguised king wants to test daughters' bravery. Task: find beautiful maiden, box with seven locks, buffalo ox, seven buffalo cows; milk and bathe in fiery milk. Buffalo curses: man shall become woman; woman, man.

GREEK, **Dawkins,** *MG,* p. 301: only motifs are hero sews horse in seven layers of wool so that when it fights with sea mare, he will not be hurt; sea horse intoxicated with wine in stream. 45, p. 56: father's profession tabu. Search for bird, ivory, beautiful girl, king's dead parents. Helper is monk. Hero and girl cause king's death; Water of Immortality causes hero to survive. P. 71: similar except for horse's role.

GYPSY, **Groome,** [Bukowina] p. 104: with help of magic horse, youngest tricks old witch, kills her daughters, runs off with feather of bird in cage. Further tasks: bring bird, beautiful girl, herd of horses, bathe in boiling milk. **Jagendorf,** p. 52: Noodlehead, youngest of three sons, discovers magic horse is destroyer of harvest, receives three colts, works as stable groom for king. One day picks up strand of golden hair, presents it to king. Tasks imposed: princess-queen of sea, bathe in hot milk, secure engagement ring of princess, wedding. King bathes in hot milk to become young, dies. **Groome,** [Polish] p. 182: King has golden apple tree; fruit is always stolen; youngest son shoots and brings down golden feathers; father is blinded. Brothers set out to find bird, are tricked, put in prison. Youngest prince befriends hare, gets advice: beware of taking bird with beautiful cage. Hero disobeys; further tasks: silver horse, princess with Locks of Gold. **Yates,** [Polish] p. 37: youngest of seven brothers is fool; finds diamond necklace, in turn, must find: beautiful girl, golden hen that lays diamond eggs, golden charger. Hero must bathe in hot milk, with help of magic horse, survives. King imitates hero, burns to death. **Groome,** [Scottish-Tinker] p. 283: fox is helper to hero instead of horse. Tasks: find most marvelous bird in world; white glaine of light, sun goddess. [Welsh] p. 107: old man befriends hero who helps everything and everyone on road and finds beautiful feather. Tasks: bird, beautiful lady, castle keys. **Yates,** [Welsh] p. 14: similar to Groome, (p. 107), above.

HUNGARIAN, **Jones,** p. 262: introduction quite different. Hero tasks: find girl with golden hair, spinning wheel and distaff, stud with golden hair. Hero must milk mares, bathe in milk. P. 288: hero task: bring water from fairies' well which will rejuvenate king. Youngest son succeeds with aid of magic horse. Test: step in hot lead. Boy and his horse succeed, proving hero father of fairy child.

ITALIAN, **Crane,** p. 40: blind king needs feather of griffin for cure. Youngest son succeeds in finding it; brothers kill and take it away. Boy's bones become whistle and sing story of deed.

ROMANIAN, **Ispirescu,** p. 241: king sends bravest child (daughter) to represent him. On road she picks up golden hair. Further tasks: find princess, her stud of mare, holy water (in so doing, receives curse: if man, become woman; if woman, become man). King bathes in milk, burns. **Kremnitz,** p. 16: king builds church; steeple continually falls down. King sends sons to find wonderful bird which will make church complete. Fox asks two elder brothers for bread; they refuse, are turned to stone. Third prince avoids this, receives magical help. Two brothers trick boy on return, take bird home. Hero, by smearing hot blood of scorpion on his feet which were cut off by his brothers, becomes whole again. Third prince, dressed as shepherd, enters church; silent bird suddenly begins to sing.

RUSSIAN, **Afanas'ev,** p. 310: only motif of hero wearing 12,000 pounds of hemp, tarring it with pitch, wrapping it around self to fight dragon. P. 494: tasks: bird, princess, wedding dress at bottom of sea; bathe in hot water. P. 612: different in motifs, but basically same. Story follows search for firebird; gray wolf takes role of magic horse. In turn, needs to find horse with golden mane, princess Elena the Fair. Wolf transforms self to these objects; brothers kill hero, take bird and girl. Gray wolf, with water of life, resuscitates hero. **Ransome**, p. 223: very similar and artistic parallel.

SCOTCH, **Campbell**, II, 344: fox is boy's supernatural helper. Hero finds falcon feather; further tasks assigned. I, lxxx: "On the Isle of Man and Highlands of Scotland, people still believe in existence of water horse."

SERBIAN, **Mijatovics**, p. 67: hunter finds golden ram. Further tasks: vineyard which must produce within two days of being planted, sufficient elephant tusks for palace, beautiful girl. Hero succeeds with help of little girl. King beheads him; girl restores to life. King tries same, dies. **Petrovitch**, p. 213: only minor variations, almost identical.

SIBERIAN, **Coxwell**, [Russian] p. 763: beginning motifs involve search for cure for father's blindness.

TURKISH, **Garnett**, [Albanian] II, 305: hero sent on difficult and impossible tasks by friend who tricks him. Beautiful girl flies away. Hero wears iron shoes and iron cane to find her. **Bain**, p. 134, **Kúnos**, *Stam*, p. 150 and *44*, p. 126: hero befriends crow who helps him find beautiful bird. Further tasks: ivory to make palace (elephants are tricked into drinking wine), bird's master, drug to cure queen's illness. King marries queen of Persis; hero marries crow (beautiful girl in disguise). **Tezel**, p. 82: hero sent by father to find remedy (figs guarded by fierce lions) for false illness of stepmother. *Dev* mother is benefactor. Further tasks: *dev's* milk, fairy cradle. Hero kills external souls of stepmother and nurse, returns eighty eyes to king's blinded wives. P. 173: only motif is hero hiding in empty golden goat to find princess. P. 140: quests for magic mirror, crying pomegranate, laughing quince; magic horse helper.

The Beautiful Feather, Version Two (Unpublished Version)

Princes seek cure for father's blindness: soil on which father has never stepped foot. Two older sons are unsuccessful. When youngest is anxious to try, father gives him magic horse, instructions to obey it.

On road hero finds beautiful feather, picks it up against horse's wishes. King hears of feather, takes it, gives further task: bird to whom feather belongs. With help of horse, hero catches bird as it alights, does not let go, no matter how great the struggle. When bird is taken to king, he is delighted and plays with it constantly. Queen is jealous and suggests hero be sent to bring sea horse's milk so that king may bathe in it and be young again, enabling him to marry princess who has taken disguise of bird.

Hero asks for forty mules, fleeces of forty sheep, forty barrels of tar, as his magic horse advises. Hero covers the horse with successive coats of tar and wool. Then the horse goes into sea, fights fiercely with sea horse, and brings her to dry land. The animal is taken to king and her fiery milk collected in large vat.

Hero is to bathe in sea horse's milk first. Magic horse blows on surface of milk; boy steps in and out quickly and is more handsome than ever. King tries same, burns to death.

Hero marries bird who is really a princess. Upon return to his home, princess touches her hands to blind king's eyes; old man sees again. (Informant: Nishan Krikorian)

The Beautiful Feather, Version Three (Unpublished Version)

Two princes set out to seek fortunes. First becomes discouraged, returns home. Second finds beautiful feather on road which is given as gift to king.

Queen suggests search for bird. With magic horse's help, hero kills a horse, removes insides, dries body. All the birds come to eat the flesh; boy hides in empty horse, catches unusual bird.

Queen next suggests search for bird cage. Hero exchanges meat and vegetable dishes placed incorrectly before vegetarian and carnivorous animals; hits correct door (one of seven), gains entrance. He unties twelve knots in belt of giantess. She gives chase; hero escapes by throwing behind: sharp knife which covers ground with sharp stones, stick which covers ground with dense trees, jug of water which creates ocean behind him.

Giantess surmounts all hazards, appears at king's palace. He suggests marriage; suitor task: quest for sea horse's milk to rejuvenate king.

Magic horse, covered with glue and plaster, fights sea horse successfully. Hero blows on fiery sea horse's milk, bathes, is unhurt. King quickly bathes and dies. Hero marries giantess and returns homeward. His jealous brother pushes him into water;

sea horse rescues hero who is then reunited with wife. (Informant: Hovhannes Kaprelian)

15. The Huntsman

AT 513C, cf AT 531, 465; EB 207; BP II, 79 ff., III, 556–58, 84–85.

ALBANIAN, **Dozon,** p. 27: king will give daughter to anyone who identifies unusual louse. This is accomplished; king refuses to fulfill promise. Girl is carried to lower world; unusual sons bring her back: listener, ground-opener, unusual seer, unusual shoemaker, searcher, thrower, catcher.

ARMENIAN, **Chalatianz,** p. 51: unusual companions. See 16. "The Dreamer and His Dream." **Khatchatrianz,** p. 99: Badakan, hero, uses wine in stream to intoxicate white bull in which external soul in form of three birds resides. P. 32: see Khatchatrianz notes for 14. "The Magic Horse." **Nazinian,** p. 20: dying father's tabu: son not to know he was fisherman. Boy breaks tabu, becomes fisherman. One day luck brings him frog; he takes it home. When house is magically cleaned and food prepared, hero stays behind, catches beautiful girl; burns frog skin. Old hag sees beauty of girl, tells king who sends great armies to take her. She takes sword in hand, slays all soldiers. Again king sends soldiers; again she destroys them. King sends husband to find fiery, heavenly horse. Wife advises: ask for seven camel loads of vinegar, seven camel loads of cotton. With caravan, hero passes seven mountains where he sees a stream, soaks water with cotton, fills river bed with vinegar. Magic horse comes to drink, becomes intoxicated; hero rides home with him. Further task: bring woman as beautiful as boy's wife. She advises hero to ask for king's own ring, strong dog, powerful wrestler, seven sheep. On travels boy meets unusual companions: drinker; eater of seven mills; two men on two mountains three days travel apart who are playing catch with millstone; listener. Boy kills a sheep, feasts as each friend joins him. Tests required: boy's dog defeats king's dog, boy's wrestler defeats king's wrestler, drinker gulps room-full of water, eater finishes great quantity of food. King realizes cunningness of boy, tries to poison food, but royal ring (king's) indicates presence of poison. Boy takes girl, returns home, kills evil king upon discovering with ring that bath water has been poisoned. P. 45: priest carries church on back into forest. Bear cub challenges him to show of strength. Priest is defeated, takes cub home with him. Bear eats so much that priest decides to make him gift to king. King finds bear too expensive to feed, sets him difficult tasks: bring back trees from forest (home of forty *devs*), bear puts *devs* to work for him; bring Frankestan's princess. Bear meets unusual companions: runner, drinker, flour-eater from seven mills, listener, *sass*-player [musician], mountain-lifter. Tests: eat enormous quantity of food; race, return with water of immortal river; take hot bath (drinker blows on, cools it); eat poisoned food (listener hears plot; musician plays; all are fascinated; food is exchanged). Bear returns with princess. King and queen die. Bear marries girl, loses skin, becomes man. Seklemian, p. 41: only motif of unusual helpers. P. 111: hero sets off to search for ivory. P. 127: hero Bedek gets bull drunk to obtain external soul of giant which is in stomach. Servantstian, p. 122: only motif of wine to intoxicate white ox in whom is external soul. See Servantstian notes for 1. "The Ogre's Soul."

GEORGIAN, Wardrop, p. 68: unusual helpers serve only as fellow travelers of hero, do not help in fulfilling tasks; instead, trick hero, keep him in well below.

GREEK, Dawkins, *MG*, p. 263: Tabu: knowledge of father's profession [hunter]. Hero shoots wonderful animal, presents it to king. Further tasks: search for ivory, beautiful girl. Hero meets unusual companions who aid him. P. 266: Tabu: profession of father [hunter] must be kept secret from son. Son shoots beautiful deer, presents to king. Further tasks: room of ivory (by substituting wine in stream). Hero joined by six companions, receives their help in fulfilling suitor tasks set by seven ogres. Hero's wife changes vizier (hero's enemy) to mouse, king to cat who chases mouse. *MGAM*, p. 383: only motif is intoxicating animals with wine to obtain external soul of villain. See Dawkins *MGAM* notes for 1. "The Ogre's Soul." P. 573: unusual helpers appear. *45*, p. 56: see Dawkins *45* notes for 14. "The Magic Horse" for story. P. 73: hero receives help from unusual companions to fulfill tasks.

GYPSY, Yates, [Welsh] p. 18: Frosty and unusual helpers win race with old witch, gain much gold.

HUNGARIAN, Ortutay, p. 227: unusual helpers appear.

ISRAELI, Noy, [Yemen] p. 143: dying father does not wish son to know his work: hunter. Boy becomes hunter, finds golden bird, takes to king. Further tasks: find Bowl of God. Demon tells boy: once a week, in seventh kingdom in palace of King of Demons, one hundred soldiers with swords carry this bowl through streets. Boy burns demon's hair as source of magic. Further tasks: find fair daughter of Sinsin, empty all reservoirs and vessels in country, sort out one hundred sacks of grain. Boy lets ants eat his supply of flour, king of ants gives him hair as source of help. Girl poisons king, marries boy.

PERSIAN, Lorimer, [Bakhatari] p. 288: only unusual helpers who aid hero in suitor tasks.

ROMANIAN, Creangă, p. 1: unusual companions.

RUSSIAN, Ransome, p. 58: unusual helpers.

SIBERIAN, Coxwell, [Little Russia (Ukrainian)], p. 981: unusual companions.

TURKISH, Bain, p. 134: much less interesting version of story. See Bain notes for 14. "The Magic Horse."

16. The Dreamer and His Dream

Cf AT 513A & 725; EB 197; BP II, 79 ff., III, 84–85, 556–58.

ARMENIAN, Chalatianz, p. 51: almost identical. Seklemian, p. 41: almost identical. P. 159: hero marries two wives. Wingate, *Folk-Lore,* XXII, 476: almost identical.

ASIA MINOR, Carnoy-Nicolaïdes, [Greek] p. 43: very similar except only one task is imposed by enemy king: pierce iron butler and iron shield. Hero is called to enemy's land, en route meets unusual companions who help him accomplish tasks set by king, marries princess.

CAUCASIAN, Dirr, [Georgian] p. 17: almost identical except greater number of supernatural helpers.

GREEK, Dawkins, *MG,* p. 346: very similar; after solution of riddles, hero must attend enemy king's palace, marries princess, has two wives, as dream predicted. *MGAM,* p. 537: boy sees dream, will tell no one about it. Similar except unusual companions do not appear.

HUNGARIAN, Jones, p. 117: identical until hero successfully solves riddles; boy is sent to enemy king with eleven others. Task: find hero among group of twelve. P. 233: similar except unusual helpers do not appear. Prediction: hero will become king of Hungary. Ortutay, p. 291: very similar except unusual helpers do not appear. Boy goes to enemy king's court, makes predictions which come true. The evil king is hanged instead of hero by trickery.

RUSSIAN, Afanas'ev, p. 427: tasks imposed by sea king are

reminiscent of hero tasks imposed on hero and his companions.
SERBIAN, **Mijatovics,** p. 248: hero dreams he will become
king, is banished.

17. The Patient Suitor

Cf AT 836F and 910B; EB 204, III 2, 3; BP IV, 149. **Clouston,** I, 197: refers to ancient Indian romance "Twenty-Five Tales
of the Demon": merchant sees beauty of the great magic who
lives in sea; they marry. Tabu: don't touch picture of fairy. When
hero does, he loses all. **MacCulloch,** pp. 228, 314–15, 333–34.

ARMENIAN, **Nazinian,** p. 92: greedy priest sees poor man
who has found gold. Man shares some of wealth; priest wants
more and more. Finally priest possesses all seven mules loaded
with gold. When farmer stops at brook to drink, he takes out
golden cup to scoop water. Priest asks for that, too. Farmer becomes angry, throws sand into priest's eyes, blinds him. "Only
this will satisfy your eye," he says, takes his treasures, returns
home. **Wlislocki,** p. 76: when tabu (can't see fairy wife's face by
light) is broken, wife disappears; husband changed to stone
forever.

CAUCASIAN, **Haxthausen,** [Persian-Armenian] p. 363: hero,
in learning answer to princess' riddle (suitor task), must die: why
are woman and dog chained together? (Woman is unfaithful;
dog helps man save himself). Boy returns, exposes baseness of
testing princess: loves monster.

PERSIAN, **Lorimer,** [Bakhtiari] p. 236: only one task set
for boy: learn why wife and dog are chained together. In travels, hero kills dragon, thus saving rare young birds. When boy
learns answer to question, he is told he must die, asks permission
to pray on roof. When he is alone there, grateful mother bird
swoops down, flies him to safety.

RUSSIAN, **Afanas'ev,** p. 255: see Afanas'ev notes for 18.
"The Country of the Beautiful Gardens."

The Patient Suitor (Unpublished Version)

[A rather disjointed story, but interesting in its use of motifs:]
Young laundry owner goes to market to buy food: there he

sees young girl who asks him to carry her purchases home. Once home, she suggests marriage but insists on one condition: husband must not complain three times.

Life is pleasant for lucky man until one day he complains that his nieces and nephews are dirty. Another time, he complains of excessive rainfall. The third time, he complains that his wife is walking through thorns in her sheer dress. As a result of breaking the condition, everything—wife, house, possessions—disappears.

A merchant leaves wife to seek his fortune. Upon his return twenty years later, he shoots his wife and son, thinking young man is the woman's lover.

Two men each have ten oxen. They enter a cave, load their oxen with gold. One is greedy, demands five, then five more of his friend's oxen. Still unsatisfied, he asks about bottle which friend has in his pocket. He learns that if medicine in bottle is applied to the eyes, man will become twenty years old again. The greedy one does this, becomes blind.

The king with a beautiful daughter gives suitor task: learn stories of characters described above. Wise man does so, marries beautiful princess. (Informant: Mrs. Katoon Mouradian)

18. The Country of the Beautiful Gardens

AT 400, cf AT 502, IV; cf EB 83, 84, 198, III 7; BP II, 318 ff., III, 406 ff. Clouston, I, 182–91: discusses maidens who remove skins and become human. 205–14: Cupid and Psyche legends. MacCulloch, p. 39: each class of animals has a chief. Pp. 328, 342–49: Swan Maiden.

ARABIAN, Campbell, *Market*, p. 105: only motif is transformation of husband to cock when tabu is broken.

ARMENIAN, Khatchatrianz, p. 125: hero catches beautiful girl as she alights. Nazinian, p. 40: girl, in disgrace because she burned animal skin, follows husband who flies in form of bird, joins him beneath the water. See Nazinian notes for 26. "The King of Snakes." Servantstian, p. 172 and Macler, *Ca*, p. 65: bride of fountain returns home for visit. Husband, in form of bird, flies to her room. Jealous sisters place broken glass at windowsill; bird is cut. Anguished husband banishes wife who in her travels learns cure: wash wound with new mother's milk and young girl's blood which has dried; sprinkle ashes over cuts three times. **Seklemian, p.** 49: similar to Servantstian version. **Surmelian, p.** 56: comparison of beauty to that of sun.

ASIA MINOR, **Carnoy-Nicolaïdes,** [Greek] p. 127: see Carnoy notes for 26. "The King of Snakes." Heroine breaks tabu: pursuit, iron shoes.

AZERBAIJAN, **Hermann,** [Armenian] p. 108: when prince breaks father's tabu, frees captive king who has been imprisoned for seven years; people become angry, dethrone boy. Meanwhile hero dreams of unusual island where three birds alight to bathe. Hero finds island, sees birds with copper, silver, gold wings bathe in water, keeps gold wings, marries girl, takes her home to his mother, returns to reclaim throne. When husband is slow in returning, girl thinks she's abandoned, wears black wings, flies to her home. Boy pursues her, wears magic hood of invisibility, finds wife, burns magic hair (received from man he freed), sits on magic horse, kills enemy in battle. Recognition symbol: royal handkerchief on wound.

BASQUE, **Webster, p.** 38: youngest of three girls is married to serpent under spell. She visits her family, returns to find him gone, wears out iron shoes in pursuit. Recognition symbol: silk handkerchief given by snake to wife.

GREEK, **Dawkins,** 45, p. 31: hero must not reveal identity of wife; when he does, she disappears. Iron shoe motif does not appear. Hero receives help from wind. P. 115: girl reveals secret of betrothed who is bullnut (born from eating lily), loses him, builds bathhouse, learns how to find youth. *MG,* p. 56: tabu: revealing husband's identity. Girl breaks tabu; husband disappears. She builds bathhouse where everyone who enters must tell his story; locates husband. P. 105: boy gives wife's plumage to mother to keep; wife gets it, flies away. Hero in pursuit.

GYPSY, **Groome,** [Polish] p. 188: introductory motifs very similar. When hero finds wife, mother-in-law sets unusual tasks which boy fulfills with wife's help. When they decide to escape, pursuit motifs are similar to those in 8. "Abo Beckeer."

HUNGARIAN, **Jones, p.** 95: pursuit of wife; hero asks help of all animals he meets. **Ortutay, p.** 84: when wife burns husband's snake skin, he disappears; pursuit.

IRAQI, **Stevens, p.** 20: youngest daughter asks for "Clusters of Pearl," a handsome prince. Father brings her box with three of his hairs. Girl loves boy; jealous sisters cause him harm. Girl wears iron shoes to find him, overhears doves, kills them, uses their blood to renew health of husband.

471

ITALIAN, Crane, p. 1: because of wife's curiosity, husband disappears. Wife wears out iron shoes, iron cane. Pursuit motifs: see 8. "Abo Beckeer." P. 7: youngest girl to marry terrible dragon; disenchantment occurs when girl agrees to marriage. P. 12: youngest girl marries king who visits her in form of bird. Jealous sisters place glass on windowsill; husband cut; girl learns use of blood as cure.

PERSIAN, Lorimer, p. 25: heroine loses husband by burning his snake skin; finds him by wearing iron shoes. Recognition: boy's ring dropped into his wash water. Rest of story follows 8. "Abo Beckeer."

POLISH, Zajdler, p. 33: beginning motifs similar to 34. "The World Below." Youngest son catches white swan and in her pursuit, acquires magic objects through trickery.

ROMANIAN, Ispirescu, p. 29: youngest princess destined to marry pig. With sorceress' advice, she ties string to pig's leg, as punishment must wear iron shoes, after much suffering, with baby in arms finally finds husband. P. 99: prince shoots arrow to select wife, finds owl, discovers owl is beautiful girl, burns feathers. Task: must do what no one has ever done to find her again. Tricks three devils, gains magic objects, finds wife and baby. Creangă, p. 1: only search motifs.

RUSSIAN, Afanas'ev, p. 580: youngest sister asks for feather of Finist the Falcon. He is transformed to man; jealous sisters hurt him. Girl wears iron shoes, trades objects to spend night with him to aid memory. P. 255: only motifs are marriage to swan maiden. Tabu: do not boast of house or wife. Man breaks tabu, loses all.

SERBIAN, Mijatovics, p. 43: hero pursues peahen; dragon given water by hero, runs off with girl. Much difficulty to find her and return. Help from grateful animals.

SIBERIAN, Coxwell, [Kalmuck] p. 206: girl marries bird in bird cage, burns cage (husband's soul); after many trials and searches, finds him, builds another cage for him.

TURKISH, Garnett, [Albanian] II, 305: boy, godson of king, learns all languages, is tricked to serve as servant of companion. Difficult quests suggested by evil friend. Hero is killed, brought back to life with Water of Life. Beautiful girl escapes in feather dress. Hero finds her after wearing out iron shoes and iron cane. Bain, [Romanian] p. 222: heroine marries hog, burns skin, eventually finds husband in tree house which she climbs with ladder built of bones of fowls given her by mothers of moon, sun, wind. She cuts off little finger to complete ladder. **Kent,** p. 79: girl marries horse who becomes man at night. Tabu: can't reveal secret. When she does, he disappears. Pursuit. Recognition: ring in wash water. Pursuit motifs similar to 8. "Abo Beckeer." **Tezel,** p. 121: similar to Kent above. P. 151: when tabu is broken, girl searches for cure for Green Pearl, her husband. **Kúnos,** *Stam,* p. 349 and *44,* p. 307: girl, because of curiosity about husband, must wear iron shoes, travel seven years as punishment.

19. The Riddles

Cf AT 851; EB 212, III; BP I, 188 ff.

CAUCASIAN, **Haxthausen,** [Persian-Armenian] p. 363: see Haxthausen notes for 17. "The Patient Suitor."

GREEK, **Dawkins,** *MG,* p. 404: division of chicken is secret of riddle.

GYPSY, **Groome,** [Turkish] p. 9: identical except letter is added which orders death of hero.

RUSSIAN, **Afanas'ev,** p. 115: close parallel although selling of hero's parents does not occur.

SCOTCH, **Campbell,** II, 36: only motif is riddle contest. Different questions used. Girls trick hero who later threatens to expose them.

TURKISH, **Garnett,** [Gypsy] II, 364: very close parallel.

20. Magic Ring

AT 560; EB 58; BP II, 451 ff., 541 ff. **Clouston,** I, 398: discovery of ring in fish's stomach; motif discussed in Jewish, Scotch, German, Arabian variants. **MacCulloch,** pp. 201–2: magic animal controls the fetish from distance; this represents form of fetishism where amulet, talisman, etc. works by itself.

ALBANIAN, **Dozon,** p. 63: similar. P. 71: tricking hero and taking magical source.

ARMENIAN, **Khatchatrianz,** p. 63: very close parallel except wife is seller of magic ring. **Nazinian,** p. 94: boy helps church singer, finds much treasure, saves *kop* [instrument used in plowing], source of magic, for self. Evil man tries three times

473

to get *kop,* dies in attempt. **Seklemian,** p. 103: almost identical to Servantstian version below; boy finds ring in net. **Servantstian,** p. 167 and **Macler,** *Ca,* p. 57: hero befriends cat, dog, snake; when he feeds snake by hand, it is transformed to handsome youth who advises hero to ask for special ring which snake father owns. Similar except mice help cat and dog retrieve ring. **Toumanian,** p. 120: only similarity is gratefulness of animals. Servant who eats small piece of king's food [flesh of white snake] can understand languages of all birds and animals; finds queen's diamond, receives freedom to travel, throws fish which have been swept ashore back into water, does not trample on army of ants, feeds his bread to hungry crows. These animals help him complete suitor tasks: find gold ring in river; collect ten bags of grain in one day; find life-tree, bring back apple.

ASIA MINOR, **Carnoy-Nicolaïdes,** [Greek] p. 57: hero, befriended by old woman, fulfills tasks set by king, rewarded with bronze ring. Suitor tasks set. Hero befriends, brands rival. Jew sells red fish for bronze ring.

BASQUE, **Webster,** p. 94: boy finds magic snuffbox, builds palace, marries princess. Jealous mother-in-law causes palace to be transported. Boy asks help from sun, moon, south wind; dressed as gardener, steals box back.

GREEK, **Dawkins,** *45,* p. 75: similar except bullnut, not snake, is magical source. *MG,* p. 41: hero buys dog, cat, snake. Almost identical except hero marries second daughter. *MGAM,* p. 329: very similar but abbreviated. Pp. 457, 507: similar but incomplete.

GYPSY, **Yates,** [Anglo-Welsh] p. 173 and **Groome,** [Welsh] p. 209: magic snuffbox with three little men is source of magic for Jack; fulfills suitor tasks. Valet steals box. Kings of mice, frogs, birds help retrieve it.

ITALIAN, **Crane,** p. 152: rusty ring found inside dead cock by youngest prince. Ring falls into possession of magician; kings of fishes and birds help in recovery.

PERSIAN, **Lorimer,** [Bakhitari] p. 269: wise sayings; hero buys animals; dreams about King Suleman's ring, finds it: source of magic; fulfills suitor tasks. Old woman finds ring; palace transported. Pigeon locates palace; dog, cat, king of mice steal ring from old woman's pocket, return it to hero's wife.

POLISH, **Zajdler,** p. 1: very similar except hero receives magic crown; mouse, king of fishes, with cat and dog find stolen crown.

474

RUSSIAN, **Afanas'ev, p.** 31: magic ring located on finger of dead princess; hero's wife tricks him, removes his ring. Dog, cat, mouse retrieve it.

SIBERIAN, **Coxwell** [Bashkir] p. 455: hero saves snake from fire; receives white box, source of magic, from grateful father. Wife, palace appear; king wars with hero but magic powers save boy. [Finn] p. 642: boy buys dog, cat, snake which are being mistreated, receives ring from snake, marries princess. She tricks and takes ring. Animals retrieve, drop it on return home, find ring in fish's stomach. [Gagaüzy] p. 401: boy befriends snake, receives magic mirror, places it under his tongue, orders princess, palace, cat, dog transported to wilderness. Old woman convinces princess to learn husband's secret; hero is tricked, left alone, cast into pit. Cat eats mice; one begs for mercy in return for retrieving magic mirror. [Kalmuck] p. 223: hero befriends mouse, ape, bear; finds magic jewel, receives great riches, trades stone, becomes impoverished. Animals retrieve jewel, drop in river, mouse has sea animals build rock wall to ward off enemy, find jewel. [Kirghiz] p. 347: cat and dog bring jewel to boy. Old woman tricks wife, runs off with jewel. Hero befriends snake and, in his need, gains jewel from snake father.

TURKISH, **Kent, p.** 143: similar except befriended snake becomes beautiful girl. Hero asks for wand under snake king's tongue. Old witch is villainess. **Bain,** p. 176, and **Kúnos,** *Stam,* p. 297 and *44,* p. 257: almost identical. Magic mirror is magic object instead of ring. Mouse is boy's helper; cat and dog do not appear. Old woman is villain. **Tezel,** p. 14: hero asks for piece of string under king snake's tongue; witch tricks youth, takes string. Four mice retrieve it from cruel king.

The Magic Ring, Version Two (Unpublished Version)

Ring is obtained as in story 20 above. Husband gives ring to wife, instructing her never to part with it. A Jew tricks her, gets magic ring, has palace removed to middle of sea.

Puppy and kitten aid tricked master. Kitten uses mouse as bait: mouse puts tail in vinegar, tickles villain's nose, ring flies out of his mouth. Story then follows published version. (Informant: Mrs. Katoon Mouradian)

The Signet, Version Three (Unpublished Version)

Poor widow and son live in great poverty. In seeking his fortune, hero befriends snake who is prince of snakes. As reward, hero receives signet from grateful father.

Hero wishes for palace across from king's, marries princess. At king's urging, princess learns husband's secret. She gives signet to king; palace is abolished. Hero's pets, cat and dog, enter king's bedroom, tickle his nose, cause him to sneeze and spit out ring.

En route home, dog loses signet in river; fish swallows it. Cat sees it in stomach of caught and cleaned fish. Return; king is destroyed. (Collected by Mardiros Tarpinian from Rouben Karagousian.)

Kingdom of Snakes, Version Four (Unpublished Version)

Boy saves life of snake who is prince of snakes. As reward, he receives magic box; trades box for magic sword; with sword, kills dervish and retrieves box. Hero trades box for magic sponge; with sword, kills dervish and retrieves box.

Hero wants to marry princess. Suitor tasks: build more beautiful palace than king's; cover walk between two palaces with rugs; cover rugs entirely with gold. Tasks fulfilled; king tricks boy into leaving magic box and sword with him. King orders sword to kill boy; it does.

Boy's mother resuscitates him with magic sponge. Everyone at king's palace, except princess and magic box, destroyed by magic sword. (Informant: Mrs. Mariam Serabian)

Variants of Version Four are:

AT 560; cf AT 561, 569. **Clouston,** I, 110–18: discussion of trading objects and regaining them through trickery.

ARMENIAN, **Seklemian,** p. 169: only motifs are resuscitation of hero. See Seklemian notes for 4. "Clever Daniel."

GREEK, **Dawkins,** *MGAM,* p. 507: very similar except trickery motifs of bride are missing. P. 457: very close parallel; magic objects are napkin, club, gourd. P. 545: only appearance of magic objects occurs. P. 375: magic objects only.

GYPSY, **Yates,** [Polish] p. 49: magic objects: small tablecloth which produces food; loaf of bread which is always full;

ducat-producing lamb; cudgels which strike enemy. These are returned to hero from thief.

HUNGARIAN, Jones, p. 161: only motif is existence of table-cloth, gold-producing lamb, magic club.

ISRAELI, Noy, [Tunisian] p. 46: poor man is given magic food-producing mill. Old witch tricks family, takes mill. She does same with tray which produces money and club which beats people until special words cause it to stop. With magic clubs, witch is beaten to death; poor man reclaims other objects.

21. Hagop's Wish

Cf AT 562 & 950, IIIa; EB 219; BP II, 535 ff. MacCulloch, p. 29: knowledge of name gives power over person.

ALBANIAN, Dozon, p. 77: spendthrift youth gets magical help; princess visits him nightly. King finally discovers clever boy.

ARMENIAN, Macler, *Cl*, p. 120: prince is unkind to old man who curses him: to love *dev's* daughter. On search, hero sees bright light near fountain on moonlight night, investigates, sees old woman dressed in white robe, reading book. She gives him book, says he'll find wounded dragon on path: touch book to dragon, read chapter of it over him, sprinkle earth over dragon who will then become well. Same procedure to be followed for wounded bird. When boy comes to sea, he is to read book: sea will divide for him. Once across, he must read from book, will reach *dev* who sets task: find, return with *dev's* wife. Befriended animals help hero. Nazinian, p. 99: boy finds brass lamp: source of magic; he rubs it, receives magical help, brings princess to him constantly. First mother, then father, disguised, take girl's place to verify story. Finally king, fearing boy's magic, permits marriage.

HUNGARIAN, Ortutay, p. 321: only motif is grateful old man who tells hero to draw circle which none will be able to cross.

RUSSIAN, Afanas'ev, p. 567: only motif is belief that spirits cannot cross circle.

SCOTCH, Campbell, II, 206: heroine draws circle, stays within to escape unearthly creatures.

SIBERIAN Coxwell, [Bashkir] p. 461: only general motifs of hero who spends legacy foolishly.

22. The Monster's Hairs

Cf AT 300; 314 V, VI, 502, III, IV, V; EB 158 IV, 257; BP III 94 ff. Clouston I, 155–67: horrible dragons threaten land, must be appeased by eating humans. MacCulloch, p. 63 ff. water of life; pp. 381–409, dragon sacrifice.

Although a number of stories share common motifs with this, none follow the plot closely.

ARMENIAN, Khatchatrianz, p. 105: youngest son-in-law acts as fool, finds unusual bird, Azaran-Belbul; hero is dropped in well. Story follows 34. "The World Below." Macler, *Cle*, p. 84: hunter sees demon at well with beautiful girl on one knee, frog on other. Hero to decide which is most beautiful; answers: beautiful is that which pleases human heart most. Demon is delighted, gives red, white, black hairs: magical source. Boy rides red horse, wrecks king's garden, is observed by princess. Girls send king, their father, apples in various degrees of ripeness, indicating their readiness for marriage. Youngest selects gardener who limps past. Enemy besieges city; hero turns armies back three times. King becomes sick; lioness' milk is only cure. Two brothers-in-law are unsuccessful. Third gets milk, removes cream, gives milk to brothers-in-law in exchange for branding them. Seklemian, p. 127: hero Bedek takes disguise of gardener. P. 169: hero sent to find lioness' milk, finds lioness in agony because of pustule on paw. Surmelian, p. 48: dragon demands girl sacrifice for use of water supply.

AZERBAIJAN, Hermann, [Armenian] p. 108: refer to Hermann notes for 18. "The Country of the Beautiful Gardens."

BASQUE, Webster, p. 22: hero lets Tartaro out of stable, receives grateful monster's promise for help, works as gardener, tramples garden. Princess is to be eaten by serpent. With magical aid of Tartaro, boy kills serpent in three-day fight. P. 111: White mare is helper. Hero Fidel works for devil, runs away, works as gardener, has golden hair, marries princess, defeats enemy army, obtains water of life, gets golden apples, reveals truth at feast.

CAUCASIAN, Dirr, [Armenian] p. 150: foolish brother catches magic horse destroying wheat field, marries princess. [Georgian] p. 50: similar except for beginning motifs: man seeks child, is given two apples. In turn, must give *dev* one son, one horse, one panther at request. Son, with help of horse, escapes giant, dresses as goose-herder. Rest of story is similar.

GREEK, Dawkins, *MG*, p. 250: childless king wants off-spring. Fate gives him child, predicts that child will be stolen by ogre at age ten. When hero escapes ogre, apprentices self as gardener. Rest of story similar. *MGAM*, p. 549: hero disguised by goat's belly worn over head marries princess, fights war, defeats enemy. Recognition motif: royal handkerchief on finger wound of hero.

GYPSY, Groome, [Polish] p. 155: foolish hero rides beautiful horse, fulfills suitor task: snatch kiss three times from princess in high tower. Hero acts humbly, fights bravely in war. King ties royal handkerchief around big toe which later serves as recognition.

HUNGARIAN, Ortutay, p. 227: only motifs are method of choosing bridegroom and treatment of brothers-in-law.

IRAQI, Stevens, p. 58: except for manner of receiving magic hairs, story is almost identical.

PERSIAN, Lorimer, p. 33: stepmother wants to harm boy, colt tells youth of impending danger. Once boy runs away, motifs follow Detroit version. Cure for king is special bird. Boy saves head and heart for self, gives rest to brothers-in-law.

ROMANIAN, Ispirescu, p. 3: monk finds child in tarred box, raises him as son. With help of magic horse, hero tricks fairies, becomes golden, works as undergardener. Rest of story follows closely. P. 227: close variant of Armenian tale up to the identification of hero after he has killed seven-headed hydra.

RUSSIAN, Afanas'ev, p. 97: strong hero, Know-Not, works as gardener, marries princess. Ripeness of apples is test for readiness for marriage. Boy wins battle; royal handkerchief serves as recognition symbol. P. 533: hero sits at father's grave for three nights. Earth opens; he gets three hairs from magic horse. Hero fulfills suitor tasks, marries princess. King sets sons-in-law tasks: duck with golden feathers (hero gives these to brothers-in-law in exchange for two fingers of two right hands); pig with golden bristles (price: toe of foot); mare with golden mane and twelve foals (price: strip of flesh from their backs). Magical source is striking bush three times.

SCOTCH, Campbell, I, 72, 95: dragon from sea is to eat princess; hero kills him. Princess leaves mark on savior; herd boy is recognized.

TURKEY, Garnett, [Armenian] I, 278: ripeness of watermelon is test for marriage readiness. [Greek] I, 178: hero and magic horse (born from eating apple) escape death. Hero disguised as gardener marries princess, finds deathless water, brands brothers-in-law. Ripeness of melons is test for readiness for marriage.

23. The Turtle Skin

AT 465; EB 86; BP II, 94.

ARMENIAN, Nazinian, p. 20: see Nazinian notes for 15. "The Huntsman." **Seklemian,** p. 155: similar to Servantstian version below. **Servantstian,** p. 158: and **Macler, Ca,** p. 45: very similar except boy marries maiden in fish skin. Last task demands hero produce three-day-old baby who can entertain king. Unusual brother of bride gives the king tongue lashing; hero finds peace. **Macler, Cl,** p. 58: youngest prince shoots arrow which falls into fountain, selecting frog for future wife. When skin is burned prematurely, prince must fill unusual tasks set by king father: piece of rug as large as hand which can be opened to seat army; bowlful of pilaff which whole army will eat and bowl remains full; bunch of raisins which will feed the army yet bunch will remain complete; man with beard twice as long as height. Prince receives help from girl's family. Little man chides king for impossible tasks, gains height as he speaks, cuts king's head off. Boy becomes ruler.

BASQUE, Webster, p. 158: beautiful girl appears at ball.

GEORGIAN, Wardrop, p. 15: hero marries frog; when he discovers her to be beautiful girl, burns her skin. Jealous king imposes impossible tasks which hero fulfills with help of girl's family.

GREEK, Dawkins, 45, p. 84: similar except mother, sister, and ball motifs do not occur. **MG,** p. 97: boys marry whomever guns shoot; youngest marries frog. P. 99: fisherman finds tortoise, brings it home. It becomes lovely girl; hero burns her skin, causing her sadness. King, jealous of girl's beauty, imposes impossible tasks on her husband. Mother of wife in sea is source of magic. **MGAM,** p. 341: prince marries enchanted frog, fulfills king's difficult requests with help of girl's family. Animal skin burned.

GYPSY, Yates, [Romanian] p. 111: although quite different introduction and many different specific motifs, story is basically marriage of hero to water creature. Tasks imposed on boy by jealous king fulfilled with help of girl's family. **Groome,** [Welsh] p. 259: king does not know how to select successor. Test: shoot arrows. Youngest son shoots into glass door of queen of fairies, marries her. Tasks assigned hero; final task brings brother forth, scaring king.

HUNGARIAN, **Jones,** p. 224: only motif is marriage to water animal. P. 15: only motif is grateful fish which becomes beautiful maiden. Tasks imposed on husband who is aided by girl's family.

ROMANIAN, **Ispirescu,** p. 99: each prince shoots arrow to find wife; hero shoots at top of tree, finds owl. Wife (owl) dances at ball; hero burns skin. Pursuit motifs similar to 18. "The Country of the Beautiful Gardens."

RUSSIAN, **Afanas'ev,** p. 119: prince shoots arrow at frog, thus selecting her as wife. King sets tasks to determine best daughter-in-law. Frog-wife proves best; prince burns skin prematurely. Pursuit and search for lost wife. P. 504: hunter spares bird who becomes beautiful girl he marries. She weaves fine rug; king desires her. Difficult tasks imposed; girl escapes king by transformation to dove. Tasks fulfilled with great difficulty. War occurs with king whom hero defeats.

SIBERIAN, **Coxwell,** [Bashkir] p. 466: hero marries water nymph, burns skin; wife disappears. Pursuit: wife throws him into fire, shakes ashes, renews life. Together, return to village. [Gagaüzy] p. 410: hero shoots arrow, selects tortoise for wife. When skin is burned, king gives hero difficult task. See Coxwell [Gagaüzy] notes for 25. "The Magic Box."

TURKISH, **Kúnos,** *Stam,* p. 84 and *44,* p. 64: hero marries unusual fish, is required to fulfill impossible tasks: golden palace, crystal bridge, unending feast, bringing forth mule from egg. Magical help from sea aids hero.

A Wonderful Statue (Unpublished Version)

Dying king tells each son to go to royal balcony and throw an apple. Wherever apple falls, there they will find future wives.

Youngest throws apple near little reindeer, therefore marries it. The day after his marriage, boy finds beautiful statue in room: his wife. Fame of statue spreads through land. However, people faint when they see the tall statue. (Informant explained that statue was a fairy woman.)

King of nearby country gives hero three tasks to fulfill (penalty: lose statue): make huge rug, find the world's greatest Bible which can be balanced on a thumb, find a man one and one-half spans high who will play cards with king all night and be able to eat supper of all the king's soldiers.

Through help of wife's relatives, all tasks are fulfilled. Little man kills the king. Statue and youth live on, having many children. (Informant: Mrs. Katoon Mouradian)

24. The Golden Box

Cf AT 510B; EB 189, 244; BP II, 45 ff.

ALBANIAN, Dozon, p. 41: very similar.

GREEK, Dawkins, 45, p. 124: girl, to escape father, cuts off own hands. Story follows 32. "The Story of Mariam." P. 181: similar. *MG*, p. 255: girl, to avoid unpleasant marriage, sets suitor tasks: three beautiful dresses, wooden chest. She prays to God to help her fly. Prince sees her in flight, takes her home as servant. Girl is known as Box with Wings, wears beautiful dresses; prince tries to recognize her at ball, gives her his ring which she places in biscuit she has made for him: recognition. *MGAM*, p. 511: Widower will marry whoever fits deceased wife's shoes. Daughter is eligible, sets three suitor tasks. Meanwhile, girl hides inside large lamp which is sold to king's son; reveals herself to him, marries prince, bears him son. When baby is killed, girl is blamed. Her eyes are put out; she is thrown in prison. With aid from heaven, baby is restored as well as her sight.

ITALIAN, Crane, p. 48: as wife dies, instructs husband to marry someone as beautiful as she was. Her ring must fit, too. Her daughter fits description. Girl sets suitor task: get four unusually beautiful silk dresses, one wooden dress. She throws herself in river, finds work as servant in palace, goes to ball. Prince gives her his ring which she later drops in his broth: recognition.

RUSSIAN, Afanas'ev, p. 351: boy can marry only girl whose finger fits his ring: sister. Rest of story is quite different. Some escape motifs from 8. "Abo Beckeer" appear.

SCOTCH, Campbell, I, 226, 232: very similar. Man will marry whomever dead wife's clothes fit. Cinderella shoe motifs end story.

TURKISH, Tezel, p. 78: king who could not have children receives magic apple from dervish. Daughter is born; mother dies. Fit of bracelet determines new wife. His daughter is thus chosen. She escapes father, hides beauty under animal pelt, finds refuge in king's palace, attends king's ball. Prince gives her gift which she puts into biscuit she prepares for him. Recognition.

25. The Magic Box

AT 461A & 425; BP I, 276 ff., II, 229 ff., III, 37 ff.

ARMENIAN, Macler, *Cl*, p. 22: similar to Wingate version below. *Cle*, p. 93: only similarity is pious man sets out to find his creator to beg for spirit and reason; on journey, meets priest, mother of brigands, large fish, seven brigands, virgin living ascetic life. All give questions for him to ask God. He finds God, an old man, at top of mountain, learns answers. Seklemian, p. 123: almost identical to Wingate version. Toumanian, p. 73: foolish man sets out to find God; various objects ask cause of their misfortune. Hero serves as supper (cure) for wolf. Wingate, *Folk-Lore*, XXI, 220: unhappy man sets out to find Luck. On road, bitter fruit, unhappy girl, lion ask him questions. He learns girl should marry, fruit is bitter because gold is buried at roots; boy is so foolish that lion eats him.

CAUCASIAN, **Dirr**, [Georgian] p. 10: lazy man seeks God; animals and objects ask him to relay messages. He is told to return and will have what he seeks. He gives God's answers to objects on road. When he tells wolf, he himself serves as food.

GREEK, **Dawkins**, *MG*, p. 360: hero sets off to find Christ to ask if what is written is ever unwritten. Various suffering people ask him to relay messages to Christ; hero does so. When he sees Christ, he becomes white instead of blackamoor but has black cross on stomach. P. 462: old woman sets out to find Undying Sun. On journey, various people and objects ask her to relay messages. *MGAM*, p. 489: only search for God to ask for child appears. Dervish gives man apple with instructions to cut it into four pieces. *45*, p. 281: king and vizier are childless, vow that if they have children, they will marry each other. Vizier's son is born black; king sends him to find God and ask Him to unwrite what has been written. On road, he meets three men, one blind, one caught in stream, one unhappy and rich. They ask youth to plead their cause to God. He does, also rolls self in mud, becomes white. Returns, opens store, marries princess. "What is written is not to be unwritten." P. 358: two brothers, one lucky, other unlucky. Unlucky one sets out to find his Luck.

Questions are asked him on way. He becomes wealthy, but must observe tabu: cannot boast of wealth as his.

GYPSY, Groome, [Transylvanian] p. 133: see notes for 47. "The Emperor's Lesson."

HUNGARIAN, Ortutay, p. 304: beginning motifs differ greatly. Only similarities are hero's suitor tasks and questions asked of God.

IRAQI, Stevens, p. 45: magic object on windowsill tells man to ask for princess. Impossible suitor tasks performed. Princess marries supernatural husband. Tabu: revealing husband's secret. When woman breaks tabu, husband disappears. P. 183: father is in search for a child. P. 263: hero is seeking Fortune, meets man and objects on road, promises to ask about their problems. Sees Fortune, receives answers.

PERSIAN, Lorimer, pp. 113, 293: identical with Wingate story discussed above except that answers learned are: lion needs fool; cultivated land is unfruitful because gold is buried; king's country is not more glorious because king is not king, but woman.

ROMANIAN, Kremnitz, p. 91: man, searching for child, is given apple by holy hermit, eats wife's half of apple; beautiful girl is born. She is snatched away by griffin, grows up in the woods. Prince, when hunting, sees and marries her.

RUSSIAN, Afanas'ev, p. 213: motif of search for King Dragon appears.

SIBERIAN, Coxwell, [Finn] p. 649: search for four hairs from Devil's Beard (similar to old man's search for God). [Gagaüzy] p. 410: hero marries tortoise wife; king sets boy to find dead mother's ring. Tortoise's mother helps boy. On road to find God, various objects ask hero to question God.

TURKISH, Tezel, p. 72: hero searches for his Fortune, his destiny, realizes that although things could be better, they could also be much worse, returns home. P. 194: man eats specially prepared pumpkin intended for wife, becomes pregnant, gives birth to girl, just like a pumpkin. Girl marries prince, transformed to beauty with lovely clothes; identity revealed.

26. The King of Snakes

AT 433B; cf EB 106; BP II, 229. Clouston, I, 205–14: Cupid and Psyche legends. MacCulloch, p. 262.

ARMENIAN, Nazinian, p. 40: childless couple are given

three apples by dervish. When woman eats apples in wrong order, little male calf is born. Years later, calf tells mother to ask for princess as his wife. Suitor tasks: produce golden platter filled with gold, make clothes for princess which no hands have touched in cutting or sewing, transport princess to boy's home so that sun doesn't touch her head or her feet touch ground. Boy fills all requirements, marries princess. When girl sees he removes skin at night and becomes man, she burns skin. Boy becomes pigeon, flies away. Girl takes three apples, starts out to find him, asks three different people if pigeon has passed by. Finally, husband makes wife pigeon; man flies into water; wife follows. They live together under water. Seklemian, p. 73: only motifs of birth of dragon child to long-suffering king.

ASIA MINOR, Carnoy-Nicolaïdes, [Greek] p. 127: unusual suitor fulfills suitor tasks.

BASQUE, Webster, p. 167: girl marries serpent, burns skin, breaks spell.

CAUCASIAN, Dirr, [Georgian] p. 47: hero marries pig who is maiden in disguise. Vizier marries pig who is real pig; bitten to death.

GREEK, Dawkins, *MGAM*, p. 453: princess to marry anyone who can make her laugh. When monkey makes her laugh, she marries him. He goes to war; she burns skin, is reunited with difficulty. P. 375: girl marries snake who gives her family magic objects: gold-producing ass, food-producing dish, man-hitting club. P. 555: snake found in woods wants to marry princess, fulfills suitor task: building palace. Marriage transforms him to man.

GYPSY, Groome, [Romanian] p. 21: similar but no burning of skin occurs.

HUNGARIAN, Jones, p. 282: befriended snake asks for princess; curse is lifted at marriage. Ortutay, p: 84: similar except burning of skin introduces search motifs. See 18. "The Country of the Beautiful Gardens."

ROMANIAN, Creangă, p. 102: old couple decide to adopt first thing they see: pig. One day pig decides to marry princess. Suitor tasks fulfilled. Animal skin burned prematurely; wife must wear iron shoes in pursuit.

RUSSIAN, Afanas'ev, p. 200: only motif is marriage of princess to goat; girl burns goat skin; man keeps human form.

SIBERIAN, Coxwell, [Polish] p. 958: woman wishes child, even if only hedgehog; one is born. When he fulfills suitor tasks, marries princess, is transformed.

27. The Nine-Seeded Apple

Cf AT 303; cf Stith Thompson and Warren T. Roberts, *Types of Indic Oral Tales* (FF Communications No. 180 [Helsinki, 1960]), 1121A Ind. BP I 115, 528 f. Clouston, I, 169–72: life tokens.

ARMENIAN, Macler, *Cle*, p. 151: rich man gets apple from dervish. Gives parings to mare, apple to wife; magic colt and brave son born. Condition made with dervish: do not name boy until dervish does so. Boy sets out to find and win princess, with help from magic colt, wins contest. Wlislocki, p. 72: queen befriends wounded bird who advises her how to conceive long-awaited child. See Wlislocki notes for 3. "The Fairy Child."

BASQUE, Webster, p. 87: grateful fish causes fertility. Births of three sons, three colts, three puppies occur. First boy kills serpent, marries princess, explores palace, is transformed. Same happens to second prince. Youngest prince does not eat, wins over evil.

CAUCASIAN, Dirr, [Georgian] p. 50: giant gives unusual fruit to barren couple with understanding that half of birth will be his. Years later, he claims one son, one magic horse, panther cub. Hero escapes with horse's help, works as bald-headed gardener, finds cure for king's illness, marries princess. Life token indicates twin needs help.

GREEK, Dawkins, 45, p. 411: slight similarity. Poor boy becomes successful at business; dervish predicts greatness for him. Together they travel to mountain which opens. Hero enters, removes box, breaks tabu by touching. Mountain closes; he remains within. When he drinks water, he is transformed to ass. Talisman in box is source of magic. Marries princess. P. 115: unusual birth occurs when lily is eaten. *MG*, p. 245: devil gives apple to childless king with condition that one son and one mare will be his. Life token indicates twin is in danger. *MGAM*, p. 489: When apple from dervish is cut into four pieces and eaten, twin boys and colts are born. First prince follows deer, shoots at it, plays dice with water fairy, loses. Second prince follows brother, wins game with water fairy, wins life.

HUNGARIAN, Jones, p. 112: life token appears: when knife stuck in tree becomes bloody, prince is in danger.

IRAQI, Stevens, p. 145: eating apple causes birth of son; apple peel causes birth of colt.

PERSIAN, Lorimer, [Bakhtiari] p. 212: dervish gives man pomegranate to share with wife. Conception occurs but dervish

claims one of twin boys who are born. Ring is left as talisman.
Old man instructs youth who kills dervish, enters water, becomes
golden. He is caught in snowstorm, finds refuge, marries girl.
In hunting, sees gazelle, follows it, finds it becomes beautiful girl.
Contest: wrestle, boy loses. Brother sets off, is mistaken for husband, follows gazelle, wrestles with beauty, wins. Brother is resuscitated.

RUSSIAN, Afanas'ev, p. 234: queen becomes pregnant from
eating pike; scullery maid eats wing, cow eats entrails of fish.
Each conceives, bears three identical human boys.

SCOTCH, Campbell, I, 72: unusual birth of three sons
whose life tokens are trees. Youngest receives help from grateful
animals, finds killer of brothers, rejuvenates them.

TURKISH, Garnett, [Greek] I, 178. queen bears sons after
eating apple. Mare bears foals from eating apple parings. See
Garnett notes for 22. "The Monster's Hairs."

28. Tanzara and Dyeer

AT 930, I, II; EB 128. Clouston, II, 187–95: eating lover's
heart. MacCulloch, p. 299: in eating any part of a man, the
qualities of that man will pass on to the eater.

AZERBAIJAN, Hermann, p. 85: king and brother who are
childless each receive apple to share with wives from dervish.
King has daughter; brother, son. Decide children will marry each
other. As years pass, king is sorry for promise. Evil *mullah*
[teacher] arranges to have Tahir's family slaughtered by Zohra's
father, the king. Tahir escapes death only when Zohra threatens
to drink poison if he is killed. Boy travels to another land, loves
another, remembers Zohra, returns to her, dressed as girl. Before
he can be killed by king, Zohra puts lover in box, pushes him
into sea. Boy reaches shores of Bulgaria, is found by princess,
marries her. Wager: Zohra is greatest beauty. Battle; lovers reunited.

GREEK, Dawkins, 45, p. 281: only beginning motifs of predestination are similar. Refer to Dawkins 45 notes for 25. "The
Magic Box." P. 286: Dawkins, speaking of a version of story
writes: "Though the text is in Greek, these curious names are
presented in Turkish: Taktirda Yazilan and Teptilde Gozulmez,
which point to the oriental character of the story." (These are
names of children whose marriage has been predestined. The

names mean: "In predestination that which is written"; "In mutability is not to be seen.")

29. Mundig

Cf AT 700; EB 288; BP I, 389 ff.

ARMENIAN, Wlislocki, p. 43: old couple want child, if only as small as hazelnut. Tiny child is very clever, rides horse, brings robbers to parents who catch them. Boy manages to ride on back of stork, gains king's favor, returns with huge diamond as reward.

GREEK, Dawkins, *MGAM,* p. 485: lazy boy sent to father with lunch, loses bread on way. Boy is instructed not to look up as he drinks water, does so, falls into hands of wicked ogre. Escapes by trickery, pushing villain's mother into boiling pot. Unpublished version reported, p. 250, from Ulghatsh: motif of chick-pea children who later annoy mother; she puts them into fire.

IRAQI, Stevens, p. 205: find girl's earrings in pot, adults realize they have been eating her.

ITALIAN, Crane, p. 242: old couple want children. One hundred peas become sons; father kills all but one, Cecino. Boy takes father's lunch, helps father attract carpentry business. Cecino hides in ear of oxen, becomes friend of robbers, is swallowed by stolen horses. Horses cut open so boy can be found, but in vain. Wolf eats horse's carcass, vomits Cecino. Boy tricks robbers, takes money to parents, is drowned in rut in road. P. 375: mother wishes beans were children; they become so. When she wishes they become beans again, all but one are transformed. Peppercorn falls into mother's soup, causing her much sadness. In chain fashion, various objects and people reflect this loss.

PERSIAN, Lorimer, p. 43: wife cooks soup; pea falls to ground; son is born. Son takes soup to father who sets him on quest for king's treasury. Cumulative events: woman washing, won't help him; he swallows stream; leopard, wolf, jackal join him. Boy is jailed; unusual friends help him through difficult times. Hero receives money, returns home.

SIBERIAN, Coxwell, [Lett] p. 912: diminutive child, Little Finger, seems to make most of every situation. [Mordvins] p. 573: wife chops wood, cuts off thumb which becomes tiny boy.

Hero is sent with father's lunch, is sold to rich lord who locks him in money chest, gets out, takes money home.

TURKISH, **Tezel,** p. 12: only appearance of thumbling-sized character. P. 49: lame chicken, attempting to retrieve money from tax collector, is joined by fox, monster, stream. Fox eats chickens; monster ruins stables; stream puts out fire.

30. Cinderella

AT 510A; EB 60; BP I, 165 ff. **MacCulloch,** pp. 110–11: continuation of life: life exists in bone, even after death. P. 376: direct supplying of gifts from parent's grave.

ARMENIAN, **Khatchatrianz,** p. 83: red cow befriends heroine and brother. When it is killed by stepmother, bones are buried, become source of magic. Recognition by slipper appears. **Nazinian,** p. 105: red cow is source of food for motherless brother and sister. Stepsister finds cow's milk bitter, gets thinner and thinner. Stepmother insists cow be killed and used for *madag* [sacrifice] offering for health of her child. Children are told to bury bones near old hag's house, keep cow's horn there which will supply them with food. Great wedding takes place at palace. Voice from burial site of bones says hag will bring beautiful clothes for children and take them to wedding. Girl is dressed in silver; boy in gold. Same thing reoccurs. Girl loses slipper in pool; everyone tries on slipper. Finally, rightful owner is found; marriage occurs. Several days later, stepmother comes to palace, takes young bride home for visit, substitutes her own daughter. Prince notices this is not his wife; stepmother is punished. **Tcheraz,** p. 87: cow gives butter and honey in horn for good girl; when stepmother sends her daughter with cow, she sucks blood and pus instead. Cow killed; girl buries bones: source of magic. Good girl goes to wedding at palace, beautifully gowned, loses slipper. Delousing scene with old woman who plunges good girl in water: hair becomes golden, tears pearls, smiles roses. Stepsister is sharp-tongued, acquires donkey's tail on head. Stepmother arranges for her daughter to marry prince who is unhappy with her ugliness. He invites all girls in country to palace to weave fabric embroidered with gold and spun with pearls, walks among them examining work, hears them telling each other stories, thus hears story of good girl. Wrong is righted. **Wlislocki,** p. 55: king will marry only if a girl can knock crown off his head from one hundred paces. No one succeeds until tall, veiled girl knocks crown off three times with diamond apple. King searches, finds poor orphan girl who has received magical help from owl.

CAUCASIAN, Dirr, [Ossetian] p. 149: abused stepdaughter receives help from horn of ram.

GEORGIAN, Wardrop, p. 63: cow gives heroine butter and honey. When stepmother has it killed, girl buries bones which become source of magic. Girl treats devi well (does not speak of lice in her hair), becomes golden, receives golden shoes. Step-mother sends own daughter who becomes uglier. Slipper: recognition token.

GREEK, Dawkins, *MG*, p. 115: three girls and mother are spinning; who breaks thread will be eaten. Youngest refuses to eat any of her mother, buries her bones which become source of magic.

GYPSY, Yates, [Welsh] p. 25: youngest of three sisters is befriended by old woman, wears lovely clothes to palace, leaves slipper behind; recognition and marriage to prince. For motifs of birth of unusual children and substitution by jealous sisters, see 31. "The Golden-Haired Twins."

HUNGARIAN, Ortutay, p. 192: only motifs of obtaining food through horn of magic animal. P. 279: beautiful girl dances at ball, gains king for husband. Mouse is her benefactor, gives her nutshell with dress inside.

IRAQI, Stevens, p. 187: very similar to Wardrop version discussed above.

PERSIAN, Lorimer, p. 79: little Fatima kills mother at mullah's direction who then marries her father. She is cruel to girl; yellow cow helps her. Girl gets moon on forehead, star on chin for being good to *dev*. Other girl does opposite, gets donkey's ears. At king's ball, prince finds slipper which girl has left behind. Stepmother hides girl in oven. Cock announces hiding place. [Bakhitari] p. 256: tattooer instructs girl to cause mother's death. Father marries tattooer who now mistreats girl. Yellow cow befriends girl, is killed at stepmother's insistence. Girl greets *dev* politely, becomes beautiful, receives golden slippers, marries prince. When bathing, bad stepsister ties girl to tree, takes her place. Tiger eats heroine but one drop of blood spills on ground. Reed grows on spot; shepherd blows in reed, sings heroine's story. Girl lives, joins husband and son.

ROMANIAN, Ispirescu, p. 177: close variant. Kremnitz, p. 179: stepmother unkind to son. He takes service with rich man, receives magic ox as payment. Ox gives boy food from horn. Rest of story is not similar.

RUSSIAN, Afanas'ev, p. 146: girl is mistreated by stepmother. Red cow is source of food and clothing. When it is killed, girl places entrails on gatepost; marries prince. Stepmother transforms her to goose, substitutes own daughter. Prince burns skin. P. 393: bullock befriends brother and sister, is killed; ashes are buried in three piles. Apple tree, dog, house become source of magic. P. 439: doll is magical source for Vasilisa, fulfills many demands of Baba Yaga, spins fine linen; girl marries king.

SCOTCH, Campbell, II, 300: dead mother becomes sheep who supplies girl with food. When sheep is killed, skin, bones and hoofs are kept as source of magic. Prince falls in love with girl. Slipper motif appears.

SERBIAN, Mijatovics, p. 59 and Petrovitch, p. 224: old man warns girls that one who drops her spindle will find her mother turned to cow. Pepelyouga thus loses mother but cow becomes magical source and helps her with spinning. Cow is killed; girl buries bones. From this spot she begs beautiful dresses which she wears to church. Slipper motif appears.

SIBERIAN, Coxwell, [Lapp] p. 603: unusual story but only similar motifs are girl picks up mother's bones, arranges them, strikes them with birch branch three times: house, food, magical help appear.

TURKISH, Tezel, p. 51: heroine becomes lovelier when old hag, grateful for delousing, instructs her to wash with unusual water. Stepmother kills girl's cow; girl buries bones which become source of magic. She attends king's ball. Slipper motif occurs. Rooster announces girl is hidden and wrong sister is being taken. Finally girl escapes evil stepmother, lives with seven *dev* brothers in mountains. Poisoned ring causes magic sleep; when removed, girl becomes well again. P. 194: See Tezel notes for 25. "The Magic Box."

31. The Golden-Haired Twins

AT 707; EB 239; BP II, 380 ff. Clouston, I, 168 ff: petrification. MacCulloch, p. 52 ff.: turning to stone; water of life.

ALBANIAN, Dozon, p. 7: very similar. Hero is sent for flower from World Beauty's garden, her handkerchief, finally for Beauty herself. Aunts attempt to poison food; evil plan exposed.

ARMENIAN, **Seklemian,** p. 111: almost identical except one child has silver hair, the other, golden. P. 33: only turning to stone motif. **Servantstian,** p. 175 and **Macler,** *Ca,* p. 71: similar except no tasks set for hero. Boy's skill as hunter gains king's attention. Boy takes precautions against treachery of aunts when he visits palace. Truth revealed. **Tcheraz,** p. 67: very similar. Third sister promises if king marries her: will bear boy with moon on forehead, girl with sun on forehead; when they wash, water will turn to gold; when they cry, tears will become pearls; when they laugh or smile, roses will fall from cheeks; as they walk, flowers will spring at their steps. Such children are born; evil sisters have midwife substitute newborn puppies; place children in box, throw into river. Young mother is tied to door of palace; face is covered; dogs, chained to her side, share her food. Each person who passes her must hit her with mallet. Old woman befriends children, keeps them in her cottage until they are young people. Boy goes hunting one day; king sees him, speaks of his beauty. Sisters hear, tell midwife who locates him. She suggests finding marvelous flute of Theodore le Danseur, which plays all melodies of the world; this will amuse his sister. Boy sets off, finds shelter with ogress, borrows donkey to reach Theodore's palace nearby. When he asks for flute, Theodore tells him, "I'm giving it to you because I pity your beauty and your youth and the unfortunate woman who cries near the palace door. But do not return." Boy is sent on further quests: Theodore's marvelous watch and mirror, Theodore himself. On last quest, hero turns to stone; birds speak of leaf from their tree which will change stone into man again. Passing shepherd follows advice, brings stone back to life. Hero convinces Theodore to accompany him, learns story of aunts' trickery and mother's punishment. Theodore warns youth aunts will serve him poisoned food. Boy tells king truth; aunts and midwife punished. Mother and family reunited. Theodore marries boy's sister.

BASQUE, **Webster,** p. 176: three sisters make wishes; youngest desires to marry king, does so. When child is to be born, king is away. Sisters throw girl baby into river; also second and third children who are boys. They substitute cat, dog, bear. New mother is put in dungeon. Children grow up; old woman tells them to seek: singing tree, bird which tells truth, water that makes life. Although monk advises them, first brother, then second, turn to stone. Sister dresses as man, sprinkles stones with water; become men again. Boys hunt, meet king, invite him to lunch, serve him peas, beans, lentils, then tell him truth.

CAUCASIAN, Dirr, [Georgian] p. 44: three girls abandoned by father and stepmother. Youngest digs way out with hands which are transformed to pick and shovel. Girls are discovered when raisins from royal stables are missing. They promise if marriage to king occurs: eldest sister will make huge carpet; second will prepare enormous dinner which can fit in egg shell; youngest will bear golden children. Rest of story follows "The Golden-Haired Twins" except no further tasks are assigned to boy.

GEORGIAN, Wardrop, p. 5: greater detail, richer version of Dirr story, above.

GREEK, Dawkins, MGAM, p. 317: very similar except children cry pearls instead of possessing golden hair. Tasks differ: obtaining girls instead of birds. Penalty is turning to stone which youth avoids. P. 371: similar except girls do not appear. MG, p. 167: mother-in-law as villainess substitutes puppy, kitten, snake for children. Monk befriends children. Magical horse helps boy on different tasks on which sister sends him (suggested by evil midwife). With help of beautiful Taitsinena, boy lives again after turning to stone.

GYPSY, Groome, [Bukowina] p. 67: villainness is servant who later marries king. Where children are destroyed, golden fir trees grow which are cut down and burned; spark escapes; golden lambs appear. After lambs are killed, in washing their bodies, two chitterlings fall into river, become two doves, later change to the two boys. In guessing contest, boys reveal identity to father. [Romanian] p. 70: very abbreviated form of substituting children and their recognition. Yates, [Romanian] p. 105: sisters are evil-doers; children are thrown before various animals to be devoured but finally find safety with old man. Midwife suggests difficult tasks for boy. Motif of turning to stone occurs. [Welsh] p. 25: see Yates [Welsh] notes for 30. "Cinderella."

HUNGARIAN, Ortutay, p. 109: similar.

ITALIAN, Crane, p. 17: youngest sister bears golden children: two sons with apples in hands, daughter with star on brow. Puppies are substituted. Fairies make gifts: deer to nurse children, purse of money, ring which will change color when misfortune befalls them. Hero tasks: find dancing water, singing apple, speaking bird. In pursuit of objects, hero must not turn around or he will turn to stone.

493

PERSIAN, **Lorimer,** p. 58: father abandons three daughters; prince befriends them, marries youngest. Two older sisters have midwife substitute puppies for beautiful twins. Woman is put on lime pillar at crossroads; everyone passing must throw stones at her. Children are saved from river, throw rose-leaves; mother cries. King investigates, recognizes children.

ROMANIAN, **Ispirescu,** p. 67: with only substitution of a gypsy as evil-doer, story is very similar to Serbian version described below. **Kremnitz,** p. 31: identical with Ispirescu version except that aspen trees grow at burial spot of children; when burned, sparks fly and become golden-scaled fish. When exposed to air for a day, they become two beautiful youths. As minstrels, they go to palace, tell story to king.

RUSSIAN, **Afanas'ev,** p. 356: youngest sister promises unusual children; three golden sons born. Substitution of cat, dog, ordinary boy is made by sisters. Youngest girl is blinded, thrown into barrel with ordinary boy. He replaces her eyesight, brings about reunion with golden children. P. 184: similar although Armenian story is richer in detail.

SERBIAN, **Mijatovics,** p. 238 and **Petrovitch,** p. 353: golden-haired children are buried alive by wicked stepmother. Two golden-leafed trees grow at spot; when burned, sparks become golden lambs. When lambs are killed, fleece is washed in river, falls into water, becomes box. When box is opened, golden-haired boys emerge; dressed as singers, entertain king, tell him their story.

SIBERIAN, **Coxwell,** [Gagaüzy] p. 414: first sister promises if she marries prince: she will put his army into walnut shell; she will encircle whole army with thread; she will bear golden-haired twins. Prince marries third girl, goes to war. Gypsy woman substitutes two puppies, throws chest and children into river. Miller befriends children. Wife is put into pit and beaten. Recognition. [Ostyak] p. 540: youngest sister promises children of unusual birth; sisters deceive her. Puppies substituted for one girl and two boy babies. Boys seek, find unusual objects, die. Girl finds them; life renewed. Find mother nailed to floor in church. Truth is told as story.

TURKISH, **Kent,** p. 69: beginning motifs differ. Wicked sisters throw children into river, substitute puppies. Miller befriends twins, warns them to watch for treachery when they visit home of their father, the dervish. **Bain,** p. 53 and **Kúnos,** *Stam,* p. 63: almost identical except golden-haired boy has half-moon on forehead, his sister has star on hers. *Dev* mother is magic source for hero on impossible tasks: twig from Fairy Queen's garden; Fairy Queen's magic mirror; Fairy Queen herself. Hero turns to stone on third pursuit, is disenchanted by Fairy Queen. **Tezel,** p. 136: similar to Kent above.

32. The Story of Mariam

AT 706; EB 246; BP I, 295 ff. **MacCulloch,** p. 67: immortal magic water restores sight or limbs.

ARMENIAN, BP I, 309: on log [angel in disguise], armless girl floats to king's palace.

ASIA MINOR, **Carnoy-Nicolaïdes,** [Greek] p. 91: combination of "The Story of Mariam" and 2. "Nourie Hadig." Teacher, who loves Marietta's father, brings about death of girl's mother. When stepmother is established, girl is mistreated, exposed on mountain top to die. Marietta is befriended by forty giants. When stepmother asks Sun who is most beautiful, she learns Marietta is still alive. After several attempts, Marietta is finally put into death-like sleep. When spell is broken, Marietta marries prince; child is born. Stepmother transforms Marietta into white pigeon, has it killed; when pine tree grows from that spot, she has it cut down. Finally pigeon emerges from tree.

GREEK, **Dawkins,** 45, p. 124: motifs from 24. "The Golden Box" introduce very similar story. P. 394: almost identical. *MG*, p. 71: only motif is teacher causes death of girl's mother, urges girl to encourage father to marry her. Father's conditions: marriage will occur when iron shoes, iron chain fall from ceiling because of rot. Girl is instructed to hurry process by throwing water up to ceiling.

GYPSY, **Groome,** [Bukowina] p. 90: hands of one man, feet of another are cut. Devil takes men to magic spring, they are made whole again.

HUNGARIAN, **Jones,** p. 49: hands of girl are cut by envious sisters. Beautiful girl marries prince, has two children. Sisters change message which is sent back and forth to prince who is away at war. Girl, with children, thrown into river; stumps grow to hands again. P. 335: Jones refers to Finnish variant similar to Armenian story. P. 182: jealous stepmother orders death of girl, wants to see liver, lungs, hands. Liver and lungs of animal are substituted, but hands are cut. Prince marries girl; she bears golden-haired boys. Message is changed by wicked stepmother; girl is thrown out. Lake of magic water cures her. Stag carries prince into deep forest where he is reunited with family. P. 250: hero's hands and feet are cut off.

IRAQI, Stevens, p. 183: only beginning motifs of child becoming motherless. Teacher persuades girl to encourage her marriage. When marriage occurs, girl is abandoned in woods.

PERSIAN, Lorimer, p. 79: teacher urges girl to select her for stepmother. See Lorimer notes for 30. "Cinderella."

RUSSIAN, Afanas'ev, p. 294: with only minor variations, close parallel.

TURKISH, Kúnos, *Stam*, p. 172 and *44*, p. 141: *dev* substitutes letter announcing birth of children. Wife and children are banished from palace. Moon-horse serves them, takes them to her country, tells girl when she (horse) dies, cut head off, set it on earth, slit stomach and lay within. When girl does so, she and her children find selves at palace, are reunited with husband.

33. Yeghnig Aghpar

AT 480 & 450, cf AT 403; EB 168; BP I, 79 ff., 207 ff., 115 ff. Clouston, I, pp. 404–11: humans swallowed by fish. MacCulloch, pp. 158–60: transformation by eating or drinking. W. R. Halliday in Dawkins, *MGAM*, p. 262, says of this story: "With reference to the metamorphosis of the brother, the following account of the origin of the Yourouks is of interest. In the mountains where rain-water has settled, they say that if a wild animal, an ibex, or a bear has drunk there and a man . . . drinks after it, he will become wild as they are. And this is how they became Yourouks."

ARMENIAN, Chalatianz, p. 1: similar to Wingate below. Macler, *Cl*, p. 10: similar to Wingate. Servantstian, p. 191: only motifs of cruel stepmother who boils wheat before planting; children are abandoned; birds befriend them. Seklemian, p. 1: see Wingate below. Tcheraz, p. 80: very similar. Stepmother slanders son so that father curses son and prays to God to transform him into stag. King meets stag with human face, leads him to palace. Good girl becomes golden; her tears turn to pearls, smiles to roses, when she befriends old hag. Stepsister becomes uglier, two udders of female dogs appear on her brow when she is sharp-tongued with old woman. Fairy helps good girl dress beautifully to attend wedding; leaves slipper behind. When shoe fits, prince marries her. Baby born; stepmother pushes beauty into sea, substitutes ugly daughter who demands stag's flesh to cure feigned illness. Stag goes to water, sings, "They have sharpened the knife and the hatchet, they have prepared the kettles of silver. Where is my sister?" Sister answers in a corner of the sea, "I wear on my back a dressing gown of silk, I carry in my hand a basin of gold. On my chest is the son of the king. How can I come near you?" King overhears, rescues wife and son, kills evil-doers. **Toumanian,** p. 77: story (told in verse) is very similar. Brother becomes lamb; villian is jealous hag. **Wingate,** *Folk-Lore,* XXI, 365: children are abandoned. Brother drinks water, becomes lamb. When children find way home, stepmother wants to eat lamb. Children run away. Rest of story is similar except slipper motif appears and girl calls to watchman from stomach of fish instead of to brother.

BASQUE, **Webster,** p. 53: good girl receives star on forehead and much gold; bad girl, donkey tail and charcoal. P. 187: see Webster notes for 7. "Seven Giant Brothers."

GEORGIAN, **Wardrop,** p. 63: good girl befriends old woman, becomes golden; stepsister becomes uglier.

GREEK, **Dawkins,** *MG,* p. 9: boy and girl, with neighbor's help, run away from wicked mother. Obstacles in pursuit: ribbon thrown down becomes a plain; comb, inpenetrable woods; salt, impossible lake. Girl marries prince; brother is lamb. Jealous queen pushes girl into fountain. Lamb sings to her. Queen orders lamb killed; sister buries bones and orange tree grows at spot. Girl tries to pick fruit, climbs to heaven, becomes star. P. 50: similar beginning motifs only, rest of story is similar to 3. "The Fairy Child." *MGAM,* p. 339: in story of Sophia and Konstandin, mother cooks liver; cat eats it. She cut off her breast and cooks it. Husband and wife decide to eat their children, so the two run away. Rest of story is similar to "Yeghnig Aghpar" except birth of child does not occur. P. 505: brother becomes fox; marriage to prince occurs. Brother takes original form again.

GYPSY, **Yates,** [Welsh] p. 21: girl befriends old woman, becomes beautiful. Stepsister does opposite, becomes uglier. Both are placed in box, thrown into river. Crop-tailed hen, born to beautiful sister, secures food for three of them. When hen is followed, find beautiful girl; marriage.

HUNGARIAN, **Jones,** p. 220: two orphan children in woods; boy drinks water, becomes roedeer. Sister marries prince. Witch gets lock of beautiful girl's hair, wraps it around toad, toasts it. This ointment is spread on ugly girl who now looks like queen.

Witch steals queen from her room, throws her into well. Whale swallows her. Ugly girl pretends illness, wants heart, liver of deer. Deer sings to sister at edge of water, is overheard. Whale is cut open; queen emerges. With ointment found in whale's stomach, she breaks brother's transformation. Ortutay, p. 255: cannibalism motifs introduce story; children run away; boy becomes fawn. Similar except villain is cook in king's palace.

IRAQI, Stevens, [Armenian informant] p. 157: very similar beginning; motifs from 2. "Nourie Hadig" appear at end.

ITALIAN, Crane, p. 331: children are abandoned; boy becomes calf; girl marries prince, befriends father. Stepmother throws girl into sea, substitutes ugly daughter. Calf is to be killed, sings to sister, is overheard.

ROMANIAN, Creangă, p. 93: motif of good and bad daughters; different concluding motifs. Kremnitz, p. 91: beginning motifs of 25. "Magic Box." Beautiful girl finds shelter in trees; old woman tricks her down. Marriage to prince.

RUSSIAN, Afanas'ev, p. 406: incomplete version. Story starts with drinking of water; brother becomes goat. Rest is similar including brother's song to sister in sea. P. 278: similar to Coxwell, p. 744, discussed below. Ransome, p. 212: close parallel.

SIBERIAN, Coxwell, [Bashkir] p. 449: Golden Knucklebone, hero, finds refuge in tree. Witch almost has it chopped down. Fox waters hewn spot; tree becomes whole again. [Ostyak] p. 537: only motif of hewn tree which is made stronger and sounder than it was before. [Russian] p. 744: only beginning motifs of father's daughter who is mistreated, is courteous to horse's head, is rewarded. Stepmother's daughter is sharp-tongued, becomes gypsy woman who dries up and dies. [White Russian] p. 975: greatly abbreviated form. Girl receives aid from ox who, when killed, has gold and silver grain in intestine. Brother drinks water, becomes ram. Substitution of bride. Girl becomes lynx.

TURKISH, Kent, p. 148: only bathing girl in special water for greater beauty. Bain, p. 1 and Kúnos, Stam, p. 3 and 44, p. 3: almost identical except children are impoverished children of emperor. Brother becomes stag; black slave is evil-doer. Tezel, p. 51: bathing in special water causes greater beauty for heroine, more ugliness for stepsister. P. 148: very similar. Cannibalism motifs begin story. Children befriend crow who tells them how to escape cruel parents. Pursuit motifs similar to 8. "Abo Beckeer."

Boy drinks water, becomes deer. Motifs of licking tree, marriage to prince occur. Villain is girl's slave.

The Abandoned Children, Version Two (Unpublished Version)

Father of two girls remarries. Stepmother has him abandon children in forest. Girls are to stay there as long as they hear sound of axe. Father hangs pumpkin on tree which is pumped by the wind, making sound of an axe. Two children are befriended by passing caravan of merchants. (Collected by Mardiros Tarpinian from Ohannes Tarpinian.)

The Cruel Stepmother, Version Three (Unpublished Version)

Man remarries; wife is cruel to children. Husband must abandon them in woods. Twice he does so, but children find their way home. Third time, they cannot. They enter a house and door closes behind them. They see two horses, red and white. Giant returns home, eats girl. Horse, next day, escapes with boy, gives him two hairs from his tail. Princess wants to marry hero. He refuses and is imprisoned, rubs hairs; horse helps him. Wearing sheepskin cap, he gets work as gardener in king's gardens. One day, rubs hairs together, sits on horse, tramples garden. Princess observes him; when it is her turn to select husband, she gives her golden apple to him. Together they travel homeward. Girl drifts downstream. Horse helps hero find her in land of short people. They befriend all they see on road and receive bag of gold. (Informant: Mrs. Katoon Mouradian)

AT 314 & 502; EB 158; BP III, 94 ff.

The Wicked Queen, Version Four (Unpublished Version)

Good king has wife who is unable to have children. He marries a good orphan, has one son. King takes trip; wicked queen decides to use magic to hurt both mother and child. She calls forth a red-headed fairy: change mother to cow, son to calf. At the same time, a female fairy appears before young mother, male fairy before son. The two are changed to animals and removed from palace.

499

King, before crossing large sea, becomes worried about his family, returns quickly. Meanwhile, wicked queen pretends to be very sick and asks for meat of red cow in stable. When red cow is killed, it gives a human cry, so queen refuses to eat it.

Next, queen demands meat of little red calf. Shepherdess asks if calf will marry her if she saves him. When he nods in agreement, she refuses to carry out king's command and will not kill calf. King asks cause of refusal and learns of wife's wickedness.

Girl goes to see queen, casts a spell on her causing her to sleep. She takes book of magic which queen keeps under her pillow and causes queen to be burned. When she puts book of magic into bowl of water, calf loses animal shape and becomes human again. (Informant: Mrs. Katoon Mouradian)

34. The World Below

AT 550 I & 301A & 300; EB 72; BP I 503 ff., II, 297 ff., 394, III, 490 ff. W. R. Halliday in Dawkins, MGAM, p. 274, says that there are two types of this story. In the first type, the strong hero is joined by two almost equally strong companions. When they take turns in preparing food, an ogre comes and conquers the two friends. But the hero wounds him on the third day, and the ogre escapes, leaving a trail of blood leading to a well.

From this point on, the first type follows the second story type:

An ogre robs the king's garden, and the three princes are given the task of catching the thief. Only the youngest prince succeeds, wounds the thief. The brothers follow the trail of blood to a well, but only the youngest prince succeeds in descending the fiery hole. Once down, he kills the ogre, rescues three princesses. His brothers cut his rope, however, and he is left below. He gets on the black ram instead of the white one and descends to even lower worlds. The hero kills a snake who is about to eat baby birds in their nest: mother bird is grateful. The hero rescues a princess who is about to be sacrificed to a dragon in order to free the town's water supply. The grateful king rewards hero with meat and drink for the powerful mother bird who takes hero to upper world. Hero cuts part of his thigh to feed the bird toward the end of journey because meat supply is gone.

Both versions, as described by Halliday, are found in the

Detroit collection as 34. "The World Below" and 35. "The Son of the Gray Horse."

If there is *one* typical Armenian folktale, it would be "The World Below" for which, in this collection alone, there are six versions. Furthermore, almost every storyteller with whom I worked knew some form of this tale.

ALBANIAN, **Dozon,** p. 35: very similar but incomplete. P. 121 and TURKISH, **Garnett,** II, 327: hero sits on grateful bird for flight to other world. See Albanian notes for 1. "The Ogre's Soul."

ARMENIAN, **Chalatianz,** p. 20: very similar. When youngest prince frees girl prisoners, finds and keeps: golden cat playing with golden mouse on golden tray; polecat playing with golden rooster in golden cage; little hunting dog playing with golden chicken on golden plate. Hero takes lightning sword and magic ring given him by third girl, removes a hair from tails of black, brown, white horses. When his brothers leave him behind, he gets on black ram, enters lower world; with lightning sword kills dragon, saves princess, frees water supply for town. Episode of eaglets and grateful mother eagle occurs. Boy asks king for forty skins of wine and forty fat tails of sheep for return flight, cuts own calf when meat is not enough. He wears sheepskin cap, is apprenticed to jeweler who must produce the above golden objects to fulfill suitor tasks imposed by princess. Apprentice asks for nuts as he works. On horseback, rushes at two princes, knocks them off saddles. Repeats on second day; on third day, hits brothers with sword; marries girl. **Khatchatrianz,** p. 105: from point where hero descends well, story is similar. See Khatchatrianz notes for 14. "The Magic Horse." **Nazinian,** p. 1: almost identical. **Seklemian,** p. 15: almost identical. **Wingate,** *Folk-Lore,* XXII, 351: almost identical except hero awakens demon by putting hot iron at feet. Girl gives hero magic ring which he later uses to fulfill suitor tasks. See Wingate notes for 14. "The Magic Horse" for story which combines plots of both "The Magic Horse" and "The World Below." **Wlislocki,** p. 27: brothers set out to find beautiful singing bird to complete church. When hero finds bird, brothers trick him, throw him into well. Pigeons bring twigs, fill well until hero can get out. Recognition of hero occurs when beautiful bird sings in church. **Surmelian,** p. 46: dragon demands girl victim for use of water supply. P. 201: striking villain only once. P. 56: beauty is compared with that of sun.

ASIA MINOR, Carnoy-Nicolaïdes, p. 75 and TURKISH, Garnett, [Greek] I, 165: almost identical.

AZERBAIJAN, Hermann, p. 33: almost identical except episode of girls being sacrificed to dragon is missing.

BASQUE, Webster, p. 77: Malbrouk, whose godfather is witch, kills daughters of godfather who had been intending him harm. He goes deep into well, rescues two girls, kills serpent. Wolf, dog, hawk, are helpers. Third girl's rescue involves destroying external soul. As marriage gift, boy steals from giant: cow with golden horns; moon which lights seven leagues; magic violin. P. 106: only motif of flight on bird, cutting of thigh when meat supply is gone.

CAUCASIAN, Dirr, [Avarian] p. 75: grateful bird and difficult flight. [Georgian] p. 36: youngest prince, to complete building of church, sets off to find cock and hen nightingale. See Dirr notes for 1. "The Ogre's Soul."

GEORGIAN, Wardrop, p. 68: hero of unusual birth is joined by unusual helpers who trick him, leave him in world below. Rest of story follows Armenian version.

GREEK, Dawkins, MG, p. 142: similar. P. 191: princes set out to find golden nightingale to complete church. Hero is assigned one task after another before he can successfully capture bird. Brothers leave hero in well. Rest of story is similar. P. 196: youngest prince seeks lamp which never goes out, kills orgres, flatters unpleasant objects which help him in pursuit, rescues three girls, finds lamp. Brothers trick him, leave him in well. He climbs up, produces three dresses inside walnut. Recognition. 45, p. 438: basically variant of 36. "The Helpful Spirit." P. 173: jealousy of brothers. Underground adventure does not occur. P. 181: only motif of apprentice eating nuts, producing magical dresses in nutshell. MGAM, p. 449: almost identical except closing motifs involving suitor tasks and recognition are missing. P. 371: similar except girls do not appear.

GYPSY, Groome, [Bukowina] p. 85: empress is carried away by dragon; three sons set out to find her. In travels, youngest eats apple, develops horns; drinks from stream, gets leprosy; eats another apple, is normal again; finds cave with three girls and mother, sends them to world above. Rope is cut; hero remains below, finds dragon's ring and a "lord" comes to his bidding. He demands to be carried above, taking with him the two kinds of water. Hero apprenticed to tailor, produces dresses. Recognition. [Bohemian] p. 151: similar except evil-doers are companions. Recognition: hero, dressed as beggar, attends wedding, asks for wine; drops ring in cup; princess recognizes him. [Polish] p. 182: only introductory motifs. [Welsh] p. 220: cure for blindness for old king is golden apple. When youngest son finds fruit, older brothers trick him. Other details of story differ. P. 252: only fragment. Hero in sheepskin cap kills dragon; girl cuts off part of his hair for recognition.

HUNGARIAN, Jones, p. 207: walnuts containing dresses. Ortutay, p. 170: underground adventure.

ISRAELI, Noy, [Turkish] p. 152: looking for thief of special golden apple tree, three brothers set out to find bird. Youngest befriends dog who helps him find special horse. He must have bird (girl) love him, otherwise he will turn to stone. He wins girl by singing to her, joins brothers who poke his eyes out, throw him in pit. Dog helps him out, advises how to cure blindness. Returns, sings song: recognition.

ITALIAN, Crane, p. 36: similar except beautiful girl gives hero crown, pomegranates, apple which later only he can produce as suitor task.

ROMANIAN, Creangă, p. 67: descent motifs to lower world occur to hero, son of mare.

RUSSIAN, Afanas'ev, p. 314: poor version of same basic plot. P. 49: hero task: move stone and find bride. Descent to lower world. Baba Yaga gives her powerful eagle to hero for return flight. He must feed bird; when meat is exhausted, cuts off part of own thigh. P. 375: queen is snatched; sons set out to find her, climb mountain. Youngest succeeds, kills giant, brings back mother and three girls. Brothers cut rope; hero stays above. Magic reed brings magical help. Hero returns, is apprenticed to shoemaker, completes suitor tasks. P. 612: only beginning motifs of disappearance of golden fruit; pursuit of firebird leads into 14. "The Magic Horse."

SCOTCH, Campbell, I, 128: hero descends cave to find beautiful girl. P. 226: similar except unusual companions. Hero remains below, not through trickery but at giant's demand. Killing of dragon, befriending birdlings are absent. See Campbell notes for 24. "The Golden Box."

SERBIAN, Mijatovics, p. 295: *kumrekusha*, very strong bird who can carry in her claws a horse and rider. Petrovitch, p. 220: unusual variant. Instead of going to worlds below, hero must climb pavilion neither in sky nor on earth to bring back sister. Rest of story is similar except suitor tasks do not occur.

SIBERIAN, Coxwell, [Kirghiz] p. 363: child-hero finds father long imprisoned, kisses old woman's breast and is befriended, receives magical horse. As scab-head, hero succeeds in marrying princess. Wife is stolen, carried to lower world; hero finds her; bird carries them to upper world. Motif of cutting thigh occurs. [Ostyak] p. 518: only motif is Aspen-Leaf's ascent to world above on bird. Feeding part of thigh occurs.

TURKISH, Bain, p. 84 and Kúnos, *Stam*, p. 95 and *44*, p. 77: interesting introduction: only sister of three brothers falls into hands of devil (*dev* in second story). After many trials, youngest brother kills giant. Rest of story is similar. Kúnos, *Stam*, p. 114: introductory motifs are similar to 35. "The Son of the Gray Horse." Companions cut rope, leave hero in lower world. Similar experiences with girl-eating dragon. Grateful mother bird; recognition of hero occurs with unusual ring. Ekrem, p. 32: very similar.

The World Below, Version Two (Unpublished Version)

King has three sons; all want to marry beautiful princess from another land. She, in turn, loves the youngest and tells them so. Older boys, through help of witch, drop girl into deep well where she is befriended by giant.

Hero and brothers try to find girl. Hero descends well and sends girl up on rope. She gives him richly colored ring with instructions to lick it if brothers trick him and leave him behind. When he does this, he will see two rams, one black, one white. He must sit on the white one; otherwise, he will go to the seventh world below.

Boy is tricked; brothers run off with princess. Boy goes to lower world. (The rest of the story, except suitor tasks, is similar.) Suitor tasks are: decoration for dressing table; shoe which will walk by itself; gown which can be folded and put inside walnut shell. Magic ring is hero's source of magic.

At wedding, hero sings outside palace. Girl answers him; story is revealed. Older brothers are punished. (Informant: Mrs. Zevart Semezian)

The World Below, Version Three (Unpublished Version)

Almost identical to published version with minor exceptions in beginning and ending motifs. When apples from unusual tree are stolen year after year, king pretends blindness. Cure: apple from unusual tree.

Befriended eagle not only brings hero to upper world, she gives him two of her feathers which serve as source of magic. With feathers, he produces objects which have been demanded of royal goldsmith as suitor tasks for oldest brother: kettle in which golden mouse and golden cat are racing and cannot catch each other; kettle in which golden dog and golden rabbit chasing each other cannot catch each other.

Mounting splendid horse, masked youngest son rides like a whirlwind in polo match, shoots ball into back of oldest brother; repeats with second brother the next day. When hero is caught and taken before king, he reveals identity by producing birth certificate, tells of treachery of brothers. (Informant: Hovhannes Kaprelian)

The Golden Apples, Version Four (Unpublished Version)

King has three sons. Test for fit ruler is catching thief who steals golden apples from garden. First and second sons fail. Youngest succeeds, discovers thief is king in disguise, testing sons. (Informant: Mrs. Mariam Serabian)

Variants of the above version are:

ARMENIAN, Khatchatrianz, p. 125: similar. Seklemian, p. 127: only beginning motif of king who sends son Bedik on expedition to test bravery. See Seklemian notes for 1. "Ogre's Soul."

GREEK, Dawkins, *MG*, p. 301: father tests bravery of daughters by disguising self in armor; youngest proves bravest.

ROMANIAN, Ispirescu, p. 241: king tests bravery of daughters; youngest is sent to represent him.

The Three Eagles, Version Five (Unpublished Version)

Old woman has three lazy, irresponsible sons who set out to seek their fortunes. They meet a dervish who predicts they will be rich because of the youngest brother. He tells them of a well which only the youngest will succeed in descending. There he will find a giant sleeping with a sword overhead; hero will kill him with only one blow.

Prediction comes true. In cave, hero finds much gold, three beautiful girls, three eagles. Money, girls and eagles are taken above; brothers return home. (Informant: Mrs. Mariam Serabian)

35. The Son of the Gray Horse

AT 301B & 302, cf AT 307; EB 215, III; BP II, 297 ff.

This long, sprawling tale does not fit an AT type classification closely. Among other things, it does have an interesting external soul motif. The similarity to the beloved Armenian epic, "David of Sassoun," (see Surmelian, *Daredevils of Sassoun*) is noteworthy. David's grandmother conceived twins by drinking water from a fountain. The boys were unusually strong, and David, in the next generation, defeated armies with only the help of his magic horse and lightning sword. The similarity of this story to 34. "The World Below" has been noted above. See all references for 34.

ARMENIAN, Khatchatrianz, p. 113: unusual statement: "hit horse hard enough to make all 360 veins in his body jump." Surmelian, p. 264: unusual feat of eating exhibited by demon.

CAUCASIAN, Dirr, [Udian] p. 220: Rustum, son of a shepherd, is very strong. On his adventures, meets unusual companions. Unusual dwarf leads hero to underworld adventure. Appearance of life token.

GEORGIAN, Wardrop, p. 68: hero of unusual birth is joined by unusual helpers who trick him, leave him in world below. Rest of story follows beginning plot of Armenian tale.

GREEK, Dawkins, *MG*, p. 46: only unusual birth motif; strong hero is born of mother's tears.

GYPSY, Groome, [Bukowina] p. 74: mare brings forth unusually strong son. On his adventures, is joined by unusual companions, has similar experience with little man, has underworld adventure. Hero befriends baby eagles; mother eagle carries boy to upper world. [Welsh] p. 243: little dwarf beats three brothers severely. Youngest follows him down well. Dwarf helps him fight three giants, liberate three girls. Dwarf is vehicle for upward journey, needs meat for nourishment; hero cuts off part of thigh.

HUNGARIAN, Jones, p. 244: similar to Groome, p. 74, above. Orphan hero is nursed by ewe. Ortutay, p. 170: woman bears three very strong sons from eating beans. Underworld adventure occurs, also meeting with little man.

ROMANIAN, Creangă, p. 67: very similar, including unusual birth of hero, except for later motifs.

RUSSIAN, Afanas'ev, p. 173: unusual conception occurs by touching tongue to human ashes; birth of very strong boy. P. 457: three girls whisked away; three brothers set out to find them. Tiny man eats food. Youngest brother wounds him, follows him to deep hole in ground, kills three dragons, brings girls up. **Ransome,** p. 248: only motifs of underworld adventure and appearance of dwarf.

SERBIAN, **Mijatovics,** p. 123: Sir Peppercorn, son of unusual birth, appears in story similar to Groome, p. 74, above.

SIBERIAN, **Coxwell,** [Kalmuck] p. 188: hero, human, long-tailed with head shaped like calf, is born, meets man descended from forest; another born of turf, another of crystal. Little old woman motifs; underworld adventure. Hero is tricked, left below but climbs up. Must blind one-eyed black bull: explains existence of seven stars in sky.

TURKISH, **Kúnos,** *Stam,* p. 114: dying king commands three sons to give his one daughter to first suitor. When they refuse dervish suitor, girl is stolen away. Brothers set out to find him, do not return. Mother sets out to find children, gets lost, is hungry, drinks urine from her horse, becomes pregnant. This son has unusual strength, finds brothers and sister, sends them back, kills *dev*. Two brothers of *dev* join hero, encounter witch who demands much food. Youth kills her, follows her below ground, finds three beautiful girls. Companions cut rope, leave him below. Rest of story follows 34. "The World Below." **Tezel,** p. 12: only appearance of thumbling who can eat great quantities of food.

36. The Helpful Spirit

AT 507C; EB 62; BP III, 490. **MacCulloch,** pp. 202–4: spirit controls magic sword.

This story, with introductory motifs of merciful burial by the hero, appears as one of the widely known forms of the "Grateful Dead." In this Detroit story, the burial motif does not occur, but the "Ransomed Woman" motifs do.

ARABIAN, **Campbell,** *Tribes,* p. 11: son is thrown into prison because he refuses to marry father's choice. Beautiful gold fish is brought to prince who throws it back into sea. Dervish helps prince meet his beloved. At marriage, dervish insists girl be divided; snakes leave her mouth. Moral: venom of women.

ARMENIAN, **Seklemian,** p. 159: similar to Servantstian version below. **Servantstian,** Part B, p. 26 and **Macler,** *Ca,* p. 149: hero befriends beautiful fish. Faithful servant kills snakes from mouth of young bride on wedding night, insists wife be divided; in fear, girl screams; snakes fall out. **Toumanian, p.** 92: hero puts fish back into water. In later years, fish answers questions which save benefactor's life.

BASQUE, **Webster, p.** 202: widow's son sets off for home with instructions to take for friend whoever gives him larger half of apple. Thus, he finds king's son. One night king is murdered but through hero, lives again. Later hero develops leprosy. King's son kills his son, washes friend in blood. Friend is cured; child lives again. Similar to 37. "Ludwig and Iskander."

CAUCASIAN, **Haxthausen,** [Persian-Armenian] p. 373: hero befriends corpse which is being beaten for unpaid debts. Later servant joins hero, enables boy to marry princess, insists on division of bride, causing snakes to leave her mouth. **Dirr,** [Zachurian] p. 99: hero frees red fish, even though it is cure for father's blindness. Friend helps in suitor task: make dumb princess speak; demands half of princess. When she screams, snakes fall out of mouth.

GEORGIAN, **Wardrop, p.** 42: prince throws fish back into sea. Later, in suitor tasks, is asked riddle, receives help from grateful fish. In division of property, princess screams; snakes fall out of mouth.

GREEK, **Dawkins,** 45, p. 438: hero befriends old man who accompanies him and as his elder, gives him magical advice and power. Hero loves princess; suitor task: contest to see who returns with greater riches. Hero cures two rich men and beautiful princess with scabby skin; reward is rich ship. Hero sets out to load salt, comes upon unusual island. Underworld adventure; lion and eagle are benefactors. Hero returns to upper world, claims princess. Elder demands half of wife; snakes leave her mouth. P. 41: friend kills snake coming from girl's mouth. *MG*, p. 209: friend demands half of wife. When girl screams, snakes leave mouth.

GYPSY, **Yates,** [Serbo-Bosnian] p. 94: hero pays dead man's debt; at end of adventures, must share everything, including beautiful princess with friend. She screams; snakes fall out of mouth. **Groome,** [Turkish] p. 1: befriended corpse helps hero win princess. When threatened by division, girl screams; snakes leave mouth.

ITALIAN, **Crane, p.** 202: divide apple to determine friendship.

ISRAELI, Noy, [Polish] p. 126: boy buys Jewish bones (dead man who owed money to Gentile), gives them Jewish burial. Later boy is joined by companion who kills robbers, helps boy gain fortunes. Boy marries landlord's daughter, must divide wife who screams; snake falls out of mouth. Companion was grateful bones.

PERSIAN, Lorimer, p. 169: hero befriends corpse. Helpful companion demands half of hero's possessions. When he wants to divide beauty, snakes fall out of mouth.

TURKISH, Garnett, [Gypsy] II, 378: hero pays debts of corpse; companion kills dragon which leaves mouth of princess. P. 370: hero saves prince and beauty but must not tell why. When he breaks tabu, turns to stone. Prince walks for seven years, takes dirt, throws it on grave; hero arises.

37. Ludwig and Iskander

AT 516 V; BP I, 42 ff. MacCulloch, p. 422: blood cures for leprosy. W. R. Halliday in Dawkins, *MGAM*, p. 254, speaks of this belief as narrated by Moses of Khorene in his *History of Armenia*, II, 83: Constantine, sick with leprosy, was told to kill children and bathe in their blood. But he could not do this because of the cries of the children and their mothers. He dreamt that if he bathed in a pool of water under the supervision of the head bishop of Rome, he would recover. The emperor did as his dream directed, was instructed in the faith, believed in God and was cured.

Encyclopaedia Britannica (1960 Edition), I, 814: "'Amis and Amiles,' is an old French romance, probably of oriental origin. It is the story of two friends, one of whom, Amis, contracts leprosy. In a vision, he learns that he can only be cured by bathing in blood of Amiles' children. When Amiles learns this, he kills children, bathes friend in blood. Miraculously, children are restored to life again and friend is cured of disease."

ARMENIAN, Macler, *Cl*, p. 71: three companions wish: first, that pine forest become vineyard; second, for many sheep; third, only for good company. Each gets wish; third marries good woman. Jesus, in guise of old man, asks for bunch of grapes, is offered withered ones; asks for milk to drink, is offered milk from black, old sheep. Goats, sheep transformed to stone; vineyard becomes forest it once was. Third companion meets old man, takes him home. Wife washes feet, seats him in place of honor. Old man tells them his illness can be cured only if he bathes in blood of seven-month-old baby. Woman kills her baby for him. When they look in cradle, baby lives again. Surmelian, p. 178: David bathes in blood of forty heifers before battle. Wlislocki, p. 59: cure for terrible wounds of townfolk caused by spit of sea bull is the killing of young children and bathing in their blood. P. 99: "The blood of young maidens and children is often used as a cleaning power." P. 169: only motif is bathing of sick count's horrible wounds in blood of good maiden.

BASQUE, Monteiro, p. 88: "It was a popular belief [in the Basque provinces] that the blood of children was useful for invigorating the weak bodies of women." Webster, p. 202: widow's son washes in blood of friend's child, cured of leprosy; child lives, too. See Webster notes for 36. "The Helpful Spirit."

GREEK, Dawkins, 45, p. 41: winning of World's Most Fair is combined with blood sacrifice motifs. P. 53: telling secret causes hero to turn to stone; blood cure. MG, p. 415: blood of three-year-old boy cures leprosy; yet child lives. P. 229: slave, who has befriended hero many times, must not tell story. When he does, turns to marble. Cure: kill friend's baby, anoint marble with blood, burn baby in oven, scatter ashes on marble. When this is done, cure effected, yet baby lives. MGAM, p. 527: motif of sacrificing children for health of friend only to find children not really dead.

GYPSY, Groome, [Turkish] p. 4: if friend reveals what he has heard, he will be turned to stone. Does so to prove friendship, becomes stone. Cure: earth sprinkled on tomb.

ITALIAN, Crane, p. 202: man kills child, bathes friend who has leprosy. Friend gets better; child lives again. P. 12: heroine learns of blood as cure for husband. P. 85: prince falls in love with statue, sets out to find someone as beautiful as statue. Prince, as he tells story, turns to stone, must bathe in blood of king's two children. As he does, becomes better; children do not die.

ROMANIAN, Ispirescu, p. 119: helpful friend who brings about marriage of prince turns to stone when he reveals secret. Cure: blood of couple's young son. Once well, friend cuts finger, spreads blood on child; both are alive again.

RUSSIAN, Afanas'ev, p. 485: hero pays debt of poor man being beaten, receives great help from this grateful friend. Girl stolen by Khousey the Deathless (external soul motif occurs).

Friend turns to stone as he tells story; life renewed with blood of children who also live again.

SIBERIAN, Coxwell, [Ostyak] p. 518: kill son, sprinkle brother-in-law with warm blood. Son brought back to life.

TURKISH, Kúnos, *Stam*, p. 256 and *44*, p. 217: helpful friend turns to stone as he reveals secret. Prince sacrifices son, bathes friend in blood. Both friend and son live again. **Tezel**, p. 190: as friend tells story to prince, he turns to stone. Only blood of slain child revives him. Garnett, [Gypsy] II, 370: see notes for 36. "The Helpful Spirit."

38. Buzz-Buzz Aunty

AT 501; EB 371; BP I, 109 ff., 490 ff.

ARMENIAN, Tcheraz, p. 117: very similar. Girl marries rich merchant who leaves large quantities of flax with her to spin while he is on business trip; she pours honey on shoulders and arms so she can lick it as she tries to spin. Child of king of fairies has tumor on neck which nothing seems to cure. Fairy servants, who have child with them, rest in front of girl's house, see her tongue darting in and out. Child laughs so hard that tumor bursts. Fairies volunteer to help girl in any way, weave cloth. Husband returns, is happy. Girl looks at spider climbing wall and says, "Grandmother, grandmother!" When husband asks why, girl tells him her grandmother was transformed into spider because she wove too much. Since husband does not want spider for wife, he never asks her to weave again.

HUNGARIAN, Jones, p. 46: close parallel except unusual name must be recognized. **Ortutay**, p. 348: similar to Jones version above.

PERSIAN, Lorimer, p. 124: somewhat reminiscent although different in every detail except girl's escape from weaving by appearance of three ugly women.

39. The *Halva*-Maker

No AT assigned.

ARMENIAN, Surmelian, pp. 236–37: arms, legs fall off as they are pulled.

TURKISH, Ekrem, p. 13: only hero who is befriended by dervish.

40. *Tushcoon* Eigna

Cf AT 561; EB 180, III.

GYPSY, Groome, [Scottish-Tinker] p. 272: unusual means of identifying child's father: when bird alights on head of man.

HUNGARIAN, Jones, p. 288: search for child's father.

41. The Rich Boy and the Poor Boy

AT 613; EB 67, 253; BP II, 468. Clouston, I, 464–65: origin of story discussed. 249: variants from Norse, Portuguese, Kabail of North Africa, Kirghiz [Siberia], Russian, Arabian, Indian versions cited.

ARMENIAN, Macler, *Cle,* p. 49: poor man is denied bread at rich neighbor's house, sets out to seek fortune. At night, finds refuge in deserted mill, overhears fox, wolf, bear, gains gold fox has hidden, cures leprosy of princess by boiling brain of shepherd's dog and bathing her in that water, finds great cauldron of gold hidden near bear's den. Hero returns home very rich man. Rich neighbor tries same procedure, dies. Nazinian, p. 71: very similar. Seklemian, p. 149: similar. Servantstian, p. 187 and Macler *Ca,* p. 92: similar. Wlislocki, p. 128: man cures his blindness, receives wealth. Evil companion tries same, is punished. BP, II, 479: rich brother has poor brother blinded because of jealousy.

BASQUE, Monteiro, p. 19: good boy overhears witches, cures sick girl, is rewarded. Second brother, who is not bad but proud, repeats pattern, is discovered, dies.

CAUCASIAN, Dirr, [Ossetian] p. 144: rich man demands eye from companion for piece of bread. Hero overhears wolf, bear, fox; heals his eye, cures sick princess, gains gold. Rich one tries to imitate, dies.

GEORGIAN, Wardrop, p. 49: almost identical.

GREEK, Dawkins, *MG,* p. 435: hero is told to work each day, no matter how little it pays; another works only for high wage. Wager: truth or lies, which pays best? Hero loses. Overhears devils, learns cure for prince and method for settling quarrel between brothers, wins much gold. Second boy tries to do same, is caught by devils. *MGAM,* pp. 389, 483: basically same story; hero overhears one secret. *45,* p. 327: boatman is blinded, cast into sea by wife and lover. Fairies help him regain sight with Water of Life. He cures princess, punishes evil couple.

GYPSY, **Groome,** [Bukowina] p. 112: good person is blinded, overhears devils talking. Rest is identical [Hungarian-Carpathian] p. 114: youngest brother blinded by greedy brothers, left by gallows, overhears remedies, cures own blindness and princess, frees abundant water supply. Brothers try same, die.

HUNGARIAN, **Jones,** p. 36: truth and falsehood are companions, share food until truth's food is gone. His eyes are gouged out in exchange for bread. Blind hero overhears cures for blindness, cause for cutting local water supply. Truth is rewarded; falsehood tries same plan, receives his punishment. P. 152: introductory motifs alone are similar. **Ortutay,** p. 399: similar.

IRAQI, **Stevens,** p. 267: almost identical.

ISRAELI, **Noy,** [Tunisian] p. 50: very similar.

PERSIAN, **Lorimer,** p. 160: although different motifs occur, same basic story form; animals are overheard.

POLISH, **Borski,** p. 52: people fear Truth's eyes; Falsehood blinds her and Truth is absent from earth. Truth hears cure for blindness, is whole again. Falsehood tries same, is destroyed.

RUSSIAN, **Afanas'ev,** p. 202: similar except Right and Wrong are companions seeking to learn which is better. Truth is blinded in exchange for bread. Voice guides him to magic spring; eyesight restored, overhears evil spirits, learns cure for princess' torment, cures and marries her. Wrong tries same, is punished.

SERBIAN, **Mijatovics,** p. 83 and **Petrovitch,** p. 240: bad brother utters: injustice is better than justice. Good brother loses money, horse, even eyesight, overhears fairies, learns healing powers of nearby water, cures his blindness and leprosy of princess. Bad brother attempts to overhear secrets, is killed.

SIBERIAN, **Coxwell,** [Kirghiz] p. 355: good man is blinded and deserted, overhears cure for his blindness, kills black dog, grinds to powder and cures dead khan. Bad companion follows routine, dies.

TURKISH, **Kúnos,** *Stam,* p. 231: similar except good brother enters secret cave, gathers treasures, uses magic words "Changa" and "Chunga" to open and close entrance. Rich brother tries same, forgets word to open door of cave, is killed by *devs.*

The Cliff (Unpublished Version)

Poor traveler shares his food with companion, is denied a share of his companion's food. Instead, he is beaten and pushed off cliff. He sees light in distance, enters cave, eats from well-provided table, hides when *dev* owners return. Overhears cure for king's blindness: leaf from certain tree crushed and applied to eyes; method for locating water supply: remove stone and dig; location of great treasure: underneath shoemaker's machine.

Poor man follows all these suggestions, gains great wealth. Rich friend, learning secret, tries to overhear more secrets, is caught and killed by *devs*. (Informant: Hovhannes Kaprelian)

42. The Devoted Son

No AT assigned; EB 251.

GREEK, Dawkins, *45*, p. 236: in a note, Dawkins reports story from Lesbos in which wife mistreats mother-in-law, sends her to school and is divorced by husband.

IRAQI, Stevens, p. 183: only sham burial.

43. The Ditch-Digger Falls into His Own Ditch

AT 837.

ARABIAN, Campbell, *Market*, p. 58: villain plans evil for hero. Intercepts king's letter ordering bearer's death. Good prevails; evil-doer is destroyed.

ARMENIAN, Wlislocki, p. 24: only the phrase used by beggar: "God will give you your reward."

ISRAELI, Noy, [Lithuanian] p. 40: very similar.

SIBERIAN, Coxwell, [Chukchis] p. 68: only general similarity: one cousin deserts the other who manages somehow to stay alive. Next year deserter returns to check on corpse and is caught in same situation while other escapes.

44. Foretelling the Future

Cf AT 934A*.

GREEK, Dawkins, *MGAM*, p. 285: only the prediction that girl will marry ash-seller and nothing can change this.

PERSIAN, **Lorimer,** [Bakhitari] p. 333: writing on forehead.

SIBERIAN, **Coxwell,** [Armenian] p. 1016: three men predicting future: one supported candle; second wrote; third dictated future of newborn. Future cannot be changed except at risk of sister's death.

45. The Soul-Taking Angel

Cf AT 332 & 1199; EB 112; BP I, 377 ff., II, 163 ff., 206 ff.

ARMENIAN, **Macler,** *Cle,* p. 142: only son of old parents sets out to see world, drinks water from well, sees old man who identifies self as St. Gabriel, the angel who takes men's souls. He shows youth where he stands at bedside, indicating whether sick one will live or die, tells hero he will die on his wedding night. Boy avoids marriage for many years, finally must comply with parents' wishes. Decides since he must die, should marry poor girl and let her enjoy some comforts of life since his family is wealthy. St. Gabriel appears to him on marriage night, gives him reprieve because he has shown mercy and understanding to those less fortunate than himself. **Wlislocki,** p. 24: St. John gives salve to poor religious boy, instructing him to apply it to lips of the sick. Pestilent bird, who perches on roof of sick, will indicate a sick one in that house. Boy does as instructed, becomes wealthy.

GREEK, **Dawkins,** *MG,* p. 466: man sets out to find just man to be godfather of son.

ISRAELI, **Noy,** [Moroccan] p. 16: only the delaying of death until prayer is completed.

RUSSIAN, **Afanas'ev,** p. 56: combination of 79. "The Talkative Wife" and beginning motifs from this story.

TURKISH, **Garnett,** [Greek] I, p. 185 and **Carnoy-Nicolaïdes,** p. 144: search for godfather; father is made famous doctor by godfather but can cure only when benefactor stands in certain position. One day death calls on doctor himself. **Kúnos,** *Stam,* p. 244 and *44,* p. 206: similar to Afanas'ev above.

46. The Gold Piece

No AT assigned.
ARMENIAN, **Tcheraz,** p. 127: identical.

47. The Emperor's Lesson

AT 930; EB 125; BP I, 276 ff. Clouston, II, 458–65: discussion of destiny.

ARABIAN, Campbell, *Market,* p. 58: letter ordering hero's death is delivered by another. See Campbell notes for 43. "The Ditch-Digger Falls into His Own Ditch."

ARMENIAN, Macler, *Cle,* p. 25: very similar. Young man is represented as Fate, who writes on forehead of newborn. On second visit, king recognizes hero by unusual name, "Son of the Goat," because goat nursed him when he was abandoned years ago. P. 133: very similar. Writers of destiny (writing on newborn's forehead) are men. When rich man locates youth, letter is written which his daughter changes. When rich man returns, finds boy is son-in-law, sends him to harvesters with food, telling them, meanwhile, they must kill any man who brings them food, no matter who. They kill rich man himself.

GREEK, Dawkins, *MG,* p. 334: similar except letter-changer is Fate, who brings about marriage predicted and death of king's son. *MGAM,* p. 493: identical. P. 307: only writing of second letter occurs.

GYPSY, Groome, [Transylvanian] p. 133: identical except even after marriage, king sets hero tasks: bring three golden hairs from head of Sun King. Motifs from 25. "The Magic Box" occur. Various people and objects ask boy to learn cause of their misfortune. Boy is hidden in water; otherwise sun would burn him. Sun's mother brushes sun's head, asks him hero's questions. On hero's successful return, king goes to lake, must take assignment of ferryman forever.

HUNGARIAN, Ortutay, p. 304: beginning motifs differ. Hero baby is befriended by miller; switched letter plays important role. Story takes on 25: "The Magic Box" motifs.

ISRAELI, Noy, [Bagdad] p. 120: very similar.

RUSSIAN, Afanas'ev, p. 213: two beggars stop at rich man's house, predict poor baby born in village will gain their landlord's wealth. Man gets baby, throws him into ravine. Child is befriended by merchants, brought back to landlord. Baby is put in tarred box, thrown in water. Box reaches monastery. Letter sent by merchant to wife orders youth's death; letter is changed. Boy marries daughter. Rich man gives boy difficult tasks. On road objects and people ask him for help. Motifs from 25. "The Magic Box" appear.

TURKISH, Garnett, [Albanian] II, 319: very similar except story continues beyond hero's marriage. King and son both perish. [Kurdish] 155: only the substitution of letter by hero occurs, thus saving his life.

The Emperor's Lesson, Version Two (Unpublished Version)

Emperor and adviser in disguise stay with poor peasants who learn prediction: their baby will marry princess. Baby is ordered killed, is only tied to stick and thrown into river. Rich merchant finds and adopts boy. From this point, story follows original version printed. (Informant: Mrs. Katoon Mouradian)

The Letter, Version Three (Unpublished Version)

King's daughter and vizier's son are in love but match is forbidden. King sends letter with hero ordering him killed. Receiver of letter, merchant, is fond of boy, cannot kill him. Boy is sent with same letter to baker. Baker cannot kill him. Queen sends baker reminder of his task. Her sweetheart, the note-bearer, is thus killed. Baker then sends boy back to king. Hero marries princess. (Informant: Mrs. Mariam Serabian)

Cf AT 910K.

The Two Blackbirds, Version Four (Unpublished Version)

Stepmother is anxious to get rid of little boy. At dinner, he overhears, interprets conversation of two blackbirds: youth will become king, father and mother will wash and dry his hands.

Father, against his will, puts boy in tarred box, throws box in river. Princess sees box, has it rescued. King befriends boy who marries princess and becomes king at death of father-in-law. King visits his home, reveals identity. (Collected by Mardiros Tarpinian from Mrs. Anoush Sarkisian)

Variants of Version Four are:

Cf AT 517; EB 214 IV; BP I, 322–25.

BASQUE, Webster, p. 137: son hears voices, learns parents will be servants to son. They get rid of him. He saves self and friends from thieves, cures sick girl, becomes Pope. Mother confesses to him.

GREEK, Dawkins, *MGAM*, p. 359: very similar.

SERBIAN, Mijatovics, p. 248: only motif is dream in which boy will be king and parents will wash his hands.

SIBERIAN, Coxwell, [Russian] p. 726: boy's prediction comes true.

TURKISH, Kúnos, *Stam*, p. 375 and *44*, p. 334: girl is punished for unusual requests made of parents: mother to hold basin, father, towels while she washes. Tezel, p. 25: only motif is king will pour water for heroine's hands.

48. Honor

AT 883A; EB 245; BP I, 13 ff. W. R. Halliday in **Dawkins, *MGAM***, p. 267, reconstructs original story. The Detroit story is very similar to the reconstructed type.

ARMENIAN, Chalatianz, p. 42: very similar. **Surmelian**, p. 56: beauty is compared with that of sun. **Wingate, *Folk-Lore***, XXII, 481: very similar.

BASQUE, Webster, p. 132: similar to Scotch version below.

GREEK, Dawkins, *MGAM*, pp. 361, 505: good versions but sketchy in detail. *MG*, p. 369: only motif is good wife is misrepresented by bad friend; misfortunes occur. P. 367: girl is left home in hands of villain. She escapes; again placed in villain's care. Dressed as boy, she insists all doors be closed as she tells story of her life.

GYPSY, Groome, [English] p. 198: heroine has all doors locked, tells story of her life (being a gypsy, mother-in-law wanted her killed; she had been taken to forest to die).

ITALIAN, Crane, p. 364: when slanderous letter is written about innocent girl, brother attempts to kill her. Prince saves, marries her. Similar events follow except that saint restores her children.

RUSSIAN, Afanas'ev, p. 415: girl accused of loose character unjustly; catches accuser in lie.

SCOTCH, Campbell, II, 2: doubt fidelity of heroine. In man's clothes, she rights wrong.

TURKISH, Kúnos, *Stam*, p. 383 and *44*, p. 342: innocent girl escapes plots laid for her, dresses as boy, works as *halva*-maker, closes door, relates life story. Tezel, p. 132: girl escapes maneating Negro, marries, has three sons. He finds her, changes self into goat, approaches her. She denies him; he kills her sons. Husband destroys him.

49. Nature's Ways

No AT assigned; BP IV, 250. **MacCulloch, p.** 198: ancient Egyptian folktale relates that magician made workmen and tools of wax, recited charm over them, gave them life. P. 199: animism in objects; ability to receive a soul.

CAUCASIAN, **Dirr,** [Kunikian] **p.** 155: figure of maiden is carved from piece of wood.

GEORGIAN, **Wardrop, p.** 25: desire to keep heroine "innocent" of nature's ways.

GREEK, **Dawkins,** 45, **p.** 105: creation of lover by heroine. *MGAM,* **p.** 465: carving figure and praying to give it life.

GYPSY, **Groome,** [Bukowina] **p.** 100: father wants to set daughter apart from world, isolates her, keeps candle at her head as she sleeps.

IRAQI, **Stevens, p.** 253: girl is alone in castle; man in iron (in the sense of an elevator), is her only contact with outside world.

SIBERIAN, **Coxwell,** [Great Russian] **p.** 731: creation of snow-child by old couple who want child desperately.

TURKISH, **Kent, p.** 23: childless couple make baby from dough, bake it in oven. Child of this unusual birth is very strong, hurts children when he plays with them. **Tezel, p.** 62: childless woman makes baby from piece of wood. Child lives in cypress tree, loves prince. In disguise of shepherd, joins prince, identity revealed; marriage. P. 99: man wants children very much. Midwife makes baby from cotton. Baby lives, becomes beautiful, has magical abilities, marries prince, does not talk to him until prince says magical charm to break silence. P. 179: similar to Kent version above. P. 202: princess kept in crystal palace, breaks window, sees light, loves prince. Disguised as dervish, follows prince; reunion.

50. The Shepherd's Dream

AT 938, cf AT 938B; Thompson-Roberts, *Types of Indic Oral Tales,* FFC 180, Type 938; EB 136; BP II, 264.

ARMENIAN, **Seklemian, p.** 9: only motifs of captain,

charmed by beauty of princess, leaves her husband on shore and takes her away. Selection of king is made by flight of bird.

CAUCASIAN, Haxthausen, [Armenian] p. 374: an abbreviated form of this story.

ITALIAN, Crane, p. 105: only introduction: the question: "When do you want your bad fortune, youth or old age?" Girl chooses old age.

TURKISH, Kent, p. 183: woman loses two sons by different accidents of fate. They meet, tell each other their stories; woman overhears. Tezel, p. 95: similar but poorly told story. P. 153: similar to Kent version above.

51. The Soul-Taker

AT 763; Clouston, II, 379–407.

52. There Is Righteousness

AT 960; cf EB 141; BP II, 531 ff.

GREEK, Dawkins, *MGAM*, p. 285: unusual names of children serve as means of establishing justice.

TURKISH, Kent, p. 186: recognition occurs because of unusual names. Tezel, p. 146: princess who has sores all over body is tricked by old witch, washes her face in stream, is cured, marries, has three sons. Names of children: "Who Was I," "Who Am I," "What Am I Going to Be." King is curious about names, discovers daughter.

53. The Test

Cf AT 949*.

ARMENIAN, Khatchatrianz, p. 68: man of high station must learn trade as suitor task. Nazinian, p. 112: king must learn trade as suitor task. Consequently, felt-making ability saves his life.

54. The Ball of Gold

No AT assigned.

55. A Treasure Hunt

No AT assigned.

56. The Curse

No AT assigned. **MacCulloch,** p. 428 ff.: beliefs concerning fairies at childbirth.

ARMENIAN, **Tcheraz,** p. 157: woman holds daughter of *Al* captive by sticking her with pin.

57. A Great Catch

No AT assigned.

58. One Way to Catch a Fish

No AT assigned.

59. What a Fish!

No AT assigned.

60. Saint Snakes

No AT assigned.

61. The Rising Snake

No AT assigned. See discussion of snakes and dragons in motif analysis, Chapter II.

62. Fool's Luck

AT 1013 & 1653B; EB 324; BP I, 520 ff.

ARMENIAN, **Nazinian,** p. 76: foolish brother takes cow to pasture, kills it as sacrifice to black crows he mistakes for priests, urges grasshoppers to witness his act of devotion. When he returns home, mother berates him, sends him back for cow. Boy asks help of grasshopper who hops away. When boy pushes rock away to find him, sees a pile of red gold, takes handful home. Brother returns, takes remaining gold home. Landlord comes to investigate source of gold; fool pushes him into well. When inquiry is made, find ox in well instead of man (wise brother had made switch).

BASQUE, **Webster,** p. 67: fool places mother in boiling water.

CAUCASIAN, **Dirr,** [Kürinian] p. 288: wife possesses door; through her stupidity, she brings financial gains to husband.

GEORGIAN, **Wardrop,** [Gurian] p. 165: bell is carried into tree; thief's tongue is cut off.

GREEK, **Dawkins,** *MG,* p. 397: very similar except among items left behind by frightened travelers is incense. When foolish hero burns this, angel asks him to name reward: pipe to play on which makes everyone dance. *MGAM,* pp. 327, 331: although stories of the same spirit, only similar motifs deal with door which is carried onto tree. P. 405: foolish brother is advised to look after mother, kills her. Fool gets much money.

GYPSY, **Groome,** [Welsh] p. 263: foolish wife in tree drops door on robbers below. Cuts tongue out of one robber.

IRAQI, **Stevens,** p. 1: only the motif of door being taken off hinges and carried on back by foolish wife. P. 287: only motifs of removing door; making water while in tree; treasure left by Arab.

PERSIAN, **Lorimer,** p. 70: door, inherited by fool, is carried up tree, dropped on those below. Bird in flight selects fool as king.

SERBIAN, **Mijatovics,** p. 256: only beginning motifs are similar. Foolish wife takes door off hinge, carries it up tree, drops it on robbers below. Rest of story differs.

TURKISH, **Bain,** p. 42, and **Kúnos,** *Stam,* p. 38 and *44,* p. 95: fool finds treasure, scalds mother, takes door off hinges. When fool enters service of rich man, the two decide neither is to get angry at other. Fool wins bargain, gets magical help from jinn: magic table; little mill which produces gold and silver; sticks. **Tezel,** p. 77: sham dead man gains fortune.

63. Ingratitude

No AT assigned.

ARMENIAN, **Tcheraz,** p. 134: peasant sees palace of king, marvels at it, asks if king built it or inherited it from father. King tells peasant he inherited it. "I'm sure that you couldn't have done it yourself," peasant replies.

ISRAELI, **Noy,** [Turkish] p. 75: Sultan in disguise is entertained by peasant who receives letter which will enable him to find his new friend in big city. At palace, peasant is served coffee, given work as gardener. Later, is appointed tax inspector of port but refuses entrance of coffee because he burned his mouth the first time he drank it with sultan. Peasant is instructed how to drink coffee; after this coffee is permitted to enter port.

TURKISH, Garnett, [Kurdish] II, 179: very close parallel except hero realizes position of host, finally accords him due respect.

64. Outwitting Giants

AT 1116, cf AT 1640; EB 162; BP I, 148 ff. **Clouston, I, 133–54**: timid hero fools dragon.

ALBANIAN, **Dozon,** p. 17: similar in theme. Dervish tricks bear into thinking he is very strong.

ARMENIAN, **Hamastdeg,** p. 79: Nazar, very lazy man, spends days dreaming of finding great treasures. Poor wife, after many years, sends him away. He enters fierce forest which is hideout for robbers. Seeing him there unarmed, robbers think he is notorious thief before whom whole world trembles. He joins them, marries one of their sisters, rides fiery horse who charges ahead and frightens enemy. When old king refuses to fight brave Nazar, the strong man is made king and now has two wives. Finally, his luck brings him happiness, not his work. **Khatchatrianz,** p. 43: very similar. **Macler, Cle,** p. 62: Chicken-Liver is thrown out by wife, takes raw egg, handful of flour, piece of bread; joins bear, wolf, snake by proving that he can crush stone (egg) to water, stone (flour) to earth. Overhears their plans, saves self. They think he has survived ordeals, share fortune. **Seklemian,** p. 53: very similar. **Servantstian, Part B,** p. 8 and **Macler, Ca,** p. 120: similar; hero goes into battle with huge rotted tree in hands. **Toumanian,** p. 103: similar to Servantstian version above.

CAUCASIAN, **Dirr,** [Tchetchen] p. 110: similar.

GEORGIAN, **Wardrop,** [Mingrelian] p. 129: old man tricks *dev* to think he is very strong and can eat much. When wolves and jackals enlighten *dev*, hero turns tables on them, too.

GREEK, **Dawkins,** *MGAM,* p. 551: similar.

GYPSY, **Groome,** [Bukowina] p. 80: dragon, fearing coward who has misrepresented his strength, joins him. Rest of story is devoted to trickery. [Slovak] p. 83: similar to p. 80 above. Clever gypsy tricks dragon into believing great strength.

IRAQI, **Stevens,** p. 224: suggestive only.

ITALIAN, Crane, p. 94: close variant.
RUSSIAN, Afanas'ev, p. 284: similar. P. 142: similar.
TURKISH, Kúnos, *Stam*, p. 56 and *44*, p. 50: a more complete version of this story.

65. *Vhy, Vhy, Vhy*

No AT assigned.
PERSIAN, Lorimer, p. 124: tell lazy, foolish girl to put mudbrick on top of pilaff to keep the food beneath compact and make it taste better.

66. The Ashman's Money

AT 1617.

67. The Clever Boy

Cf AT 875D.
GREEK, Dawkins, *MGAM*, p. 541: daughter conceives unnaturally. Son is extremely wise, interprets king's dream, exposes men dressed as maidens. P. 278: clever boy is asked to distinguish between male and female fish, exposes harem slaves as being men.
IRAQI, Stevens, p. 253: similar theme only: princess pretends chasteness; laughing fish are her undoing.

68. The Dead Snake and the Young Wife

No AT assigned.

69. The Dilemma

Cf AT 1536 & 1843.
GREEK, Dorothy Lee, "Greek Tales of Priest and Priest Wife," *Journal of American Folklore*, No. 236 (1947), p. 166: identical.

70. It Happened in a Bath

No AT assigned.

TURKISH, **Kent,** p. 133: almost identical except hero awakens to discover he has been dreaming. **Tezel,** p. 47: similar to Kent version above.

71. Quick-Witted

Cf AT 1000, 1003; Thompson-Roberts, *Types of Indic Oral Tales,* FFC 180, Type, 1537A Ind; EB 357. **Clouston,** II, 241–43: taking advantage of person already dead.

GREEK, **Dawkins,** *MG,* p. 14: hero tricks ogre, has red cow killed, kills ogre's twelve daughters, steals horse, quilt and even ogre. *MGAM,* pp. 371, 575: two older brothers break father's tabu to avoid beardless man. Youngest is able to keep alive, arranges matters so that master is killed. P. 234: Halliday speaks of a "broken-down" version of the tale collected in Aravan in which the master and his wife attempt to flee from the boy and are unsuccessful. P. 475: only motif of making a profit from man who is dead already.

HUNGARIAN, **Ortutay,** p. 392: hero manages to have woman killed instead of self, takes advantage of dead person a second time.

TURKISH, **Tezel,** p. 126: clever hero, a thumbling, saves brothers through cunning, exchanges places with *dev's* children, wears *dev's* boots, collects all his treasures.

72. Matching Wits

Cf AT 1525Q; BP III, 379 ff.

ALBANIAN, **Dozon,** p. 169: similar except tricks differ. Pasha asks thief to trick judge. Pretending he is Angel Gabriel, puts judge in box, brings him to pasha. P. 163 and **Garnett,** II, 336: Mosko and Tosko engage in contest of wits with brother-in-law. Only faintly similar.

SIBERIAN, **Coxwell,** [Kalmuck] p. 221: steal Khan's talisman.

TURKISH, **Kúnos,** *Stam,* p. 290 and *44,* p. 250: very similar.

73. The Story of the Robbers

AT 950 & 1525A; EB 342; BP III, 379 ff. Clouston, II, 121–29: Master thief. In footnote, Clouston speaks of an Armenian version in Ispahan in 1687 of which a Russian translation occurred in Moscow in 1847.

ARMENIAN, **Macler,** *Cle,* p. 15: old woman marries daughter to thief. Son wants to learn this trade, tricks mother into believing he is entering this work with God's permission, soon proves self more masterful than brother-in-law, arranges for him to fall into pit full of boiling olive oil, removes his head, tells his family not to cry but when he is away, they cry. Soldiers hear, put red mark on their door. Boy puts similar mark on all doors of block. King offers daughter to clever thief. Neighboring king mocks father-in-law because he can't catch thief. Boy wears animal skin with many bells on, climbs wall of king's palace, enters room, says he is angel who is claiming his soul. Sews king up in animal skin, returns with him to father-in-law.

BASQUE, **Webster,** p. 140: boy is servant to robbers, becomes rich, returns home. Mayor gives him tests for thievery: best horse in stable, bread in oven, sheets on mayor's bed, all money of chief priest. Boy tricks priest to think he is angel of God, gets money, puts him in sack, too, claims money from mayor also to open sack.

CAUCASIAN, **Dirr,** [Imertian] p. 276: similar to Greek *MG* below.

GEORGIAN, **Wardrop,** p. 88: contest to find more clever thief. Story is richer in detail than Detroit story.

GREEK, **Dawkins,** *MG,* p. 363: robbers trick priest, take lamb, steal gold from king's treasury, cut off uncle's head. Except for added motifs of crying tabu and using purchase of meat as bait, story is similar. *MGAM,* p. 419: motifs of tricking king are only somewhat similar.

GYPSY, **Groome,** [Romanian] p. 41: almost identical except trickery of foreign king does not occur; instead, jurist is led out of church by crabs carrying lighted candles.

ITALIAN, **Crane,** p. 163: Sicilian story is almost identical.

ISRAELI, **Noy,** [Persian-Kurdistan] p. 80: two brothers rob treasury. One falls into pit of tar, is beheaded by other to prevent identification. Bird is freed who will land on robber's roof. Boy catches, kills it, cooks meat. Old woman goes from door to door to beg for bird meat for sick son. Boy's mother gives her some; boy calls her back, kills her. Brother's body is placed on public view in hopes of catching grief-stricken one. Mother breaks glasses, cries over this as excuse.

SCOTCH, Campbell, I, 330: only similar in theme of master thief.

74. The Test of the Chicken

Cf AT 1533 & 1689A. Clouston, II, 329: in footnote, describes story from the Talmud: head of capon to master, head of house; inward part, to mistress, typical of her fruitfulness; wings, to daughters, indicating they should soon fly away; legs to sons, pillars of house; to carver, the part which most resembles boat in which he arrived and would soon depart.

GREEK, Dawkins, *MG*, p. 404: unusual division of hen used as secret of king's riddle. 45, p. 253: in note, speaks of variant from Oinoe: girl divides fowl: wings to self to fly to husband; legs to husband, pillar and support of home; head to father, head of household; bones to mother, frame of home.

RUSSIAN, Afanas'ev, p. 579: similar division of goose.

75. The Devil's Yallehr

Cf AT 1199B & 2300.

RUSSIAN, Afanas'ev, p. 308: although story is different in specific detail, story purpose and mood prevail.

76. Rooster-Brother

Cf AT 328 & 1122.

ARMENIAN, Macler, *Cl*, p. 45: boy takes goose to market to sell. Jew, king's vizier, offers to buy sparrow. Boy insists powerful vizier is mistaken; passersby confirm vizier's judgment. Boy does many things to harm vizier and king, posting sign after each episode: "I sell geese, I sell geese and I do all sorts of tricks, small or big, you won't take my goose for sparrow." Tricks: gets cooked goose back; keeps soldiers' uniforms; steals, cooks king's camel; kills old hag who will inform on him; runs off with king's daughter.

GREEK, Dawkins, *MGAM*, p. 419: two older brothers are tricked, lose fortune. Third is cunning, manages to keep alive. He successfully hurts butcher with his device for killing female lure's victims. Hero, dressed as doctor, continues to do butcher further harm. As camel driver, kills gate guards and witch-wife. King sets traps to catch hero but he steals king's signet, tricks entire town with deception. King promises immunity and rewards.

HUNGARIAN, Ortutay, p. 378: similar.

TURKISH, Tezel, p. 110: vizier buys geese as chicken; similar but not as complete as Macler, p. 45, above.

77. The Honorable Wife

No AT assigned.

ARMENIAN, Khatchatrianz, p. 68: high priest, so holy he must have road dusted to avoid stepping on insects, causes experience-wise hero to suspect villainy.

GREEK, Dawkins, 45, p. 304: great piety betrays evil-doer.

78. The Rooster's Advice

AT 670; EB 56; BP I, 131 ff.

ARMENIAN, Seklemian, p. 137: almost identical. Servant-stian, p. 196 and Macler, *Ca*, p. 103: very similar.

HUNGARIAN, Jones, p. 301: identical. Ortutay, p. 378: similar.

PERSIAN, Lorimer, [Bakhtiari] p. 225: almost identical.

RUSSIAN, Ransome, p. 240: almost identical.

SERBIAN, Mijatovics, p. 37 and Petrovitch, p. 230: almost identical.

SIBERIAN, Coxwell, [Tarantchi-Tatar] p. 319: similar except hero dies as he tells secret to wife.

79. The Talkative Wife

AT 1164D; EB 377: BP IV, 176, n. 1.

ASIA MINOR, Carnoy-Nicolaïdes, [Greek] p. 172: similar.

HUNGARIAN, Ortutay, p. 373: suggestive.

IRAQI, Stevens, p. 120: similar.

RUSSIAN, Afanas'ev, p. 56: almost identical.

80. Today's Laughter, Tomorrow's Sadness

No AT assigned; EB 332.

RUSSIAN, Afanas'ev, p. 117: although different in specific motifs, reminiscent of Armenian story.

TURKISH, Tezel, p. 6: only motif of beggar eating meat, substituting old shoe.

81–85. Gohc *Amu* Stories

These are a few stories about a local character who might have developed in the mold of Nasreddin Hodscha if World War I had not wiped out Armenian community life. Although many Detroit informants knew Nasreddin Hodscha stories, I did not collect them because it is well known that they are literary in source.

86. The Bear Husband

No AT assigned. Pertev Boratav, *Les histoires d'ours en Anatolie* (FF Communications, No. 152), pp. 3–46. **MacCulloch, pp. 267, 270–71.**

ARMENIAN, **Nazinian**, p. 45: see Nazinian notes for 15. "The Huntsman" for bear hero. Tcheraz, p. 140: "The bear has sympathy for the human race. He doesn't do any harm. He only attacks when he is attacked. When he sees a woman, he leads her to the altar, and marries her. So that she cannot escape, he licks the sole of her foot in order to rub away the skin so that she cannot run away."

RUSSIAN, **Afanas'ev**, p. 221: only beginning motifs of woman living with bear and having bear child. Both run away from bear.

SIBERIAN, **Coxwell**, [Gagaüzy] 406: priest and she-bear mate; unusually strong son is born. [Gilyak] p. 124: only motif is bear and woman mating.

87. The Town of Stone

No AT assigned. MacCulloch, p. 156.

ARMENIAN, **Chalatianz**, p. ix: "Not far from Van, at the foot of the mountain Agirpa, there is a whole wedding party which has been changed to stone. It is believed that the young people did not gain permission to marry and their parents cursed them and God punished them in this way." P. x: selfish man refused to have compassion with the poor or to share wealth with them. God punished him and made his wagons and buffalos stone. **Khatchatrianz, p.** 125: town of stone is caused by witch's curse.

GYPSY, **Groome,** [Bukowina] p. 117: existence of town made of stone; no explanation of why or how. Armenian is appointed king by hero.

88. Retribution

No AT assigned.

89. The Old Fort

No AT assigned.

90. Under Suspicion

Cf AT 922A.

ISRAELI, **Noy,** [Basra] p. 171: slave upon whose head bird perches becomes king, keeps his beggar's clothes to look at so that he can remember his past.

91. The Woman in Blue

No AT assigned.

92. The Prize Bull

No AT assigned.

93. The Sacred Sheet

No AT assigned.

94. The Servant in the Monastery

No AT assigned.

95. From Bad to Worse

AT 2040.

96. It Started with a Thorn

Cf AT 1655 & 170A; EB 19; BP II, 199–203. **MacCulloch, p.** 189; inanimate objects with human and magical abilities.

ARMENIAN, Mary Mason Paynter, in *Folk-Lore*, XXVI (1916), 311: Armenian story heard in Constantinople is almost identical except hero is a sparrow. At wedding dog is being slain; sparrow gives them his lamb. At end, hero trades bride with man riding donkey and playing on his tambourine.

GREEK, Dawkins, *MGAM*, p. 521: cock takes thorns to baker who burns them; asks for bush, gets dough and kneading trough which he takes to butcher. Dough is fed to animals. Cock asks for it again, is given sheep, takes sheep to wedding where it is cooked and eaten. Cock asks for sheep, is given bride, takes her to mountain.

ITALIAN, Crane, p. 250: sexton gives roasted pea to baker; it is eaten by cock, exchanged for various objects, finally girl. Dog is substituted; reverse order of events takes place.

SIBERIAN, Coxwell, [Buryat] p. 141: basically same theme of witty man trading one thing for something far better. Items are very different. [Yellow Ugur] p. 336: hero finds mouse, in successive profitable exchanges, gets dog and horse; places already dead woman on horse, shoves her off, blames death on heroine who, to quiet him, marries hero.

97. Munuck

AT 2040, cf AT 1931.

98. Lochman Hehkeem

Cf AT 672, 753A; cf EB 57; for Lochman the famous physician, see EB 308 III, 2w; BP II, 463–65. **Clouston, II, 407–12, 497:** resuscitation. **MacCulloch, pp. 80–100.**

ARMENIAN, **Khatchatrianz,** p. 91: almost identical. Story is entitled, "Lochman, the Physician." **Seklemian,** p. 137: boy befriends snake, learns language of snakes. See Seklemian notes for 78. "The Rooster's Advice." P. 169: put together dead body with magic objects as in 4. "Clever Daniel." **Toumanian,** p. 120: eating white snake gives hero knowledge of all animal languages.

SCOTCH, **Campbell,** II, 377: white snake is boiled in water. Boy puts finger in liquid and into mouth, suddenly knows all things, becomes doctor.

99. The Seven Stars

No AT assigned.

100. The Sunset Lad

No AT assigned. **MacCulloch,** p. 64: immortal life water. Although elements of the "magic" story are in "The Sunset Lad" and its unpublished variant, "The Wicked Stepmother," the elements of the nature myth predominate.

ARMENIAN, **Wlislocki,** p. 80: hero calls self Sun Hero, displeases Sun, eventually finds punishment for his pride. **Nazinian,** p. 28: only motif of prince who dies during day, lives at night.

CAUCASIAN, **Dirr,** [Imertian] p. 29: youngest daughter asks for rose when father goes to market. He reaches for rose; *dev* catches him, demands daughter. Once home *dev* attempts to eat girl. Escape routines similar to those in 8. "Abo Beckeer." Girl comes upon a house, sees boy who sleeps during day and wakes at night. When baby is to be born to them, girl goes to his parents' home. Mother-in-law goes to sun's mother, her sister, for help. When sun takes bath, sister is given some of that water, bathes her cursed son; he is well again.

GREEK, **Dawkins,** 45, p. 31: hero is son of Sun and Moon. Mother of Sun hides boy from man-eating Sun.

GYPSY, **Jagendorf,** p. 93: boy marries girl who is dead during day, lives only at night.

SIBERIAN, **Coxwell,** [Armenian] p. 1016: hero must secure ablutionary water from mother of Sun and Moon.

The Wicked Stepmother (Unpublished Version)

King, in disguise, is recognized by dervish who gives him almond for his barren queen. Because almond has skin, queen bears snake who must have a girl daily for supper.

In this land, poor man has grown son and daughter. His second wife has ugly daughter. Guards demand one of the girls for snake. Pretty girl dreams she must take milk, wash snake in it, and he will become a man.

When she is left with snake, she throws milk in his face. He becomes a man, tells her he didn't eat those girls, for they were taken to other lands where they married the winds and rains.

Prince has dream never to send his wife back home, instructs his parents in this matter before setting off to war. When the girl's father comes to take her home for visit, however, king permits her to go.

Reindeer says to prince if he can shoot him, wife will be all right; if he fails, he will not see wife for eight years. Prince is unsuccessful.

Stepmother, while bathing young queen in river, soaps her well, pushes her in waves, substitutes her ugly daughter in her place. When prince returns and discovers trick, he sets off to find wife.

River takes girl into dark world, washing her ashore at night. She tries to conceal her nakedness. She sees a man, learns he is blind during the day and sees only at night because he has shot two fawn of a mother deer. Girl marries him, eventually returns to home of his parents.

Mother-in-law dreams at top of mountain is a pool of water in which sun rises and sets. If her son can bathe in water after sun has bathed in it, blindness will disappear.

Both mother and son step into pool, come to beautiful palace.

Sun's mother forgives boy, instructing him not to shoot another deer. His sight is restored.

Girl bears one son. One day meets her first husband; returns home with him, leaving son with second husband. (Informant: Mrs. Katoon Mouradian)

Variants of the above are:

AT 433B & 403; EB 106; BP II 241 ff., III, 37 ff.

ARMENIAN, Servantstian, Part B, p. 37 and **Macler**, *Ca*, p. 167: very similar. Boy shoots in face of Sun, is cursed. Mother-in-law dreams must wear out iron shoes to find Sun's dwelling. **Seklemian,** p. 73: similar to Servantstian version.

GREEK, **Dawkins,** *MG,* p. 71: very similar except Sun motifs do not appear. *45,* p. 369: very similar except boy is cursed for marrying and abusing many wives. Beginning motifs similar to teacher-stepmother motifs in 32. "The Story of Mariam." Mother is girl's benefactor and adviser.

TURKISH, **Kúnos,** *Stam,* p. 221 and *44,* p. 188: very similar except magic sleep caused by forty Peris, thus hero's cure possible only with destruction of these creatures.

APPENDIX A
Narrator Sketches

At the beginning of my folklore activity, along with stories I collected beliefs, superstitions, cures, sayings and riddles. But my heart was with the folktales, particularly the *hekiat*. I collected these first, then took whatever else the informant wanted to share. Undoubtedly, this is one of the reasons why this present collection is weighted with Märchen and tales of magic.

Once the material was translated, the next problem was that few, if any, of the stories had titles; there was no way of referring to the tales. The titles which appear in the volume today are almost entirely those which Professor Gardner and I selected at the time of the collecting activity.

Stories told by a good narrator are given in an active manner, not a passive one. Questions are always directly put to the listeners; conversations as well as soliloquies are reported as direct quotations, thus making the story real to the audience. Repetition is used successfully in folktales as a unifying element since it appears so frequently throughout the narrative. It is also an excellent device for creating suspense and excitement until the climax is reached.

The techniques used by the individual narrators contribute vastly in the creation of a specific mood for the story. A good storyteller uses facial expressions, voice inflections, gestures, movements, even song and dance to help convey the emotions to his audience. The poor storyteller is more apt to use the easiest of these techniques: the inflection of voice alone.

Of the ten narrators for the Detroit collection of Armenian folktales, five were women and five men. Since both sexes contributed to this collection, it cannot be said with finality that either men or women were the medium of dissemination of the Armenian folktale. It is apparent, however, that these ten people varied in the kinds of stories which they told. In general, those who had received some formal education by church or school told the moralistic tales and the stories of cleverness. Those who had little, if any education, remembered and told the Märchen. Brief sketches of the narrators follow:

ANTRIAS AMBOIAN was born into an agricultural family in the 1890's and died in Detroit recently. He was born in Hogheh, a village of Kharput. He fled his homeland and emigrated to America in 1912.

535

Settling in Detroit, he found work at the Ford Motor Company. Mr. Amboian was married and had three children and five grandchildren.

KASAR BOGOSIAN was born in Moush in the 1890's and died in Detroit in 1959. When his family was killed during the Turkish massacres, he fled to the mountains. There he was caught by the Kurds and barely saved his life by singing a long love song. He was hidden by a Kurdish soldier for forty days and finally escaped by wearing women's clothing. He joined the guerilla forces of Armenian General Antranik and with him, went into Russia.

He emigrated to America, settled in Detroit and found work in the auto plants. Fulfilled in his new life with his wife and six children, he was renowned as a folk singer and dancer as well as an excellent storyteller.

MRS. HRIPSIMA HOOGASIAN, my mother, was born in Kharput in the 1890's. She married into the Demerjian family, known for anti-Turkish sentiments. Her husband was a skilled gunsmith; her brother-in-law was a guerilla leader who, with his men, lived in the mountains. When her husband and children were killed in World War I, Mrs. Hoogasian traveled on foot across Asia Minor into India where she and hundreds like her were befriended by the English. She finally reached America in 1920, settled in Detroit in 1921, married my father and raised two children.

KAZAR HOOGASIAN, my father, was born in Akor, a village near Kharput, about 1885 and died in Detroit in 1957. He lost his family in World War I and escaped with great difficulty to America. After working in several towns in the East, he settled in Detroit as an auto worker. Here, he met and married my mother and started a new life.

HOVHANNES KAPRELIAN is a most gifted storyteller. He was born in Kharput in the 1890's and was orphaned at an early age. Emigrating to America in 1910, he settled in Detroit, and although he worked as a carpenter, cook, restaurant owner, I know him as a cobbler. He has never married.

Mr. Kaprelian was my father's friend, and my earliest recollections of him were of a short, happy man with a pocket full of candy for my brother and me and an unlimited supply of stories for all assembled.

NISHAN KRIKORIAN was born into an agricultural family in Palu, Armenia in 1892. When he lost both his wife and daughter in the massacres, he emigrated to America in 1913. In 1916, he settled in Detroit and found work at the auto plants. Mr. Krikorian has not remarried.

Mr. Krikorian's Märchen, among the most interesting in the collection, are well-developed and rich in detail.

MRS. AKABI MOORADIAN was born in Armenia near the town of Kemack in 1904. During World War I she escaped death miraculously, found safety in an orphanage and finally escaped to Aleppo, then to France. She married and came to America, settling in Detroit about 1929. Mrs. Mooradian is an active member-worker in Armenian community organizations, particularly the church and Red Cross activities. Mrs. Mooradian is mother of three daughters and has four grandchildren.

MRS. KATOON MOURADIAN was born in Palu, Armenia in the 1890's into an agricultural family. During the Turkish massacres she fled to Kharput and finally found refuge in Aleppo, Syria. From there, she emigrated first to France, then Canada, before settling in Detroit where she died recently.

A tall, dark-haired, dark-eyed lady, Mrs. Mouradian had a fascinating supply of folk cures and remedies. The mother of two sons, Mrs. Mouradian was not only a good storyteller, but an excellent and enthusiastic folk dancer.

MRS. ZEVART SEMEZIAN was born in 1895 in Ersinga, Armenia. During the massacres she was driven from one place to another for three years. With her husband, she reached Constantinople and finally came to America in 1921. A widow for many years, Mrs. Semezian is an active member of church and community activities.

MRS. MARIAM SERABIAN, my tiny, red-haired grandmother who died in 1953, was well into her seventies at the time of this story recording.* While still in her twenties in the late 1890's, she was left a widow with two small girls. Her home, her wealth, her possessions were destroyed during the massacres of 1895. Destitute, she worked for several years until she married into the Serabian family. She bore a son, Harootyoun, the pride of her life. During World War I, she suffered greatly but somehow managed to stay alive. In 1923, she and my young uncle emigrated to America and then lived with our family for many years.

Grandmother, a short, round figure, was a master at telling fortunes by using tiny Turkish coffee cups. She was a skillful nurse, too, and an expert at using folk cures, particularly a ritual for counteracting the evil eye! Her bedtime stories, found in these folktales, are among my most vivid childhood memories.

* Using henna on her head supposedly helped her headache, grandmother said. Imagine, if you can, the vivid picture this woman made with her bright orange hair and her seventy-year-old face and figure.

APPENDIX B
Index of Motifs

Stith Thompson's *Motif-Index of Folk-Literature* has been used for reference in this study. ° numbers refer to Detroit variants which are available in outline form in the Comparative Studies. Parenthetical words are as they appear in the *Motif-Index*. Bracketed words indicate slight variations found in the Detroit collection.

A. Mythological Motifs

Motif-Index	*Motif*	*Story*
A 102.17.	Anger of God	98
A 121.2.	Sun as deity	100
A 125.	Deity in human form	25
A 165.2.0.1.	Deity's messenger can assume any guise he wishes	45
A 165.2.3.	Angels as God's messengers	45, 98
A 165.6.	Scribe of gods	44
A 185.12.	Deity [God] provides man with soul	49
A 189.7.	Deity ascertains destiny of new-born babe, inscribes it upon his forehead	44
A 220.	Sun-god	100
A 497.	Echo	100
A 511.1.3.3.	Immaculate conception of culture hero	35
A 511.4.1.	Miraculous growth of culture hero	35
A 528.	Culture hero has supernatural helpers	35
A 651.2.	Series of lower worlds	34, 34°
A 661.0.5.1.	Soul-bridge: easy for righteous to cross, difficult for others	45
A 671.0.2.1.	Fire in hell [hot descent]	34, 34°
A 681.	Sun in underworld	100

Motif-Index	Motif	Story
A 715.1.	Sun born from woman	100
A 720.	Nature and conditions of sun	100
A 722.	Sun's night journey: around or under earth	100
A 733.	Heat and light of sun	100, 100*
A 736.	Sun as human being	16, 100
A 736.1.	Sun and moon as man [woman] and woman	16
A 736.2.	Sun as woman	16
A 738.3.	Sun's healing power	100
A 751.8.	Woman in the moon [speaks]	2
A 753.	Moon as a person	2, 16
A 761.	Ascent to stars	99
A 761.3.	Stars as transformed lovers	99
A 773.	Origin of Pleiades	99
A 941.5.	Spring breaks forth through power of Saint [Moses/dervish]	32, 88
A 974.	Rocks from transformation of people to stones	87, 88
A 977.	Origin of particular stones or groups of stones	87, 88
A 1003.	Calamity as punishment for sins	87
A 1111.	Impounded water	8*, 22, 34, 34*
A 1241.	Man [donkey] made from clay	7
A 1250.	Man made from vegetable substance [dough]	49
A 1260.1.	Man made from combination of different objects	49
A 1266.	Man made from food	49
A 1438.	Origin of medicine (healing)	98
A 1562.1.	Origin of charms for pregnant woman	56

B. Animals

B 2.	Animal totems	60, 61
B 11.	Dragon	61

Motif-Index	Motif	Story
B 11.10.	Sacrifice of humans to dragon [monster/*dev*/snake]	22, 34, 100*
B 11.2.1.2.	Dragon as modified serpent	61
B 11.2.7.	Snakes issue from dragon's shoulders [tail]	61
B 11.3.2.	Dragon's home at top of mountain	61
B 11.7.1.	Dragon [snake/monster/*dev*] controls water supply	22, 34, 100*
B 16.5.1.	Giant devastating serpent	100*
B 19.1.	Brazen-footed, fire-breathing bull	35
B 19.4.	Glowing animals [bird]	14, 14*, 15
B 41.2.	Flying horse	1*, 14
B 71.	Sea horse	1*, 14, 14*
B 91.4.	Sky-traveling snake	61
B 91.5.2.	Lake serpent (monster)	22
B 113.1.	Treasure-producing parts of bird	12
B 123.1.	Wise serpent	78, 98
B 133.1.	Horse warns hero of danger	14, 14*, 33*
B 141.2.	Prophetic horse	14, 14*, 31
B 151.1.1.	Horse determines road to be taken	14, 14*, 31
B 151.2.0.2.	Birds show way to other world	34, 34*, 18
B 161.	Wisdom from serpent	78, 98
B 163.	Wisdom from other animal [eating white dove]	9
B 165.1.	Animal languages learned from serpent (not eaten)	78, 98
B 184.1.	Magic horse	1*, 14, 14*, 22, 31, 33*, 34*, 35
B 184.1.1.	Horse with magic speed	1*, 14, 14*, 34*
B 184.1.3.	Magic horse from water world	1*, 14*, 34*
B 184.1.4.	Magic horse travels on sea or land	1*, 34*
B 184.1.6.	Flight on magic horse	1*, 34*
B 184.1.10.	Magic horse makes prodigious jump	14

Motif-Index	Motif	Story
B 184.2.1.	Magic cow	33*
B 184.2.5.	Magic calf	33*
B 210.	Speaking animals	1*, 10, 14, 14*, 18, 20, 20*, 26, 31, 33*, 78, 86, 98
B 211.1.3.	Speaking horse	14, 14*, 31, 33*
B 211.2.1.	Speaking stag [transformed]	33
B 211.2.2.	Speaking lion	1*, 22
B 211.2.3.	Speaking bear	1*, 86
B 211.2.5.	Speaking fox	10
B 211.3.	Speaking bird	1, 14, 14*, 31, 34, 34*, 47*
B 211.3.2.	Speaking cock	78, 96
B 211.6.1.	Speaking snake	20, 20*, 26, 78, 98
B 215.1.	Bird language	1, 14, 14*, 18, 34, 34*
B 216.	Knowledge of animal languages	18, 78, 98
B 220.	Animal kingdoms	18, 73
B 222.	Kingdom of birds	18
B 235.	Secrets discussed in animal [dev] meeting	41, 41*
B 244.1.	King of snakes	20, 20*, 26, 98, 100*
B 244.1.2.	Serpent king resides in lake	100*
B 291.1.3.	Dove as messenger [guide]	9
B 311.	Congenital helpful animal	27
B 312.2.	Helpful animals a gift	20, 20*
B 312.3.	Helpful animals bequeathed hero	14
B 312.4.	Helpful animals purchased	31
B 312.5.	Helpful strong horse caught	1*
B 314.	Helpful animal brothers-in-law	1*
B 322.1.	Hero feeds own flesh to helpful animal	34, 34*

Motif-Index	Motif	Story
B 341.	Helpful animal's injunctions disobeyed	14, 14*
B 350.	Grateful animals	1, 1*, 8*, 14, 14*, 20, 20*, 78, 98
B 365.01.	Bird grateful for rescue of its young	1, 34, 34*
B 365.2.	Animal grateful to hero for preventing destruction of nest	1, 34, 34*
B 366.	Animal grateful for ransom from captivity	20, 20*, 78
B 375.3.1.	Grateful eagle	1, 34, 34*
B 375.9.	Grateful snake	20, 20*, 78, 98
B 386.	Tigress [lioness] grateful for opening of abcess	22
B 392.1.	Animals grateful for being given appropriate food	8*, 14
B 401.	Helpful horse	1*, 14, 14*, 31, 33*
B 411.1.	Helpful bull	92
B 413.	Helpful goat	31
B 421.	Helpful dog	20, 20*
B 422.	Helpful cat	20, 20*
B 435.1.	Helpful fox	10
B 435.4.	Helpful bear [brother-in-law]	1*
B 437.2.	Helpful mouse	20*
B 455.3.	Helpful eagle	1, 34, 34*
B 469.5.	Helpful cock	78
B 491.1.	Helpful serpent	20, 20*, 78, 98
B 501.	Animal gives part of body as talisman for summoning its aid	1, 22, 33*, 34*
B 501.4.	Birds give hero feather to burn if he is in difficulty	1, 34*
B 505.	Magic object received from animal	20, 20*, 26
B 511.5.	Bird heals man [thigh cut]	34, 34*
B 512.	Medicine shown by animals	98

Motif-Index	Motif	Story
B 513.	Remedy learned from overhearing animal [giant] meeting	41*
B 526.2.	Helpful mare cools boiling bath for master	14*
B 531.	Animals provide food for men	3, 32
B 535.0.3.	Goat as nurse for child	31
B 538.1.	Bird gives shelter with wings	34, 34*
B 542.1.1.	Eagle carries man to safety	1, 34, 34*
B 548.1.	Animals recover lost wishing ring	20, 20*
B 560.	Animals advise man	1, 18
B 563.	Animals direct man on journey	14, 14*, 31
B 571.	Animals perform task for man	14, 14*
B 571.1.	Animals help man overcome monster with external soul	1
B 575.2.	Bird rests on person's shoulders [head]	12, 50
B 581.	Animal [fox] brings wealth to man	10
B 582.1.1.	Animal wins wife for his master	10
B 593.1.	Snake as house-spirit	60
B 601.1.	Marriage to bear	86
B 601.1.1.	Bear steals woman, makes her his wife	86
B 601.10.	Marriage to deer	23*
B 604.1.	Marriage to snake	26, 100*
B 604.2.1.	Marriage to turtle	23
B 621.1.	Bear as suitor	1*
B 621.2.	Lion as suitor	1*
B 623.	Bird [eagle] as wooer	1*
B 631.	Human offspring from marriage to animal	35
B 631.9.	Human offspring from marriage of person and snake	26
B 632.	Animal offspring from marriage to animal	86
B 642.	Marriage to person in bird form	18
B 742.3.	Fire-breathing horse	1*, 14*
B 765.5.	Snake crawls from sleeper's mouth	7, 36
B 784.2.1.1.	Snake in human body enticed out by water	7

C. Tabu

Motif-Index	Motif	Story
C 31.2.	Tabu: mentioning origin of super-natural wife [husband]	25
C 31.3.	Tabu: disobeying supernatural wife	17
C 31.10.	Tabu: giving garment back to supernatural wife	18
C 41.1.	Tabu: rescuing drowning man	6*
C 66.	Tabu: murmuring against deity [God]	17
C 75.1.	Tabu: offending moon [sun]	100
C 99.1.1.	Tabu: urinating on fire [cat does]	7
C 227.	Tabu: eating human flesh	30
C 313.0.1.	Tabu: princess never to see male person	49
C 321.	Tabu: looking into box	8*
C 331.3.	Tabu: looking back during flight	14, 31
C 401.3.	Tabu: speaking while searching for treasure	55
C 411.1.	Tabu: asking for reason for un-usual action	6*
C 421.	Tabu: revealing secret of super-natural husband	25
C 423.1.	Tabu: disclosing source of magic power	21
C 425.	Tabu: revealing knowledge of animal languages	78
C 430.	Name tabu	21
C 432.	Tabu: uttering name of super-natural creature	21
C 498.	Speaking tabu: forbidden expres-sion ["Whoa!"]	7
C 510.	Tabu: touching tree	14
C 531.	Tabu: touching with iron	56
C 532.	Tabu: touching with water	8*
C 545.2.	Tabu: touching clothes of certain person	14, 87
C 600.	Unique prohibition: attempted cure for patient in certain position	45

Motif-Index	Motif	Story
C 611.	Forbidden chamber	4, 90
C 615.4.	Tabu: not to rest near the lake [sea]	5
C 621.2.1.	Tabu: touching apple	14
C 650.	The one compulsory thing	4, 40, 93
C 687.	Injunction: perform certain act daily	40
C 735.2.	Tabu: sleeping in certain place	5
C 742.	Tabu: striking monster twice	1, 4, 34, 34*
C 751.	Tabu: doing certain thing at certain time	35
C 757.1.	Tabu: destroying animal skin of enchanted person too soon	23, 26
C 833.	Tabus for journeys [father's dying words]	5
C 841.7.	Tabu: killing totem animal	60
C 841.8.	Tabu: killing deer	100*
C 842.	Tabu: exposure to sunlight	100, 100*
C 868.	Tabu: leaving land [throne] entirely unoccupied	5
C 881.	Tabu: grumbling	17
C 901.1.1.	Tabu: imposed on son by father before death	5
C 915.	Contents of forbidden casket released	8*
C 920.	Death for breaking tabu	45
C 932.	Loss of wife/husband for breaking tabu	18, 25
C 937.1.	Immortality lost because of breach of tabu	98
C 943.	Loss of sight for breaking tabu	17, 100*
C 947.	Magic power lost by breaking tabu	21
C 961.2.	Transformation to stone for breaking tabu	31
C 963.4.	Giants return to life if tabu is broken	34, 34*
C 985.	Physical changes in person because of broken tabu	31

D. Magic

Motif-Index	Motif	Story
D 29.	Transformation to person of different social class [giant: dervish]	8, 8*
D 41.	Humble man in guise of exalted	70
D 41.1.	Transformation to likeness of ruler	14
D 42.	God in guise of mortal	25
D 42.2.	Spirit takes man's shape	36
D 49.1.	Dwarf assumes human form	35
D 49.2.	Spirit takes any form	36
D 55.1.	Person becomes magically larger	35
D 55.1.3.	Pygmy [dwarf] turns into giant	35
D 55.2.5.	Transformation: adult to child	45
D 56.	Magic change in person's age	7
D 57.3.	Hair and skin turn to color of gold	27
D 61.	Magic appearance of human limbs	7, 32, 39
D 103.	Assembly or group transformed to animals	13, 12
D 114.1.1.	Transformation: man to deer	33
D 114.1.4.	Transformation: man [woman] to buffalo	13
D 132.1.	Transformation: man to ass	39, 94
D 133.1.	Transformation to cow	33*
D 133.4.	Transformation: man to calf	33*
D 141.	Transformation: man to dog	94, 39
D 142.	Transformation: man to cat	39
D 150.	Transformation: man/woman to bird	14*, 15, 25, 35
D 191.	Transformation: man/woman to snake	4, 26, 100*
D 211.5.	Transformation: man/woman to apple	8, 8*
D 215.	Transformation: man/woman to tree	8, 8*
D 231.	Transformation: man to stone	31, 87, 88
D 231.2.	Transformation: man [spirit] to marble column [slab]	36

Motif-Index	Motif	Story
D 231.2.1.	Mass transformation of wedding party to marble statues, etc.	88
D 250.	Transformation: man [woman] to manufactured object	8, 8*
D 263.2.	Transformation: man [woman] to necklace [rosary]	8, 8*
D 283.4.	Transformation: person to seafoam	14
D 293.	Transformation: man to stars	99
D 294.	Transformation to puff of dust [mist]	8, 8*
D 300.	Transformation: animal to person	26, 100*
D 332.1.	Transformation: ass (donkey) to person	12, 94
D 333.2.	Transformation: calf to person	33*
D 350.	Transformation: bird to person	5, 14, 18
D 391.	Transformation: serpent to person	26, 100*
D 399.	Transformation other animals than those already treated to person	13, 23, 23*
D 420.	Transformation: animal to object [reindeer to stone]	23*
D 422.1.2.	Horse transformed to stone	31, 87, 88
D 431.	Vegetable form [sesame seed] to person	94
D 435.	Transformation: image to person	49
D 435.1.1.	Transformation: statue comes to life	23, 36
D 437.1.	Human bone [dwarf] transforms self to person	35
D 442.1.	Transformation: stone to animal	31
D 444.	Transformation: manufactured object [clay] to animal [ass]	7
D 447.	Transformation: parts of human body to animal	39
D 449.2.	Corpse transformed to snake [dog]	94
D 451.5.2.	Transformation: blade of grass to knife/[stone]	8, 8*, 14
D 452.1.12.	Transformation: stones to dust	87
D 454.1.	Transformation: box to other object [man]	25

Motif-Index	Motif	Story
D 457.18.	Transformation: tears to other object	3
D 475.1.10.	Transformation: hair to gold	27, 33
D 475.2.2.	Transformation: water to money	3
D 475.4.5.	Tears become jewels	3
D 478.	Water changed to other substance	3
D 479.8.	Hut transformed to golden palace	17
D 492.	Color of object [river] changed	33
D 492.3.	Color of hair suddenly changed	33
D 531.	Transformation by putting on skin	23, 26
D 551.1.	Transformation by eating fruit	13
D 555.1.	Transformation by drinking from animal's tracks	33
D 571.	Transformation by throwing object	8, 8*, 14
D 591.	Transformation by immersing in magic well	33
D 621.	Daily transformation	100, 100*
D 621.1.	Animal by day; man/woman by night	23, 26
D 631.4.1.	Dwarfs change size at will	35
D 642.5.1.	Transformation to hide from ogress	8, 8*
D 661.	Transformation as punishment	12, 13, 87, 88, 94
D 665.	Transformation of enemy to be rid of him	94
D 666.	Transformation to save person	8, 8*
D 671.	Transformation flight	8, 8*
D 672.	Obstacle flight	8, 8*, 14*
D 682.	Partial transformation	39
D 717.	Disenchantment by assembling bones [resuscitation]	1*, 35, 98
D 721.3.	Disenchantment by destroying [burning] skin	23, 26
D 723.2.1.	Disenchantment by removing string [pin]	9, 56
D 753.3.	Disenchantment by obeying directions received in dream	100
D 764.	Disenchantment by eating or drinking	13

Motif-Index	Motif	Story
D 765.1.	Disenchantment by removing cause of enchantment [ring]	2
D 766.	Disenchantment by liquid [throwing water, milk into face]	8*, 33*, 100*
D 771.	Disenchantment by use of magic object	12
D 781.	Disenchantment by prayer of pope	94
D 812.11.	Magic object received from giant	12
D 812.14.	Magic object received from ascetic [dervish]	17*
D 813.	Magic object [life token] received from fairy	3
D 815.1.	Magic object received from mother	13
D 817.1.2.	Magic object received from grateful father of redeemed snake	20, 20*
D 831.	Magic object acquired by trick exchange	20*
D 832.	Magic objects acquired by acting as umpire for fighting heirs	12
D 838.	Magic object acquired by stealing	20, 20*
D 840.	Magic object found	20, 20*
D 841.	Magic object accidentally found	13
D 842.1.	Magic object [any wish] found on mother's grave	30
D 855.	Magic object acquired as reward	20, 20*
D 859.4.1.	Magic bird-heart eaten unwittingly	12
D 861.5.	Magic object stolen by hero's wife	20*
D 881.	Magic object recovered by second magic object	20*
D 881.1.	Recovery of magic objects by use of magic apples [figs]	13
D 881.2.	Recovery of magic object by use of magic cudgel	20*
D 882.	Magic object stolen back	20, 20*
D 882.1.1.	Stolen magic object stolen back by helpful cat and dog	20, 20*
D 882.2.	Recovered magic objects dropped by rescuing animals into sea	20, 20*

Motif-Index	Motif	Story
D 895.	Magic object returned as payment for removal of magic horns [reversal]	13
D 905.	Magic storm	33
D 927.2.	Magic spring guarded by demons [*devs*]	8*
D 932.	Magic mountain	7
D 935.	Magic clay [donkey]	7
D 955.	Magic leaf [remedy: blindness]	41*
D 965.3.	Magic rosebush	41
D 971.4.	Magic black cummin [sesame]	94
D 981.5.	Magic fig	13
D 991.	Magic hairs	22, 33*
D 992.1.	Magic horns [grow on person's forehead]	33
D 1005.	Magic breath [snake]	78
D 1007.	Magic bone (human) [source of magic]	30
D 1011.0.1.	Magic bird-heart	12
D 1011.6.	Magic tongue of animal [snake]	98
D 1018.	Magic milk of animal	22
D 1021.	Magic feather	1, 34*
D 1021.1.	Magic bird's power in one feather	1, 34*
D 1027.	Magic urine of animal	35
D 1050.1.	Clothes produced by magic	30
D 1053.	Magic cloak [invisibility]	18
D 1056.	Magic shirt [invisibility]	13
D 1067.2.	Magic cap [invisibility]	12
D 1069.1.	Magic handkerchief	7, 35
D 1072.1.	Magic comb	14, 15
D 1076.	Magic ring	2, 20, 20*, 34*
D 1081.	Magic sword	4, 20*, 36
D 1094.	Magic cudgel	12, 20*
D 1131.1.	Castle produced by magic	11, 20, 20*, 21, 25
D 1138.	Magic tent	13
D 1146.	Magic door	2, 89
D 1155.	Magic carpet	12

Motif-Index	Motif	Story
D 1174.	Magic box	17, 20*, 25
D 1192.	Magic purse	13
D 1209.1.	Magic bridle	1*
D 1242.	Magic fluid	98
D 1262.	Magic grinding stones	26
D 1266.	Magic book	21, 33*
D 1272.	Magic circle	21
D 1273.1.1.	3 as magic number	1, 1*, 12, 27, 30, 34
D 1273.1.3.	7 as magic number	7
D 1273.1.3.1.	9 as magic number	27
D 1282.1.	Magic knot	14*
D 1293.	Magic color	31
D 1293.4.	Black as magic color	5, 33, 34, 34*
D 1299.2.	Magic grave	30, 35
D 1300.4.	Stone gives magic wisdom	67
D 1311.4.2.	Speaking tree gives prophecy	2*
D 1311.6.1.	Moon answers questions	2
D 1311.14.	Divination from reading sacred book	21, 33*
D 1314.1.3.	Magic arrow shot to determine where to seek bride	23*
D 1318.1.1.	Stone bursts as sign of unjust judgment	2, 2*
D 1318.2.1.	Laughing fish reveals unjust judgment [adultery]	67
D 1331.3.1.	Salve causes magic sight and blindness	17, 17*
D 1337.1.2.	Water gives magic beauty	31
D 1337.2.4.	Magic water makes ugly	31
D 1338.3.1.	Rejuvenation by apple	14
D 1338.4.	Bath in magic milk rejuvenates	14*
D 1346.11.	Medicine gives immortality	98
D 1347.1.	Magic apple produces fecundity	25, 27, 28
D 1352.	Magic object has prenatal influence	35, 67
D 1361.12.	Magic cloak of invisibility	18
D 1361.14.	Magic hat renders invisible	12
D 1361.37.	Magic shirt renders invisible	13

Motif-Index	*Motif*	*Story*
D 1364.0.1.	King wakes from magic sleep	2
D 1364.3.	Flowers cause magic sleep	11
D 1364.22.	Sleep-charm [ring]	2
D 1375.1.1.5.	Magic figs cause horns to grow on person [cause transformation]	13
D 1375.2.1.	Magic fruit removes horns from person [reverses transformation]	13
D 1382.5.	Magic fire does not harm one	36
D 1400.1.4.	Magic sword conquers enemy	20*
D 1428.	Magic object fetches another object	20*
D 1438.	Magic weapon pursues victim	20*
D 1451.	Inexhaustible purse furnishes money	13
D 1454.2.1.	Roses fall from lips [cheeks]	3
D 1454.4.2.	Jewels from tears	3
D 1461.0.1.	Tree with golden fruit	34*
D 1470.1.15.	Magic wishing ring	20, 20*, 34*
D 1470.2.2.	Supplies received from magic box	20*
D 1472.1.21.	Magic chest supplies food	20*
D 1475.2.	Soldier-producing trumpet	13
D 1478.	Magic object [bird] provides light	15
D 1500.1.1.	Magic healing fountain	14
D 1500.1.7.3.	Magic healing blood	37
D 1500.1.28.	Earth as remedy	14*
D 1500.1.33.1.2.	Magic healing milk of lioness	22
D 1500.1.37.	Urine as medicine	35
D 1502.1.	Magic object [black rock pulverized to powder] cures headache	67
D 1502.4.2.1.	Blood of children as cure for leprosy	37
D 1503.10.	Magic plant heals wounds	98
D 1505.1.	Herbs restore sight	41*
D 1518.4.1.	Magic plant heals broken bone	98
D 1520.19.	Magic transportation by carpet	12
D 1524.5.	River crossed by magic	2*, 3, 11
D 1551.	Waters magically divide and close	3, 11
D 1552.	Mountains open and close	14

Motif-Index	Motif	Story
D 1561.1.1.	Magic bird-heart (when eaten) brings man kingship	12
D 1566.	Magic object [spirit] controls fire	36
D 1601.36.	Self-going shoes	34*
D 1602.2.2.	Chips from tree return to their places as cut [overnight]	33
D 1610.2.	Speaking tree	2*, 25
D 1610.35.	Speaking river	2*, 25
D 1641.12.1.	Lake is drunk dry	15, 16
D 1645.6.	Self-luminous feather	14, 14*
D 1652.1.1.	Inexhaustible bread	6, 23, 31
D 1652.8.	Inexhaustible cloth [rug]	6, 23, 31
D 1654.3.1.	Indelible mark	8*, 21
D 1654.4.1.	Sword can be moved only by right person	4, 36
D 1654.15.	Door stuck by witchcraft so it cannot be opened	2, 2*, 8*, 14
D 1658.1.	Objects repay kindness	8*, 14, 14*
D 1658.1.1.	River grateful for being praised even when ugly	14
D 1658.1.3.	Bitter water grateful for being praised	14
D 1658.1.4.	Continually slamming doors grateful for being fastened	14, 14*
D 1658.3.3.	Grateful objects give helper gifts	25
D 1658.3.4.	Grateful objects help fugitive	8*, 14, 14*
D 1710.	Possession of magic powers	36
D 1712.3.	Interpreter of dream	16
D 1715.	Last words of dying man	52
D 1720.	Acquisition of magic power	98
D 1724.	Magic power from Death	45
D 1731.	Magic power received in dream	40
D 1734.1.	Magic power of rubbing talisman	1, 22, 33*, 34*
D 1737.1.	Magic power from mother	30
D 1751.	Magic passes from body to body	36
D 1766.7.3.	Magic results produced in name of saint	40

Motif-Index	*Motif*	*Story*
D 1792.	Magic results from curse	8, 8*, 100, 100*
D 1812.3.	Means of learning future	44, 45, 47*, 50
D 1812.3.3.2.	Fortune-telling dream induced by sleeping in extraordinary place	40
D 1812.5.1.20.	Withering tree as bad omen	27
D 1815.2.	Magic knowledge of language of animals	18, 78, 98
D 1821.4.	Magic sight by putting ointment to eye	17
D 1825.3.1.	Magic power of seeing death at head or foot of bed and thus forecasting progress of sickness	45
D 1825.4.1.	Magic power of seeing things underground	17
D 1830.	Magic strength	4, 35
D 1846.5.2.	Pious man [spirit] in city renders it invulnerable	36
D 1855.	Time of death postponed	45
D 1860.	Magic beautification	33
D 1867.1.	Hut becomes mansion	17
D 1868.1.	Broken-down nag becomes magnificent riding horse	14
D 1870.	Magic hideousness	33
D 1871.	Girl magically made hideous	33
D 1921.	Magic carrying power of voice	9
D 1925.2.	Barrenness removed by bathing	7
D 1960.4.	Deathlike sleep	2, 3
D 1962.4.1.	Lullaby	100
D 2064.0.3.	Magic pestilence	36
D 2065.	Magic insanity	41*
D 2074.2.2.	Summoning by burning [rubbing] feather/hair	1, 22, 33*
D 2074.2.4.3.	Helper summoned by calling his name	21
D 2081.	Land made magically sterile	87
D 2086.	Weapons magically dulled	33
D 2101.	Treasure magically discovered	3, 40, 41*

Motif-Index	Motif	Story
D 2120.	Magic transportation [on clay donkey]	7
D 2121.	Magic journey	34, 34*
D 2126.	Magic underwater journey	1, 100, 100*
D 2141.0.7.1.	Storm produced by prayer	33
D 2144.3.	Heat produced by magic	15
D 2144.4.	Burning by magic [horse's hoofs]	1*
D 2146.2.2.	Night magically lengthened	1
D 2151.	Magic control of waters	2*, 3, 11
D 2152.1.	Magic leveling of mountains	16
D 2157.3.2.	Tree regains life and verdure after treasure it hides in roots is given away	11, 25
D 2161.	Magic healing power	36, 98
D 2161.3.1.	Blindness magically cured	14*
D 2161.3.2.	Magic restoration of severed hand	7, 39
D 2161.3.3.	Magic cure of broken limbs	39
D 2161.4.0.1.	Cure follows dream instructions by saint [old man]	100
D 2161.4.17.	Magic cure by licking	34, 34*
D 2161.5.1.	Cure by holy man	32
D 2178.5.	People created by magic	49

E. The Dead

E 1.	Person comes to life	1*, 20*, 35, 37, 98
E 2.	Dead tree comes to life	2*
E 11.1.	Second blow resuscitates	4, 34, 34*
E 12.	Resuscitation by [in spite of] decapitation	98
E 14.	Resuscitation by dismemberment	98
E 30.	Resuscitation by arrangement of members	1*, 98
E 64.	Resuscitation by magic object [sponge]	20*
E 100.	Resuscitation by medicine	98
E 102.	Resuscitation by magic liquid	98
E 155.4.	Person dead during day, revived at night	100, 100*

Motif-Index	Motif	Story
E 174.	Bones wrapped in sheepskin [handkerchief] revive	1*, 35
E 181.	Means of resuscitation learned	98
E 251.3.3.	Vampire sucks blood	7
E 323.2	Dead mother returns to aid child	30
E 410.	Unquiet grave	35
E 422.	The living corpse	93
E 586.2.	Dead returns 3 days after burial	93
E 711.4.	Soul in necklace	3
E 711.10.	Soul in sword	35
E 712.4.	Soul hidden in box	8*, 35
E 713.	Soul hidden in series of coverings	1, 1*, 35
E 714.6.	Soul (life) in the breath	78, 98
E 715.	Separable soul kept in animal	1, 1*, 35
E 715.1.	Separable soul kept in bird	1, 1*, 35
E 715.3.1.	Separable soul in bee	8*
E 741.1.	Soul in form of star	99
E 752.10.2.	Light must be kept burning by corpse to keep evil spirits away	1, 1*
E 761.3.	Life token: tree fades	27
E 765.3.	Life bound up with object [necklace]	3
E 765.3.	Life bound up with object [sword]	35
E 781.2.	Eyes bought back and replaced	3
E 782.	Limbs successfully replaced	39
E 782.1.	Hands restored	32
E 782.3.1.	Substituted arm	7

F. Marvels

F 10.	Journey to upper world	1, 34, 34*
F 12.	Journey to see deity	25
F 17.	Visit to land of sun	100
F 62.1.	Bird carries person to upper world	1, 34, 34*
F 80.	Journey to lower world	1, 34, 34*, 35, 100*
F 92.	Pit entrance to lower world	34, 34*, 35
F 93.	Water entrance to lower world	1, 100, 100*

Motif-Index	Motif	Story
F 93.0.2.1.	Well entrance to lower world	100
F 96.	Rope to lower world	34, 34*, 35
F 101.3.	Return from lower world on eagle	1, 34, 34*
F 101.6.1.	Escape from lower world on birds	1, 34, 34*
F 102.1.	Hero shoots monster, follows it into lower world	34, 34*
F 127.1.	Journey to serpent kingdom	20, 20*, 98
F 133.	Submarine otherworld	1
F 162.3.4.	Magic apple tree in otherworld	14
F 232.4.2.	Fairy princess with golden hair	15
F 233.3.	Red fairy	33*
F 234.1.15.	Fairy in form of bird	14*, 15, 18
F 235.1.	Fairies invisible	38
F 235.2.	Fairies visible only at certain times	38
F 265.	Fairy bathes	15
F 271.4.3.	Fairies spin	38
F 282.	Fairies travel through air	15
F 302.2.	Man marries fairy, takes her to his home	18
F 302.4.2.	Fairy comes into man's power when he steals her wings (clothes)	18
F 311.1.	Fairy godmother [supernatural midwives]	3
F 312.1.	Fairies bestow supernatural gifts at birth of child	3
F 312.1.1.	Fairies make good wishes for new-born child	3
F 402.1.5.	Demon [genie] causes disease	79
F 403.2.1.	Acquisition of familiar spirit	36
F 403.2.3.6.	Spirit gives counsel	36
F 412.	Visibility of spirits	36
F 417.	Spirits receive their share of everything made at certain specified time	36
F 420.1.4.9.	Water-giants	34, 34*
F 420.4.9.	Water supply controlled by water spirit [monster/dev/snake]	22, 34, 34*, 100*
F 451.2.3.1.	Long-bearded dwarf	23*, 35
F 451.3.5.1.	Dwarfs die	35

Motif-Index	Motif	Story
F 451.3.8.	Dwarfs are strong	35
F 451.4.	Home of dwarfs	23*
F 451.5.1.	Helpful dwarfs	1
F 451.5.2.	Malevolent dwarfs	35
F 451.5.18.	Dwarf loves mortal girl	1
F 451.6.5.	Dwarfs wed	1
F 480.2.	Serpent as house-spirit	60
F 493.0.1.2.	Spirit enters princess' body; she falls ill	45, 79
F 511.2.2.	Person with horse's ears	35
F 515.0.1.	Person without hands	32
F 521.1.1.	Woman with animal hair	86
F 522.	Person with wings	36
F 531.1.0.1.	Beauty of giant	8, 8*
F 531.1.0.1.1.	Beauty of giantess	9
F 531.1.2.2.	Many-headed giant	1, 5, 34, 34*
F 531.1.2.2.2.	Three-headed giant	34, 34*
F 531.1.4.1.	Giant with upper lip reaching heaven; lower, earth	34, 41
F 531.1.5.1.	Giantess throws breasts over shoulder	1, 100
F 531.1.6.3.1.	Giantess with particularly long hair	9
F 531.1.7.	Color of giant	5
F 531.1.8.2.	Giant as serpent	4
F 531.1.11.	Giants and giantess dress as human beings	8, 8*, 9
F 531.3.8.4.	Giantess sings so that it gives echo in all cliffs	9
F 531.5.1.	Giant friendly to man	1
F 531.5.7.	Giants and giantess marry human beings	4, 8, 8*, 9
F 531.5.7.1.	Mortal son of giant	4
F 531.6.2.1.	Giants live in mountains and caves	1, 7, 27
F 531.6.2.2.	Giants live under water	1
F 531.6.3.1.	Giants live in castles	9
F 531.6.7.1.	Giant possesses treasure	11, 34
F 531.6.8.6.	Giants have children	4, 8, 8*
F 531.6.12.	Disappearance or death of giants	8

Motif-Index	Motif	Story
F 531.6.12.6.	Giant slain by man	1, 5, 34, 34*
F 535.1.	Thumbling	29
F 535.1.1.	Adventures of thumbling	29
F 535.1.1.1.1.	Thumbling drives mule	29
F 535.1.1.5.	Thumbling lost in animal track	29
F 535.1.1.10.	Thumbling hides in a small place	29
F 545.2.2.	Horns on forehead	33
F 555.	Remarkable hair	33
F 555.1.	Gold hair	31, 33
F 555.5.	Multi-colored hair	33
F 556.	Remarkable voice	9
F 559.8.	Extraordinary urine	35
F 562.2.	Residence in tree	33
F 565.2.	Remarkably strong woman	9
F 575.3.	Remarkably beautiful child	2, 3
F 577.	Persons identical in appearance	70
F 577.1.	Friends identical in appearance	37
F 582.1.	Serpent damsel	7, 36
F 601.	Extraordinary companions	15, 16, 35
F 601.1.	Extraordinary companions perform hero tasks	15, 16
F 610.	Remarkably strong man	35
F 610.2.	Dwarf hero of superhuman strength	23*, 35
F 610.6.1.	Man so strong he must be chained	1*
F 611.1.6.	Strong man: son of man [woman] and mare [horse]	35
F 611.1.7.	Son of person and giant	4
F 611.3.2.	Hero's precocious strength	4, 35
F 612.2.	Strong hero kills (overcomes) playmates; sent from home	35
F 614.10.	Strong hero fights whole army alone	18, 22, 35
F 621.	Strong man: tree-puller	35
F 623.	Strong man holds up mountain	16
F 624.2.	Strong man lifts large stone	35
F 632.	Mighty eater	15, 16, 23*, 35
F 633.	Mighty drinker	15, 16

Motif-Index	Motif	Story
F 636.	Mighty thrower	15, 16
F 638.	Mighty archer	16
F 639.1.	Mighty digger	35
F 639.1.2.	Strong man finger digs ground; water gushes out	35
F 641.	Person of remarkable hearing	15, 16
F 647.4.1.	Marvelous sensitivity: woman refuses to look at male fish	67
F 668.0.1.	Skillful physician	98
F 668.1.	Skillful surgeon removes, replaces vital organs	98
F 676.	Skillful thief	72, 73
F 679.	Remarkable herdsman [shepherd]	63
F 679.8.	Skill at chess-playing	35
F 681.1.	Marvelous runner keeps leg tied up	5, 15, 16
F 702.	Land of fire	36
F 706.	Land of darkness	100*
F 710.	Extraordinary bodies of water	33
F 718.3.	Well of wine	15
F 725.9.	World at bottom of well	34, 34*
F 763.	City of fire	36
F 771.	Extraordinary castle	20, 20*, 25, 26
F 771.4.1.	Castle inhabited by ogres	5, 7, 10
F 781.	Extraordinary room [ivory]	15
F 782.	Extraordinary doors and windows	2, 2*, 33*
F 783.	Extraordinary carpet	6, 12, 23, 31
F 787.3.	Ivory bed [throne room]	15
F 796.	Dragon seen in sky	61
F 813.1.	Extraordinary apple	14, 34, 34*
F 813.1.1.	Golden apple	34*, 22
F 813.7.	Extraordinary fig	13
F 813.8.	Extraordinary pomegranate	34
F 815.5.	Extraordinary seed [sesame]	94
F 821.1.3.1.	Dress of feathers	5, 19
F 821.1.6.	Bearskin	73
F 821.2.	Dress so fine it goes in nutshell	23, 34, 34*

Motif-Index	*Motif*	*Story*
F 823.	Extraordinary shoes	34
F 823.1.	Golden shoes	24
F 827.5.	Golden comb	15
F 828.	Extraordinary crown	68
F 833.	Extraordinary sword	20*, 35
F 833.1.1.	Sword so heavy only its owner can lift it	5
F 833.5.	Sword cuts everything	20*
F 835.	Extraordinary club	12
F 852.2.	Golden coffin	10
F 866.3.	Golden cup	28
F 868.	Extraordinary saddle	1*
F 873.	Extraordinary army (soldiers)	12, 20, 20*, 25, 94
F 883.1.	Extraordinary book [tiny Bible balanced on thumb]	23*
F 911.	Person swallowed without killing	33
F 911.4.	Jonah	33
F 913.	Victim rescued from swallower's belly	33
F 914.	Person swallowed and disgorged	33
F 915.	Victim speaks from swallower's body	33
F 922.	Swallowed person bereft of clothing	33
F 929.2.	Man [woman] swallows reptiles	7
F 932.	Extraordinary occurrences connected with rivers	2*, 11, 25
F 932.12.	Speaking river	2*, 25
F 933.1.	Miraculous spring bursts forth for holy person	32
F 933.2.	Dry spring restored by moving certain stone	41*
F 942.1.	Ground opens, swallows up person	8, 8*
F 952.7.	Blindness cured by bathing	100, 100*
F 955.1.	Blood-bath as cure for leprosy	37
F 966.	Voices from heaven (or from air)	2, 2*
F 968.	Extraordinary thunder and lightning	8*

Motif-Index	Motif	Story
F 984.1.	Horse sewed in buffalo hides [tar and sheepskin]	14*
F 989.1.	Horse jumps over high wall	14
F 1041.1.2.1.	Lover dies beside dying sweet-heart	28
F 1041.1.10.	Death from envy	2
F 1041.21.3.	Refusal to eat from excessive grief	28
F 1045.	Night spent in tree	33, 62
F 1088.1.	Hero spared for his beauty	35

G. Ogres

G 11.2.	Cannibal giant	8, 8*, 33*, 34, 34*
G 15.	Human being devoured daily	8*, 22, 34, 34*, 100*
G 61.2.	Mother recognizes child's flesh when it is served to be eaten	29
G 71.	Unnatural children eat parent	30
G 84.	Fee-fi-fo-fum [I smell human flesh]	1, 8, 8*, 41, 41*
G 123.	Giant ogress with breasts thrown over shoulder	1, 100
G 242.1.	Witch flies through air on broom-stick	2
G 264.	La Belle Dame Sans Merci	9
G 265.9.	Witch [stepmother] destroys crop	33
G 301.	Monsters	22
G 302.9.7.	Demon [tiny man] eats enormously	23*, 35
G 303.3.1.	Devil in human form	75
G 303.4.6.	Devil's tail	75
G 307.	Jinn	11
G 307.2.2.	Jinn [Arab] unseen by anyone except person he wishes should see him	21
G 328.1.	Serpent inside man [woman] eats his food	7
G 346.2.	Devastating monster	22, 34, 34*
G 354.1.	Snake as ogre	100*
G 361.1.4.	Seven-headed ogre	1, 22, 34*, 41

Motif-Index	Motif	Story
G 401.	Children wander into ogre's house	33*
G 402.	Pursuit of animal leads to ogre's house	9
G 402.1.	Pursuit of bird leads to ogre's house	9
G 452.	Youth takes service with ogre [dervish]	71
G 462.	Person as servant in ogre's house	11
G 465.	Ogre/[dervish] sets impossible tasks	8*, 71
G 512.1.	Ogre killed with knife (sword)	5, 34, 34*, 35
G 526.	Ogre deceived by feigned ignorance of hero	5
G 530.	Ogre's relative aids hero	1
G 530.2.	Help from ogre's son	8, 8*
G 530.3.	Help from ogre's mother	1
G 550.	Rescue from ogre(ss)	8, 8*
G 551.4.	One brother rescues another from ogress	9
G 561.	Ogre [devil] tricked into carrying his prisoner [fellow traveler]	75
G 572.	Ogre overawed by trick	64
G 610.1.	Stealing from ogre [robbers] for revenge	76
G 661.	Ogre's secret overheard	41, 41*
G 671.	Wild man released from captivity aids [harms] hero	1*

H. Tests

H 11.	Recognition through storytelling	48
H 11.1.	Recognition by telling life history	48
H 12.	Recognition by song	42
H 13.2.	Recognition by overheard conversation with stone	2, 2*
H 13.3.	Recognition from overheard conversation of two sons	50
H 16.2.	Recognition by wounds on finger	18, 22
H 31.7.1.	Recognition by ability to shed pearls for tears	3

Motif-Index	Motif	Story
H 51.	Recognition by scar	47
H 55.1.	Recognition through branding with hoof-marks	22
H 56.	Recognition by wound	18, 22
H 57.4.	Recognition by description of woman with missing hands	32
H 58.	Tell-tale handmark	21, 34, 34*
H 61.1.	Recognition of twins by golden chain under skin [golden cane in hand]	31
H 62.	Recognition of transformed (animal) person	12
H 75.4.	Recognition by golden hair	31
H 81.1.	Hero lies by sleeping girl, leaves identification token with her	11
H 81.1.1.	Token taken from sleeping princess	1, 4, 5
H 81.2.	Clandestine visit of princess to hero betrayed by token	19
H 82.2.	Marriage tokens [ring of Solomon] identifying love	35
H 83.	Rescue tokens: proof hero has succeeded in rescue	5
H 84.	Tokens of exploits	1, 5, 22
H 86.3	Ring with inscribed names as tokens	11
H 105.	Parts of slain animal [giant] as token of slaying	1, 4, 5
H 111.	Identification by garment	40
H 111.2.	Identification by feather cloak	19
H 113.	Identification by handkerchief	18, 22
H 117.	Identification by cut garment	5
H 120.	Identification by tokens	34, 34*
H 121.	Identification by cup	28
H 152.2.	Impoverished husband in service of wife recognized	40
H 171.2.	Bird indicates election of king	12, 50
H 218.	Trial by combat	34*
H 251.2.2.	Magic stone detects perjury: sheds water [bursts]	2, 2*

Motif-Index	Motif	Story
H 301.	Excessive demands to prevent marriage	20, 20*, 24, 25, 34, 34*, 40
H 316.	Suitor test: apple/arrow thrown indicates marriage choice	22, 23*, 33*
H 318.	Suitor preferred who will pay enormous sum for bride	12, 13
H 328.	Suitor test: power of endurance [patience]	17, 17*
H 331.	Suitor contest: bride offered as prize	15, 16
H 331.2.1.1.	Suitor contest: success in battle	16
H 331.5.1.	Race with princess for her hand	15, 16
H 332.1.	Suitor in contest with bride	19
H 335.	Tasks assigned suitors: bride a prize for accomplishment	15, 16
H 335.0.1.	Bride helps suitor [husband] perform his tasks	23, 23*
H 335.0.2.2.	Suitor task: prince to learn a trade	53
H 335.3.1.	Suitor task: kill dragon to whom princess is to be sacrificed	22, 34, 34*
H 342.	Suitor test: outwitting princess	19
H 346.	Princess given to man who can heal her	41, 41*
H 355.6.	Suitor test: get wedding dress so fine it will go through ring	34, 34*
H 359.	Other suitor tests	17, 23, 28, 46, 53
H 363.	Deceased wife marriage test	24
H 465.	Test of wife's endurance: haughty princess married to beggar and must endure poverty, menial work	3
H 480.	Father tests	40
H 500.	Test of cleverness or ability	72
H 506.10.	Test of resourcefulness: find relationship among three [2] sticks	16
H 506.11.	Test of resourcefulness: discover how old, respectively, three horses are	16

Motif-Index	Motif	Story
H 507.1.0.1.	Princess defeated in repartee by means of objects accidentally picked up	19
H 542.	Death sentence escaped by propounding riddle king [princess] cannot solve	19
H 548.	Riddle contests	19
H 551.	Princess offered to man who can out-riddle her	19
H 561.1.1.1.	Clever daughter [son] construes enigmatic saying	67
H 561.5.	King and clever minister	90
H 565.	Riddle propounded from chance experience	19
H 573.	Answer to riddle found by trickery	19
H 580.	Enigmatic statements	77
H 582.2.	Riddling answers betray adultery	19
H 586.3.	One traveler to another: let us carry each other and shorten the way	75
H 601.	Wise carving of fowl	74
H 602.3.	Symbolic interpretation of names	52
H 611.1.	Melons ripe and overripe analogous to girls ready for marriage	22
H 617.	Symbolic interpretations of dreams	16
H 790.	Riddles based on unusual circumstances	19
H 901.	Tasks [repetition of phrase] imposed on pain of death	28
H 911.	Tasks suggested by courtier [vizier]	15
H 914.	Tasks assigned because of mother's foolish boasting	38
H 916.	Tasks imposed at suggestion of spouse	14*
H 919.1.	Tasks assigned at suggestion of treacherous servants	14, 15
H 921.1.	Tasks set by king to sons to determine heir to kingdom	34*

Motif-Index	Motif	Story
H 931.1.	Prince envious of hero's wife assigns hero tasks	23, 23*
H 935.	Witch [mid-wife] assigns tasks	31
H 945.	Tasks voluntarily undertaken [cure: blindness]	14*
H 962.	Tasks performed by close observation	14, 15
H 963.	Tasks performed by means of secrets overheard from tree [cave]	41, 41*
H 970.	Help in performing tasks [from mother-in-law]	23, 23*
H 971.1.	Tasks performed with help of old woman	35
H 973.1.	Task performed by fairy	38
H 974.	Task performed with help of supernatural wife	23, 23*
H 982.	Animals help man perform task	14, 14*
H 984.	Tasks performed with help of saint	40
H 991.	Unpromising hero last to try task	1, 1*, 22, 34, 34*
H 1010.	Impossible tasks	71
H 1024.2.	Task: placing frogs [turtle] in tree	32
H 1066.	Task: sweep floor and do not sweep it	8*
H 1092.0.1.	Task: spinning and weaving large amount by specified time	38
H 1131.	Task: building enormous bridge	40
H 1132.1.1.	Task: recovering lost ring from sea	20, 20*
H 1133.4.	Task: building palace of gold	20, 20*, 25
H 1141.	Task: eating enormous amount	15, 16
H 1142.	Task: drinking enormous amount	15, 16
H 1149.7.	Task: drawing spear [through iron shield]	16
H 1151.4.	Task: stealing ring from finger	14
H 1151.6.	Task: stealing elephants' tusks	15
H 1154.7.	Task: capturing bird	14, 14*, 31
H 1154.8.	Task: capturing [sea] horse	1*, 14*
H 1191.1.	Task: plant beautiful garden	20, 20*, 25
H 1193.	Task: causing dry spring to flow	41*

Motif-Index	Motif	Story
H 1210.1.	Quest assigned by father	1, 1*, 14*, 34, 34*, 46
H 1211.	Quests assigned in order to get rid of hero	14*, 23, 31
H 1212.	Quests assigned because of feigned illness	3, 4, 12, 33*, 34*
H 1213.	Quest for remarkable bird caused by sight of one of its feathers	14, 14*
H 1217.	Quest assigned because of dream	16
H 1217.1.	Quest for explanation of dream	16
H 1219.5.	Quest assigned [by] prisoner	93
H 1219.8.	Quest as punishment for [mother's] curiosity	25
H 1233.2.1.	Quest accomplished with aid of wife	23, 23*
H 1233.4.2.	Quest accomplished with aid of giantess	100
H 1233.6.1.	Horse helper on quest	1*, 14, 14*, 31
H 1236.1.	Quest over path bristling with sharp points	14, 14*
H 1236.2.	Quest over path guarded by dangerous animals	14, 14*
H 1242.	Youngest brother alone succeeds on quest	14*
H 1244.	Forgiveness the reward of successful quest	100
H 1263.	Quest to God for fortune [child]	25
H 1284.1.	Quest to place where sun sets	100
H 1286.	Quests to Fairyland	14, 15
H 1289.4.	Quests to see deity	25
H 1291.	Questions asked on way to otherworld	25
H 1292.1.1.	Question (propounded on quest): why does no one ever drink water of stream?	25
H 1292.2.	Question: why does not a certain tree flourish?	25
H 1292.5.	Question (on quest): how can girl thus far avoided by suitors marry?	25

Motif-Index	Motif	Story
H 1301.	Quest for most beautiful of women	13
H 1301.1.2.	Quest for far-away princess	16, 35
H 1320.	Quest for miraculous objects or animals	14, 14*
H 1319.3.	Quest for most beautiful [unusually large] rug	23, 23*
H 1324.	Quest for marvelous remedy	14, 14*, 22, 34*
H 1331.1.	Quest for marvelous bird	14, 14*
H 1331.1.4.	Quest for speaking bird	31
H 1331.4.	Quest for marvelous horse [sea horse]	1*, 14*
H 1333.3.0.1.	Quest for rejuvenating fruit	14
H 1352.	Quest for magic ring	20, 20*
H 1359.	Quest for marvelous objects (misc.)	34, 34*
H 1361.	Quest for lion's/sea horse's milk	14*, 22
H 1376.2.	Quest: learning what fear is	64
H 1381.1.	Quest for unknown parents	31
H 1381.3.1.1.	Quest: bride for king	14, 14*, 15
H 1381.3.1.2.2.	Quest for girl hero has seen in dream	3
H 1381.3.8.	Quest for queen of fairies	15
H 1385.3.	Quest for vanished wife	18
H 1385.4.	Quest for vanished husband	25
H 1385.8.	Quest for lost brother[s]	7
H 1416.	Test: spending night by grave	35
H 1440.	The learning of fear	64
H 1471.	Watch for devastating monster	22, 34, 34*
H 1471.1.	Watch for thieves in king's garden	34, 34*
H 1481.	Thumb cut, salt put on it in order to remain awake	1, 1*, 26, 34, 34*
H 1510.	Tests of power to survive	47
H 1511.	Heat test	15
H 1533.	Hanging test: unavailing attempt to kill hero by hanging	39
H 1553.	Tests of patience	17, 17*
H 1554.	Tests of curiosity	17

Motif-Index	*Motif*	*Story*
H 1558.	Tests of friendship	36
H 1558.0.1.1.	Apple [bread] test for worthiness for friendship	36
H 1558.7.2.	Friends desert when man reports loss of his money	13, 21, 40
H 1561.	Tests of valor	34*
H 1561.1.	Tests of valor: tournament	34*
H 1562.	Test of strength	16, 34*
H 1562.2.1.	Test of strength: lifting sword	5, 36
H 1576.1.	Test of magic powers: telling sex of unborn goat [foal]	67
H 1594.1.	Foot-race between fairy and mortal	15

J. The Wise and the Foolish

J 21.	Counsels proved wise by experience	6, 6*
J 21.2.	"Do not act when angry" counsel proved wise by experience	6, 6*, 17
J 21.6.	"Do not ask questions about extraordinary things"	6*
J 21.18.	"Do not trust the over-holy"	77
J 21.23.	Rise earlier	25
J 21.25.	Do not keep bad company	21
J 51.	Sight of deformed witches [bee] causes man to release wife from spinning duty	38
J 133.	Animal gives wise example to man	78
J 147.	Child confined to keep him in ignorance of life	49
J 152.2.	Advice from dervish	6, 25, 27, 28, 39
J 154.	Wise words of dying father	5
J 157.0.1.	Deity appears in dream and gives instructions or advice	40
J 163.4.	Good counsels bought	6, 6*
J 171.1.	Counsel: if you take it you will be sorry; if you don't you will also be sorry	14

Motif-Index	Motif	Story
J 214.	Choice: suffering in youth or old age	50
J 227.2.	Death preferred to dishonor	48
J 347.4.	Rich man poorer in happiness than poor man	54
J 514.3.	Greedy man keeps demanding one more thing from complacent man	17, 17*
J 672.2.	Cotton in ears so as not to hear abusive words [loud voice]	9
J 1113.	Clever boy	67
J 1115.9.	Clever shepherd	63
J 1117.	Animal as trickster	10
J 1124.	Clever court jester	70
J 1146.1.	Detection by pitch trap	73
J 1147.	Detection through feigned dream	77
J 1147.1.	Husband relates wife's adultery	77
J 1170.1.	Series of wise judgments settle quarrels of village [farmers]	41
J 1177.0.1.	None should interrupt or leave room while story is told: treachery revealed	48
J 1179.10.	Enoch Arden decision	100, 100*
J 1198.1.	King pleased with thieves' cleverness	72, 73
J 1263.	Repartee based on clerical ignorance	69
J 1280.	Repartee with ruler	63
J 1330.	Repartee concerning beggars	80
J 1351.2.	Envious accuser	90
J 1510.	The cheater cheated	66
J 1655.	Clever ways of concealing jewels	72
J 2349.4.	Woman [man] asks for news from home	97
J 2411.1.	Imitation of magic rejuvenation unsuccessful	14, 14*
J 2541.	Don't eat too greedily	10

K. Deceptions

K 231.3.	Refusal to make sacrifice after need is past	88

Motif-Index	*Motif*	*Story*
K 251.2.	Trickster demands return of food guest has just eaten: gets damages	96
K 301.	Master thief	72, 73
K 301.2.	Family of thieves	73
K 305.1.	Thieving contest	72
K 308.	Youngest brother surpasses elder as thief	73
K 311.1.1.	Sham dead man brought in sack by confederate	69
K 311.2.	Thief disguised as angel	73
K 311.17.	Thief disguised as beggar	80
K 315.	Thief enters treasury through secret passage	73
K 318.	Watchdog enticed away, poisoned	76
K 331.4.	Mouse's tail in mouth of sleeping owner causes him to cough up magic object	20*
K 332.	Theft by making owner drunk	12, 13, 15
K 335.0.9.	Delivery boy frightened into giving up his chickens [rooster]	76
K 335.1.	Robbers frightened from goods	62, 76
K 335.1.1.1.	Door falls on robbers from tree	62
K 341.20.	The story about theft: one thief steals, other relates the situation in form of tale to gentleman who is being robbed	72
K 407.1.	Thief has companions cut off his head so he may escape detection	73
K 423.	Stolen object magically returns to owner	20*
K 431.	Mouse's tail in mouth of sleeping thief causes him to cough up [sneeze] swallowed magic ring	20*
K 439.6.	Robbers fed poisoned food	51
K 511.	Uriah letter changed	47, 47*
K 512.1.	Compassionate executioner: bloody coat	2, 5, 48
K 523.0.1.	Illness (madness, dumbness) speechlessness feigned to escape unwelcome marriage	18

Motif-Index	Motif	Story
K 528.	Substitute in ordeal	37
K 532.1.	Escape in mist of invisibility	8
K 550.	Escape by false plea	48
K 551.1.	Respite from death granted until prayer is finished	45
K 555.2.2.	Escape [trick] by singing endless song	75
K 557.	Death cheated by moving bed	45
K 714.2.1.	Victim tricked into jumping in box by making him think he is going to heaven	73
K 730.	Victim trapped	73
K 751.1.	Capture by hiding in animal carcass	14*
K 752.	Capture by hiding under screen [wheat]	14
K 776.	Capture by intoxication [elephant trunks collected]	15
K 778.1.	Woman (Amazon) in disguise invites enemies singly into forest, overcomes them	9
K 811.	Victim lured into house, then killed	9
K 831.	Victim killed [natural death] while being bathed	70
K 832.1.1.	Victim persuaded to look into well or pond, pushed in	79
K 912.	Giants' heads cut off one by one as they enter house [climb wall]	1, 4, 5
K 955.	Murder by burning	29, 47*
K 955.1.	Murder by scalding	41, 64
K 956.1.	Gradual murder by piecemeal destruction of separable soul	1, 35
K 961.	Flesh of certain animal alleged to be cure for disease: animal to be killed	4, 33, 33*
K 963.	Rope cut and victim dropped	34, 34*
K 975.2.	Secret of external soul learned by deception	1, 35
K 978.	Uriah letter	47

Motif-Index	*Motif*	*Story*
K 1082.2.	Object thrown into air causes enemies [*devs*] to fight over it	12
K 1227.	Lover put off by deceptive respite	48
K 1322.	Girl masked as man wins princess' love	11
K 1335.	Wooing by stealing clothes of bathing girl	18
K 1336.	Magic helper brings girl to hero's bed	11, 21
K 1342.1.	Heroine in hiding-box which is brought to prince	24
K 1344.	Tunnel entrance to guarded maiden's chamber	28
K 1346.	Hero flies to maiden's room	18
K 1349.10.	Admission to woman's room by means of cap of invisibility [shirt of]	13
K 1355.	Altered letter of execution gives princess to hero	47, 47*
K 1411.	Plowing field: horse and harness destroyed	71
K 1413.	Guarding door	62
K 1462.	Washing grandmother [mother] in boiling water	62
K 1500.	Deceptions connected with adultery	77
K 1550.1.	Husband discovers wife's adultery	77
K 1570.	Adulteress and paramour outwitted by trickster [hero]	35
K 1580.	Other deceptions connected with adultery	42
K 1612.	Message of death fatal to sender	47*
K 1613.	Poisoner poisoned with own poison	4, 43
K 1733.	Ogre made to believe hero has withstood fire [hot water]	64
K 1810.1.	Disguise by putting on clothes of certain person	70
K 1810.1.3.	Taking king's place by changing dress	14

Motif-Index	Motif	Story
K 1811.4.2.	Angel [soul-taking] takes form of certain person [boy]	45
K 1812.	King in disguise	3, 6, 27, 28, 31, 47, 47*, 63, 90
K 1812.1.	Incognito king helped by humble man	90
K 1812.17.	King in disguise to spy out his kingdom	3, 6, 27, 28, 31, 47, 47*, 63, 90
K 1815.2.	Ugly disguise	22, 33*, 34, 34*
K 1816.1.	Gardener disguise	22, 33*
K 1816.6.	Disguise as shepherd	48
K 1817.1.	Disguise as beggar	53
K 1818.2.	Scald-head disguise	22, 33*, 34, 34*
K 1821.8.	Disguise as old man	5
K 1825.1.1.	Lover masks as doctor to reach sweetheart	11
K 1828.1.	Disguise as angel of death	73
K 1837.	Disguise as woman in man's clothes	11, 48
K 1840.	Deception by substitution	70
K 1851.	Substituted letter	32
K 1860.	Deception by feigned death	85
K 1867.	Trickster shams death to get food	85
K 1892.	Deception by hiding	71
K 1892.1.	Hiding in bag in order to be carried	71
K 1911.	False bride	3, 33, 100*
K 1911.1.1.	False bride takes true bride's place on way to wedding	3
K 1911.1.4.	False bride finishes true bride's task, supplants her	2, 2*
K 1911.2.2.	True bride/hero pushed into water by false [stepmother/brothers]	14*, 33, 100*
K 1911.2.2.1.	True bride lives in fish's belly	33

Motif-Index	Motif	Story
K 1911.3.1.	Substitution of false bride revealed by animal [transformed]	33
K 1917.3.	Penniless wooer; helpful animal reports master wealthy, thus wins girl for him	10
K 1920.	Substituted children	31
K 1931.2.	Impostors [brothers] abandon hero in lower world	34, 34*
K 1932.	Impostors [brothers] claim reward earned by hero	34*
K 1934.1.	Impostor takes place of king [jester]	70
K 1945.	Imposition by sham sickness	3, 4, 33, 34*
K 1951.4.	Boastful coward frightened by conspirators	64
K 1952.1.1.	Poor boy said by helpful animal to be dispossessed prince who has lost clothes while swimming [robbed]	10
K 1952.2.	Better things at home	10
K 1953.	Sham brave man	64
K 1954.	Sham rich man	10
K 1954.1.	Helpful cat [fox] borrows measure for master's money	10
K 1955.6.	Sham physician and devil (spirit) in partnership	79
K 1961.1.1.	Peasant as priest	69
K 1961.1.2.1.	Parody sermon	69
K 2015.	Child adopted by rich man in order to get rid of him	47, 47*
K 2035.	Supernatural personages [saint] seen in dream [gives advice]	40
K 2052.1.	Bride's (wife's) false modesty	67, 77
K 2058.	Pretended piety	77
K 2058.1.	Apparently pious man a thief	77
K 2101.	Falsely accused minister reinstates self by cleverness	90
K 2110.1.	Calumniated wife	31, 32, 48
K 2112.	Woman slandered as adulteress	48
K 2115.	Animal-birth slander	31, 32

Motif-Index	Motif	Story
K 2116.1.	Innocent woman accused of murder	48
K 2117.	Calumniated wife: substituted letter (falsified message)	32
K 2117.1.	Husband's letter ordering calumniated wife to be treated well is altered to order of execution	32
K 2127.	False accusation of theft	90
K 2151.	Corpse handed around	71
K 2211.01.	Treacherous elder brothers	14*, 34, 34*
K 2212.	Treacherous sister	4, 31
K 2212.0.1.	Treacherous sister attempts to poison brother	4
K 2212.0.2.	Treacherous sister as mistress of giant plots against brother	4
K 2212.1.	Treacherous stepsisters	33
K 2214.2.	Treacherous daughter-in-law	42
K 2217.	Treacherous uncle	5
K 2243.	Treacherous seneschal	48
K 2260.1.	Treacherous dark man	28
K 2272.	Crippled villain	1*
K 2277.	Treacherous dwarf	35
K 2284.	Treacherous priest	48
K 2296.1.	Treacherous robber-partner	41, 41*, 51, 52
K 2320.	Deception by frightening	73

L. Reversal of Fortune

L 10.	Victorious youngest son	1, 1*, 5, 14, 14*, 22, 27, 34, 34*
L 11.1.	Seal of humiliation put by youngest brother-in-law on back of rivals	22
L 51.	Favorite youngest daughter	30
L 52.	Abused youngest daughter/ [daughter-in-law]	23, 30
L 54.	Compassionate youngest daughter	30, 33
L 55.	Stepdaughter heroine	32, 33
L 55.1.	Abused stepdaughter	32, 33, 100*

577

Motif-Index	*Motif*	*Story*
L 111.3.	Widow's son as hero	13, 14, 15, 17, 18, 20, 20*, 40, 76
L 111.4.4.	Mistreated orphan hero	71
L 113.1.0.1.	Heroine endures hardships with menial husband	3, 6, 22
L 113.10.	Flute player a hero	63
L 114.	Hero of unpromising habits	21, 40
L 114.1.	Lazy hero	40
L 114.3.	Unruly hero	35
L 121.	Stupid hero	62
L 161.	Lowly hero marries princess	10, 12, 13, 14, 15, 16, 20, 25, 39, 40, 41, 41*
L 161.1.	Marriage of poor boy, rich girl	3, 6, 6*, 17, 17*, 22, 47, 47*
L 162.	Lowly heroine marries prince	32, 33
L 165.	Lowly boy becomes king	12, 15, 22, 41, 41*, 47*
L 351.2.	Man curses sun	100

M. Ordaining the Future

M 101.	Punishment for broken oaths	88
M 146.3.	Vow that magically conceived children shall marry	28
M 149.1.	Lovers vow to marry only each other	99
M 161.2.	Vow to revenge or death	76
M 202.0.1.	Bargain or promise to be fulfilled at all hazards	27
M 202.1.	Promise to be fulfilled when iron shoes wear out	18, 25
M 205.	Breaking of bargain or promise	10, 28
M 220.	Other bargains	19
M 225.	Eyes exchanged for food [water]	3
M 234.	Life spared in return for life-long service	71

Motif-Index	Motif	Story
M 241.	Bargain: to divide all winnings	36, 41, 52
M 241.1.	Dividing the winnings: half of bride	36
M 246.	Covenant of friendship	37
M 251.	Dying man's promise to be kept	11, 52
M 255.	Deathbed promise concerning second wife	24
M 257.2.	Murdered person's request and promise	52
M 301.	Prophets [dervish]	34*
M 301.10.	Angels as prophets	44
M 301.16.	Gods prophesy both good and evil about hero's fate	50
M 301.20.	Child as prophet	67
M 302.2.1.	Fate written on head	44
M 302.7.	Prophecy through dreams	2*, 16, 50
M 312.	Prophecy of future greatness for youth	34*, 47, 47*
M 312.3.	Eater of magic bird-heart will become rich	12
M 312.4.	Prophecy: superb beauty for girl	3
M 314.	Prophecy: child will become king	47, 47*
M 341.	Death prophecies	41, 44
M 341.1.3.	Prophecy: death before certain age	44
M 341.2.	Prophecy: death by particular instrument [fall from tree]	41, 44
M 341.3.1.	Prophecy: death in Jerusalem	93
M 353.	Prediction by bird [tree] that girl will have dead husband	2*
M 369.2.	Prophecies concerning love and marriage	2*
M 369.7.1.	Prophecy: birth of twins	31
M 369.8.	Prophecies about children born at same time	28
M 370.	Vain attempts to escape fulfillment of prophecy	2, 2*, 28, 47, 47*
M 370.1.	Death prophecy fulfilled	44
M 371.	Exposure of infant to avoid fulfillment of prophecy	47, 47*

Motif-Index	Motif	Story
M 373.	Expulsion to avoid fulfillment of prophecy	47*
M 411.	Deliverer of curse	7, 8, 8*
M 411.1	Curse by parent	8, 8*
M 411.24.	Curse on city by sage [God]	87
M 414.	Recipient of curse	7, 8, 100, 100*
M 431.5.	Curse: wound not to heal	7
M 463.	Curse on district	87

N. Chance and Fate

N 121.	Fate decided before birth	44, 47, 47*
N 122.0.1.	Choice of roads	41
N 146.	Man not fated to die cannot be killed	39, 44, 47, 47*
N 200.	Good gifts of fortune	3
N 201.	Wish for exalted husband realized	3, 6, 31
N 211.1.	Lost ring found in fish	20, 20*
N 251.	Person pursued by misfortune	50
N 252.	Messengers announce successive misfortunes	95, 97
N 271.2.	Murder revealed by unusual names of boys	52
N 311.	Separations of persons caused by looking for water	2*
N 315.	Separation by being on different banks of stream	50
N 322.	Eavesdropping person unwittingly killed	41, 41*
N 331.	Things accidentally fall, kill person	27
N 332.1.	Man accidentally fed bread which father [wife] has poisoned	43
N 334.	Accidental fatal ending to game or joke	69
N 334.2.	Hanging in game or jest accidentally proves fatal	76

Motif-Index	Motif	Story
N 338.	Death as result of mistaken identity	6*, 17, 17*
N 343.4.	Lover commits suicide on finding beloved dead	28
N 347.	Innocent man accidentally suspected of crime	90
N 451.	Secrets heard from animal [dev] conversation	41, 41*
N 452.	Secret remedy overheard in conversation of animals [devs]	41, 41*
N 452.1.	Remedy for lack of water in certain place overheard in conversation of animals [devs]	41*
N 456.	Enigmatical smile reveals secret knowledge	78
N 467.	King in disguise to learn secrets of subjects	3, 6, 31, 47, 47*
N 471.	Foolish attempt of second man to overhear secrets	41, 41*
N 512.	Treasure in underground cavern	40
N 531.	Treasure discovered through dream	55
N 534.4.	Information about treasure received from overheard conversation	41*
N 536.	Treasure pointed out by angel [saint]	40
N 553.	Tabus in effect while treasure is being unearthed	55
N 554.1.	Sacrifices at unearthing of treasure	55
N 659.1.	Poisoned cakes intended for man [beggar] by wife eaten by husband	43
N 681.	Lover arrives home just as girl is to marry another	28, 34, 34*
N 682.	Prophecy of future greatness fulfilled	34*, 47*
N 683.	Stranger accidentally chosen king	12, 50
N 711.1.	Prince finds maiden in tree/ [woods], marries her	32, 33, 48
N 711.2.	Hero finds maiden in magic castle	5

Motif-Index	Motif	Story
N 711.6.	Prince sees heroine at ball, is enamored	23, 30
N 712.	Prince first sees heroine as she comes forth from hiding box	24
N 715.1.	Hero finds maiden at fountain	8
N 716.	Lover sees beloved first while she is bathing	18
N 731.1.	Unknown son returns to father's court	50
N 731.2.	Father-son combat	34*
N 735.	Accidental meeting of mother and son	42, 50
N 743.	Accidental meeting of sisters	30
N 765.	Meeting with robber band	51
N 773.1.	Adventure from following ogre to cave	34, 35
N 774.3.	Adventures from pursuing animal (not magic) [bird]	9
N 778.	Taking refuge in grave [cemetery] leads to adventure	77
N 791.	Adventures from pursuing object carried off by river	50
N 810.1.	Invisible guardian	11
N 810.5.	Supernatural person disguised as servant as helper	36
N 811.	Supernatural godfather [angel]	45
N 812.2.	Giantess as foster mother and helper of hero	1, 100
N 812.5.	Monster grateful to hero for being spared becomes helpful	22
N 813.	Helpful spirit [genie]	21, 36
N 815.	Fairy as helper	38
N 825.3.	Old woman helper	31
N 826.	Help from beggar	53
N 831.1.	Mysterious housekeeper	7
N 836.	King as helper	63
N 836.1.	King adopts hero	90
N 844.	Dervish as helper	25, 27, 28, 29, 39, 40, 47, 47*

Motif-Index	Motif	Story
N 848.	Saint as helper	40
N 854.	Peasant as helper	7
N 884.1.	Robber helps king	73

P. Society

P 11.	Choice of king	12, 34*, 50
P 11.2.	Winner of contest to be king	34*
P 17.0.2.	Son succeeds father as king	14*
P 17.0.2.1.	At son's wedding king names him successor	34, 34*
P 17.8.	Kingship given younger brother	14*, 22, 34*
P 17.10.	Three sons each get a kingship	5
P 110.	Royal ministers	90
P 160.	Beggars	43, 53
P 171.	Branding person makes him one's slave for life	22
P 231.	Mother and son	42
P 233.	Father and son	34*
P 251.4.	Brothers scorn brother's wise counsel	5
P 251.6.1.	Three brothers	1, 1*, 5, 9, 14*, 22, 27, 34, 34*
P 252.2.	Three sisters	1, 1*, 3, 5, 6, 22, 30, 31, 34, 51
P 253.	Sister and brother	4, 31, 33
P 253.0.5.	One sister and seven brothers	7
P 253.0.2.	One sister and two brothers	36
P 253.0.3.	One sister and three brothers	4
P 253.2.	Sister faithful to transformed brother	33
P 262.	Mother-in-law	8, 23, 25, 42
P 262.1.	Bad relations between mother-in-law, daughter-in-law	23, 42
P 273.1.	Faithful foster brother	11
P 274.1.	Love between foster brother and sister	35

Motif-Index	*Motif*	*Story*
P 282.	Stepmother	12, 32, 33, 100*
P 291.	Grandfather	35
P 291.1.	Grandfather as foster father	35
P 293.1.	Mother's brother as foster father	4
P 295.	Cousins	3
P 296.1.	Godfather	35, 45
P 311.	Sworn brethren	37
P 340.	Teacher and pupil	42, 49
P 401.	Son insists on following father's trade	14, 15
P 412.	Shepherd	44, 50
P 412.1.	Shepherd as hero	50, 90
P 424.	Physician	98
P 428.	Musician	29, 96
P 431.	Merchant	6, 6*, 17, 17*, 42, 53
P 443.	Miller	10, 28, 50, 86
P 447.7.	Goldsmith as lover	77
P 452.	Dressmaker	42
P 453.	Shoemaker	41*
P 475.	Robbers	72, 73

Q. Rewards and Punishments

Q 2.	Kind and unkind	33
Q 40.	Kindness rewarded	33, 39
Q 41.	Politeness rewarded	33
Q 41.2.	Reward for cleansing loathsome person	33
Q 45.	Hospitality rewarded	39
Q 51.	Kindness to animals rewarded	20, 20*, 78, 98
Q 64.	Patience rewarded	17, 17*
Q 82.1.	Snake helps girl who permits it to wind self around her body	100*
Q 94.	Reward for cure	36, 41, 41*

584

Motif-Index	Motif	Story
Q 112.0.1.	Kingdom as reward	5, 16, 22, 47, 47*
Q 114.3.	Sword as reward	36
Q 211.4.	Murder of children punished	48
Q 223.1.	Neglect to pray punished	40
Q 223.3.	Neglect to sacrifice punished	88
Q 261.	Treachery punished	31, 32, 33, 41, 41*, 52
Q 265.4.	Punishment for undeserved curse [blindness]	100
Q 280.	Unkindness punished	33
Q 285.1.	Cruelty to animal punished	100*
Q 312.	Fault-finding punished	17, 17*
Q 312.4.	Fault-finding with God's handling of weather	17
Q 338.	Immoderate request punished	17, 17*
Q 341.	Curiosity punished	17, 25
Q 416.2.	Punishment: dragging to death by horse [jackass]	3, 31, 32, 33, 34
Q 422.	Punishment: stoning to death	51
Q 431.	Punishment: banishment	16, 18, 25
Q 433.	Punishment: imprisonment	16
Q 434.	Punishment: fettering	1*
Q 451.1.	Hands cut off as punishment	32
Q 451.3.	Loss of speech as punishment	89
Q 451.7.	Blinding as punishment	17, 100, 100*
Q 456.	Burial alive as punishment	42
Q 457.	Flaying alive as punishment	71
Q 471.1.	Persecuted queen [princess] meanly clothed, set where all are commanded to spit on her	31
Q 478.1.1.	Man sends daughter heart [flesh] of her lover	28
Q 478.2.	Adultress compelled to eat with dog	6*
Q 502.2.	Punishment: wandering until iron shoes are worn out	18, 25
Q 520.	Penances	17
Q 521.	Tedious penances	17

Motif-Index	Motif	Story
Q 522.	Self-torture as penance	17
Q 551.3.2.2.	Punishment: woman [man] transformed to birds	15
Q 551.3.2.6.	Punishment: transformation to ass	12, 39, 94
Q 551.3.2.7.	Punishment: transformation to dog	39, 94
Q 551.3.4.	Transformation to stone as punishment	87, 88
Q 551.7.	Magic paralysis as punishment	89
Q 551.7.2.	Magic paralysis as punishment for theft	89
Q 551.9.1.	Miraculous burning as punishment	33*
Q 552.2.3.	Earth swallowings as punishment	8
Q 552.3.1.	Famine as punishment	87
Q 552.3.3.	Drought as punishment	87
Q 556.	Curse as punishment	8
Q 559.2.	Punishment: man stricken blind	100, 100*
Q 559.5.1.	Birth of child prevented until girl confesses slander [mother uses certain phrases]	8
Q 571.	Magic blindness as punishment	100, 100*
Q 581.	Villain nemesis	1, 32, 33, 34, 34*

R. Captives and Fugitives

R 11.1.	Princess abducted by ogre	1, 1*, 5, 34, 34*, 35
R 13.1.5.	Wolf abducted person [child]	50
R 13.1.6.	Girl abducted by bear, made his wife	86
R 41.1.1.	Captivity in subterranean palace	1, 1*, 34
R 45.	Captivity on mountain	1*
R 45.3.	Captivity in cave	27, 32, 86
R 51.2.	Prisoner confined in chains	1*, 35
R 111.1.3.	Rescue of princess from dragon/ [dev]	22, 27, 34, 34*, 35
R 111.1.4.	Rescue of princess from giant	5
R 111.2.1.	Princess rescued from lower world	1, 34, 34*, 35

Motif-Index	*Motif*	*Story*
R 111.2.2.	Rescue of princess from mountain	3
R 131.	Abandoned child rescued	4, 47, 47*
R 131.0.2.	Miraculous rescue of all exposed children	31
R 131.2.	Miller rescues child/hero	28, 50
R 131.3.	Herdsman rescues abandoned child	50
R 131.7.	Merchant rescues abandoned child	47*
R 135.	Abandoned children find way back home	33*
R 155.1.	Youngest brother rescues elder brother	9
R 165.	Rescue by saint [dervish]	39
R 185.1.	Mortal deceives angel of death	45
R 211.3.	Escape through underground passage	16, 28
R 215.	Escape from execution	39
R 220.	Flights	23, 30
R 221.	Heroine's flight from ball	23, 30
R 222.	Unknown knight	34*
R 227.3.	Supernatural wife finds garment stolen from her husband, leaves him	18
R 231.	Obstacle flight	8, 8*, 14
R 243.	Fugitives aided by helpful animal	8*
R 260.	Pursuits	8, 8*
R 311.	Tree refuge	33, 62
R 315.	Cave as refuge	32
R 321.	Escape to stars	99
R 351.	Fugitive discovered by reflection in water	33

S. Unnatural Cruelty

S 11.	Cruel father	31
S 11.3.	Father kills child	8*
S 12.	Cruel mother	2
S 20.1.	Children [son] sell mother and father	19
S 21.3.	Son gives mother as hostage	19

Motif-Index	Motif	Story
S 31.	Cruel stepmother	12, 32, 33, 33*, 47*, 100*
S 31.5.	Girl persuades father to marry widow who has treated her kindly	32
S 42.	Cruel grandfather	35
S 51.	Cruel mother-in-law	23
S 54.	Cruel daughter-in-law	42
S 71.	Cruel uncle	5
S 72.	Cruel aunt	3
S 111.	Murder [sleep] by poisoning	2
S 112.	Burning to death	1*, 10, 33*
S 112.0.1.	City burned with all inhabitants	36
S 112.1.	Boiling to death	41
S 112.6.	Murder by roasting alive in oven	29
S 113.1.	Murder by hanging	76
S 113.2.2.	Suitor task: not suffocating in bathroom	15
S 114.	Murder by flaying	71
S 114.1.	Skin of murdered person found in enemy's house	71
S 123.	Burial alive	42
S 127.	Murder by throwing from height	7
S 141.	Exposure in boat	24, 33
S 142.	Person thrown into water, abandoned	28, 47*
S 143.	Abandonment in forest	2, 12, 31, 32, 33*, 47
S 146.1.	Abandonment in well	34, 34*, 79
S 147.1.	Abandonment on cliff	41*
S 161.	Mutilation: cutting off hands (arms)	32
S 165.	Mutilation: putting out eyes	3
S 166.	Mutilation: skin cut from back	71
S 180.	Wounding	4, 18, 22, 34, 41*, 47
S 210.	Child sold	47, 47*
S 211.	Child promised to devil [dervish]	27

Motif-Index	*Motif*	*Story*
S 223.4.	Childless couple [king] promise one of two [three] children to devil [dervish] if they may only have them	27
S 260.1.	Human sacrifices	22, 34, 34*
S 260.1.4.	Sacrifice of child to save life of another	37
S 262.	Periodic sacrifices to monster	22, 34, 34*
S 263.3.	Person sacrificed to water spirit to secure water supply	22, 34, 34*
S 268.	Child sacrificed to provide blood for cure of friend [Amis and Amulou]	37
S 268.1.	Sacrifice of child demanded as cure for feigned sickness	2
S 301.	Children exposed	31, 32, 33
S 302.	Children murdered	48
S 314.	Twins exposed	31
S 322.	Children abandoned (driven forth) by hostile relative	33
S 322.1.3.	Father condemns daughter to death because he believes her unchaste	49
S 322.2.	Jealous mother casts daughter forth	2
S 322.4.	Evil stepmother casts boy(s) forth	12
S 331.	Exposure of child in boat [basket]	31, 47*
S 338.	Father abandons daughter [children] in forest, leaves axes [pumpkin] tied so they move in wind	33, 33*
S 351.1.	Abandoned child [children] cared for by grandmother (foster mother)	31
S 353.2.	Angels feed exposed child/mother	32
S 410.	Persecuted wife	31, 32, 48
S 430.	Disposal of cast-off wife	31
S 451.	Outcast wife at last united with husband and child/children	31, 32
S 465.	Abandoned person in woods comforted by prophet and birds	32

T. Sex

Motif-Index	Motif	Story
T 11.1.1.	Beauty of woman reported to king causes quest for her for his bride	9
T 11.2.1.	Love through sight of statue	23*
T 11.3.	Love through dream	3
T 11.3.1.	Lovers meet in their dreams	11
T 11.5.	Falling in love with reflection in water	33
T 22.4.	Lovers fated to marry born at same time	28
T 24.1.	Love sickness	11, 37
T 28.	Princess falls in love with man [woman] disguised as woman [man]	11
T 32.1.	Lovers' meeting: hero in heroine's father's prison from which she helps him escape	16
T 35.5.	Lover goes to see beloved in her father's house, defiant of danger	28
T 45.	Lover buys admission to woman's room	12, 13
T 50.1.2.	Girl carefully guarded by father	49
T 50.2.	King/brothers like(s) daughter so that he does not want to marry her to anyone	49, 96
T 53.3.	Saint as matchmaker	40
T 61.5.3.	Unborn children promised in marriage to each other	28
T 62.	Princess to marry first man [suitor] who asks for her	1, 1*, 3
T 67.2.	Marriage to prince as reward for curing him	100*
T 68.1.	Princess offered as prize to rescuer	22, 34, 34*
T 69.1.1.	Three brothers married to three sisters	1, 1*, 5
T 69.5.	Father punishes daughter by giving her to poor boy in marriage	3, 6
T 81.3.	Girl falls dead on lover's body	28
T 84.	Lovers treacherously separated	28
T 91.3.	Love of mortal and supernatural person	4, 8, 8*

Motif-Index	Motif	Story
T 91.3.1.	Supernatural lover [*dev*] husband performs girl's work	8*
T 91.6.2.0.1.	King covets subject's wife	23, 23*
T 91.6.4.	Princess falls in love with lowly boy	16, 22, 33*
T 97.	Father opposed to daughter's marriage	18, 22
T 110.	Unusual marriage	100*
T 111.	Marriage of mortal and supernatural being	1, 18
T 111.5.	Marriage of mortal and dwarf	1
T 113.	Marriage to man alive by night, dead by day	100, 100*
T 117.	Marriage of person and object [magic box]	25
T 117.11.	Marriage to statue	23*
T 118.	Girls love giant	5, 8, 8*
T 121.3.1.	Princess marries lowly man	3, 6, 40
T 131.0.1.	Princess has unrestricted choice of husband	22, 33*
T 131.0.1.1.	Girl to wed man of choice	35
T 131.1.1.	Brothers' consent for sisters' marriage needed	1, 1*
T 131.1.2.1.	Girl must marry father's choice	28
T 172.0.1.	All husbands have perished on bridal night	36
T 172.2.	Bridal chamber invaded by magic serpent [in girl's mouth]	36
T 230.	Faithlessness in marriage	42, 77
T 251.1.1.	Belfagor. Devil frightened by shrewish wife	79
T 252.2.	Cock shows brow-beaten husband how to rule wife	78
T 253.1.	Nagging wife drives husband to prepare for suicide	78
T 311.	Woman/man averse to marriage	11
T 320.	Escape from undesired lover	48
T 320.1.	Oft-proved fidelity	48
T 323.	Escape from undesired lover by strategy	48
T 351.	Sword of chastity	11

Motif-Index	Motif	Story
T 381.	Imprisoned virgin to prevent knowledge of men (marriage, impregnation)	35, 49
T 411.1.	Lecherous father	24
T 482.	Day husband, night husband	72
T 511.1.1.	Conception from eating apple	25, 27, 28
T 511.8.	Conception from eating [almond]	100*
T 512.	Conception from drinking	67
T 512.2.	Conception from drinking urine	35
T 513.	Conception from wish	26
T 523.	Conception from bathing	7
T 538.	Unusual conception in old age	7
T 543.6.1.	Birth from wheat [chick-peas]	29
T 547.	Birth from virgin	35, 67
T 550.	Monstrous [unusual] birth	25
T 553.	Thumbling born as result of hasty wish of parents	29
T 554.7.	Woman gives birth to snake	26, 100*
T 572.1.	Magic prevention of birth	8, 8*
T 574.	Long pregnancy	8, 8*
T 578.	Pregnant man	25
T 586.1.	Many children at a birth	29
T 587.	Birth of twins	31
T 589.3.	Birth trees	27
T 589.6.2.	Children brought by midwife	31
T 589.7.1.	Simultaneous birth of (domestic) animal and child	27
T 615.	Supernatural growth	35
T 615.3.	Precocious wisdom	67
T 615.4.	Precocious boy supports widowed mother and self by wits	76
T 646.1.	Child cries [incessantly] because father is unknown	40

V. Religion

V 12.4.6.	Sheep (ram) as sacrifice	9
V 60.	Funeral rites	42
V 85.	Religious pilgrimage	48, 93

Motif-Index	Motif	Story
V 132.	Holy water	32
V 211.3.	Finding the cross	40
V 229.10.2.	Holy man restores cut-off hands	32
V 233.	Angel of death	45
V 256.	Miraculous healing by Virgin Mary	91
V 323.	Atheist	87

W. Traits of Character

W 26.	Patience	17
W 34.4.	[Shiek] prefers jungle [cave] life to luxury	77
W 45.	Honor	48
W 111.3.	Lazy wife	80
W 111.3.5.	Wife too lazy for spinning	38
W 125.	Gluttony	29
W 126.	Disobedience	17
W 128.	Dissatisfaction	17
W 151.	Greed	17
W 154.	Ingratitude	17, 52

X. Humor

X 31.	Dream of marking treasure	55

Z. Miscellaneous Groups of Motifs

Z 11.	Unending tale	75
Z 46.	The climax of horrors	95, 97
Z 47.	Series of trick exchanges	96
Z 61.4.	Tremendous blow [which caused mother's milk from infancy to flow through nostrils]	14
Z 71.5.1.	Seven brothers and one sister	7
Z 71.5.8.	Seven brothers marry seven sisters	7
Z 111.	Death personified	45
Z 122.	Time personified	1
Z 253.	Fool as hero	62

APPENDIX C

Bibliography of Comparative Sources

General Folklore

Clouston, A. A. *Popular Tales and Fictions.* Vol. 1–2. London: William Blackwood & Sons, 1887.

MacCulloch, J. A. *The Childhood of Fiction, A Study of Folk Tales and Primitive Thought.* London: John Murray, 1905.

Albanian

Dozon, Auguste. *Contes albanais.* Paris: Ernest Leroux, 1881.

Arabian

Campbell, C. G. *Tales from the Arab Tribes.* New York: Macmillan Co., 1950.

———. *Told in the Market Place.* London: Ernest Benn, Ltd., 1954.

Armenian

Chalatianz, Grikor. *Märchen und Sagen* in *Armenische Bibliotek,* Vol. IV. Leipzig: Verlag von Wilhelm Friedrich, 1887.

Hamastdeg. *Badmuvatzkner yev Hekiatner.* Beyoglu: Hermon Matbaasi, 1963.

Khatchatrianz, I. *Armenian Folk Tales.* Philadelphia: Colonial House, 1946.

Macler, Frédéric. *Contes arméniens* (translation of Karekin Servantstiants' *Hamov-Hodov*). Paris: Ernest Leroux, 1905.

———. *Contes et légendes de l'Armenie* (translations from Servantstiants' *Manana, Hamov-Hodov;* Hadjian's *Hin avandakan hêqiathner khotordjroy;* Yousêpheants' *Phsrankhner jolovrdakan banahewsoitiwnits*). Paris: Ernest Leroux, 1911.

———. *Contes, légendes et épopées populaires d'Armenie* (translations from Allahvertian's *Oulnia kam Zêithoun;* Hadjian's *Avandakan hêqiathner khotordjroy,* and various Armenian periodicals as indicated specifically in stories). Paris: P. Geuthner, 1928.

Nazinian, A. *Haigagan Shogovoortagan Hekiatner.* Cairo: Hoosaper, 1959.

Raffi. *Contes persans*. Paris: Librarie Charles Noblet, 1902.

Seklemian, A. G. *The Golden Maiden*. Cleveland: Helman Taylor Co., 1898.

Servantstian, G. *Hamov-Hodov*. Paris: Arax Co., Topalian Bros., 1949. (Original edition: 1884.)

Surmelian, Leon. *Daredevils of Sassoun*. Denver: Alan Swallow, 1964.

Tcheraz, Minas. *L'Orient inédit. Contes et chansons populaires*, Tome XXXIX. Paris: Ernest Leroux, 1912.

Toumanian, Hovhannes. *Badmuvatzkner yev Hekiatner*. Cairo: Nubar, 1948.

Wingate, J. S. "Armenian Folk Tales" (translated from Servantstiantz' *Manana*). *Folk-Lore*, Vol. XXI–XXIII, 1910–12.

Wlislocki, Heinrich von. *Märchen und Sagen der Bukowinaer und Siebenbürger Armenier*. Hamburg: Verlagsanstalt und Druckerei Actien Gesellschaft, 1892.

Asia Minor

Carnoy E. H. and Nicolaïdes, Jean. *Traditions populaires de l'Asie Mineure*, Tome XXVIII. Paris: Maisonneuve et Ch. Leclerc, 1889.

Azerbaijan

Hermann, Alfred and Schwind, Martin. *Die Prinzessin von Samarkand: Märchen aus Aserbeidschan und Armenien*. Koln: Greven Verlag, 1951.

Basque

Monteiro, Mariava. *Legends and Popular Tales of the Basque People*. New York: Frederich A. Stokes, 1891.

Webster, W. *Basque Legends*. London: Griffith and Farran, 1877.

Caucasian

Dirr, Adolph. *Caucasian Folk-Tales*. London: J. M. Dent & Sons, 1925.

Haxthausen, August von. *Transcaucasia*. London: Chapman & Hall, 1854.

Georgian

Wardrop, M. *Georgian Folk Tales*. London: David Nutt, 1894.

Greek

Dawkins, R. M. *Forty-Five Stories from the Dodekanese.* Cambridge: University Press, 1950.
————. *Modern Greek Folk Tales.* Oxford: Clarendon Press, 1953.
————. *Modern Greek in Asia Minor.* Cambridge: University Press, 1916.

Gypsy

Groome, Francis H. *Gypsy Folk Tales.* London: Hurst & Blackett, 1899.
Jagendorf, M. A. and Tillhagen, C. H. *The Gypsies' Fiddle.* New York: Vanguard Press, 1956.
Yates, Dora E. *A Book of Gypsy Folk-Tales.* London: Phoenix House, 1948.

Hungarian

Jones, W. Henry and Kropf, Lewis L. *Folk Tales of the Magyars.* London: Elliot Stock, 1889.
Ortutay, Gyula. *Hungarian Folk Tales.* Corvina, Budapest: Kossuth, 1962.

Iraqi

Stevens, E. S. *Folk-Tales of Iraq.* London: Oxford University Press, 1931.

Israeli

Noy, Dov. *Folktales of Israel.* Chicago: University of Chicago Press, 1963.

Italian

Crane, T. F. *Italian Popular Tales.* London: Macmillan Co., 1885.

Persian

Lorimer, D. L. R. and E. O. *Persian Tales.* London: Macmillan Co., 1919.

Polish

Borski, Lucia Merecka. *Polish Folk Tales.* New York: Sheed & Ward, 1947.

Zajdler, Zoë. *Polish Fairy Tales.* London: Frederick Muller, Ltd., 1959.

Romanian

Creangă, I. *Folk Tales from Roumania.* London: Routledge & Kegan Paul, Ltd., 1952.

Ispirescu, P. *The Foundling Prince.* New York: Houghton Mifflin Co., 1917.

Kremnitz, Mite. *Roumanian Fairy Tales.* New York: Henry Holt & Co., 1885.

Russian

Afanas'ev, A. N. *Russian Folk Tales* (tr.: Guterman). New York: Pantheon, 1945.

Ransome, Arthur. *Old Peter's Russian Tales.* London: Thomas Nelson & Sons, Ltd., 1916.

Scotch

Campbell, J. F. *Popular Tales of the West Highlands.* Vol. I–IV. London: Alexander Gardner, 1890–93.

Serbian

Mijatovics, C. *Serbian Folk-Lore, Popular Tales.* London: W. Isbester & Co., 1874.

Petrovitch, V. *Hero Tales and Legends of the Serbians.* New York: Frederich Stokes, 1914.

Siberian

Coxwell, C. Fillingham. *Siberian and Other Folk-Tales.* London: C. W. Daniel Co., 1925.

Turkish

Bain, R. N. *Turkish Fairy Tales and Folk Tales* (tr. from Kúnos). London: Lawrence Bullen, 1896.

Ekrem, Selma. *Turkish Fairy Tales.* Princeton: D. Von Nostrand Co., 1964.

Garnett, Lucy. *The Women of Turkey and Their Folklore,* Vol. I–II. London: David Nutt, 1890–91.

Kent, Margery. *Fairy Tales from Turkey.* London: Routledge & Kegan Paul, Ltd., 1946.

Kúnos, Ignasz. *Forty-Four Turkish Fairy Tales.* London, Harrap & Co., n. d.

––––––. *Türkische Volksmärchen Aus Stambul.* Leiden: Brill, 1905.

Tezel, Naki. *Istanbul Masallari.* Turkish Folklore Studies No. X. Istanbul: Burhaneddin Matbaasi, 1938.

APPENDIX D

Additional References

Aharonian, G. *Husseynik.* Boston: Hairenik Press, 1965.

Armen, Herant K. *Tigranes the Great.* Detroit: Avondale Press, 1940.

Atamian, Sarkis. *The Armenian Community.* New York: Philosophical Library, 1955.

Der Nersessian, Sirarpie. *Armenia and the Byzantine Empire.* Cambridge: Harvard University Press, 1945.

Nalbandian, Louise. *The Armenian Revolutionary Movement.* Berkeley and Los Angeles: University of California Press, 1963.

Nalbandian, Vartouhie Calantar. "About the Theory of the Babylonian Origin of the Armenian People," *Armenian Review,* I, No. 1 (1948), 15–20.

Zavrian, H. "The Polish Armenian Colony," *Armenian Review,* IV (1945), No. 1, 58–76; No. 2, 89–107; No. 3, 66–76; No. 4, 89–101.

NOTES

Preface

1. Antti Aarne and Stith Thompson, *The Types of the Folktale* (2d Rev.: FF Communications No. 184 [Helsinki, 1961]). Wolfram Eberhard and Pertev Boratav, *Typen türkischer Volksmärchen* (Wiesbaden, 1953). Johannes Bolte and Georg Polívka, *Anmerkungen zu den Kinder- und Hausmärchen der Brüder Grimm* (5 vols.; Leipzig, 1913–32).

Chapter I

1. Wayland Hand, "American Folklore After Seventy Years: Survey and Prospect," *Journal of American Folklore*, LXXIII (1960), 1–11.

2. Arshak Safrastian, "Armenia as the Cradle of the Oldest Aryan Race," *Armenian Review*, XI, No. 41 (1958), 51.

3. Ignace Gelb, *Hurrians and Subarians* (Oriental Institute of the University of Chicago Studies in Oriental Civilization, No. 20 [Chicago, 1941]), p. 89.

4. Safrastian, *op. cit.*, 59.

5. V. C. Vahan, *History of Armenia* (Boston, 1936), I, 172.

6. Jacques de Morgan, *The History of the Armenian People* (Boston n.d.), pp. 140–41.

7. H. B. Boghosian, *Highlights of Armenian History and Its Civilization* (Pasadena, 1957), pp. 43–49; Vahe Sarafian, "Paulican Protestantism Before 844 A.D.," *Armenian Review*, IV, No. 2 (1951), 118–24.

8. Aram Raffi in Noel Buxton, *Travel and Politics in Armenia* (New York, 1914), p. 193.

9. de Morgan, *op. cit.*, pp. 315–37.

10. *Ibid.*, p. 332.

11. H. F. B. Lynch, *Armenia, Travels and Studies* (London, 1901), II, 390–91.

12. August von Haxthausen, *Transcaucasia* (London, 1854), p. 225.

Chapter II

1. See Sirvart Poladian, *Armenian Folk Songs* (University of California Publications in Music, II, No. 1 [Berkeley and Los Angeles, 1942]); de Morgan, *op. cit.*, pp. 368–70.

2. Frédéric Macler, *Contes armeniens* (Paris, 1905), p. 5.

3. J. S. Wingate, "Armenian Folk Tales," *Folk-Lore*, XXI–XXIII (1910–12).

4. See Frédéric Macler, *Contes et légendes de l'Armenie* (Paris, 1911), p. 10.

5. Heinrich von Wlislocki, *Märchen und Sagen der Bukowinaer Siebenbürger Armenier* (Hamburg, 1892), foreword.

6. A. G. Seklemian, *The Golden Maiden* (Cleveland, 1898), p. xvii.

7. Garegin Servantstian, *Hamov-Hodov* (Paris, 1949), Part B, p. 12; see also Macler, *Contes armeniens*, p. 127.

8. Minas Tcheraz, *L'Orient inédit* (Paris, 1912), p. 5.

9. *Ibid.*

10. Stith Thompson, *The Folktale* (New York, 1946), pp. 367–405.

11. R. M. Dawkins, *Modern Greek Folk Tales* (Oxford, 1953), p. v.

12. R. M. Dawkins, *Forty-Five Stories from the Dodekanese* (Cambridge, 1950), p. 22.

13. de Morgan, *op. cit.*, p. 327.

14. Francis H. Groome, *Gypsy Folk Tales* (London, 1899), p. 53.

15. *Ibid.*, p. xl.

16. George Mardikian, *Dinner at Omar Khayyam's* (New York, 1944), p. 13.

17. de Morgan, *op. cit.*, p. 330.

18. Sir James Frazer, *The Golden Bough* (3d. ed.; London, 1926), I, Part I, 52.

19. John A. MacCulloch, *The Childhood of Fiction* (London, 1905), pp. 16–20, 350–80.

20. Stith Thompson, *The Motif-Index of Folk-Literature* (6 vols.; Bloomington, 1955–58).

21. Manuk Abeghian, *Der armenische Volksglaube* (Leipzig, 1899), pp. 8–28.

22. MacCulloch, *op. cit.*, pp. 118–45, 181–91.

23. *Ibid.*, pp. 30–34.

24. Tcheraz, *op. cit.*, p. 247; Grikor Chalatianz, *Märchen und Sagen* (Leipzig, 1887), p. x; Mardiros Ananikian, "Armenian Mythology," in *Mythology of All Races*, ed. John MacCulloch (Boston, 1925), VII, 87.

25. Tcheraz, *op. cit.*, p. 247.

26. Dawkins, *Modern Greek Folk Tales*, p. 23.

27. Ananikian, *op. cit.*, 85; Abeghian, *op. cit.*, p. 110.

28. Abeghian, *op. cit.*, p. 118.

29. Tcheraz, *op. cit.*, p. 158.

30. Groome, *op. cit.*, p. 62.

31. Abeghian, *op. cit.*, pp. 118–20.

32. Ananikian, *op. cit.*, 83–84.

33. Tcheraz, *op. cit.*, p. 162.

34. V. Propp, *Morphology of the Folktale* (Philadelphia, 1958), p. 18.

35. Abeghian, *op. cit.*, pp. 86–88, 101.

36. Ananikian, *op. cit.*, 73 ff.; G. Samuelian, "Totemism Among the Armenians," *Armenian Review*, II, No. 8 (1949), 61; Tcheraz, *op. cit.*, p. 147; Abeghian, *op. cit.*, pp. 74–76; Haxthausen, *op. cit.*, p. 144. See also V. Petrovitch, *Hero Tales and Legends of the Serbians* (New York, 1914), p. 23; W. H. Jones and L. L. Kropf, *Folk Tales of the Magyars* (London, 1889), p. lxi.

37. Alexander Krappe, "Indian Origin of Armenian Folk Tales," *Armenian Review*, II, No. 5 (1949), 112.

38. Chalatianz, *op. cit.*, p. xiii.

39. Abeghian, *op. cit.*, p. 82.

40. Lucy Garnett, *Women of Turkey and Their Folklore* (London, 1890), I, 217.

41. Tcheraz, *op. cit.*, p. 142.

42. See J. F. Campbell, *Popular Tales of the West Highlands* (London, 1890), I, lxxv–lxxvii.

The manuscript was edited by Francine Rosemberg and Gene Tendler. The book was designed by Richard Kinney. The text type face is Mergenthaler's Linotype Caledonia designed by W. A. Dwiggins in 1937. The display type is Venus designed and produced at the Bauer Typefoundry between 1907 and 1913.

The book is printed on Glatfelter's RR Antique and bound in Bancroft's Linen Finished cloth and Lindenmeyer Schlosser's Elephant Hide paper over boards. Manufactured in the United States of America.

Susie Hoogasian-Villa received her B.S. and M.A. degrees from Wayne State University and currently is a part-time member of the faculty of the College of Education, Wayne State University.